MW00619644

Here is what some experts have said about this and previous Smith maritime publications—

As a frequent maritime museum visitor, … I highly recommend this great new guide by Robert H. Smith.
Wally Schirra, Captain, USN (Ret.) and former astronaut

Robert H. Smith has done a remarkable job in compiling this museum guide, and I highly recommend it for the maritime buff.
Clifford D. Mallory, Jr., **Mystic Seaport Museum**

I consider all the material treated in the museum entries to be of the highest quality….The book is so well done and will be of notable use to the general public and to the more serious scholars.
Translated from a review in the Italian publication *Rivista Marittima*.

Everyone interested in our maritime heritage will enjoy a leisurely at-home perusal of this book… Since the number of maritime museums open to the public has more than doubled in recent years and attendance is now in the millions, an up-to-date take-along guide such as this fills an obvious need. *The Naval Institute's Press*

(This guide) can be seen as the fulfillment of a need and a cause for hope, namely that (it) will facilitate and promote visitations, interest, and greater public support. Garth Wilson in The Northern Mariner, The Journal of the Canadian *Nautical Research Society*

Whenever Bob Smith comes out with a new guide, I wonder if the time has come to quit serious work and hit the road. With this volume he's got me in double trouble: He lures me both on the road and back in time to an era when sails snapped crisper and the horizon was knife-edge straight and clear. Neil Morgan, Editor, *San Diego Tribune*

Whether your interest is ships or history, you will appreciate (Robert H. Smith's guide.) …Even if you're not traveling, this is a handy reference book and also interesting reading.
Jack Reber in *The San Diego Union-Tribune*

For the maritime lover planning a trip within the U.S. or Canada, Bob Smith's (book) is an essential guide.
Cheryl Ketcham in *The San Diego Log*

SMITH'S GUIDE TO

MARITIME MUSEUMS

OF

NORTH AMERICA

BY

ROBERT H. SMITH

Library of Congress Cataloging-in-Publication Data

Smith, Robert H. 1927 -

Maritime Museums of North America, including Canada: with selected lighthouse, canal, and canal lock museums / Robert H. Smith

   p. cm.
   Includes index and subject index
   ISBN 0-941786-07-2
   1. Maritime Museums—United States—Guide-books. 2. Maritime Museums—Canada—Guide-books. 3. United States—Description and travel—1998— - —Guide-books. 4. Canada—Description and travel—1998— - —Guide-books. II Title.

Printed in the United States of America on acid-free paper

8   7   6   5   4   3   2   1

Eighth printing

Publisher:
C Books
P.O. Box 176
Del Mar, CA 92014-0175
(858) 755-7753
E-Mail: cbooks@san.rr.com

Cover Photo
United States Ship

CONSTITUTION

Built in Boston to defend the young American nation, USS *CONSTITUTION* is nearly as old as the document for which George Washington and Congress named her. Both the document and the ship have proven to be resilient symbols of America's strength, courage, and liberty.

Made of timbers felled from Maine to Georgia and armed with cannon cast in Rhode Island and copper fastenings provided by Paul Revere, the vessel is truly a national ship. Launched in Boston on October 21, 1797, she first put to sea in 1798. Having remained a part of the U.S. Navy since that day, *CONSTITUTION* is the oldest commissioned warship afloat in the world.

Her first mission, during the late 1790's, was to guard American commerce in the Caribbean against French depredations. In 1803, President Thomas Jefferson sent her to the Mediterranean to protect American Ships and seamen from attack by the Barbary pirates. With Captain Edward Preble in command, *CONSTITUTION* and other ships of the squadron bombarded Tripoli. Thanks to such determination, a treaty of peace was signed in June 1805 between the United States and Tripoli onboard *CONSTITUTION*.

After returning to the Unites States, *CONSTITUTION* was named flagship of the North Atlantic Squadron. In 1810, her new captain, Isaac Hull, took her to sea. Two years later she met and defeated HMS *GUERRIERE*, the first in a grand succession of victories in the War of 1812. It was during this ferocious battle that the seaman, astonished at how the British cannonballs were bounding off *CONSTIUTION's* hull, cried our — "Huzzah! Her side are made of iron!" Hence her nickname "Old Ironsides."

In 1882, she was removed from active service and shortly thereafter retired to Portsmouth, New Hampshire Naval Shipyard. In recognition of her centennial, *CONSTITUTION* was brought back to Boston in 1897. Refitted for display and opened to the *public* in 1905, she became a national monument.

CONSTITUTION was recommissioned in 1931 for a coast-to-coast tour of ninety American cities lasting until 1934 when she was returned to her place of honor in the Boston Harbor at Charlestown Navy Yard. She rests here today as an enduring symbol of the document for which she is named and of America's determination to defend the republic she so long protected.

(Courtesy of BM2 Anthony L. Rossi, Public Affairs Officer, **USS** *Constitution*)

To my wife Helen,
whose help and assistance
made it possible
to complete this work.

AUTHOR'S PREFACE

The most asked question I receive is: "What is the best maritime museum?" And my answer is always: "Every maritime, lighthouse, canal, or canal lock museum is important as each has its own story — its own reason for having been founded. Yes, some are large museums with vast collections, artifacts, vessels, and wonderful archives — and others are smaller with wonderful artifacts, collections, and libraries and paintings. But every museum was established because of an important maritime historical fact or facts and the interested and dedicated people who expended enormous amounts of energy to create each museum, did so to make it possible for succeeding generations to more fully understand our maritime historical past and why "our museum" is important to preserve that history for now and the future.

One of the important attributes of collecting and archiving our maritime history is the increasing interest in genealogy. Where did our ancestors come from, why did they come, and how did they get here? Most, of course came by boat or ship, and almost all experienced great hardship. What kind of ships? How big or how small? We need to help our bewildering offspring to understand about their ancestors and our maritime museums will help them appreciate the past and prepare them for the roll they themselves will play out during their own lives — taking elements of the past and applying it to their lives.

Oh thank goodness for the dedication of everyone who has helped preserve our maritime history. Every time we visit a museum say thank you to those who greet you — they will appreciate it more than you might realize.

Robert H. Smith

PHOTOS ON CD (Compact Disk)

Over 400 images of maritime, lighthouse, canal, and canal lock museums, are on a compact disk for your viewing if you wish. Not, however, for commercial purposes with out express permission from the author as all images are protected by copyright. There is no charge. Please complete the following and either e-mail or send by regular mail.

Name_____

Address_____

City/State_____

Date/Place guide was purchased:_____

E-mail address if you wish to received disk on a PDF file.

MARITIME MUSEUM WEBSITE INFORMATION

A large number of the entries in this guide to Maritime Museums of North America have their own websites and these have been included in

ROBERT H. SMITH'S MASTER INDEX
TO
WORLD WIDE MARITIME AND RELATED MUSEUM WEBSITES

Those interested in maritime history and heritage have found Smith's master index to over 700 world-wide websites to be invaluable.

This website can be found using the following address on the Internet: **http://www.maritimemuseums.net**

CONTENTS

Cover Photo Information   vii

Preface by the Author   xi

PHOTOS ON CD Information   xiii
Internet Website Update Information   xiii
CONTENTS   xv
List by States and Provinces   xvii

Index: By States and Canadian Provinces   xix

CONTENTS   xv

MUSEUMS   Part 1: Unites States   1

         Part 2: Canadian Provinces   185

APPENDIX AND INDEXES
         Canal Parks   212

         List of Museums by Alpha   213

SUBJECT INDEX
         Bed and Breakfast/Overnight Encampments   226
         Boat/Ship Building   227
         Gift/Book Shops   228
         Halls of Fame   232
         Libraries   232
         Lighthouses   235
         Locks and Canals   237
         Navy Yards   238
         Newsletters & Periodicals   238
         Pirate Museums   240
         Scrimshaw   240
         Ship Chandleries   240
         Ship Models   240
         Ships and Boats   243
           By Type   243
           General   245
           Whaling   249
AUTHOR BIO   251
Note to Museum Directors   253

LIST OF MUSEUMS
LIST OF STATES -
CANADAIAN PROVINCES

UNITED STATES

Alabama	1	Nebraska	100
Alaska	2	New Hampshire	100
Arkansas	3	New Jersey	102
California	3	New York	108
Connecticut	16	North Carolina	128
Delaware	20	North Dakota	133
Florida	22	Ohio	133
Georgia	29	Oklahoma	140
Hawaii	31	Oregon	140
Illinois	33	Pennsylvania	144
Indiana	35	Rhode Island	147
Iowa	37	South Carolina	154
Kentucky	39	South Dakota	156
Louisiana	41	Tennessee	156
Maine	42	Texas	157
Maryland	50	Vermont	160
Massachusetts	60	Virginia	161
Michigan	79	Washington	169
Minnesota	92	Washington, D.C.	179
Mississippi	96	West Virginia	181
Missouri	98	Wisconsin	181

CANADIAN PROVINCES

Alberta	185
British Columbia	186
Manitoba	188
New Brunswick	189
Newfoundland	191
Nova Scotia	191
Ontario, Canada	197
Prince Edward Island	208
Québec	208
Yukon Territory	211

USA

ALABAMA
Carrolton
  Tennessee-Tombigbee Waterway,
    Tom Bevill Visitor Center   1
Gulf Shores
  Fort Morgan Museum   1
Mobile
  Museum of Mobile   1
  USS *Alabama* Battleship Memorial Park   2

ALASKA
Fairbanks
  Fairbanks Historical Preservation
    Foundation   2
Kodiak
  Kodiak Maritime Museum   2

ARKANSAS
Newport
  Mary Woods II Riverboat Museum   3
North Little Rock
  Arkansas Inland Marine Museum   3

CALIFORNIA
Alameda
  Aircraft Carrier *Hornet* Museum   3
Belvedere
  China Cabin   3
Carmel
  Point Sur Light Station   4
  The Whalers Cabin & The Whaling
    Station Museum   4
Carnelian Bay
  Tahoe Maritime Museum   4
Catalina Island
  Catalina Island Museum   5
Crescent City
  Battery Point Lighthouse   5
Dana Point
  Pilgrim (Snow Sloop)   5
Eureka
  Clarke Museum   6
  Humboldt Bay Maritime Museum   6
Fort Bragg
  Guest House Museum   6
Long Beach
  Queen Mary (Ocean Liner)   7
Marina del Rey
  Lloyd Taber-Marina del Rey
    (Nautical) Library   7
Monterey
  Monterey Maritime Museum   7
Newport Beach
  Newport Harbor Nautical Museum   8

CALIFORNIA - Continued
Oakland
  Lightship *Relief*   8
  Patomac Presidential Yacht   8
Oxnard
  Ventura County Maritime Museum   9
Pacific Grove
  Point Pinos Lighthouse   9
Point Arena
  Point Arena Lighthouse and Museum   9
Point Richmond
  East Brother Light Station   9
Port Hueneme
  Civil Engineer Corps/Seabee Museum   10
Richmond
  SS *Red Oak Victory* (Victory Ship)   10
Rio Vista
  Dutra Museum of Dredging   10
Sacramento
  Old Sacramento Waterfront and
    Riverboat *Delta King*   11
San Diego
  Cabrillo National Monument   11
  San Diego Aircraft Carrier Museum   11
  San Diego Maritime Museum   12
San Francisco
  San Francisco Maritime National
    Historical Park   12
  SS *Jeremiah O'Brien* (Liberty Ship)   13
  USS *Pampanito* (SS-33)   13
San Pedro
  Los Angeles Maritime Museum   13
  SS *Lane Victory* (Victory Ship)   14
Santa Barbara
  Santa Barbara Maritime Museum   14
Sausalito
  Bay Model Visitor Center   14
  Marinship 1942-1945 (Shipyard)   15
Vallejo
  Vallejo Naval and Historical Museum   15
Ventura
  Channel Islands National Park   15
Wilmington
  Banning Residence Museum   15

CONNECTICUT
Deep River
  Stone House   16
Essex
  The Connecticut River Museum   16
Groton
  Nautilus and Submarine Force Museum   16
Mystic
  Mystic Seaport Museum   17

CONNECTICUT - Continued
New London
    Custom House Museum   18
    U.S. Coast Guard Museum   18
Norwalk
    The Maritime Aquarium   18
Plainville
    Plainville Historic Center   19
Stonington
    The Old Lighthouse Museum   19
Stratford
    The *Glacier* Society Museum   19

DELAWARE
Bethany Beach
    Indian River Life-Saving Station   20
Fenwick Island
    DiscoverSea Shipwreck Museum   20
Georgetown
    Treasurers of the Sea Exhibit   20
Lewes
    Cannon Ball Marine Museum   21
Port Penn
    Port Penn Interpretive Center   21
Wilmington
    Kalmar Nyckel Shipyard & Museum   21

FLORIDA
Apalachicola
    Apalachicola Maritime Museum   22
Bradenton
    South Florida Museum   22
Coconut Grove
    Barnacle State Historical Site   23
Ft. Pierce
    UDT - SEAL Museum   23
Jacksonville
    Jacksonville Maritime Museum
        Society   23
Jupiter
    Jupiter Lighthouse and Museum   23
Key West
    East Martello Gallery & Museum   24
    Key West Shipwreck Historeum   24
    Lighthouse Museum   24
    Mel Fisher Maritime Heritage
        Society   24
    Pirate Soul Museum   25
    Ripley's Believe It Or Not! Museum   25
    Wrecker's Museum   25
Miami
    Cape Florida Lighthouse   25
    Historical Museum of Southern Florida   26
Palm Beach
    Palm Beach Maritime Museum   26
Panama City
    Museum of the Man in the Sea   26

FLORIDA - Continued
Pensacola
    Pensacola Historical Museum   27
Ponce Inlet
    Ponce de Leon Inlet Lighthouse Museum   27
St. Augustine
    St. Augustine Lighthouse & Museum   27
Sebastian
    Mel Fisher's Treasure Museum   27
Stuart
    Gilbert's Bar House of Refuge   28
Stuart
    Maritime & Yachting Museum   28
Tallahassee, Florida
    Museum of Florida History   28
Tampa
    SS *American Victory* Mariners Memorial
    And Museum Ship, Inc.   29

GEORGIA
Athens
    U.S. Navy Supply Corps Museum   29
Columbus
    Port Columbus Civil War Naval Center   29
St. Simons Island
    St. Simons Island Lighthouse Museum   30
Savannah
    Old Fort Jackson   30
    Ships of the Sea Maritime Museum   30
Tybee Island
    Tybee Island Historical Society   31

HAWAII
Honolulu
    Bishop Museum   31
    Hawaii Maritime Center   31
    USS *Arizona* Memorial   32
    USS *Bowfin* Submarine Museum & Park   32
    USS *Missouri* Memorial Association   32
    USS *Utah* (BB-31, AG-16)   33

ILLINOIS
Cairo
    Cairo Custom House Museum   33
Chicago
    Chicago Maritime Society   34
    U-505 (German Submarine)   34
Great Lakes
    Great Lakes Naval Museum   34
Lockport
    Illinois and Michigan Canal Museum   34
Rock Island
    Mississippi River Visitor Center   35
Sadorus
    National Museum of Ship Models &
    Sea History   35

INDIANA
Delphi
    Carroll County Wabash and Erie
        Canal, Inc.   35
Evansville
    USS LST 325   36
Jeffersonville
    Falls of the Ohio State Park   36
    Howard Steamboat Museum   36
Metamora
    Whitewater Canal State Historic Site   37
Michigan City
    Old Lighthouse Museum   37

IOWA
Arnolds Park
    Iowa Great Lakes Maritime Museum   37
Davenport
    Putnam Museum   38
Dubuque
    National Mississippi River Museum
        Aquarium   38
Keokuk
    Keokuk River Museum   38
Le Claire
    Buffalo Bill Museum of Le Claire   38
Missouri Valley
    Steamboat *Bertrand* Cargo Collection   39

KENTUCKY
Louisville
    Belle of Louisville Steamer   39
    Mayor Andrew Broaddus
        (Coast Guard Station)   40
    Portland Museum   40
Paducah
    River Heritage Center Museum   40

LOUISIANA
Baton Rouge
    Louisiana State Museum-Baton Rouge   40
    USS *Kidd* Nautical Center   41
Madisonville
    Lake Pontchartrain Basin Maritime
        Museum   41
New Orleans
    Louisiana State Museum   41
Plaquemine
    Plaquemine Lock State Historic Site   42

MAINE
Bar Harbor
    Islesford Historical Museum   42
Bath
    Maine Maritime Museum   42
Boothbay Harbor
    Boothbay Region Historical Society   43
Brunswick
    The Peary-MacMillan Arctic Museum   43

MAINE - Continued
Cape Elizabeth
    Portland Head Light   43
Castaine
    Allie Ryan Collection, Maine State
        Museum   44
Eastport
    Border Historical Society   44
    Downeast Maritime Museum   44
    Quoddy Maritime Museum   44
Friendship
    Friendship Museum   44
Greenville
    Moosehead Marine Museum   44
Islesboro
    Sailor's Memorial Museum-Lighthouse   45
Kennebunk
    Brick Store Museum   45
Kennebunkport
    Kennebunkport Maritime Museum   45
    The *Phyllis A* and Maritime Heritage   46
Kittery   37
    Kittery Historical & Naval Museum   46
Lubec
    Rier's Old Sardine Village Museum   46
Machiasport
    Gates House/Machiasport Historical Society   46
Newfield
    Willowbrook at Newfield   47
Pemaquid Point
    Fishermen's Museum and
        Pemaquid Point Lighthouse   47
Port Clyde
    Marshall Point Lighthouse Museum   47
Portland
    Osher Map Library   48
Rockland
    Maine Lighthouse Museum   48
Searsport
    Penobscot Marine Museum   48
South Berwick
    Counting House-Old Berwick
        Historical Society   49
South Portland
    Portland Harbor Museum   49
Yarmouth
    Museum of Yarmouth History   50
York
    John Hancock Warehouse & Wharf/
        Old York Historical Society   50

MARYLAND
Annapolis
    Annapolis Maritime Museum   50
    Historic Annapolis   50
    U.S. Naval Academy Museum   51
Avenue
    Longship Company, Ltd.   51
Baltimore
    Baltimore Maritime Museum   52

Baltimore - Continued
   Baltimore Museum of Industry   52
   Fells Point Maritime Museum   52
   Pride of Baltimore II, Inc.   52
   SS *John W. Brown* (Liberty Ship)   53
   USS *Constellation* (Sloop of War)   53
Cambridge
   Dorchester Heritage Museum   53
   Richardson Maritime Museum   54
Chesapeake City
   C and D Canal Museum (Chesapeake
     and Delaware Canal Museum)   54
Coltons Point
   St. Clements Island-Potomac River
     Museum   54
Crisfield
   Governor J. Millard Tawes
     Historical Museum   55
Cumberland
   C & O Canal of Cumberland, MD   55
Hagers Town
   Chesapeake & Ohio National Historic Park   55
Havre de Grace
   Havre de Grace Maritime Museum   56
   Susquehanna Museum   56
Linthicum
   Masters, Mates & Pilots Museum   56
North East
   Upper Bay Museum   57
Ocean City
   Ocean City Life-Saving Station Museum   57
Oxford
   Oxford Museum   57
Piney Point
   Harry Lundberg School of Seamanship   57
   Piney Point Lighthouse Museum   58
St. Mary's City
   Historic St. Mary's City   58
St. Michaels
   Chesapeake Bay Maritime Museum   58
Solomons
   Calvert Marine Museum   59

MASSACHUSETTS
Amesbury
   Lowell's Boat Shop   59
Beverly
   Beverly Historical Society/Museum   60
Boston
   Boston Marine Society   60
   Boston Tea Party Ship and Museum   60
   Museum of Science   60
   Old State House-The Bostonian Society   61
Buzzard's Bay
   Capt. Charles H. Hurley Library   61
Cambridge
   Hart Nautical Collections   61

MASSACHUSETTS - Continued
Charlestown
   Charlestown Navy Yard   62
   USS *Cassin Young* (DD-793)   62
   USS *Constitution*   63
   USS *Constitution* Museum   63
Cohasset
   Cohasset Maritime Museum   64
Eastham
   Salt Pond Visitor Center   64
Edgartown
   Martha's Vineyard Historical
     Society and Museum   64
Essex
   Essex Shipbuilding Museum   65
Fall River
   Battleship Cove   65
   Marine Museum at Fall River   66
   PT Boat Museum and Library   66
Falmouth
   Falmouth Historical Society's Museums   66
Gloucester
   Cape Ann Historical Museum   67
   Gloucester *Adventure* (Schooner)   67
   Gloucester Maritime Heritage Center   67
Hull
   Hull Lifesaving Museum   68
Hyannis
   Cape Cod Maritime Museum   68
Marblehead
   Jeremiah Lee Mansion   69
   Marblehead Historical Society   69
Marion
   Mary Celeste Museum   69
Medford
   Medford Historical Society Museum   69
Milton
   Captain Robert Bennet Forbes House   70
Nantucket Island
   Egan Institute of Maritime Studies   70
   Nantucket Lifesaving Museum   70
   Whaling Museum   71
New Bedford
   Lightship *New Bedford*   71
   New Bedford Free Public Library   71
   New Bedford Whaling Museum   71
   Schooner *Ernestina* Commission   72
Newburyport
   Custom House Maritime Museum   72
North Billerica
   Middlesex Canal Museum   73
North Truro
   Truro Historical Society Museum   59   73
Osterville, Cape Cod
   Osterville Historical Society   73
Plymouth
   Pilgrim Hall Museum   74
   Plimoth Plantation   74

MASSACHUSETTS - Continued

Provincetown
Expedition *Whydah* (Pirate Ship)   74
Quincy
United States Naval Shipbuilding Museum   75
Rockport
Sandy Bay Historical Society & Museums   75
Salem
New England Pirate Museum   75
Peabody Essex Museum   76
Salem Maritime National Historical Site   76
Scituate
The Maritime & Irish Mossing Museum   76
Scituate Lighthouse   77
Wellfleet
Old Harbor Life-Saving Station   77
Wellfleet Historical Society Museum   77
Woods Hole
Woods Hole Historical Collection   78
Yarmouth Port
Historical Society of Old Yarmouth   78

MICHIGAN

Alpena
Jesse Besser Museum   79
Thunder Bay Underwater Preserve   79
Bay City
Historical Museum of Bay County   79
Brimley
Point Iroquois Lighthouse & Maritime
Museum   80
Cedarville
Les Cheneaux Maritime Museum   80
Copper Harbor
Copper Harbor Lighthouse Museum   80
DeTour Village
DeTour Passage Historical Museum   81
Detroit
Dossin Great Lakes Museum   81
Douglas
Keewatin Maritime Museum   81
Eagle Harbor Lighthouse and Museum   82
Empire
Sleeping Bear Point Coast Guard
Station Maritime Museum   82
Escanaba
Sand Point Lighthouse   82
Grand Haven
Tri-Cities Historical Museum   83
Grand Marais
Grand Marais Maritime Museum   83
Gulliver
Seul Choix Point Lighthouse   83
Harrisville:
Sturgeon Point Lighthouse & Museum   84
Houghton
Isle Royal National Park   84

MICHIGAN - continued

Lansing
Michigan Historical Museum   84
Ludington
White Pine Village   84
Mackinac City
Old Mackinac Point Lighthouse Museum   85
Manistee
Manistee County Historical Museum   85
SS *City of Milwaukee* (Car Ferry)   85
Marine City
Pride & Heritage Museum and Peche
Island Lighthouse   86
Marquette
Marquette Maritime Museum   86
Muskegon
Great Lakes Naval Memorial and Museum   86
SS *Milwaukee Clipper* (Passenger Ship)   87
Northport
Grand Traverse Lighthouse Museum   87
Paradise
Great Lakes Shipwreck Museum   87
Port Austin
Huron City Museum   88
Port Hope
Lighthouse Park Museum   88
Port Huron
Coast Guard Cutter *Bramble*   88
Port Huron Lightship Museum   89
Port Huron Museum   89
Port Sanilac
Sanilac Historical Museum & Village   90
Presque Isle
Presque Isle Lighthouses   90
Rogers City
Presque Isle County Historical Museum   90
Saginaw
Castle Museum of Saginaw County History   90
St. James
Marine Museum   91
Sault Ste. Marie
Museum Ship *Valley Camp*   91
Soo Locks Information Center   91
South Haven
Michigan Maritime Museum   92
Traverse City
Madeline (Ship)   92
Whitehall
White River Light Station Museum   93

MINNESOTA

Alexandria
Minnesota Lakes Maritime Museum   93
Duluth
Lake Superior Maritime Visitor Center   93
Leif Erickson Restoration Project   94
SS *William A. Irvin* Ore Boat   94

MINNESOTA - Continued
McGregor
    Big Sandy Lake Lock and Dam   94
Moorhead
    Heritage *Hjemkomst* Interpretive Center   94
Two Harbors
    Lighthouse Point and Harbor Museum   95
    Split Rock Lighthouse Historic Site   95
Warroad
    Warroad Heritage Museum   95
Winona
    Minnesota Marine Art Museum   96

MISSISSIPPI
Biloxi
    Maritime Seafood Industry Museum   96
    Old Lighthouse   96
Pascagoula
    Scranton Floating Museum   97
Vicksburg
    Gray & Blue Naval Museum   97
    USS *Cairo* Museum   97

MISSOURI
Hannibal
    Mark Twain Home Foundation Mark Twain
Home Foundation   97
Hermann
    Historic Hermann Museums   98
Kansas City
    Arabia Steamboat Museum   98
St. Louis
    Golden Eagle River Museum   99
    Herman T. Pott National Inland
        Waterways Library   99
    Missouri Historical Society   99

NEBRASKA
Brownville
    Museum of Missouri River History   100
Omaha
    Freedom Park, Inc.   100

NEW HAMPSHIRE
Portsmouth
    John Paul Jones House   100
    Piscataqua Gundalow Project   101
Port of Portsmouth Maritime Museum
    USS *Albacore* (Submarine)   101
    Portsmouth Athenaeum   101
    Strawbery Banke Museum   101
    New Hampshire Boat Museum   102

NEW JERSEY
Atlantic City
    Absecon Lighthouse   102
    Historic Gardener's Basin   102
Barnegat Light
    Barnegat Lighthouse   102

NEW JERSEY - Continued
Beach Haven
    Museum of New Jersey Maritime History   103
Camden
    Battleship *New Jersey*   103
Cape May
    Cape May County Historical and
    Genealogical Society Museum in the
    John Holmes House and Barn   104
Edgewater
    Binghamton (Ferry)   104
Greenwich
    John Dubois Maritime Museum   104
Hackensack
    New Jersey Naval Museum/
    Submarine USS *Ling*   105
Highlands
    Fort Hancock Museum   105
    Twin Lights State Historic Site   105
Keyport
    Steamboat Dock Museum   106
Linwood
    James Kirk Maritime Museum   106
Morristown
    Canal Society of New Jersey Museum
        at Waterloo Village   106
North Wildwood
    Hereford Inlet Lighthouse   106
Ocean City
    Ocean City Historical Museum   107
Paterson
    Paterson Museum   107
Somers Point
    Atlantic Heritage Center   107
Toms River
    Toms River Seaport Society   108
Tuckerton
    Tuckerton Seaport   108

NEW YORK
Albany
    Half Moon Visitor Center/
    New Netherland Museum   108
    New York State Canal System   109
    USS *Slater* (Destroyer Escort)   109
Beacon
    Hudson River Sloop *Clearwater*   109
Bellport
    Barn Museum   109
Blue Mountain Lake
    Adirondack Museum   110
Bronx
    Maritime Industry Museum/ Fort Schuyler   110
Brooklyn
    Waterfront Museum and Showboat Barge   110
Buffalo
    Buffalo and Erie County Naval and
        Military Park   111
    Lower Lakes Marine Historical Society   111

NEW YORK -continued

Camillus
    Sims' Store Museum   112
Canastota
    Canastota Canal Town Museum   112
Captree
    Fire Island Lighthouse Preservation Society   112
Centerport
    Vanderbilt Mansion, Marine Museum   112
Chittenango
    Chittenango Landing Canal Boat Museum   113
City Island
    City Island Nautical Museum   113
Clayton
    Antique Boat Museum   113
Cold Spring Harbor
    Whaling Museum   114
Crown Point
    Crown Point State Historic Site   114
Cuddebackville
    Neversink Valley Area Museum/
      D and H Canal Park   115
East Hampton
    East Hampton Town Marine Museum   115
Dunkirk
    Dunkirk Historical Lighthouse and
      Veteran's Park   115
Fort Hunter
    Fort Hunter-Schoharie State Historic Site   116
Greenport
    East End Seaport Maritime Museum   116
High Falls
    Delaware and Hudson Canal Museum   116
Hyde Park
    Franklin D. Roosevelt Library/Museum   117
Kings Point
    American Merchant Marine Museum
      at U.S. Merchant Marine Academy   117
Kingston
    Hudson River Maritime Museum   118
Lockport
    Lockport Canal Museum   118
Massena
    Dwight D. Eisenhower Lock   119
Mayville
    Chautauqua Lakes Historic Vessels   119
Montauk
    Montauk Point Lighthouse Museum   119
New York City
    Intrepid Sea-Air-Space Museum   119
    Museum of the City of New York   120
    New-York Historical Society   120
    South Street Seaport Museum &
      Ocean Liner Museum   120
Northport
    Northport Historical Museum   121
Oswego
    H. Lee White Marine Museum   121
    Oswego Maritime Foundation   122

NEW YORK -continued

Peekskill
    National Maritime Historical Society   122
Plattsburg
    Clinton County Historical Museum   122
Port Jefferson
    Mather House Museum   123
Riverhead
    Suffolk Historical Museum   123
Rome
    Erie Canal Village   123
Sackets Harbor
    Sackets Harbor Battlefield State
      Historic Site   123
Sag Harbor
    Sag Harbor Whaling Museum   124
Saugerties
    Saugerties Lighthouse Museum   124
Sodus Point
    Sodus Bay Lighthouse Museum   125
Southampton
    Southampton Historical Museum   125
Southold
    Nautical Museum at Horton Point
      Lighthouse   126
Staten Island
    Noble Maritime Collection   126
Syracuse
    Canal Society of New York State   126
    Erie Canal Museum   126
Waterford
    Tugboat *Urger*   127
West Sayville
    Long Island Maritime Museum   127
Whitehall
    Skenesborough Museum   127

NORTH CAROLINA

Beaufort
    North Carolina Maritime Museum   128
Buxton
    Museum of the Sea and Hatteras
      Island Visitor's Center-Cape
      Hatteras Lighthouse   128
Elizabeth City
    Museum of the Albemarle   128
Fayetteville
    Cape Fear Museum   129
Hatteras
    Graveyard of the Atlantic Museum   129
Kinston
    CSS *Neuse* State Historic Site   130
Kure Beach
    Fort Fisher Historic Site   130
Manteo
    North Carolina Maritime Museum
      on Roanoke Island   130
    Roanoke Island Festival Park   131

NORTH CAROLINA - Continued
Plymouth
    Roanoke River Lighthouse Replica &
      Museum 131
Roanoke Rapids
    Roanoke Canal Museum & Trail 132
Rodanthe
    Chicamacomico Life-Saving Station 132
Southport
    North Carolina Maritime Museum
      at Southport 132
Wilmington
    Cape Fear Museum 132
    USS *North Carolina* Battleship Memorial 133

NORTH DAKOTA
Bismarck
    State Historical Society of North Dakota 133

OHIO
Ashtabula
    Ashtabula Maritime Museum 133
Bowling Green
    Historical Collections/Great Lakes 134
Canal Fulton
    Canal Fulton Heritage Society 134
Cincinnati
    Inland Rivers Library 134
Cleveland
    Steamer *William G. Mather* Museum 135
    USS *Cod* Submarine Museum 135
    Western Reserve Historical Society 135
Coshocton
    Historic Roscoe Village 136
East Liverpool
    Sandy and Beaver Canal 136
Fairport
    Fairport Marine Museum 137
Fremont
    Rutherford B. Hayes Presidential Center 137
Marietta
    Ohio River Museum 137
Newcomerstown
    USS *Radford* National Naval Museum 137
Piqua
    Piqua Historical Area 138
Put-in-Bay
    Lake Erie Islands Historical Society
      Museum 138
Sandusky
    Maritime Museum of Sandusky 138
Sugarcreek
    Warther Carving Museum 139
Toledo
    SS *Willis B. Boyer* Museum Ship 139
Vermilion
    Inland Seas Maritime Museum 139

OKLAHOMA
Catoosa
    Arkansas River Historical Society Museum 140
Muskogee
    USS *Batfish* (Submarine) Muskogee War
      Memorial Park and Military Museum/ 140

OREGON
Astoria
    Clatsop County Historical Museum 140
    Columbia River Maritime Museum 140
Bandon
    Coquille River Lighthouse 141
Cascade Locks
    Cascade Locks and Marine Park 141
Newport
    Log Cabin Museum 141
    Yaquina Bay Lighthouse 142
North Bend
    Coos Historical & Maritime Museum 142
Port Oxford
    Port Oxford Lifeboat Station 142
Portland
    Oregon History Center 142
    Oregon Maritime Center and Museum 143
    Oregon Museum of Science and Industry 143
Reedsport
    Umpqua Discovery Center Museum 143

PENNSYLVANIA
Easton
    National Canal Museum & Hugh Moore Park 144
Erie
    Erie Maritime Museum (U.S. Brig *Niagara*) 144
    Watson Curtze Mansion & Planetarium 145
Greenville
    Greenville Canal Museum 145
New Hope
    New Hope Canal Boat Company 145
Philadelphia
    American Philosophical Society Library 145
    Cigna Museum and Art Collection 145
    Independence Seaport Museum 146
    Philadelphia Ship Preservation Guild 146
Pittsburgh
    USS *Requin* (SS-481) (Submarine) 147
Wyomissing
    C. Howard Heister Canal Center 147

RHODE ISLAND
Block Island
    Block Island Southeast Lighthouse
      and Museum 147
Bristol
    Herreshoff Marine Museum/Monument 148
East Greenwich
    Varnum Memorial Armory 148

RHODE ISLAND - Continued
Jamestown
    Beavertail Lighthouse Museum 148
    The Jamestown Museum 148
Kingston
    University of Rhode Island,
      Special Collections 149
Narragansett
    South County Museum 149
Newport
    International Yacht Restoration School 149
    Museum of Newport History 150
    Museum of Yachting 150
    Naval War College Museum 150
    Rose Island Lighthouse & Museum 151
    Singlehanded Sailors Hall of Fame 152
Providence
    Alfred S. Brownell Collection of
      Atlantic Coast Fishing Craft Models 152
    Providence (Replica Sloop) 152
    Rhode Island Historical Society 153
    Steamship Historical Society of
      America Collection 153
Woonsocket
    Chafee Blackstone National Corridor 154

SOUTH CAROLINA
Catawba
    Landsford Canal 154
Charleston
    The Charleston Museum 154
Moncks Corner
    Old Santee Canal State Park 154
Mt. Pleasant
    Patriot's Point Naval and
      Maritime Museum 155
North Charleston
    The *H. L. Hunley* Museum 155
St. Helena Island
    Hunting Island State Park 156

SOUTH DAKOTA
Sioux Falls
    Battleship *South Dakota* Museum 156

TENNESSEE
Germantown
    PT Boats, Inc. Headquarters 156
Memphis
    Mississippi River Museum at Mud Island 156

TEXAS
Corpus Christi
    Corpus Christi Museum of
      Science & Industry 157
    USS *Lexington* Museum on the Bay 157
Fredericksburg
    National Museum of the Pacific War 157

TEXAS - Continued
Galveston
    Seawolf Park 158
    Texas Seaport Museum/*ELISSA* 158
Houston
    Houston Maritime Museum 158
La Porte
    Battleship *Texas* State Historical Park 159
Port Isabel
    Port Isabel Historical Museum 159
    Port Isabel Lighthouse Complex 159
    Treasurers of the Gulf 160
Rockport
    Texas Maritime Museum 160

VERMONT
Basin Harbor
    Lake Champlain Maritime Museum 160
Shelburne
    Shelburne Museum, Inc. 161

VIRGINIA
Alexandria
    Alexandria Seaport Foundation &
      Seaport Center 161
    Torpedo Factory Art Center 162
Chincoteague
    The Oyster & Maritime Museum 162
Great Falls
    The Patowmack Canal 162
Newport News
    Dorothy (The Iron Tugboat) 162
    The Mariners' Museum 163
    USS *Monitor* Ironclad 163
Norfolk
    Hampton Roads Naval Museum 164
    Nauticus, The National Maritime Center 164
Onancock
    Hopkins and Bros. Store 165
Portsmouth
    Portsmouth Lightship Museum 165
    Portsmouth Naval Shipyard Museum 165
Reedville
    Reedville Fisherman's Museum 166
Richmond
    Museum of the Confederacy 166
    Science Museum of Virginia 166
    Virginia Canals & Navigations Society 167
Triangle
    U.S. Marine Corps Museum 167
Virginia Beach
    Cape Henry Lighthouse 167
    Old and New Lighthouses 167
    Old Coast Guard Station Museum 168
Williamsburg
    Jamestown Settlement 168
Yorktown
    Watermen's Museum 168
    Yorktown Battlefield Visitor Center 169
    Yorktown Victory Center 169

WASHINGTON
Aberdeen
    Grays Harbor Historical Seaport   169
Anacortes
    W. T. PRESTON (Sternwheeler)   170
Bainbridge Island
    Bainbridge Island Historic Museum   170
Bellingham
    Whatcom Museum of History and Art   170
Blaine
    Semiahmoo Park Museum   170
Bremerton
    Bremerton Naval Museum   171
    USS *Turner Joy* Bremerton Historical
      Ships Association   171
Edmonds
    Edmonds Historical Museum   171
Gig Harbor
    Gig Harbor Peninsula Historical
      Society & Museum,   172
Ilwaco
    Columbia Pacific Heritage Museum   172
Keyport
    Naval Undersea Museum   173
Mulkiteo
    Light Station Mulkilteo 1906   173
Neah Bay
    Makah Museum   173
Pasco
    Ice Harbor - Lower Monumental
      Project Historical Society   174
Port Townsend
    Museum of the Jefferson County
    Historical Society   174
Raymond
    Willapa Seaport Museum   174
San Juan Island - Friday Harbor
    Whale Museum   175
Seattle
    Burke Museum   175
    The Center for the Wooden Boat   175
    Coast Guard Museum/Northwest   176
    Hiram M. Chittenden Locks   176
    Museum of History and Industry   176
    Nordic Heritage Museum   177
    Northwest Seaport   177
    Puget Sound Maritime Historical Society   177
    Steamer *Virginia V* Foundation   178
Tacoma
    Working Waterfront Maritime Museum   178
Westport
    Westport Marine Museum   178

WASHINGTON, D.C.
    Decatur House   179
    National Maritime Heritage Initiative   179
    The Navy Museum   179
    Smithsonian Institution   180
    Society of the Cincinnati   180

WEST VIRGINIA
Berkeley Springs
    Museum of the Berkeley Springs   180

WISCONSIN
Bayfield
    Apostle Islands National Lakeshore   181
    Bayfield Heritage Association, Inc.   181
    Hokenson Brothers Fishery   181
Fish Creek
    Eagle Bluff Lighthouse   182
Gills Rock
    Door County Maritime Museum   182
    Door County Maritime Museum at
      Cana Island Lighthouse   182
Kewaunee
    Ship's Wheel Gallery &
      Nautical Museum   182
Manitowoc
    Wisconsin Maritime Museum   183
Milwaukee
    Milwaukee Public Library   183
Portage
    Portage Canal Society, Inc.   184
Port Washington
    Port Washington Light Station   184
Sturgeon Bay
    Door County Maritime Museum   184
Superior
    SS *Meteor* Maritime Museum   184
Two Rivers
    Rogers Street Fishing Museum   185

PART 2
CANADIAN PROVINCES

ALBERTA
Calgary
    The Naval Museum of Alberta   185

BRITISH COLUMBIA
Duncan
    Cowichan Bay Maritime Centre   186
Gibson's Landing
    Sunshine Coast Museum & Archives   186
New West Minister
    Samson V Maritime Museum
Tofino
    Whale Centre and Museum   187
Vancouver
    RV *Ben Franklin*   187
    Vancouver Maritime Museum   187
Victoria
    Maritime Museum of British Columbia   188
    Royal British Columbia Museum   188

MANITOBA
Selkirk
    Lower Fort Garry National Park   188
    Marine Museum of Manitoba   189
Winnipig
    Naval Museum of Manitoba   189

NEW BRUNSWICK
Grand Manan
    Grand Manan Museum and Walter
    B. McLaughlin Marine Gallery   189
Hopewell Cape
    Albert County Museum   190
Saint John
    New Brunswick Museum   190
Shippagan
    Aquarium and Marine Centre   190

NEWFOUNDLAND
Musgrave Harbour
    Fishermen's Museum   191
St. John's
    The Rooms Provincial Museum Div.   191

NOVA SCOTIA
Annapolis Royal/ Clark's Harbour
    O'Dell House Museum   191
Barrington
    Seal Island Light Museum   192
Bridgewater
    HMCS *Fraser* (DDE-223)   192
Centreville
    Archelaus Smith Museum   192
Halifax
    HMCS *Sackville* (K-181)   192
    Maritime Command Museum   193
    Maritime Museum of the Atlantic   193
Hantsport
    Churchill House and Marine
    Memorial Room Museum   193
La Have Island
    La Have Island Marine Museum   194
Liverpool
    Queens County Museum   194
Louisbourg
    Louisbourg Marine Museum   194
Lunenburg
    Fisheries Museum of the Atlantic   194
Mahone Bay
    Settler's Museum   195
Maitland
    Lawrence House   195
Parrsboro
    Ottawa House By-the-Sea   195
Port Greville
    Age of Sail Heritage Center   196
St. Peters
    St. Peters Canal   196

NOVA SCOTIA - Continues
Shelburne
    The Dory Shop   196
Yarmouth
    Yarmouth County Museum   197

ONTARIO
Chaffey's Lock
    The Lockmaster's House Museum   196
Collingwood
    Collingwood Museum   197
Elgin
    Jones Falls Defensible Lockmaster's House   198
Gore Bay
    Mississagi Strait Lighthouse   198
Hamilton
    Hamilton-Scourge Project   198
    HMCS Haida Naval Museum
Kingston
    Marine Museum of the Great Lakes
    at Kingston   199
Mallorytown
    St. Lawrence Islands National
    Park/Brown's Bay Wreck   199
Manitowaning
    Assiginack Historical Museum and
    SS *Norisle* Heritage Park   199
Mattawa
    Voyageur Heritage Centre, Samuel
    de Champlain Provincial Park   200
Merrickville
    Merrickville Blockhouse Museum   200
Midland
    Huronia Museum & Huron Indian Village 200
Milford
    Mariner's Park Museum   201
Mooretown
    Moore Museum   201
Ottawa
    Bytown Historical Museum   201
Owen Sound
    Owen Sound Marine-Rail Heritage Museum   202
Penetanguishene
    Discovery Harbour   202
Peterborough
    The Canadian Canoe Museum   202
    Peterborough Centennial Museum   203
    Peterborough Hydraulic Lift Lock
    and Visitor Centre   203
Port Carling
    Muskoka Lakes Museum   204
Port Colborne
    Port Colborne Historical and
    Marine Museum   204
Port Dover
    Port Dover Harbour Museum   204
Prescott
    Forwarder's Museum   204

ONTARIO -Continued
St. Catharines
    St. Catharines Historical Museum   205
Sault Ste. Marie
    Museum Ship *Norgoma*   205
    Sault St. Marie Canal Visitor Centre   205
Smiths Falls
    Lockmasters Anglin's Interpretive Center   206
    Rideau Canal Museum   206
Thunder Bay
    Old Fort William Historical Park   206
Tobermory
    Fathom Five National Marine Park   207
Toronto
    HMCS *Haida* Naval Museum   207
    Toronto Port Authority   207
Wasaga Beach
    Nancy Island Historic Site   207

PRINCE EDWARD ISLAND
Port Hill
    Green Park Shipbuilding Museum   208
Souris
    Basin Head Fisheries Museum   208

QUÉBEC
Coteau-du-Lac
    Coteau-du-Lac National
        Historical Site   208
L'Islet-sur-Mer
    Bernier Maritime Museum   209
Montréal
    David M. Stewart Museum   209
Pointe-au-Père
    Pointe-au-Père Sea Museum   210
Québec
    Cartier-Brébeuf National Historical Park   210
    Grosse Ile National Historic Site   210
    Naval Museum of Québec   211
    Port of Québec in the Nineteenth
        Century National Historic Site
        (Lieu Historique National le Port
        de Québec au XIXe Siècle)   211

YUKON TERRITORY
Dawson City
    SS *Keno* (Sternwheeler)   211

PART ONE

USA

ALABAMA

CARROLTON, ALABAMA

Tennessee-Tombigbee Waterway
Tom Bevill Resource Management & Visitor
Center Tennessee-Tombigbee Waterway
Development Authority
1382 Lock & Dam Road
Carrollton, AL 35447-9648
(205) 373-8705
E-mail: ttw@tenntom.org
Location: The Visitor Center is located near
Pickensville, Alabama, one-half mile south of the
junction of Alabama State Highways 14 and 86. It
is approximately twenty-five miles south of
Columbus, Mississippi, and ten miles north of
Aliceville, Alabama.
Highlights: U.S. Snagboat *Montgomery*
Website: http://tenntom.sam.usace.army.mil/
  General Information: The Visitor Center for
the Tennessee-Tombigbee Waterway (Tenn-Tom)
is a significant historical and cultural resource
housed in a newly constructed replica of an
antebellum-style mansion and contains displays
that relate to the early history and development of
the Tombigbee River as an avenue of commerce
for the agrarian economy of the 1800s.
  Extensive documentation and displays detail the
construction of this, the nation's largest modern-
day public works project, which was begun in 1971
and completed in 1985.
  Snagboat *Montgomery* relocation: On October
2nd, 2003, the 600-ton, 78-year old U. S. Snagboat
Montgomery was lifted from the waters of the
Tennessee-Tombigbee Waterway and
Permanently placed on dry ground at Pickensville,
Alabama. The U.S. Snagboat *Montgomery*, one of
the last steam-powered stern-wheelers to ply the
rivers of the South. Her crew worked at removing
trees, sunken logs, and other debris that might
obstruct river traffic.
  The Visitor Center is adjacent to the Tom Bevill
Lock and Dam, where visitors are invited to watch
the lockage of vessels traveling between the Gulf
of Mexico and the river ports of mid-America.
  Admission: No entry fee.
Open 8:00 am to 4:00 pm CT (Nov-Mar)
Open 9:00 am to 5:00 pm CT (Apr-Oct)

GULF SHORES, ALABAMA

Fort Morgan Museum
110 Highway 180 West
Gulf Shores, AL 36542-7802
(251) 540-7125
E-mail: fortmorganmuseum@ftmorganmus.org
Location: From Mobile take I-10 east across the
Mobile Bay to the Rte. 59 south exit to Gulf
Shores. Or, for another point of reference, Gulf
Shores lies on the Gulf of Mexico Intracoastal
Waterway thirty miles west of Pensacola, Florida.
Highlights: Fresnel lighthouse lens, gift shop
Website: www.ftmorganmus.org/
  General Information: Fort Morgan Museum,
founded in 1967, is a Civil War site. The Museum
contains Fresnel lenses from two local lighthouses
— Sand Island light (from the 1870s) and Mobile
Point light (from the 1850s) and also contain
lighthouse keeper's uniforms and memorabilia.
  Admission: Entry fee. Open 9 A.M. - 5 P.M.,
year-round. Closed Thanksgiving, Christmas, and
New Year's Day.

MOBILE, ALABAMA

Museum Of Mobile
Southern Market/Old City Hall
150 So. Royal Street
P.O. Box 2068
Mobile, AL 36602
(251) 208-7569 Fax: (208) 208-7686
E-mail: museum@cityofmobile.org
Location: The Museum of Mobile is conveniently
located in historic downtown Mobile. The museum
is within walking distance from the Mobile
Convention Center, the Adams Mark Hotel, a
variety of restaurants and the Fort Condé Welcome
Center.
Highlights: Maritime history, library,
Website: www.museumofmobile.com/
  General Information: The Museum Of Mobile
exhibits and displays information on the Colonial
period, Civil War, Battle of Mobile Bay
Armaments and pre-history to present.
  The library contains 3,000 volumes, 100 vessel
technical drawings, 1,000 vessel photos, and
10,000 documents. Seventy-five paintings are
displayed and 50 are stored. The collection
includes riverboats, portraits of CSS *Hunley*, CSS
Alabama. Ship models include 25 displayed, 20
stored: full, half hull, and cutaways. Also included
full models of CSS *Hunley*, CSS *Alabama*, and the
Admiral Raphael Sommes collection.
  A full-scale historic 35' replica of Confederate
submarine — CSS *Hunley* (ca 1865). It was hand
powered by nine men and was first submarine to
sink another ship in war in the Civil War. The
Hunley has been raised and is undergoing thorough
examination by marine archeologists.

Admission: Entry fee. Open Monday-Saturday, 10 A.M.-5 P.M., Sunday, 1 P.M. – 5 P.M., Summer Season; 8 A.M.-4 P.M., Winter season. Closed all holidays except Memorial Day, Independence Day, and Labor Day.

MOBILE, ALABAMA
USS *Alabama* Battleship Memorial Park
2703 Battleship Parkway (Highway 90/98)
Mobile, Al 36601
(251) 433-2703 Fax: (251) 433-2777
1-800-GANGWAY
E-mail: kconner@ussalabama.com
Location: Easy access from east/west I-10 to Battleship Parkway where the park is at the head of Mobile Bay just off the Gulf of Mexico.
Highlights: The USS *Alabama* (BB 60) (battleship), The USS *Drum* (SS 228) (submarine), **Website:** www.ussalabama.com/
   General Information: The USS *Alabama* Battleship Memorial Park, founded 9 January 1965, is a 155-acre park dedicated to Alabama's War veterans. The park's two main attractions are the USS *Alabama* and the submarine USS *Drum*, both participants in many World War II sea battles. The park complex also features many military aircraft, including a B-52 bomber. And an aircraft exhibit pavilion with twenty-two historic aircraft honoring all services, dedicated to twenty-eight Medal of Honor recipients from Alabama.
   Most of the *Alabama's* nine battle stars were earned while serving with a strike force in the Pacific, notably in Okinawa and Japan. The vessel's gallant military career was highlighted by its dominant role close to the end of the war. The battleship was decommissioned in 1947 and in 1964 was towed 5,600 miles from Seattle, Washington, to Mobile, Alabama, where she was established as a floating shrine in 1965.
   Visitors may tour the *Alabama's* decks, turrets, mess, and berthing compartments, bridge, the wardroom, and captain's cabin. Visitors to the USS *Drum* may go into the entire boat, including the torpedo rooms and the crew's quarters.
   Activities: Overnight encampment program.
   Admission: Entry fee. Open daily; 8 A.M. – 4 P.M., October - March; 8 A.M. - 6 P.M., April - September. Closed Christmas.

ALASKA

FAIRBANKS, ALASKA
Fairbanks Historical Preservation Foundation
755 Eighth Avenue
Fairbanks, AK 99701
(907) 456-8848
E-mail: webmaster@fairbanks-alaska.com

Location: The riverboat, landlocked, is located south of town.
Highlights: Nenana (Riverboat) **Website:** http://fairbanks-alaska.com/riverboat-nenana.htm
   General Information: The sternwheel riverboat *Nenana*, the only U.S. steamboat preserved in Alaska, was built in 1922 and is only one of five surviving western rivers steamboats. Originally built as a packet for the Alaska Railroad, it was designed as a steamer rather than a diesel or diesel-electric boat, which would operate better in the harsh conditions of the north.
   The *Nenana* had compound steam engines, the most efficient type that could be applied to sternwheelers, expanded steam twice to extract more energy from a given amount of steam. She often pushed, or towed, up to six barges and could carry up to 100 tons of cargo on her main deck. In addition, she had accommodations for fifty-two passengers who could take advantage of spacious staterooms equipped with hot and cold running water and electricity.
   Admission: Call for information.

KODIAK, ALASKA
Kodiak Maritime Museum
500 Dog Bay Dr
P.O. Box 1876
Kodiak, AK 99615
(907) 486-0384
E-mail: info@kodiakmaritimemuseum.org
Location: The Kodiak Maritime Museum currently operates out of a harborside office on Kodiak Island, Alaska.
Highlights: Fishing history,
Website: http://kodiakmaritimemuseum.org/
   General Information: The Kodiak Maritime Museum is dedicated to the recognition and preservation of Alaska's rich maritime heritage. The Kodiak region was first inhabited roughly 8,000 years ago by the Alutiiq people. In 1792, Russia established its first major fur trading center in Kodiak Harbor. During World War II, the United States built a Naval Base in Kodiak that served as a major strategic center for the North Pacific Theater. The United States Coast Guard's largest base is located on Kodiak Island. Today, Kodiak consistently ranks among the top three fishing ports in the United States.
   The Museum's first permanent exhibit consists of 14 interpretive panels along the Kodiak Harbor. The panels display fishing vessel gear types commonly seen in the harbor, commercially important marine species, historical facts and other information about Kodiak's maritime heritage.
   Admission: Call for information.

ARKANSAS

NEWPORT, ARKANSAS

Mary Woods No. 2 Riverboat Museum
c/o Jacksonport State Park
205 Avenue Street
Newport, AR 72112
(870) 523-2143
E-mail: jacksonpot@arkansas.com
Location: From State Rte. 367 in Newport, take
State Rte. 69 three miles north to Jacksonport.
Highlights: The Mary Woods No. 2 (riverboat),
gift shop, **Website:**
www.arkansasstateparks.com/jacksonport/
    General Information: Jacksonport State Park
serves as a symbol of an important time in history
when steamboats carried commerce and pioneers
up the White and Black Rivers in Arkansas. An
excellent Museum is housed in the 1872 county
courthouse where, moored nearby, is the last
sternwheel riverboat to ply the White River: the
Mary Woods No. 2, (136-foot-long, 157-ton stern
paddle-wheeler).
    She was recently restored to her original
condition of a 1930s sternpaddle-wheeler,
workboat transporting freshly logged timber to the
sawmills in Arkansas. She is the last triple-decked
stern-wheeler on the White River and one of the
very few remaining on the entire Mississippi River
System. The park also offers campsites along the
river, picnic areas and bathhouses, and boat ramp.
    Admission: Entry fee. Contact Jacksonport State
Park for dates and times open.

NORTH LITTLE ROCK, ARKANSAS

Arkansas Inland Maritime Museum
P. O. Box 5757
120 Riverfront Park
DriveNorth Little Rock, AR 72114
501-371-8320
E-mail: AIMM@northlittlerock.ar.gov
Location: The museum is off W. Riverfront Drive
3 blocks S. of E. Broadway – 3 blocks W. of I-30
Highlights: USS *Razorback* SS-394
Website: www.aimm.museum/
    General Information: The Arkansas Inland
Maritime Museum, founded to provide a home for
the 311-foot submarine named after a 45-foot
whale has made North Little Rock it's new home
The USS *Razorback* SS-394.
    The City of North Little Rock bought the
submarine from Turkey for $1 plus shipping
costs, to make it the centerpiece of a planned
inland maritime museum on the north bank
of the Arkansas River.
    Activities: Tours of the Razorback.
Admission: Entry fee. Open Saturday 10 A.M. to
Dusk. Sunday 1 P.M. to Dusk.

CALIFORNIA

ALAMEDA, CALIFORNIA

Aircraft Carrier *Hornet* Museum
707 West Hornet Avenue
Alameda, CA 94501
(510) 521-8448 Fax: (510) 521-8327
E-mail: info@uss-hornet.org
Location: From the San Francisco-Oakland Bay
Bridge and I-80 east take 580, then 980 downtown
Oakland to Jackson exit, follow signs to Alameda
Tunnel. From south (San Jose), take I-880 to
Broadway exit in Oakland, turn left, take Alameda
tunnel and follow signs to the *Hornet.*
Highlights: USS *Hornet* aircraft carrier,
Website: www.uss-hornet.org/
    General Information: The Aircraft Carrier
Hornet Museum, founded in 1998, features the
894-foot USS *Hornet* (CV-12). With only a two-
week shakedown cruise she engaged the enemy in
the Pacific just 21 months after the laying
of her keel. She was constantly in the most
forward areas of the Pacific war — sometimes
within forty miles of the Japanese home islands.
Her pilots destroyed1 410 enemy aircraft and over
one million tons of enemy shipping.
    "The Grey Ghost" participated in virtually all
of the assault landings in the Pacific from March
1944 until the end of WW II, earning nine battle
stars. In 1969, *Hornet* recovered the Apollo 11
space capsule containing the first men to walk on
the moon. A short time later she recovered Apollo
12 with the all-Navy crew of "moon walkers."
    Exhibits include portrayals of the eight USS
Hornets since 1775 with emphasis on CV-8 and
CV-12; displays of aircraft that operated off
Hornet; the operational history of all other Essex-
class carriers; and the history of U.S. Navy and
Marine Corps forces in the Pacific and Far East.
    Activities: Overnight camping program, field
trips, and on-board classes for students from grade
school through university.
Admission: Entry fee and memberships available.
Open daily 10 A.M. - 5 P.M.
Limited access Fall & Winter, Labor Day to
Memorial Day.

BELVEDERE, CALIFORNIA

China **Cabin**
52 Beach Road   Mail: P.O. Box 134
Belvedere, CA 94920   Tiburon, CA 94920
(415) 435-1853
Location: The cabin is on Beach Road near
Tiburon Boulevard and the waterfront at
Belvedere Cove.
Website: www. landmarks-
society.org/landmarks/china_cabin.php
    General Information: The *China* Cabin is an
elegantly restored social saloon and two officers'

cabins that were removed from William Webb's SS *China* of 1867. In the years of 1978-86, the cabin became a maritime museum and is open to the public. The *China* was involved in transpacific trade—1867-1979.

Admission: No entry fee. Open Sunday and Wednesday, 1 P.M.-4 P.M., April-October, or by appointment. Available for private parties.

CARMEL, CALIFORNIA
Point Sur Lightstation
Point Sur State Historic Park
2211 Garden Road
Carmel, CA 93940
(831) 625-4419
E-mail: info@parks.ca.gov
Location: Point Sur Lightstation is located 19 miles south of Monterey on Highway 1 at Point Sur, California.
Highlights: Lighthouse,
Website: www.pointsur.org
General Information: Established in 1889 by the U.S. Lighthouse Service, the Point Sur Lightstation operations were transferred to the U.S. Coast Guard in 1939. The lighthouse is the only complete turn-of-the-century Lightstation open to the public on the West Coast of the U.S.

Point Sur has been considered a navigation hazard throughout history. In the 1800s most cargo ships traveling the coast stayed within two to three miles from shore and during storms made for shelter behind the protruding headlands. After 11 years of frustrating efforts, the U.S. Lighthouse Service Board finally allocated funds for the light in 1885.

One of the factors influencing the funding was the wreck of the *Ventura* in 1875. Fourteen years later, on August 1, 1889, the lightstation, fully staffed, operated the light sunset to sunrise and the fog signal when fog was present.

In 1995, the Central Coast Lighthouse Keepers (CCLK), organized in 1991, developed a Museum/Interpretive Center in the fog signal room of old Point Sur Lighthouse. It features two Fresnel lenses, fog signal equipment, and artifacts of the Lighthouse Service and Coast Guard years.

The 1st-order (huge) Fresnel lens from the Point Sur Lightstation now rests in the Monterey Maritime Museum for all to see. The light atPoint Sur is now automated for the benefit of mariners. Also, among the seven lightstation buildings, the Lantern Room, Blacksmith/ Carpenter Shop, Barn, and Water Tower have been restored.

Admission: Entry fee. Volunteer-led tours are provided on Saturdays, 10 A.M. and 2 P.M.; Sundays, 10 A.M.; Wednesdays, 10 A.M. and

2 P.M., April through October. During July and August, tours Thursdays, 10 A.M. and 2 P.M. Moonlight tours are provided during the summertime. Call for additional information. (408) 625-4419

CARMEL, CALIFORNIA
The Whalers Cabin and Whaling Station Museum
Point Lobos Natural History Association
Route 1, Box 62
Carmel, CA 93923
(831) 624-4909 E-mail: ptlobos@parks.ca.gov
Location: Point Lobos State Reserve. On the central coast of California in Monterey County. The entrance is located three miles south of Carmel on Highway 1.
Highlights: Chinese fishing, whaling,
Website: http://pt-lobos.parks.state.ca.us/WhalersCove.htm
General Information: Whalers Cabin was occupied and used from 1851 to 1983 by various families, workers, and, in later years, park personnel. Activity at Whalers Cove began around 1851, when a group of four or five Chinese fishermen and their families moved onto the west shore of Whalers Cove and built their residences, one of which still stands and houses the Museum.

This small Museum gives an excellent picture of the early whaling activities conducted here. Six whale vertebrae provide support for the floor joists, which rest on granite piers supplied from the nearby quarry. The cabin is one of the oldest buildings of Chinese origin remaining in Monterey County.

Admission: Entry fee to State Park only. Open daily, 9 A.M. The Reserve will close to incoming people and cars at 4:30 P.M. All visitors must exit the Reserve by 5:00 P.M.

CARNELIAN BAY, CALIFORNIA
Tahoe Maritime Museum
5205 West Lake Blvd.
P. O. Box 627
Homewood, CA 96141
(530) 525-9253
Fax: (530) 525-9283
E-mail: info@tahoemaritime.org
Location: Museum is located on the south side of the Homewood Mountain Resort parking lot.
Highlights: Lake Tahoe maritime history and 25 historical boats.
Website: www.tahoemaritimemuseum.org/
General Information: The Tahoe Maritime Museum's purpose is to stimulate interest, increase knowledge, and maintain watercraft and marine artifacts significant in Lake Tahoe's

maritime history through historic preservation, innovative interpretation, and public education. And be sure to see our video, "A century on the Lake."

Admission: Entry fee. Open: May 27 – June 30, Thrus-Mon, 11 A.M.-5 P.M.; July/August 7 days/week 11 A.M.-5 P.M.; After Labor Day, Sat/Sun, 11 A.M. – 5 P.M.

CATALINA ISLAND, CALIFORNIA
Catalina Island Museum
Casino Building P.O. Box 366
Avalon, CA 90704
(310) 510-2414 Fax: (310) 510-1957
E-mail: info@catalinamuseum.org
Location: Museum located in the world famous Casino Building, ground floor, facing the bay in Avalon, the major tourist port on Catalina Island, is thirty miles south of Long Beach, California, and twenty-five miles west of Newport Beach.
Highlights: Channel steamer history, ship/boat models, library, gift shop,
Website: www.catalinamuseum.org

General Information: The Catalina Island Museum showcases the varied history of Santa Catalina Island (once owned by chewing gum magnate William Wrigley, Jr.) from the Island's first inhabitants (over 7,000 years ago) to present day. Maritime enthusiasts will enjoy the permanent display *Catalina's Steamers: In All the World No Trip Like This* which features video of the steamers from the 1920s through the 1940s and artifacts from the S.S. *Avalon* and S.S. *Catalina*. Also featured is an exhibit on the 18th century Chinese Junk, *Nig Po*, which, after a checkered career involving smuggling and piracy, peacefully ended her days at Catalina Harbor as a tourist attraction and movie set. Glass bottom boat models are also on display and the development of sport fishing is also discussed.

Researchers can also access the Museum's extensive photograph collection, which includes steamer, yachts, powerboats and glass bottom boats, and the archives that contain early boat schedules, and a complete run of the local papers. (Appointments required.)
Admission: Entry fee. Open daily, 10 A.M. - 4 P.M., year-round, closed Thursdays January-March, closed Christmas Day.

CRESCENT CITY, CALIFORNIA
Battery Point Lighthouse
Del Norte County Historical Society
577 H Street
Crescent City, CA 95531
(707) 464-3089
Location: Crescent City is on the Pacific coastline about eighteen miles south of the Oregon state line on Rte. 101. Battery Point

E-mail: kraig@lighthousefriends.com
Lighthouse is reached by taking Front Street west to the intersection of A Street. Turn south on A Street one block to the parking area. The lighthouse is 200 to 300 yards from the mainland and can be reached when the tide is out by walking a short trail (used since 1856).
Highlights: Lighthouse, research files, newspapers, **Website:** www.lighthousefriends.com/light.asp?ID=58

General Information: Battery Point Lighthouse, built in 1856 and decommissioned in 1951, sits on a fully exposed small island that is accessible at low tide. The Del Norte County Historical Society maintains a maritime museum here and shines the light as a private aid to navigation. Crescent City is the site of a famous July 30, 1865 sinking of the side-wheel steam passenger ship *Brother Jonathan* that took 200 people down with it—19 survived. Salvage divers have found the site and many artifacts have been recovered.

St. George Reef Lighthouse is located six miles west of Crescent City.

The Museum contains collections in machine, naval, and shipping history. Included are local history books, photographs, diaries, manuscripts, originals of local newspapers, and research files that are available for use on premises under supervision.
Activities: Guided tours through the keeper's home to the tower.
Admission: Entry fee. Lighthouse: open April-September, Wednesday-Sunday, 10 A.M.-4 P.M., tide permitting.

DANA POINT, CALIFORNIA
Pilgrim (Snow Brig)
Ocean Institute
24200 Dana Point Harbor Drive, P.O. Box 69
Dana Point, CA 92629
(949) 496-2274 Fax: (949) 496-4296
E-mail: oi@ocean-institute.org
Location: The Institute and *Pilgrim* are located on the west end of the Dana Point Marina.
Highlights: *Pilgrim* (replica ship), *Spirit of Dana Point* Tallship, gift shop,
Website: www.ocean-institute.org

General Information: We invite you to explore with us...a world where you are not just an observer but one in which you ride the high seas aboard a historic tallship, record observations of marine mammals, observe a sea creature that can spit out its stomach, or learn the skills of a research scientist!

The 125-foot brig Pilgrim, built in 1945, is a full size replica of the hide brig immortalized by Richard Henry Dana in his classic book *Two Years before the Mast*. Owned and operated by the Ocean Institute, the *Pilgrim* is dedicated to multidisciplinary education. During the school year, the Ocean Institute offers an 18-hour award-winning living history program.

Throughout the summer, the *Pilgrim* offers an all volunteer sail training program with individuals who donate their time to maintain the vessel. In late summer the Pilgrim sets sail on her annual cruise acting as an ambassador of goodwill to Southern California ports.

Admission: Entry fee. Open Saturday & Sunday: 10 A.M. – 3 P.M.

EUREKA, CALIFORNIA
Clarke Museum
240 E Street at Third Street
Eureka, CA 95501
(707) 443-1947
E-mail: clarkehistorical@att.net
Location: Eureka is on Humboldt Bay in northern California 298 miles north of San Francisco. The Museum is in the center of town.
Highlights: Ship models, Native American history, newsletter
Website: www.clarkemuseum.org/
General Information: The Clarke Museum has a small but interesting maritime collection featuring local craft, photos, and ship models. The history of Humboldt County is the history of hard work as shown in exhibits on the maritime trade, shipbuilding, logging, sawmilling, and shipwrecks. In addition, there are displays of Native American artifacts, antique weapons, and exhibits on regional and natural history. The Museum also has a significant collection of Northwestern California Indian basketry, including examples of Yurok, Karuk, and Hupa ceremonial regalia.
Admission: No entry fee. Open Tuesday-Saturday, 12 A.M. - 4 P.M., year-round.

EUREKA, CALIFORNIA
Humboldt Bay Maritime Museum
1410 2nd Street
Eureka, CA 95501-0602
(707) 444-9440 E-mail: madaket1910@aol.com
Location: The Museum is on the west side of the downtown area.
Highlights: *Madaket* (diesel launch), USS *Milwaukee* wreck history, gift shop Web site: www.humboldtbaymaritimemuseum.com/
General Information: The Humboldt Bay Maritime Museum's historical exhibits include boats, ship-building plans, tools, models, photographs, and a 4th order lighthouse lens — parts of which can still be seen during low tides sticking up out of the beach south of Eureka at Somoa. all collected over the years from the Eureka area.

Of special interest is the historical information on the USS *Milwaukee* wreck on the beach in 1917,

The *Milwaukee* was attempting to pull the grounded submarine H-3 off the beach, but one of the tow lines parted, and the *Milwaukee* wound up on the shore never to leave — the submarine was removed and went on to serve the Navy. The 1910 diesel launch *Madaket* has been restored and is operational, giving daily bay tours during summer months.

Admission: No entry fee. Open Monday-Saturday, 11 A.M.- 4 P.M. year-round.

FORT BRAGG, CALIFORNIA
The Guest House Museum
343 N. Main Street
c/o Office of Fort Bragg City Administrator
Fort Bragg City Hall
416 N. Franklin Street
Fort Bragg, CA 95437
(707) 961-2840 (707) 964-4251
Location: Fort Bragg is 150 miles north of San Francisco on Hwy 1.
Highlights: History of coastal lumber trade
Website:
www.rvtravelog.com/ftbragg.dir/ftbragg1.htm
General Information: The Guest House Museum is situated in the 1892 Johnson family home site in Fort Bragg adjacent to the site of the family's lumber company on the headlands of Noyo Landing. The three-story Victorian home is constructed entirely of redwood. C. R. Johnson, founder of the Union Lumber Company (1859-1940), built the home and in 1912 converted it into a guest house for friends, customers, and the company's airplane pilots.

In December 1984, George-Pacific lumber company donated the home to the City of Fort Bragg. The city has continued its use as a museum and as a depository for historical pictures, artifacts, and records of the forest products industry on the Mendocino Coast and the city of Fort Bragg. Of particular import is the most interesting history of high-wire, shore-to-ship loading of lumber schooners from a high bluff at adjacent Noyo Landing, at the entrance to the present-day Fort Bragg harbor.

Photographs include loading of lumber, railroads, mills, and woods scenes. Nearby at the Depot Mall are once-used steam donkey engines, rigging blocks, locomotives, and "high" wheels used in log harvesting by Mendocino Coast forest product companies.
Admission: Call for information.

LONG BEACH, CALIFORNIA
Queen Mary (passenger liner)
1126 Queen's Highway
Long Beach, CA 90802
(562) 435-3511 877-342-0738
E-mail: historian@queenmary.com
Location: Long Beach is south of Los Angeles
and can be approached from Long Beach Freeway
via I-710, south from I-405. Follow signs via
Queen's Way Bridge. She is permanently moored
at Pier "J" in Long Beach Harbor.
Highlights: The *Queen Mary* (passenger liner),
historic tour, Hall of Maritime Heritage, award-
winning restaurants, gift shop, *Scorpion* Sub.
Website: www.queenmary.com/
   General Information: *Queen Mary* was is the
last of the great ocean liners built during the
golden age of transatlantic travel. A former
British liner, she was retired to Long Beach in
1967, and established as a tourist attraction in
1971. The *Queen Mary* contains 365 Art Deco
staterooms, 16 salons, convention and meeting
rooms, a 50,000-square-foot Exhibit Hall, three
water view restaurants, an Art Deco bar, a
wedding chapel and numerous gift shops.
   She is one of the largest passenger liners ever
built, and during her career at sea (1936-1967)
played hostess to countless celebrity and VIP
passengers. British Prime Minister, Sir Winston
Churchill, was a secret passenger on several
crossings in WWII on his way to conferences with
President Roosevelt.
   The ship is a collection of Art Deco art and
architecture featuring 56 varieties of wood,
decorative glass, memorabilia and furnishings
from the 1930s and 1940s, two 40,000-HP
engines and power train, and exhibits celebrating
the *Queen's* role as a military transport during
WWII. A retired British liner with 365
staterooms, salons, four restaurants, shops,
wedding chapel, convention accommodations, and
meeting facilities — she is one of the largest
passenger liners ever built. Prime Minister
Winston Churchill was a secret passenger during
WW II, crossing the Atlantic to visit President
Roosevelt.
   Activities: Self-guided tours include the bridge,
officers' quarters, engine room, and upper decks.
Guided tours also available.
   Admission: Entry fee. Open daily, 10 A.M.-
6 P.M., year-round with extended summer hours.

MARINA DEL REY, CALIFORNIA
Lloyd Taber-Marina del Rey Library
County of Los Angeles Public Library
4533 Admiralty Way
Marina del Rey, CA 90292-5416
 (310) 821-3415

E-mail: colapl@lhqsmtp.colapl.org
Location: The library is just west of Lincoln
Blvd. and north of the intersection of Bali Way
and Admiralty Way. *Highlights:* Library, reading
room facing the harbor,
Website: www.colapublib.org/libs/marina/
   General Information: This public Library
houses the Nautical Collection for the County of
Los Angeles Public Library and primarily services
the recreational boater. Consisting of books
(5,000), videos (550), periodicals (25) and audio
cassettes (50), the collection covers all facets of
boating: purchasing, building or maintaining a
boat, sailboat, yacht, or dinghy; navigation; first-
aid; naming your craft; cooking in a limited space,
and boating skills. The history of boats and ships
is briefly covered, as are charts for various
waterways and the recollection of sea adventures
and nautical fiction. For those interested in
peripheral nautical subjects, we have books on
building model ships; lighthouses; painting
watercolors of sea subjects; and nautical
dictionaries.
   Three Internet computers in the William Pagen
Nautical Wing have nautical software available to
the public: charts of Southern California and
Catalina Is, chart planning, tide tables, sailboat
racing strategy and power boating rules of the
road. The library's collection, in existence since
1976, is available through Interlibrary Loan and
the catalog is available on the county library's
website.
   Admission: No entry fee. Open Tuesday
11 A.M.-8 P.M.; Wednesday and Thursday 12
P.M.-8 P.m.; Friday 12 P.M. - 6 P.M.; Saturday
10 A.M. - 5 P.M. Closed Sunday, Monday and
Holidays. The library is accessible to the
disabled.

MONTEREY, CALIFORNIA
Monterey History & Maritime Museum
5 Custom House Plaza
Monterey, CA 93940
(831) 375-2608   Fax: (831) 655-3053
E-mail: tim@montereyhistory.org
Location: Monterey is ninety miles south of San
Francisco on Pacific Ocean coastline on SR-1;
exit to center city. The Museum is adjacent to
Fisherman's Wharf.
Highlights: Library, (2,000 volumes) on maritime
and shipping, ship models including Frigate
Savannah and Vizcaino's ship *San Diego*,
scrimshaw, first-order Fresnel lens from the Point
Sur Lighthouse, **Web Site:**
www.montereyhistory.org/a-contact.htm
   General Information: Portraying the sailing-
ship era, the fishing and whaling days in
Monterey, California, the local naval history

(1846), the Maritime Museum of Monterey (previously named the Allen Knight Maritime Museum), opened in January 1971 to exhibit a large private collection of maritime artifacts and relics accumulated by the late Allen Knight of Carmel, California. His devotion to ships and the sea was lifelong. Early on he served as a young deck hand on the sailing ship *Falls of Clyde*, which is now restored and moored at the Hawaii Maritime Museum in Honolulu.

The Museum has a variety of collections that Include sailing-ship models, steering wheels, bells, blocks, compasses, lanterns, scrimshaw, navigation instruments, ship name boards and other parts of old ships, prints, and paintings of ships.

Special features include the ship *San Diego*, captained by Spanish Explorer Sebastian Vizcaino in his 1562 west coast explorations. When he came upon a great bay on the southern coastline, he re-named it San Diego. Juan Rodriguez Cabrillo, in his earlier 1542 exploration had named this same great bay San Miguel. Another special feature is a beautiful large model of the frigate *Savannah*, which was the flagship of Commodore John Drake Sloat when he captured Monterey in 1846, making California a part of the United States. A comprehensive maritime library includes many volumes of old *Lloyd's Register*. The library is primarily for researchers: writers, scholars, and artists.

Activities: Guided tours and lectures.

Admission: Entry fee. Memberships are available. Open daily except Wed, 10 A.M.-5 P.M. Closed Thanksgiving, Christmas Day, and New Year's Day.

NEWPORT BEACH, CALIFORNIA
Newport Harbor Nautical Museum
600 East Bay Avenue
Newport Beach, CA 92661
(949) 675-8915
E-mail nhmm@nhnm.org
Location: Newport Beach is south of Long Beach and ten miles east of I-405. Exit Rte. 55 west to Newport Beach. Turn off onto Pacific Coast Hwy south to Museum on Ferryboat.
Highlights: Maritime history, ship models,
Website: www.nhnm.org/
General Information: Established in 1986, the Newport Harbor Nautical Museum now resides in a replica ship first used as a major restaurant in Newport Harbor. The Museum preserves the history of Newport Harbor in photographs, artifacts, and memorabilia reflecting the recreational and industrial lore of the area. From the early days when the harbor was visited by the U.S. Coast Guard schooner *Humboldt* in 1870

to the Ensenada races which now originate here, the Museum has assembled an intriguing collection to perpetuate the region's maritime heritage.

In addition to permanent displays of boats, ship models, navigational and nautical instruments, and fishing trophies, the Museum provides a series of special exhibits highlighting various class boats, sports-fishing history, race events, boat building, art displays, and other subjects of maritime interest.

Admission: No entry fee. Open Tuesday-Sunday, 10 A.M.-5 P.M. Closed on Monday.

OAKLAND, CALIFORNIA
Lightship *Relief* – WLV 605
Jack London Square
57C Clay Street
Oakland, CA
(510) 272-0544
Location: The lightship is at Jack London Square in Oakland adjacent to the former presidential yacht *Potomac*, used by President Franklin Delano Roosevelt.
Highlights: Lightship WLV 605 Relief
Website: www.uslhs.org/inner/lightship.html
General Information: The WLV 605 *Relief* was built in Boothbay, ME at Rice Brothers Shipyard, along with her sister ship, the 604 (which are now a floating museum in Columbia, WA.

The relief is a 600-class lightship - the last class of lightship built by the U.S. Coast Guard. The 605 served in Delaware, off Blunts Reef, and as the Relief ship for all west coast lightships. Today, after 15 years of restoration and 20,000 volunteer hours, she is open to the public at Jack London Square in Oakland, CA and is a national historic landmark.

Admission: Open for Tours
Thursday and Friday, 10:00 am to 3:00 pm
Saturday and Sunday, 11:00 am to 4:00 pm
Jack London Square, Oakland, California
Phone (510) 272-0544

OAKLAND, CALIFORNIA
***Patomac* Presidential Yacht**
540 Water Street
P.O. Box 2064
Oakland, CA 94604
(510) 627-1215)
Location: Parking
Washington Street Garage between 2nd and Embarcadero Streets, one block from the *Potomac*. Sorry, we do not validate.
Highlights: *Patomac* Presidential Yacht
Website: www.usspotomac.org
General Information: The U.S.S. *Potomac* originally was built in 1934 as the Coast Guard

376 gross tons and with a cruising speed of 10 to 13 knots, was converted to the presidential yacht U.S.S. *Potomac* by Franklin Delano Roosevelt, who had her recommissioned as a U.S. Navy vessel in 1936.

Activities; Group tours – call for reservations.

Admission: Dockside tours: Wednesday 10:30 a.m. to 3:30 p.m., Friday and Sunday 12:00 noon to 3:30 p.m.

OXNARD, CALIFORNIA
Ventura County Maritime Museum
2731 So. Victoria Avenue
Oxnard, CA 93035
(805) 984-6260 Fax: (805) 984-5970
E-mail: vcmm@aol.com
Location: Oxnard is north of Los Angeles on the southeastern end of the Santa Barbara Channel. Take Rte. 101 to the Victoria exit, and then head south five miles to Channel Islands Boulevard. The Museum is at the intersection of Channel Islands Boulevard and Victoria.
Highlights: Ship models, maritime paintings,
Website: www.tfaoi.com/newsmu/nmus162.htm

General Information: The Ventura County Maritime Museum, founded in 1989, is a recreational, educational, and research facility emphasizing the Pacific Rim, the California coast, and the Channel Islands.

The Museum also houses the Almar Fine Arts Collection of seventy significant maritime paintings, 1750 to date, and seventy-four exquisite ship models including the Marple Fleet of nine world-class scratch-built sailing vessels. The Museum also brings to life the shipwrecks and maritime adventures of the nearby Channel Islands.

Admission: Contact Museum for hours and fees.

PACIFIC GROVE, CALIFORNIA
Point Pinos Lighthouse
c/o Pacific Grove Museum of National History
165 Forest Avenue
Pacific Grove, CA 93950-2612
(831) 648-3176
Location: The Lighthouse is in north central California 123 miles south of San Francisco near Monterey. From Monterey, go west pass through Pacific Grove to the end of Lighthouse Avenue.
Highlights: Point Pinos Lighthouse,
Website: www.93950.com/steinbeck/3.htm

General Information: Point Pinos (point of pines) Lighthouse is the oldest, continuously operating lighthouse on the West Coast. The Cape Cod-style lighthouse is located at the western edge of the town of Pacific Grove, near

Monterey. Point Pinos light has shone since 1855 and had two female keepers in the 19th century who served a combined period of 40 years. The building and third order Fresnel lens are all original. A small maritime museum is in the lighthouse.

Admission: No entry fee. Open Thursday through Sunday, 1 P.M.-4 P.M. For special tours, phone ahead.

POINT ARENA, CALIFORNIA
Point Arena Lighthouse and Museum
P.O. Box 11, 45500 Lighthouse Road
Manchester, CA 95459
1-877- 725-4448 (707) 882-2777
E-mail: palight@mcn.org
Location: North on Hwy 1 one mile from the City of Point Arena (near Mendocino), then west 2 miles on Lighthouse Road.
Highlights: Lighthouse, on-sight vacation rentals, whale-watching, museum, overnight lodging,
Website: www.pointarenalighthouse.com/

General Information: the 1906 San Francisco earthquake fractured The Point Arena Lighthouse, originally built in 1870. It was condemned, along with the ornate Keeper's residence, and had to be torn down. Later, the 115-foot tower was rebuilt as the first poured concrete steel-reinforced lighthouse. The two-ton first-order Fresnel lens is still in place, but has not been used since the lighthouse was automated in 1977. The non-profit Point Arena Lighthouse Keepers, Inc. has occupied Point Arena Light Station and keeps it open as an historic and recreational area.

A museum in the adjacent fog signal building houses maritime and historical artifacts, and photographs. The Lighthouse keepers have renovated the three homes on the station, and these are now available to the public as vacation rentals. Each home is approximately 1400 square feet, with three bedrooms, two full baths, and completely furnished.

Activities: The lighthouse is open to the public for tours and three bungalows on site are available for lodging.

Admission: Entry fee. Open daily, 10 A.M.-4:30 P.M. daily year round.

POINT RICHMOND, CALIFORNIA
East Brother Light Station
117 Park Place
Point Richmond, CA 94801
(510) 233-2385 Fax: (510) 291-2243
E-mail: info@ebls.org
Location: East Brother Light Station is one-quarter mile west of Point San Pablo in San Pablo Bay and closest to Point Richmond.

9

Access is by ten-minute ferryboat ride.
Website: www.ebls.org/
Highlights: East Brother Light Station, Bed and
Breakfast, Website: www.ebls.org
  General Information: East Brother Light
Station was constructed in 1873-74, one of the
second group of lighthouses to be built along the
west coast of the U.S. Manned continuously, the
Coast Guard
automated the light and fog signal, and in 1969 it
was added to the National Register
of Historic Places. In 1979, with the determined
efforts of volunteers and perched on a 1-acre slab
of rock off Richmond's shore, the island's
facilities were totally restored as a living museum
and a unique adventure that accurately preserves
the essence of an important chapter in American
maritime history.
  Activities: Overnight visitors will delight to a
five-course dinner with San Francisco sparkling
twelve miles to the south. Victorian furnishings,
brass beds, and fresh flowers highlight the five
comfortably appointed guest rooms that once
served as the lighthouse keeper's quarters.
  Admission: Reservations are required. Call or
write for information and rates.

PORT HUENEME, CALIFORNIA
Civil Engineer Corps/Seabee Museum
Naval Construction Battalion Center
Code HO, Building 99
1000 23rd Avenue
Port Hueneme, CA 93043-4301
(805) 982-5165 Store: 805-982-5168
Location: From Oxnard (northwest of Los
Angeles) take Rte. 101 to the SR-1 exit. Follow
signs to the Naval Construction Battalion Center
in Port Hueneme (pronounced Y-Ne-Me).
Highlights: Keepsakes from countries and islands
Seabees have visited, dioramas depicting Seabee
construction feats, unusual hunting and farming
implements, gift shop,
Website: https://portal.navfac.navy.mil/nfelc
  General Information: The Civil Engineer
Corps/Seabee Museum, founded in 1947, is a
lasting monument to the history and fighting spirit
of the Seabees and Naval Civil Engineer Corps.
The name "Seabee" is derived from the initials
"CB" for Construction Battalion.
  The Museum contains numerous artifacts such
as weapons, swords, unusual hunting and farming
implements, personal memorabilia, and many
other items relating to the customs and culture of
the various countries and islands where Seabees
have served and are still serving. It also features
dioramas depicting some of the Seabee's larger
construction feats.

Admission: No entry fee. Open Tuesday-
Saturday, 9 A.M.-4 P.M. Closed Federal
holidays, Easter, and the week between Christmas
and New Year's Day

RICHMOND, CALIFORNIA
SS *Red Oak* (Victory Ship)
Richmond Museum of History
1337 Canal Blvd., Berth 6A
Richmond, CA 94804
(510) 237-2933
Richmond Mus. of History 510-235-7387
Email: info@ssredoakvictory.org
Location: The ship is located at Terminal 11,
Richmond, CA.
Highlights: SS *Red Oak* Victory,
Website: www.ssredoakvictory.org/
  General Information: The SS *Red Oak*
Victory is one of the few remaining Victory ships,
and one of the last produced at the Kaiser
Shipyard in Richmond, CA. She is named for the
city of Red Oak, Iowa which suffered the highest
per capita casualty rate of any American
community during World War II. She was turned
over to the Museum of History in Richmond
September 20, 1988 where she is permanently
moored. See other Victory ships now museum
ships: SS *American* (Victory) (FL) and SS *Lane*
(Victory) (CA).
  The ship departed San Francisco for Pearl
Harbor on January 10, 1945. She then began her
career as an ammunition ship and departed Hawaii
loaded with munitions needed in the Marshall and
Caroline Islands. She then sailed for the
Luckenback Steamship Company in 1947 and
between 1950 and 1953 as a Merchant Marine
vessel.
  Admission: Entry fee. Open Sat/Sun 10 A.M.
– 3 P.M. Tues/Thurs 10 A.M. – 3 P.M.

RIO VISTA
Dutra Museum of Dredging
345 St. Gertrude Avenue
Rio Vista, CA 94571
(415) 258-7876 or (650) 207-6489
E-mail: pdutra@dutragroup
Or jbobcal@comcast.net
Location: Rio Vista is a small, quaint river town
located in the heart of the California Delta.
Highlights: California Delta Dredging and Dutra
family history, historic home
Web site: www.dutragroup.com
  General Information: The Dutra Museum of
Dredging is a private collection of materials
representing the history of sidedraft clamshell
dredging in the Sacramento-San Joaquin Delta
and the role the Dutra family and Dutra

companies have played in building the Delta infrastructure. The collection, unique in its scope and size, spans the century that has elapsed since the introduction of steam-powered dredging equipment to the California Delta.

The collection is housed in a craftsman style mansion built in 1907. Originally built for local farmer John McCormak, the Dutra family became the home's fourth owner when Ed and Linda Dutra purchased it in 1978. The home is currently owned by the Dutra Museum Foundation.

The museums content includes many photographs, log books, ledgers, dredge models, original engineer drawings on linen, mammoth bone extracted from a Delta island and a family history mural (by Marty Stanley) that details the Dutra family's beginnings as Portuguese whalers.

The Dutra family's involvement in sidedraft clamshell dredging began more than a century ago. Since then, members of the family have been continuously engaged in this highly specialized branch of dredging science.

Antone Dutra, began the companies' historic association with the construction and maintenance of the Delta levee system in 1904. His son, Edward Dutra, continued these efforts beginning in 1933, followed by Antone's grandson, Bill, in 1962 role in protecting one of California's most important natural resources.

Admission: We are currently open by appointment only. To schedule a tour please call one of the directors, Patty Dutra Bruce at (415) 258-6876 or Janet Bennett at (650) 207-6489. Admission: $3 for adults & $2 for seniors/Stds.

SACRAMENTO, CALIFORNIA
Old Sacramento Waterfront and Riverboat
Delta King

1000 Front Street
Sacramento, CA 95814
1-800-825-5464 916-444-5464
E-mail: mcoyne@deltaking.com
Location: The Riverboat *Delta King* is located at the intersection of Front and K Streets on the Sacramento River Waterfront in the western part of downtown. *Highlights:* Riverboat *Delta King* (hotel, meeting rooms, restaurant),
Website: www.deltaking.com/
   General Information: A $10 million reconstruction of Sacramento's historic river waterfront includes a two-block-long wooden wharf; four historic buildings; the store ship *Globe*; *Delta King* riverboat; and a freight depot.

The 285-ft sternwheeler *Delta King* carried passengers between Sacramento and San Francisco in the 1920s and 1930s, as did its sister ship the *Delta Queen*, which now plies the waters of the Mississippi River. The *Delta King* is now permanently docked on the waterfront with forty-four deluxe hotel staterooms and suites, theatre, and meeting facilities, and she is, herself, a riverboat museum.

Admission: Call or write Sacramento Convention and Visitors Bureau, 1421 K Street, Sacramento, CA 95814, (916) 264-7777 for information.

SAN DIEGO, CALIFORNIA
Cabrillo National Monument

1800 Cabrillo Memorial Drive
San Diego, CA 92106-3601
(619) 222-4747
Fax: (619) 226-6311 E-mail on Website.
Location: The Monument is at the south end of Cabrillo Memorial Drive atop Point Loma Peninsula, west of downtown San Diego. Follow Rosecrans Street (SR 209) to Canon Street. Turn right on Canon and follow Canon Boulevard, turning left on Catalina Boulevard. The Monument is approached through the gates of the Navy's SPAWAR facility.
Highlights: Old Point Loma Lighthouse, Gray Whale observation point, statue of Juan Rodríguez Cabrillo, bookstore, Coast Defense exhibit, Tide pools, Bayside Trail,
Website: www.nps.gov/cabr/
   General Information: Cabrillo National Monument overlooks the city and harbor of San Diego. A statute commemorates Juan Rodríguez Cabrillo, who landed near here in 1542. Just up the hill, the historic 40-foot high lighthouse, first lit in 1855, served passing ships for nearly forty years. Five rooms in the restored lighthouse are furnished with antique furniture from 1887 and Lighthouse Service artifacts.
   Activities: The Visitor Center features exhibits on Cabrillo's voyage and films. Various audiovisual and gray whale programs. The whale overlook provides a point from which to observe the annual gray whale migrations (December-February). Recorded interpretive messages are at the lighthouse and whale overlook, statue, and Visitor Center. Also, birding and hiking along Bayside Trail. Tide pooling in winter, call for low tide information.
   Admission: Entry fee. Open daily, 9 A.M.-5:15 P.M., summer 9 A.M. – 6:15 P.M. year-round.

SAN DIEGO, CALIFORNIA
San Diego Aircraft Carrier Museum –
USS *Midway*

910 N. Harbor Drive
San Diego, CA 92101-5811
(619) 544-9600
Fax: (619) 238-1200 E-mail: THRU WEBSITE
Location: The carrier is on the south side of the Navy Pier at Broadway and Harbor Drive on the

San Diego Embarcadaro.
Highlights: Aircraft carrier USS *Midway*,
Website: www.midway.org/
General Information: The San Diego Aircraft
Carrier Museum - USS *Midway* is now a reality.
The Museum will contain a variety of naval
aircraft including two F-4s Phantom II fighters,
an A-4E Skyhawk light attack bomber, and a C-
1A Trader cargo/transport. In addition there will
be a wide collection of exhibits and displays
offering the visitor full knowledge of the carrier
Midway's role in support of the military during
WWII.

The naval museum features a corridor of
displays that tell the history of the ship. Several
of the ship's veterans also have given the museum
personal possessions, including pea coats,
photographs, sea bags and even lice powder.
Admission: Entry fee. Open daily 10 A.M. –
5 P.M.

SAN DIEGO, CALIFORNIA
San Diego Maritime Museum
1492 N. Harbor Drive
San Diego, CA   92101
(619) 234-9153 Fax: (619) 234-8345
E-mail: info@sdmaritime.org
Location: The floating museum on board five
ships are located in downtown San Diego on the
colorful Embarcadero.
Highlights: The *Star of India* (1863 bark), The
Berkeley (1898 San Francisco ferry), The *Medea*
(1904 steam yacht), The *Californian* (replica
Revenue cutter), Pilot, ship models, *Full & By*
(Newsletter) and *Mains'l Haul* (Historical
Journal), gift shop, library,
Website: www.midway.org
General Information: Founded in 1948, the
Maritime Museum of San Diego resides in three
historic ships representing both sail and steam
power. Both *Star of India* and *Berkeley* are State
and National Historic Landmarks and Guiness
Book of World Records recognizes the Star
as the "oldest active ship in the world." Step back
into history to view fine craftsmanship, life at sea,
steam engines, naval history, demonstrations of
maritime skills, and an interesting variety of
exhibits for all ages.

Exhibits on board the ships interpret regional
and Pacific maritime history including: the age of
exploration; seaborne trade; whaling, fishing, and
other maritime resources; oceanography; yachting
and sport fishing; the U.S. Navy; the
Development of San Diego's harbor; the
technological history and folklore of sailing
ships; and the technological history and the
Folklore of steam ships. In addition, the ships
always house one or more temporary exhibits that
focus on some aspect of maritime art, history, and

folklore. Docent interpreters are usually on hand
to explain the ships and exhibits.
Activities: Guided tours, speakers' bureau,
lectures, films, loan exhibits, and demonstrations.
Admission: Entry fee. Memberships are
available. Open daily, 9 A.M.- 8 P.M., year-
round.

SAN FRANCISCO, CALIFORNIA
**San Francisco Maritime National Historic
Park**
Lower Fort Mason, Building E, Room 265
San Francisco, CA 94123
(415) 447-5000
Maritime Library (415) 567-7030
Maritime Museum Store
2905 Hyde Street
San Francisco, CA 94109
(415) 775-2665 E-mail: lynn_cullivan@nps.gov
STORE: maristore@maritime.org
Web site: www.maritime.org
Location: The Museum and Hyde Street Pier are
located on San Francisco Bay, at the west end of
Fisherman's Wharf. The Museum is at the foot of
Polk Street: the pier is at the foot of Hyde
Street. The library is located further west, in Fort
Mason Center, Building E.
Highlights: Boardable national historic landmark
vessels, maritime artifacts and ship models,
marine paintings, scrimshaw, J. Porter
Shaw Library and archives, 1st Order Fresnel
Light, Hyde Street Pier, Maritime Museum Store
(Hyde Street), **Website:** www.nps.gov/safr/
General Information: Created in 1988, San
Francisco Maritime National Historical Park has
displays on the West Coast maritime history from
the 1800's to the present. Collections include
250,000 photographs and negatives of ships and
shipping ports, primarily West Coast; 120,000
sheets of ship plans; 3,000 logbooks
and 5,000 charts; manuscripts; scrimshaw; fine
art; ship models; 142,000 books and periodicals;
oral histories of interviews with seafaring men
and shipowners; artifacts from historic vessels;
steam machinery; and small craft.

Historic ships on Hyde Street Pier include:
Balclutha, a square-rigged ship; *C. A. Thayer*, a
schooner; *Eureka*, a walking-beam ferry; *Alma*, a
scow schooner; *Eppleton Hall*, a paddle-wheel
tug; *Hercules*, a steam tug; and a Monterey
fishing boat. At one time, the *Hercules* towed
1,000-foot-long log rafts from the Columbia River
to San Diego, where the logs were cut in a local
waterfront sawmill. San Diego had no trees!
Activities: Lectures, special tours, small boat
restoration program, films, changing exhibits,
boatbuilding classes, and sea music programs.
Admission: Entry fee-donations accepted.
Open daily: Memorial Day to Octo. 15, 9:30 A.M.
– 7 P.M.; Oct. 16 - May 30, 9:30 A.M. – 5 P.M.

SAN FRANCISCO, CALIFORNIA
SS *Jeremiah O'Brien* (Liberty Ship)
National Liberty Ship Memorial
Pier 45, Fisherman/s Wharf
San Francisco, CA 94123-1382
(415) 544-0100 Fax: (415) 544-9890
E-mail: liberty@ssjeremiahobrien.org
Location: The ship is berthed at (and sails from)
Pier 45 on the San Francisco Embarcadero, in the
heart of Fisherman's Wharf.
Highlights: SS *Jeremiah O'Brien* (Liberty Ship),
Store, Newsletter: *The Jeremiah*, docked,
the club operates their radios as a "Special
Events" station during the summer cruises.
Website: www.ssjeremiahobrien.org
   General Information: The *Jeremiah O'Brien*, a
World War II cargo ship, is one of two remaining
Liberty Ships and the last unaltered examples, in
operating condition, of 2,751 vessels of identical
design built between 1941 and 1945 by eighteen
U.S. shipyards. From 1943-1946, she was
operated by Grace Lines for the Government's
War and Shipping Administration and made
eleven round trips from the United Kingdom to
the Normandy beachheads, as well as voyages to
South American, Australia, India, Mainland
China, and the Philippines.
   In June 1994 the *Jeremiah O'Brien* was the only
1944 Normandy invasion ship to participate in the
50th anniversary of D-Day activities
commemorating the landings at Normandy, France,
in 1944. She sailed from San Francisco, through
the Panama Canal, and across the Atlantic
to England. From there, she sailed an old familiar
route to Normandy with many other vessels to
observe this important anniversary.
   She was manned by merchant seamen and
defended by contingents of Navy Armed Guard,
assisted when under fire by the Merchant Marine
crew. The U. S. Maritime Administration now
owns the *O'Brien*.
   Activities: Programs and special events are
conducted aboard at her berth on the San
Francisco Embarcadero Pier 32. She also sails
twice a year in the spring and fall.
   Admission: Entry fee. Open daily, 10 A.M.-
4 P.M.

SAN FRANCISCO, CALIFORNIA
USS *Pampanito* (SS-33)
Maritime Park Association, Pier 45
P.O. Box 470310
San Francisco, CA 94147-0310
(415561-6662 Fax: (415) 561-6660
E-mail: On Web Site
Location: The submarine is located at Pier 45,
near San Francisco's Fisherman's Wharf.
Highlights: USS *Pampanito* submarine,
Overnight encampments,

Website: www.maritime.org/pamphome.htm
   General Information: One of the best restored
World War II fleet boats; *Pampanito* earned six
battle stars for her WW II service in the Pacific,
sinking five vessels. Her biggest day came on
September 12, 1944, when she and two
other submarines surprised an 11-ship convoy and
sank seven vessels. Later, *Pampanito* rescued
more than 73 Allied prisoners of war who had
been carried aboard the enemy transports
unbeknown to the submariners.
   Laid up after the war, *Pampanito* was acquired
by the Maritime Park Association (formerly the
National Maritime Museum Association) and
opened to the public.
   Admission: Entry fee. Open May – Oct,
9 A.M.- 8 P.M.; Oct. – May, 9 A.M. - 6 P.M.

SAN PEDRO, CALIFORNIA
Los Angeles Maritime Museum
Berth 84 at foot of 6th Street
San Pedro, CA 90731
(310) 548-7618 Fax: (310) 832-6537
E-mail: museum@lamaritimemuseum.org
Location: I-110 south to the City of San Pedro —
west of Long Beach — immediately north of
the Ports of Call Village at the foot of 6th Street in
the old Ferry Building
Highlights: 700 ship and boat models, maritime
art, naval and marine history, *The Compass Rose*
(newsletter), gift shop,
Website: www.lamaritimemuseum.org
   General Information: Los Angeles Maritime
Museum, built in 1941, is housed in what was the
Public Works Administration (PWA)
"Streamlined Modern" building, which was the
base for an auto ferry that crossed the channel at
regular intervals form San Pedro to a sister
building on Terminal Island. Among a wide
variety of displays are historical photographs of
Los Angeles harbor and assorted hardware and
equipment from the USS *Los Angeles*. The
Museum also houses a twenty-one-foot scale
model of the *Queen Mary* and cut-away   Once
operated as a ferry building, the promenade deck
offers an excellent view of the harbor, and the
Museum offers some fascinating glimpses into the
ships of World War II.
eighteen-foot scale models of the *Titanic* and
Lusitania.
   Activities: Daily tours by prior appointment.
   Admission: No entry fee, but donations
accepted. Open Tuesday - Saturday, 10 A.M. –
5 P.M., Sundays 12 Noon - 5 P.M. Last entry is
4:30 P.M. Closed Mondays.

SAN PEDRO, CALIFORNIA
SS *Lane* (Victory Ship Class Freighter)
U.S. Merchant Marine Veterans - World War II
Berth 94
P.O. Box 629
San Pedro, CA 90733-0629
(310) 519-9545 Fax: (310) 519-0265
E-mail: info@lanevictory.org
Location: The *Lane Victory* is in the Los Angeles
Harbor at Berth 94 in San Pedro.
Highlights: The SS *Lane* (Victory ship),
newsletter *Anchor Light*, gift shop,
Website: www.lanevictory.org/
     General Information: The SS *Lane* Victory
was donated to the U.S. Merchant Marine
Veterans WWII by of an act of Congress in 1988
and was intended to be used as an educational
memorial museum vessel. The vessel saw service
in World War II, the Korean, and Viet Nam
conflicts, as well as many years in peace-time
commerce. The *Lane* is now a National Historic
Landmark and is a fully operational WWII cargo
ship. Other Victory ships now museum ships: SS
*American (*Victory) (FL) and SS *Red Oak*
(Victory) (CA).
     Exhibits include ship models, memorabilia of
the WWII era which are displayed in two
excellent maritime museum areas aboard the
Lane. The all-volunteer, non-profit, tax-exempt,
nationwide organization welcomes all persons
who are interested in our maritime heritage, and
especially Victory ship historian buffs, to join it as
members.
     During daily visits and cruises all areas are
open for viewing, including the engine room,
cargo holds, crew, and armed guard quarters.
     Radio Rooms: Two radio rooms are on board.
On the top deck is the ship's radio room with the
original WWII Morse Code radio system. Fully
licensed with the ship's call sign KECW, the
ship's radio is fully operational. The
WWII equipment is augmented by modern radios.
The SS *Lane* Victory Amateur Radio Club
operates the ship's "home" station with call
sign W6LV. In addition to when the ship is
docked, the club operates their radios as a
"Special Events" station during the summer
cruises.
     Admission: Entry fee. Open daily, 9 A.M.-
4 P.M.

SANTA BARBARA, CALIFORNIA
Santa Barbara Maritime Museum
113 Harbor Way Suite 190
Santa Barbara, CA 93109-2344
(805) 962-8404 Fax: (805) 962-7634
E-mail: museum@sbmm.org
Location: The Museum is located on Harbor
Way. Turn left here and enter into the harbor
parking area. SBMM is located at 113 Harbor

Way, in the large white building that faces the
harbor.
Highlights: Maritime history of the Santa Barbara
Channel, ROV Submarine, Pioneer II
Submersible, **Website:** www.sbmm.org/
     General Information: The Santa Barbara
Maritime Museum, founded in 1994, was created
to preserve and present the maritime history of
California's Central Coast, while providing an
ongoing educational platform to study and record
human interaction with the marine environment.
     Santa Barbara's seafaring tradition began well
before the fifteenth century, when native
indigenous peoples, the Chumash Indians,
paddled 280-foot-long, six-man, wood-plank
tomols (canoes) across the Santa Barbara Channel
to Santa Cruz Island—a 26-mile trip. Then came
explorer Juan Rodridguez Cabrillo followed by
Sabastian Vizcaino and then Spanish Mexico.
     In 1821, Mexico won its independence, and
trade increased as Boston-based vessels filled
with goods sailed around Cape Horn, stopping at
Refugio Beach and Santa Barbara to barter for
hides and tallow to take back to the shoe factories
and candle makers of New England. Richard
Henry Dana describes such commerce in his book
"Two Years Before the Mast."
     Admission: Entry fee. Open year round:
Summer Hours-Memorial Day to Labor Day:
10 A.M. to 6 P.M. daily, Labor Day to Memorial
Day hours, 11 A.M. to 5 P.M.,

SAUSALITO, CALIFORNIA
Bay Model Visitor Center
2100 Bridgeway
Sausalito, CA 94965-1764
(415) 332-3871 Fax: 415-289-3004
E-mail: keley.d.stock@spd02.usace.army.mil
Location: The Bay Model Visitor Center is in
Sausalito — follow signs from highway 101. Use
Marinship Way access road.
Highlights: Complete (often watered) model of
San Francisco Bay and Delta, bookstore,
Marinship 1942-1945 Museum.
Website: www.spn.usace.army.mil/bmvc/
     General Information: The Bay Model, built
and operated by the U.S. Army Corps of
Engineers, is a one- and one-half-acre working
hydraulic model of the entire San Francisco Bay,
South Bay, San Pablo Bay, and Sacramento/San
Joaquin Delta. It is housed in the former outfitting
warehouse of the Marinship yard, a WW II
shipbuilding facility constructed under the
sponsorship of the W. A. Bachtel Co.
     At the present time the Model's tidal
simulation is used for the purposes of
demonstration and no longer for testing purposes.
The Model operates daily. In addition, the Bay
Model Visitor Center features the Marinship

14

1942-45 exhibit, numerous interactive exhibits, audio tours in several languages and guided tours by appointment.

Admission: No entry fee. Memorial Day through Labor Day, Tuesday thru Friday, 9 A.M. – 4 P.M., Saturday & Sunday 10 A.M. – 5 P.M. Closed Mondays Labor Day thru Memorial Day, Tuesday thru Saturday 9 A.M. – 4 P.M. Closed Sundays and Mondays

SAUSALITO, CALIFORNIA
Marinship 1942-1945
Bay Model Visitor Center
2100 Bridgeway
Sausalito, CA 94965
(415) 322-3871
Location: The museum is located in the Bay Model Visitor Center in Sausalito — follow signs from highway 101. Use Marinship Way access road.
Highlights: Marinship 1942-1945 (history of wartime merchant ship construction),
Website: www.spn.usace.army. mil/bmvc/teachers/teacher_guide/15.html
General Information: Marinship 1942-1945 is a mini-museum within the Bay Model building where exhibits commemorate the prodigious efforts of workers at the Marinship yard in Sausalito during World War II at which ninety-three ships were built in record time — fifteen liberty ships, sixty-two tankers, and sixteen oilers.

Artifacts from the last surviving Marinship tanker and oral histories of former shipyard workers are included. The Bay Model building was originally the outfitting warehouse for this important West Coast shipyard. Other exhibits and visitor aids include audio tours of the Bay Model, an hydraulic model of San Francisco Bay, videos and interactive programs about San Francisco Bay and its environment.

Activities: Guided tours are available by appointment.

Admission: No entry fee. Open daily between Memorial Day and Labor Day, Tuesday-Friday, 9 A.M.-4 P.M.; Saturday, Sunday, and holidays, 10 A.M.- 5 P.M.; winter, Tuesday-Friday, 9 A.M.-4 P.M.

VALLEJO, CALIFORNIA
Vallejo Naval and Historical Museum
734 Marin Street
Vallejo, CA 94590-5913
(707) 643-0077 Fax: (707) 643-2443
E-mail: valmuse@pacbell.net
Location: Vallejo is twelve miles north of Oakland. Take I-80 to Vallejo. The Museum is located in the old city hall building downtown on the corner of Capitol and Marin Streets.
Highlights: Working submarine periscope, ship models, ship paintings, bookstore,
Website: www.vallejomuseum.org
General Information: The Vallejo Naval and Historical Museum, founded in 1974, interprets the history of Vallejo and the adjacent area, including the Navy at adjacent Mare Island and on the San Francisco Bay.

Partners for 142 years, Vallejo and the Navy grew together following the 1853 purchase of Mare Island by the Government to establish a Navy Yard in California. Many ships and submarines were constructed here during WW II. Mare Island Shipyard closed in 1966.

The Museum exhibits are maintained in five galleries: Hall of History; South Gallery; Staircase of Seapower; The Heritage Chamber; and Saginaw Gallery. Displays include selections from the permanent collections, local private collections, traveling exhibitions, and borrowed artifacts from the extensive collection at Mare Island.

Admission: Entry fee. Open Tuesday-Saturday, 10 A.M.-4:30 P.M., year-round.

VENTURA, CALIFORNIA
Channel Islands National Park
Visitor Center
1901 Spinnaker Drive
Ventura, CA 93001
(805) 658-5730 Fax: (805) 658-5700
E-mail: on web site.
Location: The Visitor Center is located on the ocean side spit of Ventura Harbor.
Highlights: History of Santa Barbara Channel Islands, bookstore, living tidepool, auditorium, native plant garden, weekend ranger programs,
Website: www.nps.gov/chis/
General Information: The Visitor Center contains the Channel Islands National Park headquarters and features exhibits and presentations on the Channel Islands National Park. Important historical events took place on these islands, including the ultimate death and burial of Juan Rodridguez Cabrillo, the founder of San Miguel which became San Diego. Also, information on shipwrecks on the islands is available.

Admission: No entry fee. Open daily, 8:30 A.M.-5 P.M., year-round.

WILMINGTON, CALIFORNIA
Banning Residence Museum
401 East "M" Street
Wilmington, CA 90748
(310) 548-7777
E-mail: visit@banningmuseum.org
Location: From the Harbor Freeway, exit onto Pacific Coast Hwy east. Travel east to Avalon Boulevard, then south two blocks to "M" Street,

15

turning east to the Museum.

Highlights: History of Los Angeles Harbor, library, museum shop,

Website: www.banningmuseum.org/

General Information: The Banning Residence Museum is in the mansion General Phineas Banning built. Its grounds are parkland maintained by the City of Los Angeles. Banning, upon arrival in 1851 in Southern California, established a ship-to-shore transportation business, first from a rowboat, then expanding it to provide freight and passenger hauling from Wilmington, California, to Los Angeles, Arizona, and as far as Salt Lake City, Utah.

Naming Wilmington for his birthplace — Wilmington, Delaware — he established the Los Angeles Harbor for which he is mostly remembered. The Museum houses Banning family furniture, and the historic stagecoach barn is a fully outfitted example of a nineteenth-century working barn. A research library is located in the barn, where a wide variety of books and papers describe the history of Southern California, most particularly Banning's influence in the area.

Admission: Small donation requested for entry. Memberships are available. Open for tours Tuesday-Thursday, 12:30 P.M.-2:30 P.M. with tours by reservation only. Tours Saturday and Sunday 12:30-3:30 P.M. The Museum shop is open during public tour hours and for special programs or by appointment. Closed national holidays. Groups of ten or more by appointment.

CONNECTICUT

DEEP RIVER, CONNECTICUT

Stone House Marine Room
245 Main Street (Rte. 154)
P.O. Box 151
Deep River, CT 06417
(860) 526-5811 E-mail: lhostetler@wesleyan.edu
Location: Via I-95 exit at Old Saybrook north on to Rte. 9 seven miles to the Deep River Exit 5.
Highlights: Local maritime history **Web Site:** http://home.mindspring.com/~historicalsociety/id1 1.html
General Information: The Stone House Marine Room contains oil paintings of ships commanded relate to vessels with local ties: built, owned, captained, or manned by local people.

Admission: By donations. Open Saturday and Sunday, 2:00 P.M.-4:00 P.M., July-August. Other times by appointment. by local shipmasters, rare early photographs of shipyards, navigation instruments, rare documents, and other nautical material. In addition, the Mather Collection of

town memorabilia includes scrapbooks, pictures, and other town history notes, and provides an invaluable reference source of local history. Most of the articles in the museum

ESSEX, CONNECTICUT

The Connecticut River Museum
Steamboat Dock
67 Main Street
Essex, CT 06426
(860) 767-8269 Fax: (860) 767-7028
E-mail: jroberts@ctrivermuseum.org
Location: The Museum is located at the foot of Main Street on the Connecticut River in Essex. From the west: Take I-95 to Exit 69, then Essex/Rte. 9 north three miles to Exit 3 (Essex). From the east: Take I-95, then take Route 9 north to Exit 3 and follow signs to the Museum. From I-91, get off at Exit 22S to Rte 9 to south to Exit 3 and follow signs to the Museum.
Highlights: The *American Turtle* (first submarine), ship models, small craft (seasonal), *Steamboat Log* (newsletter), Thomas A. Steven Library (a research facility), gift shop, changing exhibits, **Website:** www.ctrivermuseum.org

General Information: The Connecticut River Foundation, founded in 1974, and located in a warehouse building on the 1879 Steamboat Dock, at the foot of Main Street. The dock served as a port of call for steamboat service from New York City to Hartford, Connecticut. The Museum displays a working reproduction of *American Turtle*, the first submarine, invented by David Bushness in 1775.

Permanent exhibits include Lay's Wharf (c.1650); small craft exhibits on river hunting, fishing, yachting; steam boating; brownstone schooners; models and paintings on Revolutionary War, the 1812 burning of fleet at Essex and valley archaeology. The Museum offers seasonal in-water exhibitions of antique and classic boats as well as hosting the Traditional Vessels Weekend in September.

Activities: Guided tours, lecture series, films, formally organized education programs, Traditional Vessel Weekend, changing exhibitions, and a permanent collection
Admission: Entry fee. Memberships are available, which may include docking privileges. Open Tuesday-Sunday 10 A.M.- 5 P.M. Closed national holidays.

GROTON, CONNECTICUT

Nautilus — **Submarine Force-Library Museum**
Naval Submarine Base New London
1 Crystal Lake Road
Groton, CT 06349-5571
(860) 694-3558 Fax: (860) 694-4150
Toll Free: 1-800-343-0079

E-mail: gregory.caskey@navy.mil
Location: Groton is forty-five miles east of New Haven at exit 86 on I-95. The submarine and Museum are off Rte. 12 near the entrance to the Naval Submarine Base.
Highlights: The USS *Nautilus* (1954), first nuclear-powered submarine in the U.S. Navy, also captured Italian, German, and Japanese mini-submarines, submarine periscopes,
Website: www.ussnautilus.org/

General Information: The Historic Ship *Nautilus* and Submarine Force and Library Museum (founded in 1964) are located outside the main gate of the naval base. The Museum is a repository for the records and history of the U.S. Submarine Force, from its humble beginnings at the turn of the century to the modern Navy.

In the Museum entrance is an eleven-foot model of the fictional Captain Nemo's *Nautilus* from Jules Verne's "20,000 Leagues Under the Sea." The Museum displays working periscopes, an authentic submarine control room, an extensive wall of ship models that depict the development of the U.S. Submarine Force.

The collection of historic submarines includes the first nuclear-powered submarine *Nautilus* (launched June 14, 1952 and commissioned in 1954). These submarines, and the Albacore at the Port of Portsmouth Maritime Museum, were both designed for specific purposes — the *Nautilus* for the newly designed propulsion system (nuclear) and the *Albacore* for a new hull design. Other exterior exhibits include: the Japanese HA-8; Italian *Maiale*; a German *Seehund*; and an early American research submarine; Simon Lake's *Explorer*. Interior collections include pictures, models, battle flags, paintings, brow canvases, submarine parts, medals, and personal memorabilia from submariners. 20,000 photographs of submarines and related subjects are available for perusal in the adjoining research library. The Museum has been expanded to include a larger museum store, a 70-seat theater, and extensive cold war era exhibits.

Activities: Self-guided tours of the world's first nuclear- powered vessel, the *Nautilus*; working models of navy periscopes; submarine control room and two mini-theatres with twenty-five-minute films depicting the growth and history of the Submarine Force and the U. S. *Nautilus*.

Admission: No entry fee. Museum, summer hours: Closed Tuesday, 9 A.M.-4 P.M., Winter hours: Wednesday-Monday, 9 A.M. to 4 P.M. Tuesday, 1 P.M. 5 P.M.
Library: Open Monday, Wednesday, Thursday, and Friday, 8:30 A.M.- 3:30 P.M., by appointment only. Closed Thanksgiving, Christmas, and New Year's Day. (The *Nautilus* is closed the first two weeks in May and the last two weeks in October for maintenance.)

MYSTIC, CONNECTICUT
Mystic Seaport Museum
75 Greenmanville Avenue
P.O. Box 6000
Mystic, CT 06355-0990
(860) 572-5315 Fax: (860) 572-5328
Toll Free: 888-973-2767
E-mail: info@mysticseaport.org
Location: Mystic is ten miles east of New London along the Mystic River on SR 27.
Highlights: Boardable 19th- and 20th-century vessels, ship models, scrimshaw, boatbuilding, G. W. Blunt Whale Library, 60,000 ship/boat plans, *The Log* (quarterly), *The Windrose* (newsletter), Rosenfeld photograph collection, 60,000 (±) ship/boat plans, library (research and archives of American yachting and boating), gift shop,
Website: www.mysticseaport.org

General Information: Founded in 1929, Mystic Seaport is the nation's leading maritime museum, housing the largest collection of boats and maritime photography in the world. Renowned for its village area of historic buildings and tall ships, Mystic Seaport includes exhibit galleries and a working shipyard where the art of wooden shipbuilding endures.

In the village are of historic buildings, trade she ops and homes that give the visitor an understanding of life in a seaport during the mid-nineteenth century.

Visitors may board the last of the wooden whaling ships, the Charles W. Morgan, the 1882 training ship Joseph Conrad, and the fishing schooner L.A. Dunton. More than 100 other ships and boats are on display in the Museum.

Exhibit galleries offer ship models, scrimshaw, figureheads, paintings, artifacts, small boats, and other relics that trace the history of ships, shipbuilding, and maritime activities. Don't miss Voyages: Stories of America and the Sea, the country's first exhibit to offer a national perspective of the sea's profound role in defining our national identity. Visitors may watch skilled shipwrights restore historic vessels in the seaport's preservation shipyard. Sea chantey concerts, as well as demonstrations of fireplace cooking, boat building, sail setting, and maritime arts, are given seasonally. Craftspeople may be seen working in some shops. A planetarium offers daily shows. There is also a children's museum where youngsters may play with toys, clothing, and games popular in the 1800s.

The Museum has purchased the entire Rosenfeld Collection of photographs. The collection, which comprises more than one million images, documents more than 100 years of maritime and yachting history, and is the single largest collection of marine photographs in the world.

Mystic Seaport provides opportunities for college-level maritime studies. The Munson Institute conducts graduate-level courses during the summer months while undergraduate maritime studies courses are offered through the Williams College/Mystic Seaport Program during the academic year.

Admission: Entry fee. Memberships are available. Museum open daily: 9 A.M.-5 P.M., to 5 P.M. in summer; Winter, 10 A.M.-4 P.M. Closed Christmas Eve and Christmas, but open limited hours on Thanksgiving, and New Year's Day.

NEW LONDON, CONNECTICUT
Custom House Museum
New London Maritime Society
150 Bank Street
New London, CT 06320-6024
(860) 447-2501   Fax: (860) 447-8086
E-mail: nlmaritime.society@snet.net
Location: Town center, walk toward River on Golden Street, right on Bank Street.
Highlights: Maritime history
Web Site: www.nlmaritimesociety.org/
    General Information: The Custom House Museum was created to collect and show maritime history and artifacts are displayed that are especially relevant to southeast Connecticut. The Custom House, constructed in 1833 of granite in Greek revival style, now serves as a museum. It is a major restoration of the oldest operated Custom House in America, designed by Robert Mills, the nation's first Federal architect, who also modified the building.
    Admission: Entry fee. Open Tuesday/Saturday 1 P.M. – 5 P.M.

NEW LONDON, CONNECTICUT
U.S. Coast Guard Museum
U.S. Coast Guard Academy
15 Mohegan Avenue
New London, CT 06320-4195
(860) 444-8511 e-mail: On web site
Academy: 1-800-883-USCG (8724)
Location: New London is fifty miles east of New Haven. In town, follow signs on Rte. 32 to the U.S. Coast Guard Academy.
Highlights: The *Eagle* (training barque), library (150,000 volumes), gift shop in Visitor's Center,
Website: www.uscg.mil/hq/cg092/museum/
    General Information: The U.S. Coast Guard Museum in Waesche Hall was founded in 1967. Collections include ship and airplane models; paintings and artifacts; flags and figureheads relating to the U.S. Coast Guard and its

predecessors — the Revenue-Cutter Service, Lighthouse Service, Life-Saving Service — and the barque *Eagle*.

    The Museum tells the story of the unique services the U.S. Coast Guard provides and has provided for the two hundred years of our nation's history. Since the Coast Guard provides the infrastructure services for the maritime industries, a visit to the museum adds an important dimension to anyone's tour through maritime and military museums around the country. Only here can one explore all the aspects of marine law enforcement, aids to navigation, search and rescue, and marine safety that make the sea-lanes and waterways of America save for mariners the world over.

    One of the most distinctive landmarks at the Academy, when it is in port, is America's Tall Ship, the training barque *Eagle*. This beautiful, 295-foot vessel came to the Academy as a reparation prize from Germany after World War II. Perhaps the finest training ship afloat for young sailors, it is on Eagle's decks and aloft in the rigging where future officers get their first tastes of the challenges of life at sea. The *Eagle* celebrated her sixtieth anniversary in 1996.

    The Museum's collection of some 6,000 works of art and artifacts depicts the service's diverse and proud history—U.S. Coast Guard (1915 to present), Lighthouse service (1870s - 1939), Life Saving Service (1870s - 1915), and Revenue Cutter Service (1870s-1915).

    Admission: No entry fee. Pavilion and Museum open, Monday-Friday, 9 A.M.-4:30 P.M. Closed national holidays. If the training barque *Eagle* is in port, she may be boarded.

NORWALK, CONNECTICUT
The Maritime Aquarium
10 North Water Street
Norwalk, CT 06854
(203) 852-0700, ext. 206 Fax: (203) 838-5416
Location: Norwalk is just six miles east of Stamford. The Aquarium is in historic "SoNo," a revitalized area of South Norwalk along the waterfront of the Norwalk River and Long Island Sound. It is a short distance from I-95 and a brief walk from the AMTRAK/Metro North railroad station.
Highlights: Connecticut's only IMAX Theatre New gift shop and cafeteria, research vessel *Oceanic* and *The Glory Days*,
Website: www.maritimeaquarium.org/
    General Information: The Maritime Aquarium at Norwalk, founded in 1988, is devoted to the maritime history and marine life of Long Island Sound. In the Maritime Hall: boatbuilding, touch tank with live rays, animal adaptation exhibits, main and gallery exhibit area. Falconer Hall:

Historic and contemporary vessels and several historic replicas. The Maritime Aquarium is home to the research vessel *Oceanic*, the historic Hope oystering sloop, and *The Glory Days*, an elegant steam tender. In the Aquarium: sharks, seals, river otters, and over 1000 marine animals indigenous to Long Island Sound. A permanent sea turtle exhibit has been established.

Activities: Boatbuilding, marine science programs, teacher enrichment, field studies, IMAX films, parties, member events and group tours.

Admission: Entry fee. Memberships available. Open daily, 10 A.M.-5 P.M., July and August until 6 P.M. Closed Thanksgiving and Christmas.

PLAINVILLE, CONNECTICUT
Plainville Historic Center
29 Pierce Street
Plainville, CT 06062,
 (860) 747-6577 or 0081   Fax: 860/747-6577
Location: The Center is in Plainville via I-84, take exit 34.
Highlights: Farmington Canal, library
Website: www.plainvillelibrary.org/PHSI/
General Information: The Plainville Historic Center is in the former town hall (1890). The museum focuses on Plainville's early days, including the era of the Farmington Canal (1827-47). The museum displays toys, period costumes, tools, clocks, bakery wagon, museum shop, and a large diorama of Center of Plainville in 1830 with bridges, three boats, and dry dock. Extensive canal research material available by appointment.

Admission: Open May-December, Wednesday and Saturday, noon-3 P.M. Research: Wed/Thurs 9 A.M. – 2 P.M.

STONINGTON, CONNECTICUT
Old Lighthouse Museum
7 Water Street
P.O. Box 103
Stonington, CT 06378-1422
(860) 535-1440
E-mail: director@stoningtonhistory.org
Location: Stonington is fifteen miles east of New London. From I-95, take exit 91 South (N. Main Sreett to the stop sign. Then turn left and that the next right over the bridge to Water Street. The Museum is at the south end of Water Street.
Highlights: Lighthouse, ship models, local history of maritime interest,
Website: www.stoningtonhistory.org/light.htm
right over the bridge to Water Street. The Museum is at the south end of Water Street. Street) to the stop sign. Turn left and take the next
General Information: The Old Lighthouse Museum, founded in 1925, operated by The

Stonington Historical Society, is housed in a stone lighthouse built in 1823. The lighthouse was moved back from the seashore several hundred feet north to the present location where the keeper's house was added. The lighthouse was important to the captains whose steamships transported thousands from New York City to the harbor in Stonington, where they transferred to railroad trains for the balance of the trip to New England areas.

The Museum's exhibits include ship models, whaling gear, firearms, stoneware, and early maritime portraits. Also displayed are furniture; silver and pewter; utensils at Whitehall; seventeenth- and eighteenth-century historical treasures of the town including whaling and War of 1812 relics; manuscript collections. The Pequot Indians, until their defeat in 1637, were dominant in the area. Then the first white settlement was established.

Activities: Guided tours; lectures; formally organized education programs, permanent and temporary exhibits.

Admission: Entry fee. Memberships available. Open daily, May/Oct, 10 A.M.-5 P.M. In July, the Museum is open daily.

STRATFORD, CONNECTICUT
The *Glacier* Society Icebreaker
905 Honeyspot Road
Stratford, CT 06615
(866) ICE PLAY (423-7529) TOLL FREE
 (203) 375-6638 E-mail: info@glaciersociety.org
Location: Bridgeport, Connecticut
Highlights: The *Glacier* Icebreaker, Newsletter: *The Icebreaking News*,
Website: www.glaciersociety.org
 General Information: The *Glacier* Society, an Education Foundation, is dedicated to the restoration and operation of the icebreaker USS/USCGC *Glacier* in honor of all who served in the exploration of the North and South Poles. Historically, she holds the honor of serving as Admiral Richard Byrd's flagship In addition to her record-breaking deployments; the *Glacier* is one of only a few United States ships to serve under the control of both the US Navy and the US Coast Guard.

The USS/USCGC *Glacier* will be placed back into service as a marine science, research, and education platform providing hands-on training to children, students, and adults while teaching the history of Pole exploration. Contact The *Glacier* Society for information.

DELAWARE

BETHANY BEACH, DELAWARE
Indian River Life-Saving Station
P.O. Box Z 25039 Coastal Highway
Rehoboth Beach, DE 19971
(302) 227-6991 Fax: (302) 227-6438
E-mail: parkinfo@state.de.us
Location: The Station is located on the ocean side of Route 1, 3.5 miles south of Dewey Beach and 1.5 miles north of the Indian River Inlet
Highlights: Lifesaving history,
Website:
www.beach-net.com/history/irlifestation.html
General Information: The former Indian River Life-Saving Station building, under the direction of the Delaware Seashore Preservation Foundation, has stood on its current location for more than 100 years. The Station is the object of a restoration effort by a group of local volunteers. The learning center will feature information on the lifesaving history of the Delaware coast focusing on the period of 1905. Also included is information on the Revenue Cutter Service, the U.S. Lifesaving Service, the U.S. Coast Guard Service, and sunken ships, famous rescues, and Pirates. The hope is to restore the Venetian red-roofed structure to its original appearance when it was constructed in 1876.
Admission: Entry fee. Open daily Memorial Day-Labor Day. Call for off-season hour's rest of year.

FENWICK ISLAND, DELAWARE
DiscoverSea Shipwreck Museum
708 Ocean Highway (2nd Floor)
Fenwick Island, DE 19944-4408
Toll Free: 1-888-743-5524 (302) 539-9366
E-mail: dsmuseum@aol.com
Location: From Georgetown south on Rte. 113 nineteen miles to Rte. 34. Then east eleven miles to Fenwick Island.
Highlights: Thousands of artifacts from shipwrecks such as the Spanish ship *Atocha*, 1715 Fleet, *Titanic*, *R.M.S. Republic*, *Faithful Steward*, *Edmund Fitzgerald*, China Wreck, and many more. **Website:** www.discoversea.com
General Information: DiscoverSea Shipwreck Museum is a continuing exhibit that expands and diversifies with the acquisitions of new artifacts as they are recovered. The Shipwreck Museum opened in July 1995 and has a goal of recovering and preserving our maritime heritage. For hundreds of years the great ports of Delaware and Chesapeake Bay brought to the Delmarva Penninsula one of the highest concentrations of shipping in the early Americas. Today, through the use of proper archeology and recovery, you can experience Delmarva's forgotten maritime history.
If the Delaware Coast could talk, its story would be of merchantmen and galleons, pirates and privateers, men who sailed the ships and wreckers who laid in wait for them. Other interactive displays include aquariums, and theatre makes this a unique gateway to our maritime heritage.
Through your DiscoverSea Shipwreck Museum visit, lecture or beach tour, you will travel through a hands-on experience which will enable you to shake hands with history.
Admission: No entry fee. Open: June-August, daily 10 A.M. – 9 P.M.; September – May, Saturday – Sunday, 11 A.M. – 4 P.M.

GEORGETOWN, DELAWARE
Treasures of the Sea Exhibit
Delaware Technical & Community College
Rte. 18, P. O. Box 610
Georgetown, DE 19947-0610
(302) 856-5700 Fax: (302) 858-5462
Location: The Treasures exhibit is located in the Delaware Technical & Community College library building, Rte. 18, Georgetown.
Highlights: Gold, jewels, and silver from a Spanish galleon *Atocha*, gift shop,
Website: www.treasuresofthesea.org/
General Information: Treasures of the Sea Exhibit contains the lost treasures of the ill-fated *Nuestra Senora de Atocha*, a Spanish galleon that was helplessly driven by hurricane-force winds into a coral reef, off Key West, Florida, ripping a hole in her bow. May 20, 1973, treasure hunters discovered 1,500 silver coins dated no later than 1621. On July 4, 1973, three silver bars and a coral and gold necklace were recovered; numbers on one of the silver bars matched those listed on the *Atocha's* manifest located in the library in Seville, Spain. July 13, 1975, saw the recovery of nine bronze cannons with markings that confirmed Mel Fisher* had discovered the *Atocha*. However, it was not until July 20, 1985, that the "motherlode" of the *Atocha* was found, a cargo estimated to be worth $400 million. Melvin Joseph, a Georgetown investor, and others assigned their stock or investment interest to the Delaware Technical and Community College Education Foundation, which made it possible for the establishment of the Treasures of the Sea Exhibit.
Admission: Entry fee. Open Monday, Tuesday, 10 A.M.-4 P.M.; Friday, noon-4 P.M.; Saturday, 9 P.M.-1 P.M. Suggest phoning to verify days and times exhibit is open. *-See also Mel Fisher Maritime Heritage Society, Key West, FL. and Mel Fisher Treasurer Museum, Sebastian, FL.

LEWES, DELAWARE

Cannon Ball House & Marine Museum
c/o Lewes Historical Society
110 Shipcarpenter Street
Lewes, DE 19958
(302) 645-7670   Fax: (302) 645-2375
E-mail: infol@historiclewes.org 1
Location: Lewes (pn. LOO - is) is on Rte. 9, thirty
miles southeast of Dover near the Atlantic
coastline.
Highlights: The *Overfalls* (lightship), *U.S. Coast
Guard Newsletter,*
Website: info@historiclewes.org
   General Information: Cannonball Marine
Museum, founded in 1972, is housed in the
Cannonball House, noted for having been hit by a
cannonball in the War of 1812. The Lewes
Historical Society has been restoring six or seven
historical homes in Lewes including the
Cannonball House, which now houses maritime
exhibits of ship models, a "Pilot Room" devoted to
artifacts and items about the ship pilots of the area.
The Lightship *Overfalls* is a part of the Museum
and is located on the canal at Ship Carpenter Street.
   Activities: Lectures, films, annual craft fair,
annual flea market, and seminars
   Admission: Entry fee. Open Tuesdays,
Thursdays, and Saturdays, 10 A.M.-3 P.M., June-
September.

PORT PENN, DELAWARE

Port Penn Interpretive Center
Fort DuPont State Park
P.O. Box 170
Port Penn, DE 19706
(302) 836-2533   Fax: (302) 836-2539
E-mail: travis.sauerwald@state.de.us
Location: The Center is located at the intersection
of Delaware Rte. 9 and New Castle County Road 2
(Port Penn Road) in the old schoolhouse.
Highlights: Decoy exhibits, floating fishing cabin,
Fort Delaware State Park, Port Penn Wetland Trail,
Website: www.destateparks.com/fdsp/fdpp.htm
   General Information: The village of Port Penn
is one of the many stops along Delaware's Coastal
Heritage Greenway. This Greenway that extends
from urban Fox Point State Park to the beaches of
Cape Henlopen State Park, encompasses many of
Delaware's finest cultural and natural resources.
   Throughout its history, Port Penn has looked to
the Delaware River and its marshes for sustenance
and contact with the outside world. The
Interpretive Center focuses on life during the
eighteenth and nineteenth centuries and how the
landscape evolved over time in this Delaware
Riverbank community.
   Since settlement in 1764, the people of Port
Penn have relied on the wetlands through such

enterprises as hunting, fishing, and trapping. And
original dikes built by the Dutch settlers provided
fresh-water farming. Nearby is the Chesapeake &
Delaware Canal (C & D Canal) from the Delaware
River to the head of the Chesapeake Bay, a major
shipping route. The wetlands have played a major
role in the lives of Port Penners — then and now.
   Floating cabins: one- or two-room watermen's
houses mounted on shallow-draught hulls that were
once a common maritime tradition in the Delaware
River area. The one cabin that remains gives a
glimpse of a tradition that almost disappeared
without being recorded.
   The Port Penn Interpretive Center is
administered by nearby Fort Delaware State Park.
On Pea Patch Island, the state park provides
programs about the fort focusing on the period
between 1863-1864 (Civil War) and emphasizes
learning history through examining abundant
records of the guards and prisoners. Besides the
fort and its living history program, Pea Patch
Island hosts an intricate habitat. A walk along the
nature trail takes you through the area that in Civil
War times were the prisoners and guards barracks
(a replica is being completed) and hospital.
   Fort Delaware also administers nearby Fort
DuPont State Park, both in Delaware City, four
Port Penn has four boats in its inventory. The
boats, a Delaware ducker, a sneak-box, and two
flat-bottomed bateaus are being developed as either
stationary exhibits or as working craft for teaching
boatmanship to students. For information on either
Fort DuPont of Fort Delaware, telephone (302)
834-7941.
   Activities: Decoy-carving workshops, wetland
talks, The Atlantic Sturgeon Series and town tours.
   Admission: No entry fee but donation requested.
Museum open: please contact Port Delaware Park
Office for hours of operation
(302) 834-7941

WILMINGTON, DELAWARE

Kalmar Nyckel **Shipyard and Museum**
Kalmar Nyckel Foundation
1124 E. 7th Street
Wilmington, DE 19801
(302) 429-7447
E-mail: info@kalmarnyckel.org
Location: The Museum is located on a small
peninsula on the Delaware and Christina Rivers
near downtown Wilmington and can be reached
from Rte. 13 on Church Street turning east on E.
7th Street.
Highlights: The *Kalmar Nyckel* (replica ship),
small craft (Swedish), and wooden boat shop,
Website: www.kalmarnyckel.org/

General Information: The *Kalmar Nyckel* Shipyard and Museum brings to life the heritage of "New Sweden," the first permanent European settlement in the Delaware River Valley. A living history shipyard at the settler's site has been re-established. The *Kalmar Nyckel* replica is now the Delaware Tall Ship.

The *Kalmar Nyckel* ("the Key of Kalmar," name of fort that protects the city of Kalmar) is a 97-foot, 317-ton replica of a 1629 Dutch pinnace. The ship, launched in September 1997, was constructed at the *Kalmar Nyckel* Shipyard and Museum by shipwrights, blacksmiths, ship riggers, carpenters, and many other trades people. A cadre of volunteers is on sight to assist also.

The Museum exhibits, in what was the lofting building for the construction of the replica ship, seventeenth-century shipbuilding tools, ship plans, flags, navigation, and marine artifacts from 1700 to 1900. The Museum's small-craft include: *Little Key*, an eighteen-foot ship's boat; *King's Launch*, a twenty-foot Swedish naval whaleboat.

Activities: The Shipyard has a community Challenge School, an alternative educational program for at-risk youth teaching boat-building skills; Delaware Valley History Program; teaching cruises and Summer In-Service Programs.

Admission: Entry fee. Summer hours: due to sailing schedule, call or check website for hours open. Open Thursday-Sunday, 10 A.M. to 4 P.M., winter hours only.

FLORIDA

APALACHICOLA, FLORIDA

Apalachicola Maritime Museum
103 Water Street
Apalachicola, FL 32320-1736
(850) 653-2500 (phone/fax)
E-mail: admin@apalachicolamaritimemuseum.org
Location: Museum on Ave. "D," *Governor Stone* (schooner), is in Battery Boat Basin, Bay Avenue.
Highlights: *Governor Stone* (schooner)
Website: www. ammfl.org/
General Information: The Apalachicola Maritime Museum is dedicated to informing the public about the maritime history of the American South, and especially that of the Apalachicola Bay area. Sailing vessels have plied these waters for century commerce and pleasure since the eighteenth. And steamboats operated here in countless numbers for over 100 years. Today, Apalachicola's maritime tradition continues with the proud fleet of working vessels of independent fishermen, oystermen, and shrimpers.

In addition, a maritime library is available for use by Museum members and those interested in maritime history—particularly that of the Gulf Coast area. The forty-one-foot (sixty-three-feet counting bowsprit and boom) *Governor Stone*, named for the post-Reconstruction governor, is being restored to serve as a training vessel and sailing goodwill ambassador along the Gulf Coast. She is the only surviving 1877 fixed-keel, two-masted coasting schooner in the Gulf area. As a buyboat, she purchased oysters from local tongers —Apalachicola to Alabama.

Admission: No entry fee but donations requested. Hours by appmt; office 10A-5: 30P Call or write for days/times Museum is open and for times/locations for viewing and boarding the *Governor Stone* (schooner).

BRADENTON, FLORIDA

South Florida Museum
201 10th Street West
Bradenton, FL 34205-8635
(941) 746-4131 Fax: (941) 746-5671
E-mail: info@southfloridamuseum.org
Location: Bradenton is 25 miles south of St. Petersburg and 40 miles south of Tampa off I-75.
Highlights: The Fogarty Family and Manatee County's boatbuilding industry,
Website: www.southfloridamuseum.org
General Information: The South Florida Museum "charts a course" through the boat-building history of this west coast Florida community. In conjunction with the Florida Maritime Historical Society, the Museum provides a journey through local history via maps, charts, and navigation arranged for orderly and logical understanding.

John Fogarty sailed into the mouth of the Manatee River in 1865, having been blown off course. He remained here (in the Bradenton area) developing community buildings and founded a shipyard for the construction of ships and boats. The family descendants continued in the business until 1944. Since then, the original shipyard buildings have been moved to Manatee Village Historical Park, where original equipment has been restored and small boat-building is again underway but in a museum setting.

Admission: Entry fee. Open Tuesday-Saturday, 10 A.M.-5 P.M.; Sunday, 12 Noon – 5 P.M. We are closed on New Years Day, the first Saturday in November, Thanksgiving Day and Christmas.

COCONUT GROVE, FLORIDA
Barnacle State Historical Site
3485 Main Hwy
Coconut Grove, FL 33133
(305) 442-6866
E-mail: Katrina.boler@dep.state.fl.us
Location: Coconut Grove is approximately three miles south of downtown Miami. The Barnacle is in Peacock Park off Main Highway.
Highlights: Historic home, ship model, native plants in a hardwood hammock, boat house with old fashioned tools on Biscayne Bay,
Website: www. thebarnacle.org/tbs/
General Information: Ralph Munroe, noted designer/builder of shallow-draft boats, built the cottage in the 1891 and later enlarged it by raising the seven rooms to accommodate an additional floor underneath. Most of the furnishings belonged to Monroe, and many of his photographs are displayed. Monroe became commodore of the Biscayne Bay Yacht Club in 1877, remaining in that position for twenty-two years. Wrecking, the profession of salvaging wrecked ships, was a mainstay of Monroe's interest and work. The Barnacle displays remnants of his wrecking adventures, boat models, and maritime artifacts.
Admission: Entry fee. Open 8 A.M sundown.

FT. PIERCE, FLORIDA
UDT - SEAL Museum
3300 N. A1A North Hutchinson Island
Ft. Pierce, FL 34949-8520
(772) 595-5845
E-mail: navysealteams@juno.com
Location: The Museum is located on the ocean side across from Pepper Park on North Hutchinson Island.
Highlights: "Top Secret" exhibit, Seal's gear/history, Apollo Space Capsule, wet swimmer delivery vehicles (submersibles), *Fire in the Hole* (quarterly newsletter), **Website:** www.navysealteams.com/options.htm
General Information: The Museum, the only one of its kind, is the repository of the history of part of the U.S. military service shrouded in secrecy. Displays and exhibits explore the work of the Frogmen, Scouts & Raiders, Naval Combat Demolition units, and SEAL teams - The Sea Air Land Commandos of the U.S. Navy. The men of this group were drawn from the Underwater Demolition Teams, which began as FROGS at this *Location* in 1943 during World War II.
Admission: Entry fee. Open Tuesday through Saturday from 10 A.M. until 4 P.M.; open Sundays from Noon until 4 P.M. Closed on Mondays.

JACKSONVILLE, FLORIDA
Jacksonville Maritime Museum Society, Inc.
2 Independent Drive
Jacksonville, FL 32207
(904) 398-9011 Fax: (904) 398-7248
E-mail: jaxmarmus@bellsouth.net
Location: The Museum office/exhibit building is located immediately adjacent to the south end of Main Street bridge: Southbank Riverwalk, St. John's River.
Highlights: Ship models, 16-foot model of aircraft carrier *Saratoga*,
Website: www. jaxmaritimemuseum.org
General Information: The Society was organized in 1985 to establish a world-class maritime museum dedicated to the preservation of the maritime history of Jacksonville and Florida's First Coast. The Museum exhibits arts and sciences showing the origin, history, and development of the continuing impact of the Maritime trade on the First Coast and Florida. The Museum is an educational and entertainment resource for the community and its visitors.
Admission: No entry fee. Open daily, Monday-Friday, 10:30 A.M.-3 P.M.; Friday, 10:30 A.M.-5 P.M.; Saturdays and Sundays, 1 P.M. - 5 P.M.

JUPITER, FLORIDA
Jupiter Lighthouse
Florida History Center and Museum
Loxahatchee River Historical Society
500 Captain Armours Way
Jupiter, FL 33469
(561) 747-8380 E-mail: visit@LRHS.org
Location: The lighthouse is located in Lighthouse Park.
Highlights: Lighthouse
Website: www.lrhs.org/JIL.htm
General Information: The red Jupiter Lighthouse was built between 1853-1860. It was first lit on June 10, 1860 and has been in operation everyday, except for a brief period during the Civil War. The Lighthouse still serves as a guide and aid to navigation. The United States Coast Guard maintains the lens. The lighthouse is maintained and operated by the Loxahatchee River Historical Society. At the base you will find the Oil House. This building serves as a museum for lighthouse artifacts.
Admission: The Visitor Center located at 500 Captain Armour's Way in Lighthouse Park and is open Saturday -Wednesday each week from 10 A.M. until 4 P.M. The Loxahatchee River Historical Society's phone is (561) 747-6639. The Museum presents a permanent exhibit called "History Shaped By Nature." The history of the Jupiter, Florida area can be traced to pre-historic times. The exhibit portrays life at various stages of history. On site are a replica Seminole Village and the 1892 pioneer Tindall Home. A second exhibit hall houses exhibits of varied interest on a temporary basis, usually three months in duration. The Museum is open Tuesday-Friday, 10 A.M.-5 P.M. and Saturday/Sunday, 12 Noon - 5 P.M. There is an entry fee.

23

In addition, the Loxahatchee River Historical Society operates the DuBois Pioneer home in DuBois Park in Jupiter. The home is open Tuesday & Wednesday, 1 P.M. – 4 P.M. All three facilities are closed Christmas, Easter, and New Year's Day.

KEY WEST, FLORIDA
East Martello Towers Gallery and Museum
3501 So. Roosevelt Boulevard
Key West, FL 33040
(305) 296-3913   Fax: (305) 296-6206
E-mail: kwahs@kwahs.org
Location: Follow US-1 to A1A beachside to the Towers.
Highlights: Maritime artifacts, ship models, Fort Zachary Taylor, East Martello Towers, Gift Shop,
Website: www.kwahs.com/martello.htm
   General Information: East Martello Tower was built in 1862 by the U.S. Army to protect Fort Zachary Taylor from Confederate attack. It is the only Martello fort in the US still intact with eight-inch thick walls.

Gun galleries where wreckers brought survivors and cargo ashore after unwary ship captains crushed their ships on unseen reefs now houses artifacts and displays of Florida Keys history. Robert the Haunted Doll, junkyard sculptures by Stanley Papio and the painted woodcarvings of folk artist Mario Sanchez now fill this Civil War Fort.
   Admission: Entry fee. Open daily, 9:30 A.M.- 5 P.M., year-round. Closed on Christmas.

KEY WEST, FLORIDA
Key West Shipwreck Historeum
1 Whitehead Street
Key West, FL 33040-6634
(305) 292-8990 Fax: (305) 293-7898
E-mail: shipwreck@historictours.com
Location: In old Mallory Square
Highlights: Shipwrecked packet *Isaac Allerton* history, **Website:** www.shipwreckhistoreum.com
   General Information: The Key West Shipwreck Historeum is housed in a reproduction of the wrecker's warehouse that originally stood on the site. Costumed actors interact with visitors and recreate the events of the wreck and salvage of the 137-foot, square rigged packet *Isaac Allerton*, which sank in 1856.
   In her hold was a general cargo of household goods, marble floors, capitol, and lintels for the Federal Customs house at New Orleans. In 1985, the wreck was rediscovered and claimed. Artifacts from the shipwreck are on display and videotapes are shown. A 65-foot observation tower, originally a ship-wrecker's watch tower, provides a magnificent view of the Atlantic Ocean and the

Gulf of Mexico like it did 150 years ago when wreckers were on the lookout.
   Admission: Entry fee. Open daily 9:45 A.M.- 4:45 P.M.

KEY WEST, FLORIDA
Lighthouse Museum
938 Whitehead Street
Key West, FL 33040
(305) 294-0012   E-mail: naberle@kwahs.org
Location: Key West is on the southern most tip of Rte. 1, 156 miles south of Miami. The Museum is several blocks east of the downtown area in a residential section.
   Highlights: Lighthouse and keeper's quarters museum,
Website: www.kwahs.com/lighthouse.htm
   General Information: The Key West Lighthouse was completed in 1848. In 1895, twenty feet were added to achieve a height of ninety-five feet. The Museum is housed in the former lighthouse keeper's quarters, where items concerning the lighthouse history are displayed highlighting the history of the Key West Light Station.

Key West Arts Historical Society maintains several very important historical sites in the community including The Key West Lighthouse, East Martello Towers, and the Custom House. It also is involved in the "Remember the Maine" battleship famous from the Spanish –American War where Key West played an important part in support.

The Key Lighthouse Restoration Project began in 1987 and took three years to complete. Each historic building was returned to its appearance at the turn of the century. Visitors touring the award-winning restoration discover what life was like for a Lighthouse Keeper   in the days before electricity and automation. Eighty-eight spiral steps lead to the top of the 90-foot Lighthouse where a panoramic view of the Island can be seen.
   Admission: Entry fee. Open daily, 9:30 A.M.- 4:30 P.M., year-round. Closed Christmas.

KEY WEST, FLORIDA
Mel Fisher Maritime Heritage Society
200 Greene Street
Key West, FL 33040
(305) 294-2633 800/434-1399
E-mail: office@melfisher.org
Location: Key West, the southern most tip of US-1, is 156 miles south of Miami.
Highlights: Changing museum exhibits, research library, newsletter, laboratory,
Website: www.melfisher.org/
   General Information: The history of shipwrecks begins with those unknown mariners who first ventured out onto the uncharted sea and

24

for millennia; the sea has guarded their secrets. Today, shipwreck archaeologists recover more and more of this priceless heritage every year.

The Mel Fisher Maritime Heritage Society, founded in 1982, displays gold jewelry, silver coins, and numerous artifacts recovered from the wreckage of the Spanish treasure ships *Atocha* and *Santa Margarita*. The two vessels sank 40 miles off Key West in a hurricane on September 6, 1622, on their return voyages to Spain from Havana, Cuba. Also here are exhibits detailing techniques of underwater archaeology, the history of the transatlantic slave trade, and other maritime subjects.

Activities: A theatre, conservation, archaeological research facilities.

Admission: Entry fee. Memberships available. Open daily 9:30 A.M.-5 P.M. year round.

KEY WEST, FLORIDA
Pirate Soul Museum
524 Front Street
Key West, FL 33040
877-243-2378
305/292-1113 Fax: 305/292-1125
Location: In downtown Key West one block west of Duval Street on Front Street
Highlights: Authentic pirate artifacts, pirate flags, pirate treasure chest
Website: www.piratesoul.com
General Information: The Pirate Soul museum opened in 2005 to collect and display pirate memorabilia. The museum features nearly 500 authentic artifacts, many from founder Pat Croce's private collection, depicting piracy's golden age from 1690 to 1730. The museum used audio-animatronic elements to explore the lives of such notorious buccaneers as shipmates Anne Bonny and Mary read, and Florida Keys pirate Black Caesar.

Visitors also can view the original journal of Captain Kidd's last voyage; a blunderbuss owned by Blackbeard; and many other interesting exhibits.

Admission: Entry fee: Open daily 9 am to 7 pm

KEY WEST, FLORIDA
Ripley's Believe It Or Not! Museum
108 Duval Street
Key West, FL 33040
(305) 293-9939
E-mail: museum@ripleyskeywest.com
Location: The Museum is in the heart of downtown Key West in the old Strand Theatre.
Highlights: "Pirates: Pain and Torture" exhibit,
Website: www.ripleyskeywest.com/
General Information: Ripley's Believe It Or Not! Museum, housed in the refurbished Strand

Theatre in Key West, provides exhibits on Key West history, deep-sea diving, and a nautical display entitled "Pirates: Pain and Torture." Also exhibited is the largest collection of "hard hat" diving helmets in the world, including an original "20,000 Leagues Under the Sea" helmet, and the helmet used by John Wayne in "wake of the Red Witch." Words like "keelhaul, Norwegian barrel, Mongolian box," and other pirate terms are brought to life through wax figures dramatizing the life of those rascals that roamed the shores of Florida and the Caribbean.

Admission: Entry fee. Open daily from 10 A.M. until 5 P.M., Labor Day until Memorial Day. After Memorial Day, the Light Station will be open from 10 A.M. until 9 P.M.

KEY WEST, FLORIDA
Wrecker's Museum
(The Oldest House in Key West)
322 Duval Street
Key West, FL 33040
(305) 294-9502
Location: Key West, 156 miles south and west of Miami (the southernmost tip of Florida), is reached via US-1 or by air.
Highlights: Ship models, history of the wreckers,
General Information: The Wrecker's Museum, established in the Oldest House in Key West, highlights the life of the ship wrecker. Key West has the distinction of being the only community in the U.S. where ship wreckers were licensed. This created a cooperative, rather than a competitive relationship, between the wreckers — all eager to first bring in the survivors and then the cargo of the wrecked ship, for sale. The "wreckers" would put out to sea in any weather to save lives, cargoes, and vessels from the reefs and shoals.

The Wrecker's Museum, in an 1829 house with a ship's hatch in the roof and "The Landlubbers Tilt" inside, maintains a variety of items on display, including ship models, marine artifacts, even a doll's house. There are three buildings to view from a spacious garden, wrecker's documents, fine paintings, and antiques.

Admission: Entry fee. Open daily, 10 A.M.-4 P.M., year-round.

MIAMI, FLORIDA
Cape Florida Lighthouse
Bill Baggs Cape Florida State Recreation Area
1200 S. Crandon Blvd.
Miami, FL 33169
(305) 361-5811 Off. (305) 361-8771
Fax: (305) 365-0003
Location: The Lighthouse is located at the southern tip of Key Biscayne.
Highlights: Lighthouse
Website: http://users.erols.com/lthouse/cflt.htm

General Information: A 900-acre state recreation area on the southern tip of Key Biscayne contains a museum complex that includes the Cape Florida Lighthouse and a reconstructed keeper's home and office.

Admission: Entry fee. Park open daily,8 A.M.-sunset; tours of lighthouse and museum Wednesday-Monday 10:30 A.M., 1 P.M., 2:30 P.M. and 3:30 P.M. (limit 25 persons per tour).

MIAMI, FLORIDA

Historical Museum of Southern Florida
101 W. Flagler Street
Miami, FL 33130
(305) 375-1492
E-mail: info@hmsf.org
Location: The Museum is in downtown Miami.
Highlights: Ship models, early Florida history, gift shop, **Website:** www.hmsf.org/
General Information: Historical Museum of Southern Florida uses artifacts, dioramas, audiovisual displays, photographs, and a variety of other media to illustrate the past 10,000 years of the region's history and development. Of special note is the John C. Harrison Recreational Maritime Collection including over 350 outboard engines — a representative cross-section of their development from 1915-1950. The outboard engines are stored in an off-site warehouse. The Museum also displays periodically thirty-three boats from the same period — most less than twenty feet in length.
Admission: Entry fee. Open Monday-Saturday, 10 A.M.-5 P.M.; third Thursday, 10 A.M.-9 P.M.; Sunday, noon-5 P.M. Closed Thanksgiving, Christmas Day, and New Year's Day.

PALM BEACH, FLORIDA

Palm Beach Maritime Museum
7719 S. Dixie Highway
West Palm Beach, FL 33405
P.O. Box 2317
Palm Beach, FL 3480
(561) 540-5147 Fax: (561) 540-5196
E-mail: museum@pbmm.org
Location: The Museum's principal location is at the Lake Worth Lagoon Education Center in Currie Park 1/2-mile north of Palm Beach Lakes Blvd. on Flagler, and on the shores of Lake Worth — West Palm Beach's largest park on the Intracoastal Waterway.
Highlights: President Kennedy's Bunker, now a Museum, U.S. Coast Guard Station on Peanut Island, **Website:** www.pbmm.org/
General Information: The Palm Beach Maritime Museum, founded in 1990, was established to bring to life the events in the maritime history of Florida and the Caribbean Basin. It presents a collection of artifacts and exhibits through the use of advanced communications and interactive technologies. Although the primary mission is educational, this will be balanced and complemented by continuous programs of entertainment and recreation.

An underground bunker and command post on Peanut Island near Palm Beach was President John F. Kennedy's A-bomb bunker. The bunker and an adjacent coast guard station will be turned into a museum on this seventy-nine-acre island, which will be connected by ferry to the mainland. The bunker was built in 1960 to house the vacationing President John F. Kennedy and his family in the event of enemy attack during the difficulties with Cuba.

Activities: Multiple sites, Ferryboat rides.
Admission: Entry fee. Museum open: Wednesday-Saturday from 9 A.M. – 1 P.M. Sundays from 10 A.M. – 2 P.M. Ferry Schedule from Currie Park, Tour times at Peanut Island: Wednesday – Friday: 10:30 A.M., 11:30 A.M. & 12:30 P.M.; Saturday and Sunday, 11:30 A.M., 12:30 P.M., 1:30 P.M. & 2:30 P.M.

PANAMA CITY, FLORIDA

Museum of the Man in the Sea
17314 Panama City Beach Parkway (Hwy 98)
Panama City Beach, FL 32413-2020
(850) 235-4101 (Phone/Fax)
E-mail: info@maninthesea.org
Location: Panama City is ninety-five miles east of Pensacola on US 98 and ninety miles west of Tallahassee.
Highlights: Shipwrecks Around Florida exhibit, treasures from *Atocha* Fleet (lost 1622 off Key West),
Web Site: http://maninthesea.org/
General Information: Sponsored by the Institute of Diving, the Museum specifically focuses on our under-sea environment. The exhibits include artifacts from Civil War transport ship *Maple Leaf,* SS *Tarpon* that carried passengers and goods between Mobile, AL and Carabelle, FL, a permanent collection of commercial, government, and sport-diving equipment, such as Sealab I, a Mark I deep-dive system, only known collection of Seal-Team-Swimmer-Delivery Vehicles VI, VII, VIII, and IX, and full diving dress with helmets, air pumps, armored diving suit, and other items.
Admission: Entry fee. Open daily, 10 A.M.-5 P.M., year-round.

PENSACOLA, FLORIDA
Pensacola Historical Museum
115 East Zaragosa Street
Pensacola, FL 32502
(850) 433-1559 Library: (850) 434-5455
E-mail: phstaff@pensacolahistory.org
Location: The Museum is in the Arbona Building
Highlights: Maritime history, Lelia Abercrombie
Historical Library, Irish famine tall ship *Jeanie
Johnson*,
Website: www.pensacolahistory.org/
   General Information: The Museum presents
the history of the City of Pensacola in the Arbona
Building, conveniently situated in the midst of the
restaurants and shops of the historical district. The
library contains information on shipping and the
fishing industry and an extensive photograph
collection.
   Admission: Entry fee. Open Monday-Saturday,
10 A.M.-4:30 P.M.

PONCE INLET-VOLUSIA, FLORIDA
Ponce De Leon Inlet Lighthouse
4931 S. Peninsula Drive
Ponce Inlet, FL 32127
(386) 761-1821
E-mail: lighthouse@ponceinlet.org
Location: The inlet is just south of Daytona Beach
on the Atlantic Ocean. The Lighthouse is west of
Atlantic Avenue on South Peninsula Drive (off
Rte. 1 and I-95).
Highlights: The *F. D. Russell* (tugboat), quarterly
newsletter, lighthouse ship store,
Website www.ponceinlet.org/
   General Information: Night after night from
1887 to 1970 this 175-foot tall sentinel of brick and
granite flashed its faithful warning "to the men who
go down to the sea in ships." The Lighthouse was
started with the purchase of ten acres of land on
March 21, 1883, and completed in 1887. Ponce de
Leon Inlet Lighthouse museum, founded in 1972,
is on the grounds of the restored light station. The
Coast Guard reactivated the light in 1982.
   In addition to the Lighthouse there are eight
other buildings: The 2nd assistant keeper's
cottage artifacts documenting the background of
Ponce Inlet; the principal light-house keeper's
house operating as a sea museum; the 1st assistant
keeper's cottage named the Gladys Meyer Davis
House (Davis was a life-long resident of Ponce
Inlet whose father was the last Head Keeper).
   Activities: Self-guided tours
   Admission: Entrance fee. Open daily, 10 A.M.-
5 P.M., Summer hours begin May 31: Open10
A.M. to 9 P.M. daily.

ST. AUGUSTINE, FLORIDA
St. Augustine Lighthouse and Museum
Anastasia Island
81 Lighthouse Avenue
St. Augustine, FL 32080
(904) 829-0745
E-mail: info@staugustinelighthouse.com

Location: Take Rte. A1A south from St. Augustine
one mile then left on Old Beach Road across from
Alligator Farm on Anastasia Island, to the
lighthouse.
Highlights: Lighthouse,
Website: www.staugustinelighthouse.com/
   General Information: The days of the blue-
uniformed lighthouse keeper — checking his oil
supply, slowly climbing the tower to clean the lens
— have passed forever, yet his lighthouse remains.
In 1565, Spanish settlers erected a wooden
watchtower at the inlet. On March 16, 1824, the
tower officially became Florida's first lighthouse. It
was replaced in 1875. A brick light keeper's house
was added, and the light keepers and their families
lived and worked on site until 1955. The St.
Augustine Lighthouse remains an active aid to
navigation with its first-order Fresnel lens, which is
beamed 19 nautical miles out to sea.
   Admission: Entry fee. Open daily, 9 A.M. –
5 P.M.

SEBASTIAN, FLORIDA
Mel Fisher's Treasure Museum
1322 U.S. Hwy One
Sebastian, FL 32958-3889
(772) 589-9875
Location: From Orlando: Travel east on Beeline
Expressway to I-95, then south to exit 69
(Fellsmere Road). Then go east to U.S. 1 and turn
north. The Museum is six blocks on the right.
Highlights: Spanish treasure, preservation
laboratory, gift shop
   General Information: Mel Fisher's Treasure
Museum is an extension of the treasure museum in
Key West. Here, you will join millions who have
witnessed the most spectacular collection of
Spanish artifacts and treasure ever assembled.
   Even now, treasure is being uncovered from a
fleet of eleven Spanish galleons and one French
ship that set sail from Havana for Spain and sank in
the year of 1715.
   All the ships perished in a storm off the east
coast of Florida, near present-day Sebastian. Seven
hundred lives and fourteen million pesos worth of
treasure went down. Recovery from the fleet
continues to grow in quantity and spectacle and is
shown in the recent recovery display. Observe on-
the-spot preservation techniques through a special
viewing window in the Museum's laboratory.
   Admission: Entry fee. Open Monday-Saturday,
10 A.M.- 5 P.M., Sunday, noon-5 P.M. year-round.
Closed some holidays.

STUART, FLORIDA
Gilbert's Bar House of Refuge
301 SE MacArthur Blvd.
Stuart, FL 34996
(772) 225-1875 Fax: (772) 225-2333
E-mail: info@elliottmuseumfl.org
Location: The House of Refuge is ninety-five
miles north of Miami. Take Exit 133 from the
Florida Turnpike east or Exit 61, 61C east from I-
95. Follow signs several miles to Hutchinson
Island and Indian River Plantation. Turn south on
MacArthur Boulevard one and three-tenths miles to
the House of Refuge.
Highlights: Boathouse, surfboat reproduction, gift
shop, **Web site:** http://
elliottmuseumfl.org/houseofrefuge/index.html
   General Information: Commissioned in 1875
by the U.S. Life-Saving Service to assist those
shipwrecked off the east coast of Florida, the
Gilbert's Bar Station is the only one (of nine)
restored and remaining in use. The House of
Refuge was maintained to handle up to ten
survivors in a second-story dormitory room
furnished with cots. Here, survivors would stay a
day or two until they felt well enough to continue
on with their journey—often by land.
   On the site is a boathouse containing early life-
saving equipment, maritime exhibits, and pictures
and books. A surfboat, clinker-built, is exhibited
based on its 1875 plans. The main house is
furnished in late Victorian period. In it, as many as
ten rescued survivors could be accommodated, at a
time.
   Admission: Entry fee. Open: Tuesday through
Sunday from 11 A.M. until 4 P.M.

STUART, FLORIDA
Maritime & Yachting Museum
3250 S.W Kanner Highway
Stuart, Florida 34995
(772) 692-1234 E-mail: mym34994@comcast.net
Location: The Maritime is approximately 40 miles
north of West Palm Beach on Florida's Atlantic
coast, on the South Fork of the St. Lucie River.
From I-95: Take Exit 61 and drive east toward
Stuart on Kanner Highway (State Route 76) for 4.2
miles. The museum will be on your left. From US
Highway 1 (Southeast Federal Highway) in Stuart:
Take State Route 76 (Kanner Highway) south,
cross Monterey Road, and continue for 0.7 miles
just past Martin County High School. The museum
will be on your right.
Highlights: Wooden boat building, boat
restorations, boat models, library,
Web site: www.mymflorida.com
   General Information: The Maritime &
Yachting Museum's mission is to collect, preserve,
and display artifacts and vessels that provide a
tangible link to the past. The library provides a
permanent record of maritime and yachting events
that have contributed to the development of the
Treasure Coast and Florida.

Educational programs in restoration, model
building, small-boat building, and *Activities* to
stimulate interest in our maritime heritage are
provided. The Museum sponsors Sea Scout ship
#81.
   The Indian River Lagoon provides Tea-Talks by
Widow's Walk Tea Room, with a view of
knowledgeable marine speakers. Other evening
programs enhance the educational opportunities.
   Admission: No fee but memberships and/or
donations are encouraged. Open Monday-
Saturday, 11 A.M. - 4 P.M. Sundays, 1 P.M.-
5 P.M.

TALLAHASSEE, FLORIDA
Museum of Florida History
R. A. Gray Building
500 South Bronough
Tallahassee, FL 32399-0250
(850) 245-6400 E-mail: pastanley@dos.state.fl.us
Location: Take I-10 into Tallahassee, then bear
south on Rte. 27 to center city. The Museum is
downtown one-block west of the State Capitol.
Highlights: Spanish Maritime Exhibit, Florida
waterways exhibit, gift shop,
Web site: http://dhr.dos.state.fl.us/museum
   General Information: The Museum of Florida
History was established to promote and encourage
knowledge and appreciation of the maritime
history of Florida and to preserve and exhibit
artifacts that relate to the history of the state.
   The Museum's "Plate (silver) Fleet" exhibits
covers Spanish colonial shipping of gold and silver
from the New Word to Spain. Artifacts from 1715
and 1733 shipwrecks are displayed, including
treasure lost when the fleets were struck by
hurricanes.
   A major exhibit, "Waterways: The History of
Water Transportation in Florida," touches on the
entire story of water transportation in Florida with
a main focus on the "golden era of steamboating."
The forward quarter of the re-created steamboat
Hiawatha, has been fashioned to house the exhibit.
   The original *Hiawatha* traveled the St. John's-
Ocklawaha Rivers run to Silver Springs from 1904
to 1920.
   Activities: Audiovisual presentations; quilting
workshops
   Admission: No entry fee - donations accepted.
Hours of Operation: Monday-Friday 9 A.M.- 4:30
P.M.; Saturday 10 A.M. - 4:30 P.M.;
Sunday and holidays Noon - 4:30 P.M.

TAMPA, FLORIDA

SS *American Victory* Mariners Memorial and Museum Ship, Inc.

705 Channelside Drive
Tampa, FL 33602
(813) 228-8766   Fax: (813) 228-8769
E-mail: amvic@americanvictory.org
Location: The ship is docked at Channelside Drive in Tampa. From I-275 Northbound, Take the Downtown East (Scott Street) EXIT 25 Continue straight on Scott Street to Orange/Jefferson Street. Right on Jefferson (which becomes Pierce Street) to Twiggs Street. Left on Twiggs Street to Channelside Drive. Right on Channelside Drive to York Street. Left on York Street to the Florida Aquarium Parking Lot.
Highlights: SS *American* Victory ship, *Steaming as Before* Newsletter,
Web site: www.americanvictory.org
   General Information: SS *American Victory* was named after American University in Washington, D.C., to honor the school's contributions to war training and weapons research during both WW II and I. From June until September 1945, she carried ammunition and other cargo from U.S. West Coast ports to Southeast Asia. She ferried cargo, equipment and troops back to the U.S. after the war ended. Other Victory ships now museum ships: SS *Lane Victory* (CA) and SS *Red Oak Victory* (CA).
   During the Vietnam War effort, under the Military Sealift Command, she carried bombs, military equipment, and supplies to South Vietnam and Thailand. In September 1967, she was severely battered by Typhoon Diana en route from Japan to South Vietnam. *American Victory* was deactivated in 1969, and placed in the James River Reserve Fleet remaining there until April 1999 when she was towed to her new home.
   Admission: Open: Monday through Saturday 10 AM. - 5 PM., Sundays: 12 Noon - 5 PM.

GEORGIA

ATHENS, GEORGIA

U.S. Navy Supply Corps Museum

U.S. Navy Supply Corps School
1425 Prince Avenue
Athens, GA 30606-2205
(706) 354-4111 Fax: (706) 354-7239
E-mail: daniel.atha@navy.mil
Location: From Atlanta: I-85 north to SR 316 east, to Loop Road 10 (Athens Bypass), north to Prince Avenue exit. East on Prince Avenue - 3 blocks to base entrance. From points north: I-85 south to Commerce, GA exit. South on U.S. Rte 441 to Loop Road 10 (Athens Bypass). South on Bypass to Prince Avenue exit. East on Prince Avenue 4-block to base entrance.
Highlights: Ship models, uniforms, Galley gear,

personal memorabilia; archives; garden with gazebo, fountains, stream and seasonal plantings,
Web site: www.npdc.navy.mil/css/nscs/default Cfm?a=services.getServices&ACTYid=6
   General Information: The U.S. Navy Supply Corps Museum, established in 1974, is housed in the 1910 Carnegie Library of the former State Normal School/Teachers College.
   The Museum stands as a tribute to the men and women of the U.S. Navy Supply Corps. Exhibits trace the growth and development of the Supply Corps, explains its many functions in supplying today's Navy, and commemorates noteworthy Individuals associated with the Corps. Facilities include an archive with vintage manuals and cookbooks, photos, newsletters, scrapbooks, curriculum materials, directories, and yearbooks.
   Displays include models of namesake ships USS Supply, both past and present, a 12-foot model of USS *Neptune*.
   Admission: Free admission and parking. Open Monday-Friday, 9 A.M.-5:15 P.M. Closed Federal holidays.

COLUMBUS, GEORGIA

Port Columbus National Civil War Naval Museum

1002 Victory Drive, P.O. Box 1022
Columbus, GA 31901
(706) 327-9798
E-mail: cwnavy@portcolumbus.org
Location: Columbus is on the Chattahoochee River in western Georgia. From Atlanta, take 85 W towards Montgomery, take 185 S. to Columbus, then take exit 1b, Victory Drive. Proceed 5 miles and turn left into South Commons.
Highlights: The CSS *Jackson* (ironclad ram, partial hull — Albemarle Class), The CSS *Chattahoochee* (gun boat), ship models, gift shop,
Website: http://portcolumbus.org/
   General Information: This 40,000 square foot museum opened in March of 2001 and is the only museum in the nation to take a comprehensive look at the Civil War at sea. Included in the exhibits are the hulls of two original Confederate warships, the CSS *Jackson*, a 225 ft ironclad ram, and the CSS *Chattahoochee*, a more conventional wooden gunboat.
   Rebuilt portions of three other famous Civil War ships have been installed so visitors may see how Civil War sailors, North and South, lived and worked. These include the USS *Hartford*, the USS *Monitor* and the CSS *Albemarle*.
   Conventional exhibits featuring the nation's rarest Civil War naval artifacts fill the main gallery and a special naval battle theater has been constructed to allow visitors a taste of what it was like inside a Confederate ironclad ship during several famous sea battles.
   Admission: Entry fee. Open Monday - Sunday 9 A.M. – 5 P.M. Open 364 days a year - Closed December 25th

ST. SIMONS ISLAND, GEORGIA
St. Simons Island Lighthouse Museum
101 12th Street
P. O. Box 21136
St. Simons Island, GA 31522-0636
(912) 638-4666 Fax: (912) 638-6609
E-mail: ssi1872@comcast.net
Location: The lighthouse is in the Village District overlooking Saint Simons Sound. Take U.S. 17 in Brunswick, then take the Torras Causeway to St. Simons Island. After the bridge over the Frederica River, turn right on King's Way. Stay on King's Way past the blinking light at Sea Island Causeway, and past the traffic signal at Frederica Road. (At this intersection, you will see the airport on your left). At the next traffic signal, turn right on Mallory Street, go one block to Beachview and turn left. Go 1/4 mile to 12th Street and turn right.
Highlights: Lighthouse and museum,
Website: www.saintsimonslighthouse.org/
General Information: The Saint Simons Lighthouse Museum, operated by the Coastal Georgia Historical Society, is located in the restored lighthouse keeper's dwelling reconstructed in 1872 on the same site to replace the original which was destroyed by retreating Confederate forces in 1862. Changing exhibits depict the island's lighthouse history and offer a fine view of the island and the adjacent.

In 1738, General James Oglethorpe built Fort St. Simons as a defense against Spanish invaders from Florida. America's shipping industry led to the site's next historic role. James Gould began building a seventy-five-foot lighthouse in 1807. Completed in 1810, the octagonal tower tapered from its twenty-five-foot base to a ten-foot-diameter top. Charles Cluskey was the builder of the second lighthouse.

Admission: Entry fee: Open daily: Monday-Saturday, 10 A.M.- 5 P.M., Sunday, 1:30 P.M.-5 P.M. Lighthouse closes 4:45 P.M. Museum and Lighthouse closed on Thanksgiving Day, Christmas Eve, Christmas Day and new Year's Day.

SAVANNAH, GEORGIA
Old Fort Jackson
1 Fort Jackson Road
Savannah, GA 31404-1039
(912) 232-3945 Fax: (912) 236-5126
Location: Fort Jackson is three miles east of Savannah. Take Islands Expressway to President Street to Woodcock Road on the Savannah River.
Highlights: The CSS *Georgia* (a rail ironclad) model, Gift Shop,
Website: www.sas.usace.army.mil/CSS/
General Information: Old Fort Jackson Museum, founded in 1976, is in the oldest standing fort in Georgia. It was built on Salter's Island, the site of an earlier fort and Colonial brickyard. Four garrisons of soldiers manned the cannons on Salter's Island during times of revolution, civil war, foreign invasion, martial law, and epidemic disease. The height of the Fort's military use was as the Confederate headquarters of the river batteries. The Fort's collection includes cannons, small arms, tools, and machinery that are demonstrated and employed during the many special events held each year.

The 250-foot long CSS *Georgia*, a rail iron-clad vessel, was located by dive teams from the U.S. Army Corps of Engineers and the Cultural Resources Laboratory of Texas A & M. Because of the "black water," resulting in zero visibility, the divers must "feel" the wreckage to determine the exact location of its features and the extent of damage she has sustained through the years. During the course of diving some artifacts have been recovered and are located in the museum. Well worth seeing!

For two hundred years the maritime history of the South Atlantic Coast has been hidden from view. Today the Coast Heritage Society is undertaking a project to uncover this resource. A research project was begun in 1980 to locate information about small boats used in this area by our ancestors. Results of this study were published in 1982 in "Tide Craft, The Boats of Lower South Carolina and Georgia."

Activities: Educational programs, June-15 to August 15, daily cannon firings,
Admission: Entry fee. Open Monday-Sunday, 9 A.M. - 5 P.M., year-round.

SAVANNAH, GEORGIA
Ships of the Sea Maritime Museum
41 Martin Luther King Boulevard
Savannah, GA 31401-2435
(912) 232-1511 E-mail:
contact@shipsofthesea.org
Location: Take I-10 into center of Savannah. The Museum is a mere 100 feet from the Savannah River on East River Drive (several blocks east of the City Hall).
Highlights: Ship models, figureheads, chandlery, ships-in-a-bottle collection, scrimshaw,
Web site: www.shipsofthesea.org/
General Information: Ships of the Sea Maritime Museum, founded in 1966, is in the 1819 restored William Scarbrough House which was built for one of the principal owners of the *Savannah*, the first steamship to cross the Atlantic Ocean. The Museum exhibits ship models, scrimshaw, paintings, and maritime artifacts. The Museum's collections have been enhanced with newly commissioned large-scale models of the greatest ships in Savannah's history, a comprehensive display of navigational instruments,

a variety of other seafaring artifacts, and video presentations.

Activities: Guided tours, maritime-oriented classes for children.

Admission: Entry fee. Open Tuesday-Sunday, 10 A.M. - 5 P.M., year-round. Closed Christmas Eve, Christmas, and New Year's Day.

TYBEE ISLAND, GEORGIA

Tybee Island Historical Society
Tybee Island Light Station
P. O. Box 366
Tybee Island, GA 31328
(912) 786-5801 Fax: (912) 786-6538
Location: Tybee Island is eighteen miles east of Savannah. Take I-95 to I-16 from Savannah to US-80, then fifteen miles to Tybee Island.
Highlights: Tybee Lighthouse, lighthouse history,
Website: www.tybeelighthouse.org/

General Information: "From Rabun Gap to Tybee Light" — a phrase employed by nineteenth-century Georgia politicians to measure the great expanse of the state from the north to the south. Today it signifies the importance of the Tybee Lighthouse, which marks the mouth of the Savannah River. Built in 1773 and reconstructed after the Civil War, Tybee Light is 154 feet tall. Visitors may climb the lighthouse for a breathtaking view of Fort Screven and Tybee Island.

A small museum is housed in the 1881 keeper's cottage. A restored 1812 kitchen is open. The Tybee Museum (founded in 1961) is housed in Battery Garden, a Spanish American War coastal defense battery and contains exhibits on coastal defense, the Martello Tower, the Tybee Train, the North Gun Collection, and the Erichsen Doll Collection.

Activities: Tours and lectures

Admission: Entry fee. Memberships are available. Open daily , 9 A.M.- 6 P.M., April-September. Closed Tuesdays year-round. After Labor Day-March, open daily 9 A.M. to 4 P.M.

HAWAII

HONOLULU, HAWAII

Bishop Museum
1525 Bernice Street
Honolulu, HI 96817-2704
(808) 847-38205 Fax: (808) 841-8968
E-mail: museum@bishopmuseum.org
Location: The Museum is east of downtown Honolulu on Bernice Street. Exit I-H1 at Rte. 63 to Bernice St.
Highlights: Planetarium, ship models, library (90,000 volumes), gift shop,
Website: www.bishopmuseum.org/

General Information: Bishop Museum was founded in 1889 and is famous for its extensive array of Pacific cultural and economic artifacts. Polynesians charted the position of the stars in the heavens, observed the currents of the ocean and the flights of birds which allowed them to create bamboo stick charts that enabled them to sail a great distances to the north, settling in the area first known as the Sandwich Islands and later renamed Hawaii.

In its extensive collections, the Museum also contains several small but important exhibits in honor of the mariner, a depiction of the freighter/passenger business, a small whaling exhibit, and an exhibit of the way finding ocean voyaging in ancient Polynesia.

Activities: Lectures, films, and education programs.

Admission: Entry fee. Memberships are available. Open daily, 9 A.M.-5 P.M. year-round.
NOTE: See also Hawaiian Maritime Center.

HONOLULU, HAWAII

Hawaii Maritime Center
Pier 7, Honolulu Harbor
Honolulu, HI 96813-2704
(808) 848-4138 (808) 536-1519
E-mail: museum@bishopmuseum.org
Location: The center is on Pier 7, off Ala Moana Boulevard, at Honolulu Harbor near downtown Honolulu. Call (808) 536-6373 for information on free parking.
Highlights: The *Falls of Clyde* (1878 sailing ship, a National Historic Landmark), The *Hokule'a* (Polynesian double-hull voyaging canoe), Pier 7 (international steamship pier), Aloha Tower, gift shop, **Website:**
www.bishopmuseum.org/exhibits/hmc/hmc.html

General Information: The Hawaii Maritime Center opened in 1989 where you can "experience Hawaii's Ocean Legacy." There are fifty displays on the maritime history of the Hawaiian Islands: From ancient Polynesian non-instrument navigation and voyaging, through rowdy nineteenth-century whalers, the romantic luxury liners of the 1930s, Pan Am's classic Flying Boats, surfing, and tattooing.

See photographs of Kind David Kalakaua's boathouse, which was once situated near the Hawaii Maritime Center, and mementos of sculling another racing events of the early 1900's. In the boathouse you can take a fascinating journey through the days of Captain Cook to the monarchy more vividly than ever with a stereo Walkman audio tour, laser disc videos, and audio exhibits available in several languages — it's all here and more!

The Center's Whaling Exhibit includes a gigantic humpback whale skeleton, one of only two in the world. Another exhibit on the grand "Boat Days" of the passenger ocean liners is worth seeing.

Visitors can walk the decks of the only four-masted; full-rigged ship left in the world—an historic landmark—the *Falls of Clyde*. This vessel served the Islands form 1889-1920. (See Monterey Maritime Museum for information on one of the *Clyde's* crewmembers by the name of Allen Knight.) National Geographic has documented the historic voyaging canoe Hokule'a. This Polynesian Sailing Canoe made history by retracing the voyages of ancient Hawaiians throughout the South Pacific by using the stars and ocean currents to navigate.

Admission: Entry fee. Open daily, 8:30 A.M.-5 P.M., year-round. Limited free parking: call 536-6373 for information before coming.

HONOLULU, HAWAII
USS *Arizona* Memorial
1 Arizona Memorial Place
Honolulu, HI 96818-3145
 (808) 422-3300 Fax: (808) 483-8608
E-mail: On Web Site
Location: The Memorial is in Pearl Harbor, adjacent to Honolulu on the island of Oahu. Take H-1 to State Highway 99, following signs to the National Park Service Visitors Center.
Highlights: The USS *Arizona* Memorial, museum, research library, bookstore, *Broadside* Newsletter,
Website: www.nps.gov/usar/
 General Information: The USS *Arizona* Memorial, established in 1962, commemorates the December 7, 1941, Japanese attack on Pearl Harbor and all the men who died in the attack. All bodies of those killed have long since been removed from the hulk. The museum contains exhibits related to the attack on Pearl Harbor. A research library relating to Pearl Harbor and World War II is available for use on the premises. Advance appointments.
 Activities: Guided programs, shuttle boat to the memorial, lectures, a film, and educational programs.
 Admission: No entry fee. Visitor's Center: open 7:30 A.M.-5 P.M., year-round. Boat trip to the Memorial: open daily, 8 A.M.-3 P.M. Closed Thanksgiving, Christmas, and New Year's Day.

HONOLULU, HAWAII
USS *Bowfin* Submarine Museum and Park
11 Arizona Memorial Drive
Honolulu, HI 96818
Toll Free: 1-866-836-0317
E-mail: info@bowfin.org

 (808) 423-1341 Fax: (808) 422-5201
Location: Bowfin Park is located at Pearl Harbor, adjacent to the USS *Arizona* Memorial Visitor Center. Take H-1 to State Highway 99, following signs to the *Arizona* Memorial.
Highlights: USS *Bowfin* (SS-287 — restored WW II submarine), U.S. Submarine Memorial honoring fifty-two submarines lost in World War II, museum and mini-theatre, library, gift shop,
Website: www.bowfin.org
 General Information: USS *Bowfin* Submarine Museum and Park is a privately maintained memorial to World War II submariners, the men of the "Silent Service." Launched on December 7, 1942, *Bowfin* performed with distinction during her nine war patrols in the Pacific. After serving as a reserve training ship in the 1960s, she was saved from the scrap heap and restored by the Pacific Fleet Submarine Memorial Association.

The Museum exhibits artifacts and documents that relate the story of the "Silent Service." Library and archives include World War II patrol reports and files on submarines since 1900. Outdoors exhibits include the conning tower of USS *Parche*, a Japanese one-man suicide torpedo (*Kaiten*), and assorted missile and torpedo displays.
 Activities: cassette player receivers aid a self-guided tour of the boat. Attendants are on hand to ensure safety and to answer questions.
 Admission: Entry fee. Open daily 8:00 A.M.-5 P.M. Closed Thanksgiving, Christmas, and New Year's Day.

HONOLULU, HAWAII
USS *Missouri* Memorial Association
P.O. Box 879
Aiea, HI 96701
(808) 455-1600 Fax: (808) 423-0700
Toll free: 1-877-MIGHTYMO (1-877-644-4896)
 E-mail: William.hughes2ATtx.rr.com
Location: The Battleship *Missouri* Memorial is in Pearl Harbor, adjacent to Honolulu on the island of Oahu. Take H-1 to State Highway 99, following signs to the *Arizona* Memorial Visitors Center.
Highlights: The USS *Missouri* Memorial museum, Ship's Store, *Broadside* Newsletter,
Website: www.ussmissouri.com/
 General Information: The USS *Missouri*, launched January 29, 1944, participated in the invasions of Iwo Jima and Okinawa, and served as Admiral William F. Halsey's flagship. The *Missouri* is best remembered as the place where, on board, General of the Army Douglas MacArthur officially accepted the surrender of Japan, on September 2, 1945, ending World War II.

During the Korean War *Missouri* supported American forces during the Inchon Landings, provided support of the evacuation of Hungnam, and conducted extensive shore bombardment of North Korea. *Missouri* was recalled to service in 1986 when she was recommissioned in San Francisco and departed on a round-the-world shakedown cruise, the first battleship to circumnavigate the world since President Theodore Roosevelt's "Great White Fleet" of 1907-1909. In 1987, the *Missouri* supported shipping operations in the Persian Gulf and participated in a variety of Pacific Fleet Exercises.

In 1991, "Mighty Mo" once again sailed into troubled waters during Desert Storm where her 16-inch guns and missile batteries supported American and Coalition forces in the liberation of Kuwait.

The *Missouri* has now joined the battleships USS *Arizona* (BB-39) and USS *Utah* BB-31, and the submarine USS *Bowfin* (SS 287) as fitting memorials in Pearl Harbor to those who served and gave their lives for our country.

Admission: Open daily 9 A.M. – 5 P.M. Ticket window closes at 4 P.M. Closed Thanksgiving Day, Christmas Day, & New Year's Day.

HONOLULU, HAWAII

USS *Utah* (BB-31/AG-16)
Naval Base Pearl Harbor, Code 013
Attn: PAO.
Pearl Harbor, HI 96860-5020
1-800-471-0281
E-mail: William.hughes2ATtx.rr.com **OR**
peglee@nts-online.net
Location: The memorial and ship are reached from Ford Island in Honolulu at Pearl Harbor.
Highlights: USS *Utah* (BB-31 and AG-16) sunk on December 7, 1941, at Pearl Harbor.
Website: www.ussutah.org/

General Information: Sunk in the attack on the United States Pacific Fleet at Pearl Harbor on December 7, 1941, the *Utah* is a tomb for fifty-eight members of her crew. The battle-scarred and partially submerged remains of the battleship are the focal point of a shrine erected by the people of the United States to honor *Utah's* crew, some of whom lost their lives while trying to save their torpedoed ship.

Along with the submerged hulk of the USS *Arizona* on the other side of Ford Island, *Utah* is a frozen moment of time, lying much as she did in the immediate aftermath of the Pearl Harbor attack. While Pearl Harbor and its surrounding bases were repaired and ultimately modernized after the Japanese attack, *Utah*, like *Arizona*, was not. The ship is now a national shrine and memorial to her crew. The memorial, on Ford Island, is accessible to the public by arrangement and appointment. The USS *Utah* is a National Historical Landmark.

Admission: No entry fee. Call for times open.

ILLINOIS

CAIRO, ILLINOIS
Cairo Custom House Museum
1400 Washington Avenue
Cairo, IL 62914
(618) 734-1019
Location: Cairo is on the very southern tip of Illinois and two blocks from the Ohio River.
Highlights: Where Lewis & Clark mapped trip.
Website:
www.lib.niu.edu/ipo/1999/ihy990446.html

General Information: The Alexander County city of Cairo, in southern Illinois, is home to many historical buildings. One of these famous buildings is the Cairo Custom House.

Constructed in 1872, this historic building houses a museum exhibiting local memorabilia.

What exactly is a custom house? Customs, also known as tariffs, are "duties or taxes imposed by a government on imported and, occasionally, exported goods." The Cairo Custom House collected customs for all of the imports traveling past Cairo by river. Imports were sent through New Orleans to Cairo, which was part of the collection district of New Orleans.

Stephen A. Douglas picked the site for the building in 1859 but postponed construction of the Custom House until after the Civil War. In 1866 John A. Logan returned to Congress and lobbied successfully for $50,000 dollars to start construction, with $50,000 dollars each following year until construction was completed. Construction began in 1867, and the building opened to the public on the evening of June 16, 1872.

Admission: No entry fee: Open Monday – Friday, 10 A.M. - Noon & 1 P.M. – 3P.M.

CHICAGO, ILLINOIS
Chicago Maritime Society
310 S. Racine – #6N
Chicago, IL 60607
(312) 421 9096 E-mail: geraldhthomas@cs.com
Highlights: Gift Shop
Website: www.chicagomaritimesociety.org/

General Information: The Chicago Maritime Society currently maintains a maritime history research facility, which is open by appointment.

Activities: Lectures, meetings, and school programs on site.

CHICAGO, ILLINOIS
U-505 (German WW II Submarine)
Museum of Science and Industry
57th Street and Lake Shore Drive
Chicago, IL 60637-2093
(773) 684-1414   Fax: (773) 684-8853
1-800-468-6674 E-mail: msi@msichicago.org
Location: The submarine is housed at the Chicago
Museum of Science and Industry (on the south
side of Chicago near the lake front) at 57th Street
and South Lake Shore Drive.
Highlights: Captured German U-Boat, gift shop,
Website:
www.msichicago.org/exhibit/505/index.html
   General Information: The WW II German
Submarine U-505 is a type IXC U-boat. Captured
on June 4, 1944 by Hunter Killer group 22.3
commanded by Captain Daniel V. Gallery, U-505
is the first enemy man-of-war to be captured by
the US Navy since 1815. The boat as well as nine
mailbags with over 1100 pounds of secret
publications revealed secrets useful to the Allies.
U-505 exhibits give an introduction to the
background of the Battle of the Atlantic. One of
two German Enigma code machines taken from
U-505 is on display as are artifacts relating to the
personal life of the crew. A 10-minute film
describes the capture by crewmembers of the
escort carrier USS *Guadalcanal* .
   Activities: 20-minute guided tours of the U-
Boat and ten-minute film of the capture.
   Admission: Entry fee for the Museum of
Science and Industry. Memberships available.
Open: May-September, Monday through
Saturday: 9:30 A.M. to 5:30 P.M.. Sunday: 11:00
A.M. to 5:30 P.M.; September 7 - November 25
Monday through Saturday: 9:30 a.m. to 4:00 p.m.
Sunday: 11:00 a.m. to 4:00 p.m.; Call for Winter
hours.
NOTICE: Ground was broken in March of 2003
at the site of the new underground building on the
northeast side of the Museum. Current plans call
for moving the U-505 in the spring of 2004 and
preparing to re-open The New U-505 Experience
in 2005.

GREAT LAKES, ILLINOIS
Great Lakes Naval Museum
Building 158 Camp Barry
610 Farragut Avenue
Great Lakes, IL 60088
(847) 688-3154
E-mail: Therese.Gonzalez@navy.mil
Location: From the main gate, take Farragut
Street
to Sampson Street, turn right on Barry Road.
Look for signs directing you to the museum and
Camp Barry.
Highlights: Continuing acquisition of naval gear
Website: www.greatlakesnavalmuseum.org/
   General Information: The Naval Training
Center Great Lakes Museum Exhibit is a

government-owned and operated museum
dedicated to telling the story "boot camp" training
in the United States Navy, and in particular, the
Naval Training Station/Center Great Lakes,
Illinois. Although originally one of four boot
camps, it is now home to Recruit Training
Command, the only Navy recruit training
command. A special section of the museum is
dedicated to the expanding role of women in the
United States Navy.
   Activities: Group Tours
   Admission: No entry fee. Open Friday
1 P.M. – 4 P.M., Sat/Sun 7 A.M. – 3 P.M.
Due to the increased security precautions, please
bring a photo ID and, if driving, a driver's license,
vehicle registration and proof of insurance.

LOCKPORT, ILLINOIS
Illinois and Michigan Canal Museum
200 W. 8th Street
Lockport, IL 60441
(815) 838-4830 E-mail: cca@canalcor.org
Location: Lockport is in the Des Plaines River
Valley seven miles north of Joliet on SR-171.
The Museum-one block north of the junction of
SR-7. *Highlights:* Canal history, newsletters,
Website: www.canalcor.org/
   General Information: The Illinois and
Michigan Canal Museum, founded in 1969, is
housed in the 150-year-old canal commissioner's
office and residence building. It is the only canal
museum in the United States that illustrates the
construction, operation, and demise of a single
waterway. The Museum is owned and operated by
the Will County Historical Society and is part of
the National Heritage Corridor-Illinois
administered by the National Park Service.
   The first stop in the Museum is the canal room,
where many of the century-old artifacts are
displayed with pictures and documents relevant to
the history of the building and operation of the
Canal. The Canal opened in 1848, and over ten
million tons of commerce traversed the Canal
during its sixty-two years of operation.
   Collections include artifacts; pictures;
documents relevant to the history of the Canal;
log cabin; root cellar; village jail; blacksmith
shop; tinsmith shop; workshop; railroad station;
one-room country school; smokehouse; herb
garden; settlement house; and mid-nineteenth-
century farmhouse.
   The massive stone walls of the first lock built
on the Canal remain, but the wood gates are gone.
Interpretive signs allow one to envision how the
lock might have been when it held water to a
depth of six feet and "locked" boats through.
   Activities: Guided tours.
   Admission: No entry fee. Memberships are
available. Open daily, 1 P.M.-4 P.M., January-
mid-December. Closed national holidays and
Thanksgiving week.

ROCK ISLAND, ILLINOIS
Mississippi River Visitor Center
USAED, Rock Island
P.O. Box 2004
Attn: Mississippi River Visitor Center
Rock Island, IL 61204-2004
1-800-645-0248 (309) 794-5338
Fax: (309) 794-5741
E-mail: mvrodmn15@usace.army.mil
Location: Rock Island Arsenal Island. From I-80
on Iowa side, take Brady Street Exit south, stay on
US 61 until West 2nd St. turn left and cross
Arsenal Bridge, turn left onto Arsenal Island,
proceed to second drive on left, and turn into
Center's parking lot.
Highlights: Operation of Lock and Dam #15 on
the Mississippi River,
Website:www.mvr.usace.army.mil/missriver/VC
%20Page/Mississippi%20River%20Vistor.htm
    General Information: The U.S. Army Corps of
Engineers maintains several visitor centers,
including this one on the Mississippi River at the
Quad City *Location*. Watch the locks operate and
learn watch the pilots maneuver tons of cargo,
enjoy looking over exhibits and learn more about
the Mississippi River's use as a part of our
national water highway system.
    Admission: No entry fee. Open daily, Summer
hours, 9 A.M.-5 P.M.; Winter hours. Closed
Christmas and New Year's Days.

SADORUS, ILLINOIS
**National Museum of Ship Models & Sea
History**
201 S. Market Street
Sadorus, IL 61872-9771 or P.O. Box 11451
Champaign, IL 61826
(217) 352-1672
E-mail: info@lincolnshireprop.com
Location: The Museum is in the small town of
Sadorus, about 3 hours south of Chicago and 12
miles south of Champaign-Urbana.
Highlights: Ship models, 1931 Trumpy Yacht,
Disneyland hotel 16ft. QUEEN MARY model,
14 ft Taylor Test Basin *Nautilus* sub test hull &
Web site: www.lincolnshireprop.com/museum
    General Information: The National Museum
of Ship Models and Sea History, founded in 1999,
contains over 250 ship models, housed in an 1878
two-story county store, and include a half-inch
Chinese riverboat carved from a walnut, to the 16
foot long, 17th century flagship, *Victory* from
Nelson's Battle of Trafalgar. Models were
purchased or donated from builders, museums,
and families attempting to preserve our nautical
heritage. Some of the larger models are from
famous movies, and were purchased directly from
studios in California before being restored in

Illinois. Tugboat Annie, Cleopatra, Ben Hur, and
other famous screenplays are represented.
    Recently acquired large models: 27 ft long
scale model of the *Queen Mary*, made of 1 million
toothpicks; beautiful USS Arizona model 7 ft
long, made entirely of brass; and 2 large models
of aircraft carriers; also the 1929 wooden
50' *Trumpy* yacht *Chicora*.
    Activities: Lectures, meetings, and school
programs on site
    Admission: Entry fee. Saturdays, 10 A.M. –
4:30 P.M.

INDIANA

DEPHI, INDIANA
Carroll County Wabash and Erie Canal, Inc.
1030 North Washington Street
Delphi, IN 46923
(765) 564-2870   Canal hotline: (765) 564-6572
E-mail: mccain@carlnet.org
Location: Northwest central Indiana in the
Wabash River Valley between Lafayette and
Logansport.
Highlights: Canal history,
Web site: www.wabshanderiecanal.org
    General Information: The Carroll County
Wabash and Erie Canal, Inc. has a 2 and 1/2-mile
segment of the old canal and towpath. The upper
half is a watered section much like the heyday of
1850. In Canal Park there is a village with old
buildings like the Federal style house built in
1843-44 by Reed Case, superintendent for building
the canal in Carroll County. Case was 34 years of
age and destined to become a leader in the
community. He then added an extension to his
Front Street property and used it as an Inn for canal
travelers. It was only three blocks from the canal
port on West Main.
    The Reed Case House, centerpiece of the Canal
Park, is located near two additional restored
structures. One is the Bowen Cabin and Inn while
the other is the Kuns Cabin. The Canal Association
and the City of Delphi are preparing to build a new
Interpretive Center. It will also serve as a
community center, Wabash &Erie Canal, Inc's
headquarters, and as a canal museum for the state
of Indiana.
    Admission: No entry fee. Open April-
December, the first Sunday of the month from
2 P.M. - 4 P.M

EVANSVILLE, INDIANA
USS LST 325
840 LST Drive
Evansville, IN 47713
812-435-8678
E-mail: WebSkipper@LSTMemorial.Org
Location: I-64 S., to Veteran's Mem. Pkwy, exit
to Waterworks Road, Follow signs to Marina
Point.
Highlights: The USS LST Ship Memorial
Web site: http://www.lstmemorial.org
   General Information: After ten years of work,
the United States LST Association undertook an
incredible voyage with a crew of twenty-nine
WW2 and Korean War veterans under 61-year-
old Capt Robert Jornlin from Earlville, IL After
her epic 4350-mile return voyage from Greece she
arrived at Mobile on the 10th of January 2001.
Lloyd's List of 11 Jan 2001 carried photo of LST-
325 arriving.
   Activities: USS LST 325 is now open for
public tours in Evansville, Indiana.
   Admission: Entry fee. Mondays - Closed for
maintenance work , Tuesdays thru Saturdays -
Tours 10 a.m. - 4:00 p.m, Sundays - Tours noon
to 4:00 p.m.

JEFFERSONVILLE, INDIANA
Falls of the Ohio State Park
P.O. Box 1327
Jeffersonville, IN 47131-1327
(812) 280-9970 E-mail: park@fallsoftheohio.org
Location: Located on the banks of the Ohio River
in Clarksville, near Jeffersonville, IN, at I-65 exit
0, the end of West Riverside Drive.
Highlights: River maritime history, Interpretive
Center, gift shop, **Website:**
www.fallsoftheohio.org
   General Information: The Ohio State Park lies
within the boundaries of the 1404-acre National
Wildlife Conservation Area where the Visitor
Center contains exhibits pertaining to the history of
the McAlpine Locks and Dam; a large-scale model
of the Falls area today; and a giant mural depicting
The Falls of the Ohio before navigational changes.
   In addition to the vast amount of geological
information at the Interpretive Center, there are
exhibits about barges, ferries, and showboats. Also,
a collection of steam whistles is exhibited along
with information about women river pilots, models
of four-paddlewheel-boats, and a video on
navigating through locks. An exhibit panel
describes the Ohio River navigational structures
(McAlpine locks and dam) on the deck overlooking
the river.
   The George Rogers Clark home site is located at
the bottom of the Falls of The Ohio, known for
almost 200 years as Clark's Point and situated in a
sharp curve enabling Clark to have a spectacular
view of the falls and also see downriver for a
considerable distance. The seven-acre tract is now
a part of The Falls of The Ohio State Park.

   Activities: Hands-on river exhibits for pre-
school children in the Children's Activity Area,
special events, education programs, hiking,
picnicking, bird watching, fishing, and naturalist
services. Also Ohio River and Coral Reef
Aquariums.
   Admission: Entry to Park free. Entry fee for
Center. Open seven days a week, dawn to dusk.
Interpretive Center open Monday-Saturday 9 A.M.-
5 P.M., Sunday 1 P.M.- 5 P.M.

JEFFERSONVILLE, INDIANA
Howard Steamboat Museum and Mansion
Clark County Historical Society
1101 E. Market Street
P. O. Box 606
Jeffersonville, IN 47130
1-888-472-0606 (812) 283-3728
Fax: (812) 283-6049
E-mail: HSMSteam@aol.com
Location: Jeffersonville lies on the Ohio River
across from Louisville, Kentucky. Take the Court
Avenue exit off I-65 to the intersection of Spring
Street. Head south to Market, then east to the
Museum.
Highlights: History of the Howard Shipyards, boat
models, gift shop,
Website: www.steamboatmuseum.org
   General Information: Clark County Historical
Society Howard Steamboat Museum, Inc. was
founded in 1958 and is located in the 1893
historic home of Edmunds J. Howard, son of
Howard Shipyard's founder James E. Howard.
The Museum itself is famous for its original
furnishings, and displays include artifacts and
scale models of famous steamboats.
   In addition, the Museum contains much
information about the original Howard Shipyards
(1834-1941). The shipyard began in 1834 when
founder James Howard built his first steamboat —
the *Hyperion*. Quickly thereafter, Howard side-
wheelers became noted for their beauty, speed, and
durability. When James Howard died in 1876, a
new era began — that of the sternwheeler.
   The shipyard's letterhead boasted of its being
"the oldest continuously-operated shipyard in
America." During World War II, Jeffboat, under
contract with the government, produced landing
ship tanks on the site of the old Howard Yards,
thus marking the end of shipbuilding by the
Howard family.
   Among the 3,000 steamboats built by the
Howard family were the *Glendy Burke* (1851), the
Robt. E. Lee (1876), the *J. M. White* (1878), the
City Of Louisville (1894), the *Cape Girardeau*
(1924), later re-named the *Gordon C. Greene* and
appeared in the film classic "Gone with the Wind."
   Activities: Guided tours, lectures, and work-
study for students.
   Admission: Entry fee. Memberships are
available. Open Tuesday-Saturday, 10 A.M.-4
P.M., Sunday, 1 P.M.-4 P.M.

METAMORA, INDIANA
Whitewater Canal State Historic Site
19083 North Clayborn Street
Box 117
Metamora, IN 47030
(765) 647-6512 Fax: (765) 647-2734
E-mail: wwcshs@franklin.cnz.com
Location: Metamora is sixty-one miles
southeast from Indianapolis on Rte. 52.
Highlights: Six-mile restored water section,
covered canal-boat aqueduct, **Website:** www.
byways.org/explore/byways/10423/places/12
764/
   General Information: Whitewater Canal State
Historic Site is adjacent to a fourteen-mile section
(six miles of which is restored) of the old waterway
built between 1836 and 1845. The restored
gristmill produces cornmeal, corn grits, which can
be purchased here. And where else can you take a
thirty-minute cruise in a horse-drawn canal boat?
A charming ride from Metamora through the
Whitewater Valley, across the only covered
aqueduct in existence to Lock 24 at Millville, and
back.
   Activities: Concerts are periodically staged
in a nineteenth-century-style gazebo
bandstand, and picnicking facilities are near
the gristmill.
   Admission: Gristmill: no entry fee. Open
Wednesday-Saturday, 9 A.M.-5 P.M.,
Sunday, 1 P.M.-5 P.M. Closed Easter and
Thanksgiving days. Canal boat season: May
1-October 31 each year. Canal Boat Ticket
required. Open Monday-Friday, noon-4
P.M., on the hour; Saturday and Sunday,
12 Noon - 4 P.M., on the hour. Closed on
Mondays, Thanksgiving, Christmas Eve,
Christmas Day, New Year's Day and Easter.

MICHIGAN CITY, INDIANA
Old Lighthouse Museum
1 Washington Park Marina, P. O. Box 512
Michigan City, IN 46360
(219) 872-6133/3273 E-mail: mchistorical@att.net
Location: Michigan City is at the southern end of
Lake Michigan, twenty-five miles east of Gary via
I-94. The Museum is on Heisman Harbor Road in
Washington Park at the city's harbor.
Highlights: Lighthouse, Fresnel lens, Old
Lighthouse Museum,
Website: www.oldlighthousemuseum.org
   General Information: Old Lighthouse Museum
was founded in 1973 and is housed in an 1858
lighthouse, Indiana's only one. It was here in 1847
that the first submarine to ply the Great Lakes
(built by L. D. Phillips), was launched.
   The Museum portrays the long and interesting
history of Michigan City, bound to the lake with all

its mysteries and beauties. Featured are a keeper's
living room and bedroom, Fresnel lens, stories of
shipwrecks, shipbuilding tools, the top of the
Lincoln Funeral Train, Michigan City history, and
periodic changing displays.
Collections include lighthouse service artifacts;
boat builder's tools; shipwreck artifacts; local
Indian artifacts; local historical articles; early farm
tools. A library of material on county and area
history, lakefront, and shipping is available for use
in the Museum by appointment.
   Activities: Guided tours, lectures, and library.
   Admission: Entry fee. Memberships are
available. Open every day except Monday from
1:00 P.M. until 4:00 P.M.

IOWA

ARNOLDS PARK, IOWA
Iowa Great Lakes Maritime Museum
On Lake Okoboji at the Arnolds Park
   Amusement Park
243 West Broadway Street P. O. Box 726
Arnolds Park, IA 51331-7779
(712) 332-2183 Fax: (712) 332-7714
E-mail: ap@arnoldspark.com
Location: On West Okoboji Lake—Iowa Great
Lakes Region located in the northwest corner of
Iowa. Take I-90 south on Hwy. 86 near Lakefield,
MN, 22 miles to Hwy 71. Turn left 3 miles to
Arnolds Park town and Arnolds Park Amusement
Park. The Museum is located near the waterfront
and the pier of the *Okoboji Queen II* excursion
boat.
Highlights: Classic wooden runabouts
Web site: www.okobojimuseum.org/
   General Information: The Iowa Great Lakes
Maritime Museum, founded in 1986, was opened
in 1991. The Museum is dedicated to the
preservation and presentation of unique
Midwestern lake nautical heritage, displays,
nautical artifacts, and memorabilia from the local
area.
   The Museum maintains a collection of classic
wooden runabouts and photographs of our 1880s
steamboat heritage. A premier treasure is a 1939
Barrelback Chris Craft that was sunk in a boating
mishap in 1946. Recovered in 1995, it is
preserved
as it was found. The Chris Craft, a rare version of
the Barrelback series, was one of a fleet of
speedboats that gave rides to visitors to the
amusement park. The Museum is a repository for
many of the research materials that the late Bob
Speltz used in his outstanding seven book series,
The Real Runabouts.
   Activities: 50-seat-theater show *Experience
the Legend*, a history of our *Protecting the
Legend*, an ecological appeal for lakes region, and

the continued preservation of our beautiful lakes. The Iowa Great Lakes Antique and Classic Boat Society conducts an annual boat show on the first Sunday of August. Several past A. C. B. S. show winners are proudly on display in the Museum.

Admission: No entry fee. Open daily, Memorial Day to Labor Day from 10 AM to 8 P.M.

DAVENPORT, IOWA

Putnam Museum
1717 West 12th Street
Davenport, IA 52804-3597
(800) 435-3701 (563) 324-1933, Ext. 253
E-mail: museum@putnam.org
Highlights: Ship models, photographs,
Website: www.putnam.org

General Information: The Museum exhibits maritime and natural history of the region, and the Riverboat Gallery holds paintings of early river transportation and ship models. Of particular maritime interest is the regional history exhibit "River, Prairie, and People." Researchers may request access with advance notice to many other photographs and artifacts.

Admission: Entry fee. Open: Monday-Friday, 9 A.M. - 5 P.M.; Saturday 11 A.M. - 5 P.M. Sunday, 12 P.M.- 5 P.M.

DUBUQUE, IOWA

National Mississippi River Museum and
  Aquarium
350 East Third Street
Port of Dubuque
Dubuque, IA 52001-2302
1-800-226-3369 (563) 557-9545
E-mail: info@rivermuseum.com
Location: Dubuque is on the Mississippi River sixty-four miles north of Davenport via I-80. Go east on 3rd Street to the Ice Harbor and Museum Complex.
Highlights: William M. Black (1934 riverboat) Boat & Breakfast, National Rivers Hall of Fame, The award-winning "River of Dreams" (film), the *Woodward* Riverboat Museum,
Website: www.mississippirivermuseum.com/

General Information: The Mississippi River Museum, housed on the *Fred W. Woodward* Riverboat, was founded in 1979 and exhibits artifacts of upper Mississippi Riverboat history; canoes; towboats; flatboats; steamboats; and steam engines.

Of special note are the *William M. Black*, a former Corps of Engineers side-wheel dredge, and the National Rivers Hall of Fame, established to honor men and women of the inland waters and to collect and preserve river artifacts and to conduct seminars and educational programs.

The historic 277-foot paddlewheeler *William*

M. Black, built in 1934, is one of the last of the steam-powered riverboats that maintained clear channels for river navigation. She offers guests the opportunity to view its mighty engines and massive boilers, pilothouse, staterooms, crew's quarters, and galley.

Activities: Guided tours, school programs, and publications.

Admission: Entry fee. Memberships are available. Open daily May-October, 10 A.M. – 6 P.M.,; daily November-April 10 A.M.-5 P.M., Closed national holidays.

KEOKUK, IOWA

Keokuk River Museum
117 So Water Street
Keokuk, IA 52632
(319) 524-4765
Location: Keokuk lies on the Mississippi River in the southeast tip of Iowa, right at the Missouri state line. Take I-380 directly south out of Cedar
Highlights: The *George M. Verity* (paddlewheel steamboat) National Historic Landmark,
Website: www.keokuki.net

General Information: Keokuk River Museum, founded in 1961, is housed in the *George M. Verity*, a Mississippi River Steamboat. A visit to the Museum takes you back to the era of the river steamboats before the modern-day diesels came into being.

Originally the SS *Thorpe* when she was built in 1927 by the U.S. Government at Dubuque, Iowa, (renamed the *Verity* after the founder of Armco Steel Corporation) and inaugurated barge service on the upper Mississippi. The first of four steamboats built to revive river transportation, she was the first to move barges from St. Louis north to St. Paul. The *Verity* was retired in 1960 after thirty-three years of service on the Mississippi and Ohio Rivers. Now berthed at Victory Park, she houses a museum of Upper Mississippi River history and beckons you to come aboard.

Activities: Lectures

Admission: Entry fee. Open daily, 9 A.M.- 5 P.M., mid April-November.

LE CLAIRE, IOWA

Buffalo Bill Museum of Le Claire
199 North Front Street
P.O. Box 284
Le Claire, IA 52753
(563) 289-5580 Fax: (563) 289-4603
E-mail: museum@buffalobillmuseumleclaire.com
Location: Le Claire is on the Mississippi River ten miles north of the Tri-cities area (Davenport, Rock Island, and Moline). Immediately off I-80, follow River Drive upriver at the foot of Jones Street on the Levee.

Highlights: *Lone Star* steamer (sternwheel), gift shop,

Website: www.buffalobillmuseumleclaire.com/

General Information: Buffalo Bill Museum of Le Claire, founded in 1957, was created to preserve the history of Le Claire through its river captains, pilots, shipyards, and other areas of maritime interest. Exhibits include the *Lone Star* Steamer, one of the last working river, wooden hull, coal fired boats on the Mississippi River, which was decommissioned in 1966 and dry docked in 1968. Also, a display of the work of James Ryan, inventor of the flight recorder for airplanes and seat belts.

Admission: Entry fee. Open:mid-May-mid-October, Monday-Saturday, 9 A.M.- 5 P.M., Sunday, 12 Noon-5 P.M.; mid-October-mid-May, weekends only, Saturday, 9 A.M.-5 P.M., Sunday, 12 Noon—5 P.M.

MISSOURI VALLEY, IOWA
Steamboat *Bertrand* Cargo Collection
DeSoto National Wildlife Refuge
1434 – 316th Lane
Missouri Valley, IA 51555-7033
712-642-4121 Fax: 712-642-2877
E-mail: r3bertrand@fws.gov
Location: The wildlife refuge center is located some thirty miles north of the Omaha-Council Bluffs metropolitan area via I-29, Nebraska Rte. 75, or Rte. 133. The visitor center is located one mile south of the refuge entrance on US 30, between Missouri Valley, Iowa, and Blair, Nebraska.
Highlights: Artifacts from the *Bertrand* (sternwheeler riverboat), gift shop
Website: http://midwest.fws.gov/desoto/
General Information: The *Bertrand* was a mountain packet sternwheeler designed for the shallow, narrow rivers of the West. The 178-foot ship was built in 1864 at Wheeling, West Virginia, and carried cargo estimated between 250 to 400 tons. While traveling up the Missouri River to the Montana Territory, the *Bertrand* sank April 1, 1865, in twelve feet of water, approximately twenty-five miles north of Omaha. The gangplank was lowered, and those on board walked ashore.

Some items were removed, but most of the cargo stayed with the ship until it was rediscovered and excavated from under thirty feet of Missouri River mud in 1968. Exhibits of the *Bertrand* are housed in the Visitor Center and include a Cargo Viewing Gallery and Artifact Storage where you step into a time capsule filled with an amazing variety and quantity of munitions, tools, clothing, food-stuffs, and household goods. The excavation site, where the

steamboat remains buried is three miles from the visitor center.

Admission: Entry fee. Visitor Center open daily, 9 A.M.- 4:30 P.M. Closed Thanksgiving, Christmas, and New Year's Day.

KENTUCKY

LOUISVILLE, KENTUCKY
***Belle of Louisville* Steamer**
401 West River Road
Louisville, KY 40202
(866) 832-0011 (502) 574-2992 Fax: (502) 574-3030 E-mail: webcrew@belleoflouisville.org
Location: From north/south on I-65, take I-64 west to the 3rd Street exit. Eastbound on I-64, take 9th Street exit turning left on Market Street, then take another on 4th Street to River Road
Highlights: *Belle of Louisville* Steamboat (cruising with calliope music),
Website: www.belleoflouisville.org

General Information: Originally commissioned as the *Idlewild* in 1914, the present day *Belle of Louisville* began her career on the Lower Mississippi. Built by James Rees and Sons in Pittsburgh, she originally served as ferry and day packet for the West Memphis Ferry Co. By 1928, she had served as far south as New Orleans as the ferry and packet business dried up. Sold to the New St. Louis and Calhoun Packet Co., she started a career of "tramping" the different rivers of the Western Rivers System. She still holds the distinction of being the most widely traveled excursion steamer ever.

She was sold once again and in 1947 she was renamed the *Avalon*. She continued traveling "anywhere there was 5 feet of water" until the wear and tear finally put her out of service. She was put on the auction block in 1962 and was purchased by Louisville, Jefferson County, KY. for $34,000. Restored and renamed the *Belle of Louisville*, she is now a jewel in Louisville's crown. She is 200-feet long and can carry over 900 passengers. Her paddlewheel alone weights 17.5 tons. As the oldest Authentic Mississippi-style sternwheel steamboat running, she continues to make history. She participates every year against her rival the Delta Queen in the Great Steamboat Race.

The hundred-year-old simple, non-condensing steam engines remain the sole means of propulsion for the boat, and the *Belle* herself remains the best place to experience 1890s steamboat technology first hand. She has served commerce as a packet and ferry. She has served her country as a USO boat and as a towboat pushing oil barges for the war effort in the 1940s. She now continues to serve the present generation as an historical icon, the last of her kind.

Admission: Cruising fee. For cruise times and dates, check our website or call (502) 574-2992

LOUISVILLE, KENTUCKY

Mayor Andrew Broaddus
(River Coast Guard Station)
c/o *Belle of Louisville*
401 River Road
Louisville, KY 40202
(502) 574-2992 Fax: (502) 574-3030
Location: The retired Coast Guard Station is located at 4th Avenue and River Road.
Highlights: U.S. Life-Saving Station #10 (retired), National Historic Landmark, **Website:** www.cr.nps.gov/maritime/nhl/mayor.htm
   General Information: Life-saving stations, established by the Life- Saving Service, precursor to today's Coast Guard, were set up by the Federal Government along the western rivers in 1881 to provide aid to endangered river travelers. Louisville was the first locale chosen for a station because the Falls of the Ohio River, treacherous rapids, presented numerous navigation challenges.
   Louisville's first Life-Saving Station was placed in service November 4, 1881, and was replaced in 1902 and again in 1928 with new ones; all called life-saving station #10. The U.S. Coast Guard decommissioned the vessel in 1972 and renamed the *Mayor Andrew Broaddus* in honor of a former Louisville mayor.
   The *Mayor Andrew Broaddus* life saving #10 station was built in Dubuque, Iowa, in 1928 based on a design resembling its predecessor. Equipped with life-saving skiffs, and a six-oar surf boat, its crew rescued stranded passengers, salvaged cargo, saved drowning swimmers, recovered bodies, and extinguished fires on water and land. It is the only floating life-saving station to survive and one of very few life-saving stations of any kind in the nation. It has been moored at its present location since 1981 and was named a National Historic Landmark in 1989. It serves as offices and wharf boat for the *Belle of Louisville* steamboat.

LOUISVILLE, KENTUCKY

Portland Museum
2308 Portland Avenue
Louisville, KY 40212
 (502) 776-7678 E-mail: turnerm@iglou.com
Location: The Museum is near downtown Louisville. **Website:** www.goportland.org
   General Information: The Portland Museum tells the history of the Ohio River region with dioramas, exhibits, and video documentaries.
   Activities: This museum harks back to the days when Louisville and Portland were rival river ports. It features a 23-minute light-and-sound show, Portland: The Land, The River and The People; an arts-and-humanities gallery; 1937 Flood

newsreels, historic urban architecture exhibit.
   Admission: Entry fee. Open Tuesday – Friday, 10 A.M.-4:30 P.M.

PADUCAH, KENTUCKY

River Heritage Center Museum
117 So. Water Street
Paducah, KY 42001-0787
(270) 575-9958
E-mail: jharris@riverheritagemuseum.org
Location: The Museum overlooks the confluence of the Ohio and Tennessee Rivers.
Highlights: Steamboat ship models, art displays
   General Information: The River Heritage Museum was developed to preserve the history of the Ohio River and Western Rivers system. Exhibits include model steamboats and riverboat paintings.
   There will be exhibits on the life on the river: How the river influenced migrations to the area, history of river transportation, pirates on the river, and a variety of contributed artifacts. Also to be included is information on the river's locks and dams, re-creating travel through interactive working models of the locks, and modern river towing.
   Admission: Entry fee. Open Monday – Friday, 10 A.M. – 5 P.M.

LOUISIANA

BATON ROUGE, LOUISIANA

Louisiana State Museum-Baton Rouge
660 N. Fourth St.
Baton Rouge, LA 70802
(225) 342-5428 (800) 568-6968 (# for Louisiana State Museum in New Orleans temporarily)
E-mail: srykels@crt.state.la.us
Location: Museum is located 3 blocks east of Mississippi River north of North Street. Take Exit 1H off I-110 to North Street west7 blocks.
Highlights: "Father of Waters" exhibit and steamboat information
Website: http://lsm.crt.state.la.us/BR/br.htm
   General Information: The Louisiana State Museum-Baton Rouge will open with an exhibit that highlights the significance of the "Father of Waters" in creating and sustaining much of the state.
   The approximately 3,000 square foot exhibit, located in the center of the first floor gallery, explores the unique river in three of its roles — as a natural system, an avenue of commerce, and an adversary to mankind. Within these broad topics, the display examines the development of the river from fledgling stream to its present size and course, the evolution of commerce and shipping on its waters, and the continuing struggles of man to span its banks and tame its floods.

The exhibit features a wealth of images and maps, steamboat, other shipping artifacts, and interactive components. It is dominated by the recreation of a steamboat pilothouse on one end and a 48-foot long wooden shrimp boat on its "Gulf" end.

Admission: Entry fee. Tues/Sat 9 A.M. – 5 P.M., Sundays, 12 Noon – 5 P.M.

BATON ROUGE, LOUISIANA
USS *Kidd* & Nautical Center
305 South River Road
Baton Rouge, LA 70802-6220
(225) 342-1942 Fax: (225) 342-2039
E-mail: info@usskidd.com
Location: Baton Rouge is approached on either I-10 east/west or I-110 north/south. It is eighty miles upstream from New Orleans. The war memorial is on the Mississippi River (across from the Baton Rouge Centroplex) at Government and Front Streets.
Highlights: The USS *Kidd* (DD-661, destroyer), P-40 fighter plane, *Kidd's Compass* (newsletter), gift shop, overnight camping program,
Website: www.usskidd.com/

General Information: The USS *Kidd* &Nautical Center includes displays from the former Louisiana Maritime Museum. The State of Louisiana has a varied and colorful nautical history. Situated at the end of the Mississippi River and reaching into New Orleans, Louisiana, the Gulf of Mexico has made it a central trading area. Colonized under France and Spain, plantations lined the river and steamboats were in constant motion.

The river became an economic highway. The Nautical Center is an educational facility where mankind and water, war and peace themes are represented by displays and changing exhibits. Galleries with ship models relate to the sea-going vessels and also to the boats that ventured upon our many rivers.

Of special note is the USS *Kidd* (DD-661), opened in 1983. She is a Fletcher Class World War II destroyer and rests in a cradle that allows viewers to walk under the hull when the river is at its lowest level (in late summer). Collections include training manuals, publications, and nautical charts relating to the destroyer.

Activities: Guided tours, lectures, shipboard, and overnight camping program for youth groups

Admission: Entry fee. Memberships are available. Open daily, 9 A.M.-5 P.M., year-round. Closed Thanksgiving and Christmas.

MADISONVILLE, LOUISIANA
Lake Pontchartrain Basin Maritime Museum
133 Mabel Drive
Madisonville, LA 70447-9301
(985) 845-9200
E-mail: info@lpbmaritimemuseum.org
Location: From the North side of the Causeway Lake Pontchartrain Cswy becomes N Causeway Blvd 0.62 miles. Turn sight left to take the ramp toward Madisonville/LA-22 W. 0.18 miles Merge onto W causeway approach 1.90 miles. Turn slight left onto LA-22 3.18 miles. Cross Bridge at Tchefuncta River and turn LEFT onto Main St/LA-1077 .29 miles. Turn left onto Mabel Dr. 0.20 miles.
Highlights: The Wooden Boat Festival in the fall.**Website:**
http://www.lpbmaritimemuseum.org/

General Information: The idea of a Lake Pontchartrain Basin Maritime Museum was established to provide seems educated tourism, cultural continuity, a rebirth of interest in our maritime heritage, and a wealth of historic material that needs interpretation and protection. Since Iberville's voyage of discovery in March of 1699, three hundred years ago, this watery basin of swamp, bayou, and lake has been unified by water transportation and the evidence thereof is around us, out of sight and inaccessible to the inhabitants. It is known that literally hundreds of watercraft from all eras and of all types lie in the silt of our river bottoms.

Shipyards, brick kilns, lumberyards and landing places for all manner of farmed and manufactured goods line the banks of our waterways. Our mission is to provide an education and research center to collect, interpret, and preserve the maritime and cultural history and artifacts of the Lower Mississippi River Basin for public benefit.

Activities: Our mission is to provide an education and research center to collect, interpret, and preserve the maritime and cultural history and artifacts of the Lower Mississippi River Basin for public benefit on the scenic Tchefuncte River, featuring a wide variety of family fun, food, artists, and children's activities, and of course, music. The Wooden Boat Festival: Every year, St. Tammany hosts a tribute not to seafood, but to the hand crafted wooden boats that originally made it possible for us to enjoy these marine delicacies.

Admission: Entry fee. Open Tuesday – Saturday, 10 A.M. – 4 P.M., Sunday, 12 Noon – 4 P.M.

NEW ORLEANS, LOUISIANA
Louisiana State Museum
751 Chartres Street, P.O. Box 2448
New Orleans, LA 70116-3205
(504) 568-6968
Fax: (504) 568-4595 E-mail: lsm@crt.state.la.us
Location: The Cabildo and Arsenal are at Jackson Square in the French Quarter.
Highlights: Louisiana and the Mighty Mississippi

Exhibit, **Web site**: lsm.crt.state.la.us/

General Information: Entry through the Cabildo brings the visitor to "The Old Man River Rolling Along" permanent exhibit, featuring some of Louisiana's most treasured pieces — ship models, steamboat artifacts, paintings — that tell a fascinating and compelling story.

The history of local river transit is described in a section on the ferryboats that carried New Orleanians from bank-to-bank and in another area, circa 1850 models of the sailing ship *Lawrence Delap* and the *Neptune*, and an 1872 lighthouse lens from South Pass. Even the "Great Mississippi Steamboat Race" of 1870 inspired enormous public sentiment, as did the "age of floating palaces." All is recalled when you visit the Museum.

Admission: Entry fee. Open Tuesday-Sunday, 9 A.M.-5 P.M. Closed all legal holidays.

PLAQUEMINE, LOUISIANA
Plaquemine Lock State Historic Site
57730 Main Street
Plaquemine, LA 70764
1-877-987-7158 (225) 687-7158 or Fax: (225) 687-8933 E-mail: plaqlock@crt.state.la.us
Location: Take LA-1 south thirteen miles out from Baton Rouge. The Plaquemine Lock is on the Mississippi River off Main Street in the downtown area. *Highlights:* A Mississippi river-system lock, History of the Mississippi River and its boat traffic, **Web site:** www.crt.state.la.us/crt/parks/plaquemine_lock/plaqlock.htm

General Information: Plaquemine Lock State Historic Site was founded in 1983 and encompasses the original lock structure and lockhouse built at the turn of the century. The lockhouse now serves as a museum and historic site.

The Mississippi River and its surrounding waterways have long been considered vital assets to the people and economy of Louisiana. Yet the waters have also posed serious threats of flooding to the low-lying areas of the state, so controlling the waterways became as important as the waters themselves. Eventually, Congress was petitioned by the residents of Iberville Parish to authorize funding for a lock system to control the water level between Bayou Plaquemine and the Mississippi River.

At the time the lock was completed, in 1909, it had the highest fresh-water lift of any lock in the world, namely, fifty-one feet, and functioned on a unique engineering plan utilizing a gravity principle. This was modernized at a later date by the installation of hydraulic pumps. In 1961 a larger lock began operating at Port Allen, and the Plaquemine Locks was closed after fifty-two years of service.

Admission: Entry fee. Open daily, 9 A.M.-5 P.M., year-round. Museum closed Thanksgiving, Christmas, and New Year's Day.

MAINE

BAR HARBOR, MAINE
Islesford Historical Museum
P.O. Box 177
Bar Harbor, ME 04609-0177
(207) 288-3338
E-mail: Brooke_Childrey@nps.gov
Location: Bar Harbor is forty-six miles southeast of Bangor, Maine, on Mount Desert Island. The museum is actually situated on Little Cranberry Island, just south of there, approachable by ferry from both Northeast and Southwest Harbors.
Highlights: Maritime history, Island history
Website:www.nps.gov/acad/planyourvisit/islesfordhistoricalmuseum.htm
General Information: Islesford Historical Museum, founded in 1919, preserves a part of the history of maritime New England and also exhibits items depicting island life.

Admission No entry fee. Open daily, 10 A.M.-5 P.M. Mid-June - September.

BATH, MAINE
Maine Maritime Museum
243 Washington Street
Bath, ME 04530
(207) 443-1316 Fax: (207) 443-1665
e-mail: maritime@bathmain.com
Location: Follow I-95 to Rte. 1. Head east one mile to Bath (thirty-five miles northeast of Portland on Boothbay) on the west side of the Kennebec River.
Highlights: The *Sherman Zwicker* (Grand Banks Schooner), "Lobstering and the Coast of Maine" Exhibit, Maritime history exhibit building, Small-craft collection, The apprentice shop (wooden boat building), *Long Reach Log* (newsletter), Library (6,000-volumes) on Maine maritime history, **Web site**: www.bathmaine.com/
General Information: For centuries mariners have built wooden ships, sailed them to faraway ports, and fished from them on banks and bays for elusive cod and lobster. This rich seafaring heritage comes to life at the Maine Maritime Museum, founded in 1962.

The museum includes a restored ten-acre shipyard — with over 1,000 feet of river frontage, it's the last shipyard intact in the country where sailing vessels were built — a boatbuilding school, a lobstering exhibit, and a new major exhibit building on Maine's maritime heritage. Exhibits depict local shipbuilding families and traditions as well as regional history and models; half-models; tools; instruments; trade goods; seamen's possessions; small boats; and dioramas.

For exhibits on dory fishing, go on board the Grand Banks schooner S*herman Zwicker* when she is in port. The shipyard also houses an apprentice shop where traditional boatbuilding skills are taught, exhibits on wood ship construction, a and a fine collection of small craft used along the Maine coast and inland waterways.

Activities: Hour-long tours of the Percy & Small Shipyard, where one learns how wooden ships were built, begin April 15. Shipyard demonstrations of blacksmithing, draft horses, ship launchings, treenail making, and signal flags begin June 22. Two video presentations, training programs in small wooden boat building, group tours by appointment, and an annual symposium on maritime history.

Admission: Entry fee. Open daily, 9:30 A.M.-5 P.M., year-round. Closed national holidays.

BOOTHBAY HARBOR, MAINE
Boothbay Region Historical Society
72 Oak Street   P.O. Box 272
Boothbay Harbor, ME   04538-0272
(207) 633-0820 E-mail: brhs@gwi.net
Location: At Bath, head east on Rte. 1 ten miles to State Highway 27. Boothbay Harbor is on the peninsula between the Sheepscot and Damariscotta Rivers and shares the peninsula and adjacent islandswith a dozen other communities, including Boothbay (settled 1730), of which it was once a part.
Highlights: Maritime history
Website: www.boothbayhistorical.org/
General Information: The Boothbay Region Historical Society is a nineteenth-century sea captain's residence. It is of Italianate design, period furnishings. The exhibits include implements of the fishing and shipbuilding industries, plus nineteenth- century household appliances, old photographs, and documents.
Admission: No entry fee. Open: July-Labor Day, Wednesday - Saturday, 10A.M.- 2 P.M; year round..

BRUNSWICK, MAINE
Peary-MacMillan Arctic Museum
Bowdoin College
9500 College Station
Brunswick, ME 04011 -8495
(207) 725-3062/3416
E-mail: ahawkes@bowdoin.edu
Location: Brunswick is twenty-five miles north of Portland just off I-95 or Rte. 1 and eight miles from historic Bath. The museum is located in Hubbard Hall, main floor, on the campus of historic Bowdoin College.
Highlights: Arctic exploration,
Web site: www.bowdoin.edu/arctic-museum/location/index.shtml

General Information: Named after alumni Robert E. Peary and Donald B. MacMillan (1898), the museum preserves the long association between Bowdoin College and the Arctic and features displays of Arctic natural history specimens, exploration equipment and photographs, and Inuit (Eskimo) art and artifacts.

Peary graduated from Bowdoin in 1877 and began his Arctic explorations in 1886 in Greenland. He culminated his Arctic work with his expedition to the North Pole in 1909. The museum's exhibits focus on Peary's career where exhibits include several models of the explorations ships S.S. *Roosevelt* and Schooner *Bowdion.*

The Special Collections of Bowdoin's Hawthorne-Longfellow Library contain the personal papers and photographs of several arctic explorers and prominent sea captains.

The Elisha Kent Kane Historical Society in New York City strives to be a clearinghouse for information on Arctic exploration
Admission: No entry fee. Open Tuesday – Saturday 10 A.M.-5 P.M., Sunday 2 P.M.-5 P.M., year round. The museum is closed on Mondays and national holidays.

CAPE ELIZABETH, MAINE
Portland Head Light
1000 Shore Road
Cape Elizabeth, ME 04107
(207) 799-2661 E-mail: cephl@aol.com
Location: On Casco Bay, Cape Elizabeth is four miles south of South Portland, off Rte. 77. The head light is on the south side of the harbor entrance. *Highlights:* Portland Head Light
Website: www.portlandheadlight.com/
General Information: Portland Head Light was erected in 1791 on orders from George Washington, after seventy-four ship owners petitioned for a beacon to guide them into Maine's busiest harbor. It was the first light authorized by the United States and is one of the oldest lighthouses in continuous use.

Henry Wadsworth Longfellow frequently hiked from Portland to compose under the tower. Waves swept away the 2,000-pound fog bell in 1869, deposited the ship *Annie C. McGuire* at the base of the cliffs in 1886, and smashed the whistle house wall 1973, knocking out the foghorn and temporarily extinguishing the light.

Portland Head Light is one of the most visited lights on the Atlantic seaboard. The tower's hurricane deck provides a view of more than 200 islands in the sweep of Casco Bay.
Admission: No entry fee. Park: open daily, sunrise-sunset year-round. Open April 17 (weekends only until June 1), then daily 10 a..m. – 4 p.m. through October.

CASTINE, MAINE

Allie Ryan Maritime Collection of the
Maine State Maritime Museum
(See also: Maine Maritime Academy)
Pleasant Street
Castaine, ME 04420-5000
(800) 464-6565 (In State) (800) 227-8465 (Out of State)
Location: The collection is in Quick Hall at the Maine Maritime Academy, located on Ste. 199 in Castine.
Highlights: Maine/New England Maritime History, Steamboat history, Ship models, Library (350-volumes) **Website**:
http://www.mainemaritime.edu/
General Information: Allie Ryan Maritime Collection details the importance of the steamboat through hundreds of paintings, lithographs, and photographs. A replica of the pilothouse from the steamer *Golden Rod*, an engine room telegraph and other materials are also here.

Exhibits include paintings, prints, broadsides, photographs, ship models, navigation instruments, main steam engine, steamboat pilothouse replica, ships papers, steamboat line schedules, and brochures, plus a 350-volume library on maritime history.
Admission: No entry fee, but donations accepted. Open Monday, Wednesday and Friday, 9 A.M.-Noon and 1 P.M.-3 P.M.; Tuesday-Saturday 9 A.M.-4 P.M. Other times by appointment.

EASTPORT, MAINE

Border Historical Society
74 Washington Street   P.O. Box 95
Eastport, ME 04631-1228
(207) 853-2328
E-mail: borderhistoricalsociety@yahoo.com
Location: Eastport, Maine is adjacent to Nova Scotia in the southeast corner of the state.
General Information: The Society preserves maritime items of the fishing industry including the boats, the factories, and industry along the U.S. and Canadian shores of Passamaquoddy Bay.
Admission: Open: June-August, 1 P.M.-4 P.M.

EASTPORT, MAINE

Downeast Maritime Museum
74 Washington Street P.O. Box 95
Eastport, ME 04631
(207) 853-0644
Location: The museum is on the second floor of Barracks Museum Building.
General Information: The museum displays relate to maritime and natural history of Passamaquoddy and Cobscook Bays. Artifacts and records tell the unique story of the Downeast coastal area.
Admission: Open June/August, 1 P.M. – 4 P.M.

EASTPORT, MAINE

Quoddy Maritime Museum
68 Water Street, P.O. Box 98
Eastport, ME 04361
207-853-4297 E-mail: Charlton@acadia.net
Location: Follow Rte. 190 to downtown Eastport, turn right at the Post Office, Museum is on the right in the last two buildings of the first block:
Highlights: Local maritime history, gift shop,
  General Information: The Quoddy Maritime Museum, opened in 1988, and its collections contain maps of area, 14' x 15' model of the proposed Passamaquoddy Tidal Power Project, a video oral history display as well as other VHS tapes of maritime interest, and more. Currently on exhibit is "Lewis Hine visits Eastport, 1911." Also, Quoddy Crafts features the work of 20 local crafters. A Museum gift shop is on site. A visitor center is maintained to answer tourist inquiries.
  Admission: No entry fee. Open Memorial Day to Salmon Festival (Second Saturday in September), Monday-Saturday, 9 A.M. – 5 P.M. Call for additional information.

FRIENDSHIP, MAINE

Friendship Museum
Rt. 220 & Martin's Point Road
P. O. Box 321
Friendship, ME 04547
(207) 832-4221
E-mail: info@friendsshipmuseum.org
Location: Friendship is approximately seventy-two miles north of Portland, Maine. Follow Rte. 1 to Waldoboro, and take Rte 220 south to Friendship. *Highlights:* Memorabilia of the town of Friendship,
  General Information: Friendship Museum was founded in 1964 and housed in an old brick schoolhouse built in 1850. The museum contains exhibits on the community and the history of the sailing craft known as the Friendship Sloop.
  Admission: No entry fee, but donations accepted. Open July-Labor Day, Tuesday-Saturday, 1 P.M.-4 P.M., Sunday, 2 P.M.-5 P.M.

GREENVILLE, MAINE

Moosehead Marine Museum
12 Lily Bay Road
P. O. Box 1151
Greenville, ME 04441
(207) 695-2716
E-mail: info@katahdincruises.com
Location: The museum is located in the center of Greenville, seventy-five miles northwest of Bangor at the south end of Moosehead Lake.
Highlights: The *Katahdin* (steamboat), The *Katahdin Knots* (newsletter) **Website**:
http://www.katahdincruises.com/museum.html

General Information: For many years, before the opening of the road system in the United States, water traffic was the primary mode of transportation around the country, including the area around Moosehead Lake. Steamboats carried livestock, railroad equipment, supplies, and passengers. Steamboat history began there in 1836 with the steamboat, *Moosehead.* Many of the boats were built at Greenville and the West Cove shipyard.

The Moosehead Marine Museum, founded in 1970, is a floating museum aboard the Lake Steamer SS *Katahdin.* Exhibits include artifacts and photos concerning the steamboat era on Moosehead Lake, logging, and the Mount Kineo Hotel, considered one of the finest resort properties in the world during its heyday. The museum has two rooms of area memorabilia: one room is devoted to the ships of the lake, the other to the great hotel era, the Mount Kineo House in particular.

The SS *Katahdin*, a 1914 lake ferry steamship used on the last log drive in the Nation; has undergone restoration and is once again carrying passengers on happy voyages on Moosehead Lake.

Activities: Head of Lake Cruises and Mt. Kineo Cruises

Admission: Cruises: Moosehead Lake — Monday-Friday, 10 A.M.-4 P.M., Memorial Day - September 30. Other times by appointment.

ISLESBORO, MAINE
Sailor's Memorial Museum and Lighthouse
Grindle Point
c/o Islesboro Town Office
P. O. Box 76
Islesboro, ME 04848
(207) 734-2253 or 789-5611
Location: Take I-95 to Augusta, exiting onto Rte. 202. Travel east forty-six miles to Belfast, then south on Rte. 1 thirteen miles to Lincolnville. At the Grindle Point board the auto ferry to Islesboro Island (or board the auto ferry at Lincolnville Beach).
Highlights: Lighthouse
Website: www.lighthouse.cc/grindle/history.html
General Information: Sailor's Memorial Museum, founded in 1936, contains collections that include maritime and other historic coastal artifacts and materials, primarily about local heritage. The Grindle Point keeper's house is also open to visitors.
Admission: No entry fee. Open Tuesday-Sunday, 10 A.M.-4 P.M., mid June-Labor Day.

KENNEBUNK, MAINE
Brick Store Museum
117 Main Street
P. O. Box 177
Kennebunk, ME 04043
(207) 985-4802 Fax: 207-985-6887
E-mail: info@brickstoremuseum.org
Location: Kennebunk lies twenty-five miles south of Portland on Rte. 1, one mile east of I-95. The museum is located downtown at 117 Main Street.
Highlights: Maritime history, Research library,
Website: www.brickstoremuseum.org
General Information: The Brick Store Museum, founded in 1936, *is* a complex of four restored nineteenth-century buildings, including William Lord's brick store (1825). The museum contains changing exhibits of fine and decorative arts, historical and maritime collections and a research library.
Activities: Architectural walking tours every Friday at 2 p.m., 10 June -14 October. Leaving from the Museum, the tours pass by homes in the Kennebunk Historic District (1760-1900).
Admission: Entry fee for museum and Taylor-Barry House. Open Tuesday-Saturday 10 A.M.-4:30 P.M. year round. Closed on all national holidays.

KENNEBUNKPORT, MAINE
Kennebunkport Maritime Museum/Gallery
Ocean Avenue
P.O. Box 765
Kennebunkport, ME 04046
(207) 967-4195 (207) 967-3218
Location: The museum is located at "The Floats" on the historic Kennebunk River. Follow Rtes. 9 or 35 to Dock Square in Kennebunkport. Turn right onto Ocean Avenue along river and follow approximately one mile to museum. *Highlights:* Navigational instruments, Marine paintings, Scrimshaw, Ship models,
General Information: The museum is located in the fully renovated boathouse of celebrated New England author, Booth Tarkington. Here you'll find the last remnants of Tarkington's schooner Regina, a longtime Kennebunkport landmark, including the ship's wheel, all her bow carvings, her quarter boards, and the ship's name flag.

Displays include: artifacts from throughout New England's seafaring history; eighteenth- and nineteenth-century navigational instruments including quadrants, sextants, chronometers, and spyglasses; a large collection of antique scrimshaw; eighteenth- and nineteenth-century ship models, builders one-half models; and a collection of marine paintings by Bard, McFarlane, Badger, Jacobsen, Raleigh, and York.
Admission: Entry fee. Open daily, 10 A.M.-4 P.M., May 15-October 15.

KENNEBUNKPORT, MAINE
The *Phyllis A* & Maritime Heritage Association
P. O. Box 1149
Kennebunkport, ME 04046
(207) 967-8809 E-mail: visit@phyllisa.org
Location: Exit 3 (Kennebunk) off Rte 95 Southeast
on SR 35 for 8.35 miles to US 1 (SR 35|Main St,
Kennebunk). Left on US 1 (SR 35|Main St) one
block to SR 35 (Summer St). Bear right on SR 35
(Summer St) for 3.52 miles to SR 9 (Western Ave).
Left on SR 9 (Western Ave) for 0.30 miles to Dock
Square, Kennebunkport, Right on Ocean Ave to the
Arundel Wharf Restaurant (43 Ocean Ave)
Highlights: The *Phyllis A*
   General Information: The *Phyllis A's* return in
2001 to the site of the Bernie Warner Shipyard on
the Kennebunk River where she was built in 1925
marked the beginning of her new career as a living
monument to Kennebunkport's boat-building
heritage and to the region's fishing families and
working waterfront.
   Join us in the exciting adventure of preserving
this unique vessel. Explore our website. And be
sure to visit the *Phyllis A* and the Maritime
Heritage Association Boatshop Museum when you
come to Kennebunkport.
   Admission: No entry fee. Open Mid-May to
Mid-October, 8 A.M. – 5 P.M.

KITTERY, MAINE
Kittery Historical and Naval Museum
200 Rogers Road
P. O. Box 453
Kittery, ME 03904
(207) 439-3080
Location: Just north of Portsmouth, New
Hampshire, off I-95 at Rte. (by the circle at Rte.
236).
Highlights: Artifacts from early seacoast life,
Genealogy of Kittery families and local culture,
Ship models, Gift shop, Library,
   General Information: Kittery Historical and
Naval Museum, founded in 1975, has assumed the
responsibility of preserving and interpreting the
history of the oldest incorporated town in Maine, as
well as that of the Naval Shipyard and related on-
shore activities.
   Kittery, the "Gateway to Maine" was first settled
in 1623. From 1695 to 1749, three English
warships were constructed by local craftsmen. In
1776, the first Continental Naval vessel, the
Raleigh, was launched on the Piscataqua. On June
12, 1800 the Department of the Navy purchased
Seavey Island in Kittery and established the first
government installation of its kind in the U.S.
   The museum exhibits objects and manuscripts
related to the history of the town and the
Portsmouth Naval Shipyard. At the museum, you
will see a thirteen-foot model of the sloop *Ranger*,

models of eighteenth-, nineteenth- and twentieth-
century naval vessels including a gundalow, a naval
Gatling gun, photographs, dioramas, paintings of
bygone days, ships plans, and logs. Manuscripts
are also available for researchers.
   Activities: Special exhibits, lectures, and
special events
   Admission: Entry fee: reduced rates for
children, seniors, and groups. Open Monday-
Friday, 10 A.M.-4 P.M., June 1-October.

LUBEC, MAINE
Rier's Old Sardine Village Museum
Route 189
Lubec, ME 04652
(207) 733-2822
Location: Take I-95 to Bangor, then east on US
1A/1 approximately ninety miles to Whiting, then
Rte, 189 some eleven miles to Lubec. The
Museum, is on the most eastern coast of Maine
adjacent to the Canadian Province of New
Brunswick.
Highlights: Ship models
   General Information: A block of shops and
displays illustrate the growth of the food canning
industry from the first, primitive hand-formed
can of the 1830s to the thriving canneries of the
1930s. Displays include: model ship collections;
early nineteenth-century corn cannery; rare model
corn cooker and can filler; original double
steamer; and early blueberry cannery with original
stamping presses and dies.
   Admission: Entry fee. Open Wednesday-
Sunday 1 P.M.- 5 P.M., June-September.

MACHIASPORT, MAINE
Gates House/Machiasport Historical Society
Route 92
P.O. Box 301
Machiasport, ME 04655
(207) 255-8860, (207) 255-8898
Location: Machiasport lies about ninety-five miles
due east of Bangor on Machias Bay. Take Rte. 1 to
SR-92. The society operated the Gates House in
town.
Highlights: Ship models, Library, Genealogy
   General Information: The Gates House, built
circa 1800, is a Federal-style house with several
rooms furnished in period fashion. The maritime
room exhibits include ship models and a maritime
library.
   Admission: No entry fee, but donations
accepted. Open mid-June-mid-September,
Tuesday-Saturday, 12:30 P.M.-4:30 P.M.

NEWFIELD, MAINE

Willowbrook at Newfield

Willowbrook Museum Village
P. O. Box 28   70 Elm Street
Newfield, ME 04056
(207) 793-2784
E-mail: director@willowbrookmuseum.org
Location: Willowbrook is 21 miles north of
Sanford via US 202 for 11 miles, then north ten
miles to Newfield.
Highlights: Ship models, Restored small craft,
Web site: www.willowbrookmuseum.org/

General Information: A nineteenth-century
restored village on a ten-acre site represents many
aspects of rural New England life. Displays in a
marine room contain navigational tools,
shipbuilders' tools, uniforms, ship models,
paintings, maps and other memorabilia. Several
marine engines and about five restored small craft
are also on display.

Admission: Entry fee. Open daily, 10 A.M. –
5 P.M., mid-May-September 30.

NORTHEAST HARBOR, MAINE

The Great Harbor Maritime Museum

125 Main Street, P.O. Box 145
Northeast Harbor, ME 04660
(207) 276-5262 E-mail: sarakmurray@yahoo.com
Location: North East Harbor lies ten miles
southwest of Bar Harbor on Mount Desert Island.
Highlights: History of Maine coastal life
General Information: The Great Harbor
Maritime Museum, founded in 1982, is the result of
the hand work and generosity of the local
townspeople. Virtually all of the exhibit items are
on loan to the collection and depict almost all facets
of Maine coastal life —fishing and lobstering,
domestic life, many trades, professions, and a host
of other objects and photographs celebrating "the
way things used to be."

Special exhibits of maritime interest include
models of the steamboats *Rangeley* and *J. T. Morse*
as well as "Life at Mt. Desert Rock Lighthouse," a
series of glass-plate photographs taken at the Light
in 1907.

Activities: Various heritage activities depicting
the area's culture
Admission: Open: June-Columbus Day,
Tuesday-Saturday, 10 A.M.-5 P.M.

PEMAQUID POINT, MAINE

**Fishermen's Museum and
    Pemaquid Point Lighthouse**

Lighthouse Park P.O. Box 353
Pemaquid Point Road
Pemaquid Point, ME 04539-0353
(207) 677-2494 Email: sprek@tidewater.net
Location: Pemaquid Point Lighthouse is located
sixty-miles northeast of Portland. From US Route 1
in Damariscotta, take ME 130 south to Bristol
(about 14.5 miles). The route leads to the parking
lot (small fee) at Pemaquid Point. There is a
museum in the keeper's house.

Highlights: Wall-size chart of all coastal
lighthouses in Maine, Fresnel lighthouse lens built
in France, Working half-models of fish boats and a
whaler, lobster boat, Ship models
Website: www.lighthouse.cc/pemaquid/
General Information: The Pemaquid Point
Lighthouse was commissioned by John Quincy
Adams in 1827. Its 1,000-candlepower beam is
visible up to fourteen miles at sea. The town of
Bristol owns and maintains the surrounding park
and the Fishermen's Museum, now housed in the
old lightkeeper's dwelling. The light, though not
attended, is a familiar navigational aid to fishermen
and all coastal traffic. It is a working light and not
open to the public.

Displays at the Fishermen's Museum, opened in
1972, include pictures of lighthouses along the
coast of Maine which are numbered to correspond
to a wall-size navigational chart; a bronze buoy bell
with iron chain; and a Lyle gun for shooting a
lifeline to ships in distress. Also presented are
tools used in Lobstering and gear for several
different methods of harvesting the sea. A lens
identical to the one in the tower of the lighthouse is
featured.

The Museum exhibits are located in four
rooms: the Navigation Room, with navigation
displays; the Fish House, with work-benches, tools,
and gear used in the lobstering and fishing
industries; the Net Room, where several different
methods of harvesting fish are displayed, including
a small scallop dredge and a sink-
gill net used to catch cod and haddock; and the
Gallery, where working half-models of fish boats
as well as models of a whaler are displayed. A
photograph record of the building of a schooner,
scrapbooks containing information on fishing
shrimping, and shipwrecks, as well as albums of
old postcards, documents, and newspaper articles
pertaining to the area, are of special interest.

Admission: No entry fee, but donations
accepted. Open (Memorial Day to Columbus Day)
to the public every Tuesday from 1 P.M. to 5 P.M.,
Wednesday from 9 A.M. to 5 P.M., Sunday 1 P.M.
to 5 P.M., and by chance.

PORT CLYDE, MAINE

Marshall Point Lighthouse Museum

P.O. Box 247
Port Clyde, ME 04855
(207) 372-6450
Location: The Museum is located in Port Clyde.
From Rte. 1 in Thomaston take Rte. 131 to Port
Clyde, follow the signs to the lighthouse.
Highlights: Lighthouse, gift shop **Website**:
www. lighthouse.cc/pemaquid/history.html

General Information The Marshall Point
Lighthouse Museum is in the 1985 keeper's house.
It used seven lard-oil lamps with fourteen-inch
reflectors. The current tower, built in 1858, was
equipped with a fifth-order Fresnel lens. A fog bell
added in 1989, was replaced by a fog horn in 1969.
In 1935 the light was electrified and automated in

1971. The current keeper's house built in1985 — deserted in 1980 — was taken over by the local Historical Society and restored.

The Museum was opened on the first floor and now welcomes 10,000 visitors each year. The Museum has exhibits on fishing, lobstering, quarrying, and of course, the lighthouse itself. A set of three-ring scrap books preserve local stories in photos, postcards, newspaper, and magazine articles. They lend a feeling of sharing in family remembrances as they preserve the town's sense of history. As part of the Maine Lights Program the ownership was officially transferred in June 1998. The Museum is an example of successful community involvement and hard work.

Admission: No entry fee. Open: May – October, Saturday 1 P.M. to 5 P.M.; June – September, Sunday through Friday 1 P.M .to 5 P.M.; Saturday 10 A.M. to 5 P.M.

PORTLAND, MAINE
Osher Map Library
P.O. Box 9300
Portland, ME 04104-9301
(207) 780-4141 or 1-800-800-4USM
E-mail: oml@usm.maine.edu
Location: The Library is on the Portland campus of the University of Southern Maine, at the intersection of Forest Avenue and Bedford Street.
Highlights: Rare Map Library
Web site: www.usm.maine.edu/maps/library.html
General Information: The Osher Map Library and Smith Center for Cartographic Education is the only separately established rare map library in northern New England. L The Smith and Osher collections comprise fine examples of original maps, atlases, geographies, and globes spanning the years from 1475 to the present. They constitute a rich and multifaceted resource for the study and teaching of geography, history, art, and cultural development. For the University, the people of Maine, scholars, students, and visitors, and collections are indeed a treasure.
Activities: The Osher Map Library is committed to sharing its collection with a broad constituency by means of exhibitions, lectures, conferences, and other special events. It encourages collaborative efforts with other institutions including museums, historical societies, and teaching institutions ranging from primary schools to the university level. It serves the University and residents of Maine and Northern New England, including the general public and local school systems, as well as the global community of scholars and researchers.
Admission: No entry fee. Open Monday: Closed Tuesday, Tuesday, 12:30 P.M. – 4:30 P.M.; Wednesday, 12:30 P.M. – 4:30 P.M. and 6 P.M.- 8 P.M. ; Thursday 12:30 P.M. – 4:30 P.M. and 6 P.M. – 8 P.M.; Friday, school groups by

appointment; Saturday, 9 A.M. – 1 P.M. Because the university schedule changes between the academic year and vacations, it is advisable to call ahead — (207) 780-4850 — to confirm these times.

ROCKLAND, MAINE
Maine Lighthouse Museum
1 Park Drive, PO Box F
Rockland, ME 04841
(207) 594 3301
e-mail info@mainelighthousemuseum.com
Location: From Portland, follow I-95 twenty-three miles north to Rte. 1. Head east for fifty-five miles into Rockland. The Museum is at the Gateway Center on Park Drive in Rockland at the former site of the Courier Gazette newspaper.
Highlights: Lighthouse lenses, ship models, scrimshaw, Civil War records,
Website: www.mainelighthousemuseum.com
General Information: Shore Village Museum, also known as "Maine's Lighthouse Museum," founded in 1977, contains collections of Civil War records; weapons; uniforms; lighthouse artifacts; John W. Flint collection of nautical instruments and marine artifacts; related books; marine items from the U.S. Coast Guard, including working foghorns and lights.

Also exhibited are thirty-four dolls dressed in historic costumes, scrimshaw;, lobstering tools, ship models, items of local historic interest, and the largest collection of lighthouse lenses and artifacts on display in the America. A "please touch" museum invites children to come and enjoy. A Wyeth print unveiling launched a capital campaign for the Museum that will house America's finest collection of lighthouse memorabilia including the most extensive collection of fresnel lenses in the world.

Activities: Guided tours, lectures, gallery talks, and special programs
Admission: No charge. Open: Mon/Fri, 9 A.M.-4:30 P.M; Sat/Sun 10 A.M. – 4 P.M. Closed Sundays in Winter & early Spring.

SEARSPORT, MAINE
Penobscot Marine Museum
5 Church Street at US Route 1
P. O. Box 498
Searsport, ME 04974
(207) 548-2529 Toll-Free: 800-268-8030
E-mail: nparker@penobscotmarinemuseum.org
Location: Searsport is equidistant between Bangor (to the north) and Camden (to the south) on the upper Penobscot Bay. The museum sits at the corner of Rte. 1 and Church Street.
Highlights: Ship models, finest collection of marine paintings in Maine, *The Bay Chronicle Journal* (newsletter), Phillips Memorial Library

(4,000-volumes), Gift shop,
Web site: www.penobscotmarinemuseum.org/
General Information: Penobscot Marine Museum, founded in 1936, consists of an historic district of 13 buildings (eight listed on the National Register of Historic Places). Attractions include Captain Jeremiah Merithew's house (1860), Fowler House (1820) Old town hall (1845), Former Church Vestry (1846), Duncan House (1850), modern library and art gallery, two small craft barns and a boat house. The Josiah Dutch House contains the educational center.

PMM's Marine Watercraft collection is now centered in multi-level barns and a boathouse with both wooden fishing craft and early 20th,century sailing craft. Rotating exhibits in the art gallery, permanent exhibits include "Challenge of the Down Easter" and "Working the Bay."

The Museum contains 300 paintings, ship models, builders' half-models, shipbuilders' tools, and American and Oriental furnishings. The County's largest collection marine paintings by Thomas and James Buttersworth are also on display.

Activities: Docent tours at every exhibit. Children's activities: capstan drills; yard-in-the-yard; story time; etc.

Admission: Entry fee. Open Monday through Saturday - 10 A.M. to 5 P.M., and Sunday - 12 to 5 P.M.

SOUTH BERWICK, MAINE
Counting House - Old Berwick Historical Society (circa - 1830)
Routh 4, Main & Liberty Sts. P.O. Box 296
South Berwick, ME 03908
(207) 384-0000 E-mail: Info@obhs.net
Location: From Kittery north on Rte. 236 14-miles to South Berwick on corner of Main and Liberty Streets.
Highlights: Gundalow ship models (freight boats), Nautical library,
Web site: www. seacoastnh.com/dct/berwick.html
General Information: The society's 160-year-old restored factory building is situated at the head of navigation on the Salmon Falls River. Also exhibited are shipbuilder's tools, ship models, navigational instruments, photos, and other items of local nature. The museum contains gundalow models, photos, and technical drawings on gundalows. The Counting House contains an archive with 3,000 documents and photographs.

Admission: No entry fee, but donations accepted. Open, July-October, Saturday 1 P.M.–4 P.M., and by appointment.

SOUTH PORTLAND, MAINE
Portland Harbor Museum
Southern Maine Technical College
Fort Road
South Portland, ME 04106
(207) 773-3800 - 207-799-6337
E-mail: info@portlandharbormuseum.org
Location: From I-295 in Portland, take Exit 6A and follow Rte. 77 over the Casco Bridge to South Portland. From the bridge, go straight ahead and follow Broadway until it ends. Follow signs to the Museum. The museum is located on the waterfront at Fort Preble on the campus of Southern Maine Vocational Technical Institute (SMVTI).
Highlights: Annually changing exhibits plus permanent exhibits on the only surviving clipper ship Snow *Squall*, and the lighthouses of Casco Bay, Spring Point Ledge Lighthouse, Historic Fort Preble, Willard Beach and a Signed Shoreline Walkway.
Web site: www.portlandharbormuseum.org/
General Information: The Portland Harbor Museum (formerly the Spring Point Museum) was founded in 1985 to interpret the history of the harbor, its islands and surrounding communities. The bow of the extreme clipper ship *Snow Squall* was brought to the museum from the Falkland Islands in 1987 to form the centerpiece of a major research and preservation project.

Built at South Portland in 1851, the 7420ton vessel sailed out of New York for thirteen years to San Francisco and the Far East, in 1864, she sustained severe damage trying to round Cape Horn and lay in Port Stanley, Falklands Islands, for almost a century and a Squall Project in 1995, sections of the bow were given to three other maritime museums but the major pieces were retained by Portland Harbor Museum for exhibition and as a memorial to Maine's role in the greatest age of sail.

In 1998 Portland Harbor Museum was awarded stewardship of the adjacent Spring Point Ledge Light under the Maine Lights Program, with a goal to preserve the century old lighthouse. It is opened for public tours four times each years. The Museum also maintains collections of maritime artifacts and archival material.

Activities: The 2001 exhibit is titled, "They came by Sea: Portland Harbor, A Tourist Destination."

Admission: Entry fee. Open May-December on weekends, and Friday-Sunday in June, July, August open daily, 10 A.M. – 4:30 P.M.

49

YARMOUTH, MAINE

Museum of Yarmouth History
215 Main Street
P. O. Box 107
Yarmouth, ME 04096-6722
(207) 846-6259
E-mail: yarmouth-history@inetmail.att.net
Location: Take exit 16 on I-295 to Rte. 1. Exit
onto Rte. 115, the main street in Yarmouth.
(Yarmouth is just nine miles north of Portland on
Casco Bay.) Merrill Memorial Library houses the
museum.
Highlights: History of Yarmouth and North
Yarmouth, Bookshop, **Web site:**
www.mainemuseums.org/htm/museumdetail.php3?
orgID=119
   General Information: The Museum of
Yarmouth History focuses on the history both
Yarmouth and North Yarmouth, a coastal
community settled in 1636. Yarmouth history has
always been linked to the sea, especially in the
Nineteenth century when it was the home to many
shipyards and sea captains.
   Museum exhibits may include photographs,
shipbuilding tools, instruments, ship paintings.
Research materials include journals, documents.
   Admission: Donations welcome. Open
Monday-Friday, 1 A.M.-5 P.M., July and August;
Tuesday-Friday, 1 A.M.-5 P.M.; Saturday,
10 A.M. - 5 P.M.

YORK, MAINE

John Hancock Warehouse and Wharf/
   Old York Historical Society
P. O. Box 312
York, ME 03909
(207) 363-4974   E-mail: oyhs@oldyork.org
Location: Exit off I-95 onto Rte. 1A in the
southeast corner of Maine. The wharf and
warehouse are on Lindsay Road and the bank of the
York River.
Highlights: The *Captain Edward H. Adams* (open-
decked barge, seasonal only), Library, Gift shop,
Website: www.oldyork.org/
   General Information: John Hancock
Warehouse and Wharf were built in the eighteenth
century and established as a museum and
historical site in 1974. It documents three hundred
years of commercial life along the York River. Of
the many wharves and warehouses that fronted the
river and York Harbor (then Lower Town) in the
eighteenth century, the John Hancock Warehouse is
the only remaining commercial building from
the colonial period in York. A reproduced
nineteenth-century "gundalow" (an open-decked
barge with a sixty-nine foot lateen sail used since
the mid-1600s as a river freighter), the *Captain
Edward H. Adams* is usually tied up at the wharf
when it is not on tour.
   Guides will lead you through six museum
buildings that date from 1740 to 1940 and portray
community, commercial, maritime, and family life

from those periods. Collections include furnishings
and other maritime artifacts from wealthy
shipowners and merchants.
   Activities: Guided tours, library for research,
decorative arts, genealogy, early manuscripts,
documents pertaining to York County, and some
maritime materials.
   Admission: Entry fee. Tickets at Jefferd's
Tavern Visitor's Center open: June – mid-October,
Tuesday-Saturday, 10 A.M.-5 P.M.

MARYLAND

ANNAPOLIS, MARYLAND

Annapolis Maritime Museum
723 Second Street
P.O. Box 3088
Annapolis, MD 21403
(410) 295-0104
E-mail: office@amaritime.org
Location: The Museum is located at the foot of
2nd Street and Back Creek in the Eastport section
of Annapolis.
   Highlights: Maritime history and culture of
Annapolis and Anne Arundel County, MD, of
Eastport including history of yacht racing,
waterman's work on the Bay, and boats that
brought early settlers and supplies to the area.
Website: www.annapolismaritimemuseum.org/
   General Information: The Annapolis Maritime
Museum (AMM) started over 12 years ago. The
Museum collects photographs, artifacts, and oral
history on the maritime history and culture of the
Annapolis area. The collection includes two
historic boats, artifacts from watermen who worked
the Bay, the history of boatbuilding, and the
records of yacht racing in the area.
   The AMM is one of four partners in a
consortium that took over ownership of the
Thomas Point Shoal Lighthouse May 1, 2004, with
The City of Annapolis. The United States
Lighthouse Society and its Chesapeake Chapter,
and Anne Arundel County
   Admission: Open Saturdays 11 A.M.-4 P.M.,
Sundays 1 P.M.-4 P.M., and by appointment.

ANNAPOLIS, MARYLAND

Historic Annapolis Foundation
   Victualling Warehouse Maritime Museum
77 Main Street/194 Prince George
Annapolis, MD 21401.
Historic Annapolis:
18 Pinkney Street
Annapolis, MD 21401
(800) 603-4020 (410) 267-7619
Fax: (410) 267-6189
E-mail: john.guild@annapolis.org
Location: Annapolis sits on the Chesapeake Bay
thirty-two miles east of Washington, D.C., off Rte.
50.

Highlights: The general historical past of Annapolis, The William Paca House, Tobacco Prise House, Victualling Warehouse Maritime Museum, **Website:** www.annapolis.org/

General Information: Collections include: architecture and decorative arts, Hancock's Resolution (1765), William Paca House; Old Treasury Building; Tobacco Prise House; barracks; and the Victualling Warehouse Maritime Museum. The latter features a diorama of the Annapolis waterfront circa 1751-91, when Annapolis was the principal seaport of the upper Chesapeake Bay. Also exhibited are shipbuilding tools, half-woven sails, military clothes, oak barrels, wine bottles, and other displays.

Activities: Guided tours, lectures, films, educational programs, research programs, and special events.

Admission: Entry fee. The maritime museum is open daily, 11 A.M.-4:30 P.M., year-round. Contact the office for the opening hours of the various historic buildings.

ANNAPOLIS, MARYLAND
U.S. Naval Academy Museum
118 Maryland Avenue
Annapolis, MD 21402-5034
(410) 293-2108 Fax: 293-5220
E-mail: cheevers@usna.edu
Location: Annapolis sits on the Chesapeake Bay. The Museum is located in Preble Hall on the grounds of the U.S. Naval Academy in Annapolis, MD. It is 35 miles east of Washington, D.C. via U.S. Route 50 (Exit 24), and 26 miles south of Baltimore via Maryland Route 2 or Interstate 97. The area is served by three major airports, several private airfields, Amtrak, buses, and marinas.
Highlights: The Gallery of Ships featuring renowned models of the Henry Huddleston Rogers Collection, 1650-1850; the Beverley R. Robinson Collection of Naval Prints; "100 Years and Forward," a new permanent exhibition on the U.S. Navy's role in the 20th century; and the John Paul Jones Crypt,
Web site: www.usna.edu/Museum/

General Information: The U.S. Naval Academy Museum originated in 1845 as the Naval Academy Lyceum, a collection of historic and natural objects, scientific models and apparatus, and works of art brought together for study and discussion by students and faculty. Today the museum continues to serve as an educational and inspirational resource for the Brigade of Midshipmen at the Academy, as well as for visiting scholars and the general public. It is open seven days a week and uses, in its galleries of historical exhibits objects and graphic material, to demonstrate the Navy's role in war and in peace. The museum's holdings

include ship models, paintings, prints, flags, uniforms, and weapons, Visitors Center. The U.S. Naval Institute Bookstore is located in the Museum.

Many other buildings on the Naval Academy grounds also exhibit items form the collection. A large display can be found in the crypt of John Paul Jones located in the Naval Academy Chapel.

The Museum's holdings include ship models, paintings, prints, flags, uniforms, weapons, medals, sculpture, manuscripts, rare books, photographs, ships' instruments, gear, and a wide variety of personal memorabilia associated with famous naval leaders. The Naval Institute Press provides a wide variety of publications of maritime interest and its Bookstore is located in the Museum.

Admission: No entry fee. Open Monday-Saturday, 9 A.M.-5 P.M.; Sunday 11 A.M.-5 P.M. Closed Thanksgiving, Christmas, and New Year's Day.

BALTIMORE, MARYLAND
Longship Company, Ltd.
21924 Oakley Road
Avenue, MD 20609
(301) 390-4089 or 762-0887
E-mail: longshipco@hotmail.com
Location: The community of Avenue is two miles north of Coltons Point, which is on the Potomac River some forty-five miles southeast of Washington, D.C.
Highlights: The *Fyrdraca* (Viking warship),* The *Gyrfalcon* (landing boat), **Web site:** www.wam.umd.edu/~eowyn/Longship

General Information: The Longship Company, Ltd. is dedicated to the research, and operation and maintenance of vessels from the Viking and Early Medieval periods, and study of the history of those time periods. Two vessels currently in the collection are the 32-foot *Fyrdraca*, a replica ninth-century Viking warship built in 1979 and a 21-foot *Gyrfalcon*, a replica of the *Gokstad* faering used as a ships dinghy.

The vessels make frequent training voyages and appear at waterfront festivals, boat shows, and marine exhibits throughout the Chesapeake region. The company researches and reconstructs artifacts, clothing, weapons, and tools of the Viking and Early Medieval period.

Activities: Training voyages, Living history encampments, museum, and school demonstrations.

Admission: No entry fee. Phone for schedule and latest information.

• See also Heritage *Hjemkomst* Interpretive Center and *Leif Erikson*

BALTIMORE, MARYLAND
Baltimore Maritime Museum
301 E. Pratt Street. Piers 3 & 5
Mail: 802 South Caroline Street
Baltimore, MD 21202
(410) 396-3453   Fax: (410) 396-3393
E-mail: admin@baltomaritimemuseum.org
Location: The Baltimore Maritime Museum is located at Pier 4 on Pratt Street in Baltimore's Inner Harbor.
Highlights: The *Chesapeake* (lightship), The USS *Torsk* (submarine), Cutter *Taney*, lighthouse,
Web site: www.baltomaritimemuseum.org/
General Information: The Baltimore Maritime Museum offers guided tours through the USS *Torsk*, the last U.S. submarine to sink enemy shipping in World War II. Across the pier is the lightship *Chesapeake*, a floating lighthouse designed to aid shipping in the Chesapeake Bay. The U. S. Coast Guard Cutter *Taney* is also exhibited. She is the only surviving warship afloat that was present in Hawaii during the attack on Pearl Harbor. And a screw pile lighthouse.
Activities: Overnight camping program on USCGC *Taney*.
Admission: Entry fee. Open: Summer Hours 7 days a week; USCGC *Taney* 10A.M. - 5 P.M.; Lightship *Chesapeake* & Seven Foot Knoll; Lighthouse 10A.M. – 6 P.M.; *Torsk* submarine 10A.M. - 8:30 P.M. ; *Torsk* special evening tickets available on board Ticket Booth closes 1/2 hour earlier than ships; Spring & Fall Hours, Sunday - Thursday: 10:A.M. – 5 P.M.; Friday - Saturday: 10A.M. – 6 P.M., Ticket Booth closes 1/2 hour earlier than ships; Winter Hours, Friday - Sunday: 10 A.M. – 5 P.M.; Ticket Booth closes 1/2 hour earlier than ships; Spring hours start in March

BALTIMORE, MARYLAND
Baltimore Museum of Industry
Baltimore Harbor on Key Highway
1415 Key Highway
Baltimore, MD 21230
(410) 727-4808 Fax: (410) 727-4869
E-mail: tours@thebmi.org
Location: Exit off I-395 onto Montgomery Street, then head south toward Fort McHenry. The Museum is near the steam tug *Baltimore*, which is docked on the south side of the old Baltimore Harbor on Key Highway.
Highlights: The *Baltimore* (steam tug), library,
Website: www.thebmi.org/
General Information: The Baltimore Museum of Industry, founded in 1981, is housed in an oyster cannery. A wide variety of industry- related exhibits are displayed, and machinery is demonstrated.
Activities: Tour of steam tug *Baltimore* (by appointment)

Admission: Entry fee. Open Tuesday-Saturday 10 A.M. – 4 P.M., Sunday, 11 A.M. – 4 P.M.

BALTIMORE, MARYLAND
Fells Point Maritime Museum
Maryland Historical Society
1724 Thames Street
Baltimore, MD 21231
(410) 732-0278 E-mail: museum@mdhs.org
Location: The Society, from downtown, go north on Charles Street, stay in left lane, turn right on Park Ave., then turn left on Monument to parking
Highlights: Extensive maritime collection,
Website: www.mdhs.org/
General Information: The Fells Point Maritime Museum closed in 2007 and all exhibits are at the Maryland Historical Society for the Preservation of Federal Hill and Fells Point. The Museum displays the Society's maritime collections including artifacts, models, and paintings.
Among Fells Point's fascinating people include such well-known historic figures as privateer Thomas Boyle and shipbuilder Thomas Kemp, as well as the everyday residents who made Fells Point famous. The Museum's exhibit Fells Point's Fast Ships Follow the design, technology, and skill involved in building and operating the famous Baltimore clipper schooner that impacted international trade-carrying fruit, exotic spices, and tobacco. Not all trades needing the fast ships were legal, however. Fells Point produced slave ships and even played a role in the opium trades.
Admission: Entry fee. Open Thursday through Monday 10:00 A.M. to 5:00 P.M.

BALTIMORE, MARYLAND
Pride of Baltimore II, Inc.
1801 So. Clinton Street Suite 250
Baltimore, MD 21224
Toll free: 888-557-7433 (410) 539-1151
Fax: (410) 539-1190 E-mail: Pride2@Pride2.org
Location: The *Pride*, when in town, is located in Baltimore's Inner Harbor.
Highlights: The *Pride of Baltimore II* (top-sail schooner), The *Pride of Baltimore* Memorial,
Website: www.intandem.com/NewPrideSite/
General Information: The Baltimore Clippers were the preferred vessels of privateers — legal pirates — during the American War of 1812 against the British. These swift vessels were used as revenue cutters (the forerunner to the Coast Guard Cutters), merchant ships, and privateers at a time when the U.S. Navy was in its infancy.
The *Pride of Baltimore II* is a painstaking re-creation of a nineteenth-century topsail schooner built to the lines of a Baltimore Clipper. Built in 1988, the *Pride of Baltimore II* is the successor to the first replica *Pride of Baltimore* that visited more than 125 ports in her nine years of operation.

After a highly successful European visit, the first *Pride of Baltimore* replica sank during a sudden storm in May 1986, while sailing home from the Caribbean.

Admission: Contact the office for location and dates available for boarding. The memorial is on the south side of Baltimore's Inner Harbor.

BALTIMORE, MARYLAND
SS *John W. Brown*
Project Liberty Ship
Bethlehem-Fairfield Shipyard
P. O. Box 25846 Highlandtown Station
Baltimore, MD 21224-0546
(410) 558-0646 Fax (410) 558-1737
E-mail: john.w.brown@usa.net
Location: The ship is located at Pier One on the 2000 block of South Clinton Street. I-95, Exit 56 (Keith Ave.), turn right at light.
Highlights: The *John W. Brown* (liberty ship), ship's store, *The Ugly Duckling* and *Liberty Log* newsletters, Ship's Store
Website: www.liberty-ship.com
   General Information: Project Liberty Ship is an all volunteer organization engaged in the restoration, preservation, and operation of the "Oldest Operating Liberty Ship" remaining of the 2751 built (only two ships remain). This historic ship is a Living Memorial Museum, honoring the those men and women who built, sailed, and defended these "Ships for Victory." The SS *John W. Brown* is 441-feet, six-inches in length and has a beam of 56-feet, 10 3/4-inches. The draft is 27-feet 9 1/4 inches and can hold 8500 long tons of cargo. The first Liberty Ship launched was *The Patrick Henry* at the Bethlehem-Fairfield shipyard in Baltimore on September 27, 1941.
   Activities: 4-day cruises (6/hrs) on the Chesapeake Bay (ticket reservation required), tours of entire ship, engine room while underway. Live music and entertainment, flybys of vintage aircraft (P-51, B-24), and catered "all you can eat" continental breakfast and luncheon. For cruise reservations, call (410) 558-0164.
   Admission: No entry fee. Donations are recommended. The ship is open on Wednesday and Saturday, 9 A.M.-2 P.M. Groups should call 2 weeks ahead of intended visit. * See also Marin Ship 1942-1945 and SS *Jeremiah O'Brien.*

BALTIMORE, MARYLAND
USS *Constellation* (Sloop-of-War)
Historic Ships in Baltimore
Pier One, 301 East Pratt Street
Baltimore, MD 21202-3134
(410) 539-1797 Fax: (410) 539-6238
E-mail: crowsom@historicships.org
Location: Inner Harbor near the intersection of Pratt and Light Streets.

Highlights: The USS *Constellation* Sloop-of-War,
Web site: www.constellation.org/
   General Information: The USS *Constellation* is the last all-sail warship built by the US Navy, and only remaining naval vessel of the American Civil War afloat. She was built at the Gosport Navy Yard in Portsmouth, Virginia and launched in 1854 as a 22-gun sloop-of-war (meaning her main battery of 20 guns was located on one deck) to replace the 38-gun frigate of the same name that was launched in Baltimore in 1797. She measures 176 feet in length on the gun deck, with a maximum beam (width) of 41 feet, 6 inches, and draws 21 feet of water when fully armed and rigged.
   She has been the centerpiece of Baltimore's Inner Harbor renaissance since 1968, when a misguided "restoration" attempted to make her into a representation of the 1797 frigate. By 1994 she was in a deteriorated condition, and was condemned as unsafe. Her rigging was removed, and she was closed to the public. Subsequently, she underwent an extensive restoration that returned her to her proper 1854 appearance while retaining almost 50% of her historic fabric.
   USS *Constellation* returned to her permanent berth on July 2, 1999, and was reopened to the public. An audio-tour with 20 stops, over 40 graphic panels, and a number of artifact exhibits interpret the history, restoration, operation of and life on board this historic naval vessel.
   Activities: Cannon firing demonstrations daily, living history programs interpreting Civil War naval life, docent guided-tours, special lectures, presentation and demonstrations of shipbuilding and restoration methods on selected weekends.
   Admission: Entry fees. Open daily, Apr/Oct 10 A.M.- 5:30 P.M., Nov/Mar, 10 A.M.- 5:30 P.M. Extended hours may be available June/July/August.

CAMBRIDGE, MARYLAND
Dorchester Heritage Museum
Dorchester Heritage Museum
1904 Horn Point Rd.
Cambridge, MD. 21613
(410) 228-5530
Location: Cambridge is located on Maryland's Eastern Shore approximately forty-five miles south of the Chesapeake Bay Bridge on US-50.
Highlights: Last Eastern Shore gunning boat (water-fowl hunting)
   General Information: Dorchester Heritage Museum contains maritime, aircraft, farming, and Indian exhibits in a working museum. Exhibits include one of the last Eastern Shore gunning boats used by legal and illegal water-fowl market hunters.

Activities: An annual antique aircraft fly-in the weekend May 15, 2001, Saturday, 8 A.M. to 5 P.M.

Admission: Open: April-Oct/Sat & Sun, 1 P.M. to 4:30 P.M.

CAMBRIDGE, MARYLAND
Richardson Maritime Museum
James B. Richardson Foundation, Inc.
401 High Street,   P.O. Box 1198
Cambridge, MD 21613-1198
410-221-1871 Fax: 410-228-5471
E-mail: info@richardsonmuseum.org
Location: The Foundation is housed in the extensively renovated old Maryland National Bank building.
Highlights: Wooden boat building
Website: www.richardsonmuseum.org
General Information: The James B. Richardson Foundation, ultimately to include Richardson Maritime Heritage Center: Richardson Maritime Museum; the Ruark Boatworks; and the Brannock Education and Research Center

The Richardson Maritime Museum is located at 401 High Street. Devoted to the preservation and heritage of Dorchester County and the surrounding Area. The Museum's collection includes an extensive display of Chesapeake Bay ship models, and the history of wooden boat building, including various tools and artifacts.

Admission: Open Wednesday & Sunday 1-4 PM, Saturday 10 AM - 4 PM The Museum is closed New Years Day, Easter Sunday, Fourth of July, Thanksgiving and Christmas.

In addition, the Ruark Boatworks located at 100 Maryland Avenue & Hayward S. is passing on the knowledge and skills of area boatwights to volunteers and visitors alike. Watch boatbuilding and restoration in action as the Foundation fulfills its mission of "Putting History on the Water."

Admission: Hours are 9 A.M.-2 P.M. Mon., Wed. and Fri. but may vary with work in progress. Docent on duty Saturday 1- 4 P.M.

CHESAPEAKE CITY, MARYLAND
C & D Canal Museum
(Also known as: Chesapeake and Delaware Canal Museum)
815 Bethel Rd
Chesapeake, MD 21915
(410) 885-5622 Fax: (410) 885-5926
Location: Chesapeake City is on the west end of the canal that links the Delaware and Elk Rivers. The most direct route from Maryland is to take the Elkton exit off I-95 north/south, take Rte. 279 west to 213 South, then follow back roads southeast the few miles to Chesapeake City.

Highlights: Old lock pump house, working model of a water wheel and lock, steam engines,
Website: www.pennways.com/CD_Canal.html
General Information: Housed in the original canal pump/house complex, the Museum includes a working model of a water wheel and lock, paintings, maps, documents, and artifacts pertaining to the history of the waterway. The Old Lock Pump House, built over a century ago, contained a steam engine, boilers, and pumps to replace water lost in opening and closing a nearby canal lock. The U.S. Army Corps of Engineers has carefully preserved the pump complex since it went out of use in 1926.
Admission: No entry fee. Open Easter- October 31, Monday-Saturday, 8 A.M.-4 P.M. Closed Sundays and holidays.

COLTONS POINT, MARYLAND
St. Clements Island - Potomac River Museum
38370 Point Breeze Road
Colton's Point, MD 20626
(301) 769-2222 Fax: (301) 796-2225
E-mail: Kim_cullins@co.sint-marys.md.us
Location: Twenty-five miles upstream from the Chesapeake Bay on the Potomac River, at Coltons Point, the Museum is accessible by water or land. Take Rte. 301 forty miles south of Washington, D.C., exiting onto SR-234. Head east to Clements and Rte. 242 south to the end at Coltons Point.
Highlights: The *Doris C* and the *Early Times* (dory boats), mural of first landing of Maryland colonists, research library, Little Red Schoolhouse, Crab Claw Gift Shop and water taxi,
Website: www.stmarys.com/recreate/museums
General Information: St. Clements Island – Potomac River Museum is a nationally accredited museum whose mission is to interpret, exhibit, and preserve the significant history of St. Clement's Island, the "Birthplace of Maryland," the Potomac River, its inhabitants, and culture.

Arriving from England, March 25, 1634, the first Maryland colonists landing on St. Clement's Island escaping religious persecution and civil disabilities and founded a new colony offering economic opportunity and religious toleration. Here they gave thanks celebrating the first Roman Catholic mass in the English speaking colonies and negotiated with the Piscataway Indians for a permanent settlement.

Activities: Pre-arranged tours, self-guided tours, picnic facilities, public pier, lectures, special events, water taxi to St. Clement's Island weekends Memorial weekend to Labor Day weekend.

Admission: Entry fee for Museum. Open weekdays 9 A.M. to 5 P.M., weekends 10 A.M. to 5 P.M.

CRISFIELD, MARYLAND
Governor J. Millard Tawes Historical Museum
Somers Cove
3 Ninth Street P. O. Box 253
Crisfield, MD 21817
(410) 968-2501 Fax: (410) 968-0350
E-mail: ctyler@crisfieldheritagefoundation.org
Location: Crisfield is on the southernmost point of
Maryland's Eastern Shore, approached via SR-413
south out of Salisbury.
Highlights: Artwork, folk art, maritime and
local history, and seafood industry, **Website:**
http://skipjack.net/le_shore/visitsomerset/tawes_m
useum.html
General Information: Governor J. Millard
Tawes Historical Museum, founded in 1982,
exhibits a collection of photographs, paintings and
much more from the life of the late Crisfield
resident and former Maryland governor. There
are also exhibits relating to the history of Crisfield
and the seafood industry.
Admission: Entry fee. Open daily, Memorial
Day thru Oct 30th 9-4:30 (M-F) 10-3:00 (Sa & Su)
Nov 1st to Memorial Day 9-4:30 (M-F)
Closed Weekends

CUMBERLAND, MARYLAND
C & O Canal of Cumberland, MD, Inc.
Chesapeake and Ohio Canal
300 Bel Air Drive
Cumberland, MD 21502
(301) 722-8226
Highlights: C & O Canal
Website: www.fred.net/kathy/canal.html
General Information: C & O Canal of
Cumberland, MD., Inc., was established to promote
historical significance of the C & O Canal for
educational and charitable purposes, to promote
interest in historical western Maryland, and to
recreate certain portions of the C & O Canal. Other
Chesapeake and Ohio Canal Historic Park Sites.
Visitor Centers at:
Georgetown: 1057 Thomas Jefferson St. NW,
Washington, D.C. 20007, (202) 653-5190
Great Falls Tavern: 11710 MacArthur
Blvd, Potomac, MD 20854 (301) 299-3613
Hancock: 326 E. Main Street,
Hancock, MD 21750 (301) 678-5463
Williamsport: 205 W. Potomac Street,
Williamsport, MD 21795 (301) 582-0813
Western Maryland Station: Canal Street,
Cumberland, MD 21502 (301) 722-8226

HAGERSTOWN, MARYLAND
Chesapeake and Ohio National Historical Park
Crystal (IBM) Building
1850 Dual Highway #100
Hagerstown, MD, 21740-6620

(301) 739-4200 Fax: 301-739-5275
E-mail: CHOH_Superintendent@nps.gov
Location: Visitor Center and canal boat ticket
sales located in Georgetown, D.C. at Georgetown
Visitor Center, 1057 Thomas Jefferson St., NW.
Great Falls Tavern visitor center at 11710
MacArthur Boulevard, Potomac, MD, about ten
miles northwest of Washington, D.C., Clara Barton
Parkway to MacArthur Boulevard. Other visitor
centers noted below. Hours of operation very.
Highlights: Canal boat trips at Georgetown and
Great Falls, lockhouses, aqueducts, Paw Paw
Tunnel, **Website:** www.nps.gov/choh
General Information: The Chesapeake and
Ohio Canal National Historical Park, founded in
1971, stretches for 184.5 miles from Georgetown
(Washington, D.C.) to Cumberland, MD. The C &
O Canal parallels the Potomac River, offering
countless sites of incredible beauty and a wealth of
historical data. Locks and lockhouses, dams,
aqueducts, and remnants of once-thriving
communities that remind us of the almost 100
years (1828-1924) of active canal traffic.
Seventy-four lift locks were built, averaging
100 feet long, 15 feet wide, and 16 feet deep and
capable of lifting or lowering boats 8 feet. A set of
wooden lock gates, weighing over two tons, was at
each end of the lock. Originally, numbers identified
the locks. But numbers gave way to names like
Swains Lock and Pennyfield Lock. Eleven
aqueducts built between Georgetown and
Cumberland allowed numerous tributaries to flow
into the Potomac River; some even flowed under
the canal via culverts with six miles of bends. The
canal is watered 22 miles from Georgetown to
Violette's Lock.
To avoid a six-mile bend in the Potomac, canal
builders bored through a knobby spur in a
mountain and created the Paw Paw Tunnel. It is
3,118 feet long and took fourteen years to build
(1836-1850). It is situated ten miles east of
Oldtown, Maryland, on SR-51.
Activities: Films, educational walks and talks,
and living history demonstrations at Seneca
lockhouse. During the season, the National Park
Service sponsors one-hour trips aboard a replica
boat on the historic canal from Georgetown and at
Great Falls, MD. Along the way, Park rangers and
volunteers in period costumes relate the history of
the canal, lead group singing, and tell anecdotes.
(For information on these boat trips, phone (301)
767-3714).
Admission: Entrance fee at Great Falls only.
Call Park headquarters at (301) 739-4200 for more
information. **OTHER** Chesapeake and Ohio Canal
Historical Park Sites: Visitor Centers at:
Brunswick, MD, 40 W. Potomac Street
Brunswick, MD 21716 (301) 739-4200
Cumberland, MD, 300 Bel Air Drive,
Cumberland, MD 21502 (301) 722-8226

Georgetown: 1057 Thomas Jefferson St. NW, Washington, D.C. 20007, (202) 653-5190
Great Falls Tavern: 11710 MacArthur Boulevard, Potomac, MD 20854 (301) 299-3613
Hancock: 326 E. Main Street, Hancock, MD 21750 (301) 678-5463
Williamsport: 205 W. Potomac Street, Williamsport, MD 21795 (301) 582-0813
Western Maryland Station: Canal Street, Cumberland, MD 21502 (301) 722-8226

HAVRE DE GRACE, MARYLAND
Havre de Grace Maritime Museum
100 Lafayette Street
P.O. Box 533
Havre de Grace, MD 21078-3542
(410) 939-3739 Fax: 410-939-0019
E-mail: museum@comcast.net
Location: Take I-95, exit 89 (MD 155) to Havre de Grace. Proceed straight under railroad bridge, right at Juniata Street to first light. Left on Otsego Street. Bear right under railroad bridge onto Union Avenue. Follow to Lafayette Street. Turn left and three blocks to the Museum.
Highlights: Martha Lewis (skipjack)
Web Site: www.hdgmaritimemuseum.org/
General Information: Havre de Grace was a major hub for water-related commerce and recreational
Activities on the Upper Chesapeake Bay. The Museum was founded in 1988 to preserve the great maritime heritage and lifestyle of the area.
Havre de Grace Maritime Museum displays artifacts, memorabilia, and photographs from past exciting times. Highlighted in the historical information exhibits are local lighthouses, commerce-carrying canals serving central Pennsylvania, and skipjacks *Martha Lewis*, one of 8 working models on the Chesapeake Bay.
Activities: Offers educational programs and events on local maritime history
Admission: No entry fee. Open May-October, Saturdays and Sundays, 1 P.M. - 5 P.M.

HAVRE DE GRACE, MARYLAND
Susquehanna Museum at Havre de Grace
817 Conesteo Street
P. O. Box 253
Havre de Grace, MD 21078-0253
(410) 939-5780 Fax: (410) 939-1755
E-mail: director@lockhousemuseum.org
Location: Off I-95 north/south take the exit at SR-155. Havre de Grace lies at the mouth of the Susquehanna River, the southern terminal of the Susquehanna and Tidewater Canal that empties into the upper Chesapeake Bay.

Highlights: Restored lock house
Website: www.lockhousemuseum.org/
General Information: The Susquehanna Museum "at the Lock House", founded in 1970, is committed to preserving the history of Havre de Grace. The Museum building is the restored lock house, which was originally built in 1840, and furnished in keeping with the mid-1800s. In addition to the restored house, the pilot bridge over the lock has been restored and work has started on restoring the lock.
In the forty-five mile run to the Susquehanna and Tidewater Canal's northern terminal at Wrightsville, Pennsylvania, the mule-drawn canal boats had to be raised a total of 233 feet. This was accomplished with twenty-nine lift locks. With the canal boat moving about three miles per hour and encountering a lock about every mile and a half, the trip would take a couple of days.
Admission: Entry free, donations accepted. Open June-August: Friday-Sunday 1 - 5 P.M.; group tours available daily by appointment.

LINTHICUM HEIGHTS, MARYLAND
Masters, Mates, and Pilots Museum
Maritime Institute of Technology and Graduate Studies (MITAGS)
5700 Hammonds Ferry Road
Linthicum Heights, MD 21090
(410) 859-5700 Fax: (410) 859-5181
Location: From south take I-95 north through Baltimore Harbor Tunnel. From the north via Baltimore/Washington Parkway: take the Baltimore/ Washington Parkway to Beltway I-695 to Towson. Go off at Exit 8 (Nursery Road)- Hammonds Ferry Road. Proceed south on Hammonds Ferry Road. School entrance on the right 0.7 mile. From South via Baltimore/ Washington Pkwy, go to Beltway I-695 to Glen Burnie. Go off at Exit 7 (Linthicum South). Proceed south on Camp Meade Road (Rte. 170). Right on Twin Oaks Road. Right on Hammonds Ferry road. The Maritime Institute of Technology is on the left 0.3 mile.
Highlights: Ship models, Merchant Marine history,
General Information: The Maritime Institute of Technology and Graduate Studies is the training facility of the International Organization of Masters Mates and Pilots, a division of the International Longshoremen's Association (AFL-CIO). The school maintains a small memorabilia room that contains art, ship models, and artifacts concerning the Merchant Marine. Exhibits contain photographs, posters, etc. of the Merchant Marines' contribution during World War II.
Admission: No entry fee. Open Monday-Friday, 8:30 A.M.-4:30 P.M., year-round.

NORTH EAST, MARYLAND
Upper Bay Museum
W. Walnut Street & North East Community Park
P.O. Box 275
North East, MD 21901
(410) 287-2675 info@upperbaymuseum.org
Location: I-95 South to Maryland exit for Rt. 272
South. Town Park entrance (North East Comm.
Pk) is about 1 mile south of Rt. 40, right at Walnut
Street to the and Upper Bay Museum.
Highlights: Antique outboard engines, original
boats, tools, antique decoys, shotguns, decoy
maker's workshop, a rare punt gun, rare double
Sink Box (boat) and local Indian artifacts,
Website: http://upperbaymuseum.org
   General Information: The Upper Bay Museum
is unique in its extensive variety of artifacts, which
document the history of water related industry,
commerce, and sport in the Upper Chesapeake
Bay. Housed in the H.L. Harvey Fish Co. Building,
are items used by local families for generations.
   Nets, traps, lures, boats, tools and an extensive
collection of antique outboard engines represent
the fishing industry. Sneak, Skiff, Railbird, and
Bushwack boats represent the waterfowl hunting
and sport industries. A large collection of sculling
oars which is unique to the silent and deadly use of
the Bushwack Boat. A large punt gun is displayed
in the Boat which carried it to the hunting area.
Antique shotguns, original hand-crafted waterfowl
decoys, tools and a double Sink Box which is the
only one known of. It insured that the duck hunters
would leave the waters undisturbed and glide along
almost soundlessly. The Sink Box was so deadly
against the waterfowl population that in the 1930s
the Federal Government outlawed its use.
   Local hunters provided waterfowl to many
markets including Baltimore, Philadelphia, and
New York. Local boat captains guided many
notable, "Sports" to gun on the world famous
Susquehanna Flats, including President Grover
Cleveland, Walter Chrysler, and the DuPonts.
   Activities: Scheduled guided tours, long
running Decoy Show 3rd week in October, decoy
carving demonstrations, and competitions, Student
Young Writers Competition, artifact restoration,
raffles and auctions
   Admission: Entry fee-small donation. Open
Memorial Day - Labor Day, Saturday 10 A.M. –
3 P.M., Sunday 10 A.M. – 4 P.M.. Open all
holidays, 10 A.M. – 4 P.M.. Open other times by
appointment. Tours scheduled by appointment any
time (410) 287-0672).

OCEAN CITY, MARYLAND
Ocean City Life-Saving Station Museum
813 Atlantic Ave.
Ocean City, MD 21842-4088
(410) 289-4991 Fax: (410) 289-0384

E-mail: curator@ocmuseum.org
Location: If entering Ocean City by Rte. 50
Bridge, bear right at bottom of bridge. Follow
Philadelphia Avenue south to the Inlet Parking Lot.
Museum located on Boardwalk at the Inlet.
Highlights: Life-Saving Service artifacts,
shipwreck research, marine aquarium, Sands of the
World, Mermaid Exhibits, gift shop,
Website: www.ocmuseum.org/
   General Information: The original life-saving
station was commissioned by Congress and built
in 1878 and rebuilt in 1891. The building was used
to house the crewmembers and equipment
of the United States Life-Saving Service. Stations,
such as these, were located on the more than
10,000 miles of America's coastline.
   In 1915 the Life-Saving Service merged with
the Revenue Cutter Service to form the United
States Coast Guard. The Museum preserves the
colorful history of Ocean City, Maryland, through
exhibits of U.S. Life-Saving Service from 1875-
1914 on the barrier islands of Delaware,
Maryland, and Virginia. Exhibits include a life car,
a restored apparatus cart, a Manby line-throwing
mortar and surf rescue boat—beautifully restored.
   Admission: Entry fee. Open daily, June-
September 11 A.M.-10 P.M.; open daily, October-
May 11 A.M.-4 P.M.; winter, open 10 A.M.-
4 P.M., weekends.

OXFORD, MARYLAND
Oxford Museum
100 South Morris Road, P.O. Box 131
Oxford, MD 21654
(410) 226-0191
E-mail: oxford_museum@verizon.net
Location: Take the SR-333 exit off Rte. 50 on
Maryland's Eastern Shore. Bear west five miles
into Oxford. The Museum is at the corner of
Morris and Market Streets.
Highlights: Home of Robert Morris of American
Revolution fame, *Port of Entry* (publication),
   General Information: The Oxford Museum,
founded in 1964, is a personal marine museum
with mementos dating from the time that Robert
Morris, the financier of the American Revolution,
lived in the house that the Museum now occupies.
Many items displayed pertain to the first port of
entry in Maryland.
   Admission: Open Friday-Sunday, 2 P.M.-5
P.M., or by arrangement

PINEY POINT, MARYLAND
Harry Lundeberg Seamanship School , Inc.
45353 St. George's Avenue
Piney Point, MD 20674
(410) 994-1471
Location: Follow Rte. 301 south from
Washington, D.C., forty miles to the junction of

SR-235. Head east twenty-two miles to the junction of SR-249. Head south to Piney Point on the Potomac River, fifteen miles upstream from the Chesapeake Bay.
Highlights: The *Manitou* (yacht)
General Information: Harry Lundberg School of Seamanship is a training school of the Merchant Marine. Several vessels are on exhibit.
Admission: No entry fee. Open the first Sunday of each month, 9 A.M.- 5 P.M.
Note: See Coltons Point for Piney Point Lighthouse Museum

PINEY POINT, MARYLAND
Piney Point Lighthouse Museum
44701 Lighthouse Road
Piney Point, MD 20626
(301) 994-2222   Fax: 301-769-2225
E-mail: Kim_cullins@stmarys.com
c/o St. Clements Island - Potomac River Museum
38370 Point Breeze Road
Coltons Point, MD 20626
(301) 769-2222 Fax: (301) 796-2225
Location: The Lighthouse is fourteen miles upstream from the Potomac River mouth on the Chesapeake Bay and approximately forty-five miles from the St. Clements Island - Potomac River Museum. Travel southeast on Rte 5 south, to Rte. 249 south at Callaway. Drive nine miles and turn right on Lighthouse Road, follow to the end. Pier available.
Highlights: Piney Point Lighthouse, exhibit of U-1105 (*Black Panther* German U-Boat), Lighthouse Lens Gift Shop, **Website:** www.baygateways.net/general.cfm?id=28
Website: for the *Black Panther*: www.stmarys.com/recreate/museums
General Information: The Piney Point Lighthouse, built in 1836, is one of only four remaining lighthouses on the Potomac River. Standing on its original site and adjacent to its keeper's quarters, this restored lighthouse served as a working beacon from 1836 until 1964. The Museum contains exhibits on the lighthouse history, and the U-1105 German U-Boat, submerged in the Potomac one mile off shore. The U-1105 site is Maryland's first *Historic Shipwreck Dive Preserve.*
Activities: Boardwalk with descriptive placards, picnic area, and public dock.
Admission: By donation. Grounds open all year, sunrise to sunset. The Museum is open May 1-October 31, noon - 5 P.M., Friday-Monday, call for weekday hours.

ST. MARY'S CITY, MARYLAND
Historic St. Mary's City
18551 Hogaboom Lane P. O. Box 39
Rosecroft Road
St. Mary's City, MD 20686

Toll Free: 800-762-1634 (240) 895- 4990
Fax: (240) 895-4960
E-mail: sgwilkinson@smcm.edu
Location: From Annapolis: take Rte. 2 south continuing on merged Rtes. 2/4. Cross Gov. Johnson bridge at Solomons and continue to Rte. 235, then south through Lexington Park, thirteen miles to Mattapany Road (sign: Historic St. Mary's City), turn right onto Mattapany Road, proceed two miles to Rte. 5, turn left and then right on Rosecroft Road (follow signs to Visitor Center located in blue barns).
Highlights: The *Maryland Dove* (replica ship), **Website:** www.stmaryscity.org
General Information: The seventy-six-foot, forty-two-ton replica *Maryland Dove* and ship's boat are displayed on the waterfront of the outdoor museum at the site of Maryland's first capital. This working re-creation of a square-rigged merchant carrier of the mid-seventeenth century was named for the pinnace *Dove,* which accompanied the first colonists as a supply ship, scouted the settlement site, and later conveyed trading missions for the Colony. Other major exhibits at Historic St. Mary's City include a reconstructed portion of the town center, a tobacco plantation, and ongoing archaeological excavations.
Admission: Entry fee. Memberships available. Open Wednesday-Sunday, 10 A.M.-5 P.M., June 16 – September 12. Call for hours for other times of the year.

ST. MICHAELS, MARYLAND
Chesapeake Bay Maritime Museum
213 N. Talbot Street,
Navy Point P. O. Box 636
St. Michaels, MD 21633-0636
(410) 745-2916 Fax: (410) 745-6088
E-mail: lschaefet@cbmm.org
Location: The Museum complex is located on a peninsula in the harbor of historic and picturesque St. Michaels on the Eastern Shore at Navy Point. From the Bay Bridge follow Rte. 50 east to the Easton Bypass (SR-322). Bear west on SR-33 into St. Michaels, turning right onto Mill Street.
Highlights: Hooper Strait Lighthouse (restored and a National Landmark, 9 log-bottom longeye (boat), Wooden Boat Building, *Weather Gauge* (semi-annual publication), *On the Beam* (newsletter), library (9,000 volumes), museum store, **Website:** www.cbmm.org/
General Information: Chesapeake Bay Maritime Museum is dedicated to preserving the history of the Chesapeake Bay region. The Museum has grown from a single house in 1965, when it was established, to an eighteen-acre campus of restored buildings and new structures erected to exhibit a comprehensive collection of Bay artifacts and to preserve the lore of the area.

58

The Museum traces the geologic, social, and economic history of the Chesapeake Bay through the age of sail and steam to the advent of gasoline- and diesel-powered engines. Exhibits include: the largest collection of historic Chesapeake Bay craft; the 1879 "screwpile" Hooper Strait Lighthouse; a working boat shop; a working decoy gallery and steamboat exhibit.

Activities: Education classes (including wooden boat building), seminars and lectures on maritime history, research projects

Admission: Daily passes. Memberships (one with special docking privileges) available. Open daily, Hours vary by season.

• Spring: March 1 to May 30, 9 A.M. -5 P.M.
• Summer: June 1 to Sept. 30, 9 A.M. -6 P.M.
• Fall: 9 A.M. -5 P.M.
• Winter: 9 A.M. -4 P.M.
• Closed Thanksgiving, Christmas and New Year's days

SOLOMONS, MARYLAND

Calvert Marine Museum
14200 Solomons Island Road
P. O. Box 97
Solomons, MD 20688
(410) 326-2042 Fax: (410) 326-6691
E-mail: alvescd@co.cal.md.us
Location: Solomons is at the mouth of the Patuxent River (first river north of Potomac River) on the Chesapeake Bay. Take SR-4 south off Rte. 301 (east of Washington, D.C.) Calvert Marine Museum is located on State Route 2 in Solomons, Calvert County, Southern Maryland, and twenty miles south of Prince Frederick.
Highlights: Drum Point Lighthouse, Cove Point Lighthouse, *Wm. B. Tennison* (historic bugeye), small craft collection, art collection, J. C. Lore Oyster Processing Plant, *Bugeye Times* (newsletter), library (1,600 volumes on maritime history),
Website: www.calvertmarinemuseum.com
General Information: The Calvert Marine Museum was founded in 1969. It is ideally situated for interpreting the natural history of this tidewater region as it has evolved from prehistory through human utilization. The Museum relates its three areas of interest — paleontology, estuarine biology, and maritime history — to the public in an educational manner, maintaining a repository of specimens and artifacts pertinent to these themes and stimulating research in these areas for better understanding and more accurate documentation of the estuarine and cultural history of the region.

Two lighthouses dominate the Museum's waterfront: Drum Point Lighthouse and Cove Point Lighthouse. Constructed in 1883 at Drum Point to mark the entrance of the Patuxent River, this

screwpile, cottage-type light is one of only three remaining from forty-five which once served the Chesapeake Bay at the turn of the century. Cove Point Lighthouse (1828) is the oldest operating lighthouse in Maryland and is now under the administration of the Museum. Decommissioned in 1962, the lighthouse fell victim to vandals until moved in 1975 to its present site. Authentically restored, it has become the Museum's main attraction.

The marine museum is housed in a 30,000-square-foot exhibition building on the waterfront. Exhibits include: vessels constructed by an important local commercial boat-building enterprise; a fine art collection; a historic 1899 log oyster boat; and a 1600-volume library on maritime history. Also exhibited are artifacts excavated from a vessel of the Chesapeake Flotilla, which defended the Chesapeake during the War of 1812.

The J. C. Lore Oyster Processing Plant, a half-mile south, provides a look at commercial fishing in the region from the perspective of people engaged in the industry.

Activities: Guided tours, lectures, craft demonstrations, slide and film programs, field trips, educational programs, boat rides, and a special hands-on discovery room for young visitors.

Admission: Entry fee. Memberships available. Open daily from 10 A.M.-5 P.M. Closed Thanksgiving, Christmas, and New Year's Day. (Discovery Room hours vary.) Drum Point Lighthouse, open daily, 10 A.M.-5 P.M., May - September, (Winter hours are different). Cove Point Lighthouse, is open May-October weekends, holiday, other days to be determined. The J. C. Lore Oyster House, open daily, 1 P.M.-4:30 P.M., May-September.

MASSACHUSETTS

AMESBURY, MASSACHUSETTS

Lowell's Boat Shop
459 Main Street
Amesbury, MA 01913-4207
(978) 834-0050
E-mail: info@lowellsboatshop.com
Location: Amesbury is one mile west of I-95 on the north bank of the Merrimack River in the northeast corner of Massachusetts.
Highlights: Wooden boat (dory) history, boat building, rowing/sailing, **Website:** www.lowellsboatshop.com
General Information: Lowell's Boat Shop, a National Historic Landmark, is the oldest continuously operating manufacturer of wooden boats in the country—since 1793. The dory shop

is owned by the Newburyport Maritime Society, which also operates the Custom House Maritime Museum, Newburyport, Massachusetts. The Society operates Lowell's as a museum and working boat-building shop to preserve the knowledge and history of the traditional craft of building small wooden boats. The heart and soul of LBS is continuing to build new boats for customers and repairing boats that were built here.

Activities: Boatbuilding, repair, and restoration; classes for adults and youth (year round); row a handcrafted traditional wooden boat from the shop's boat livery (seasonal). Group tours by appointment.

Admission: No entry fee; fee for pre-scheduled group tours. Museum open Mem/Day – Labor Day, Tuesday-Sunday, 11 A.M. – 4 P.M. Labor Day/Mem. Day, please call for appointment.

BEVERLY, MASSACHUSETTS
Beverly Historical Society and Museum
117 Cabot Street
Beverly, MA 01915-5196
(978) 922-1186   Fax: 978-922-7387
E-mail: info@beverlyhistory.org
Location: Beverly (established in 1693) is on SR-1A, twenty-five miles northeast of Boston.
Highlights: Library (3,000 volumes)
Website: www.beverlyhistory.org
General Information: Beverly Historical Society and Museum, founded 1891, includes general maritime history through a 3,000-volume library that include extensive shipping papers andlog books. (Of historical note, George Washington, on September 5, 1775, at Glovers Wharf in Beverly, commissioned the schooner *Hannah*.)
Admission: Entry fee. Memberships are available. Open Tuesday, Thursday through Saturday 10:00 A.M. - 4:00 P.M. Wednesday 1:00 P.M. - 9:00 P.M.

BOSTON, MASSACHUSETTS
Boston Marine Society
National Historical Park – 1ST & 6TH Ave.
Building 32, Charlestown Navy Yard
Boston, MA 02129
(617) 242-0522 (617) 244-241-0505
E-mail: info@bostonmarinesociety.org
Location: In Boston, take I-93 to Rte. 1 north. Follow the signs to Charlestown Navy Yard across Charlestown Bridge — USS *Constitution* site.
Highlights: Oil Paintings, Ship models
Website: www.bostonmarinesociety.org/
General Information: Boston Marine Society, founded in 1742, maintains a collection of artifacts, oil paintings, and ship models at its site in the Charlestown Naval Shipyard.

Admission: No entry fee. Open Monday-Friday, 10 A.M.-3 P.M., year-round.

BOSTON, MASSACHUSETTS
Boston Tea Party Ship and Museum
Congress Street Bridge on Harborwalk
Boston, MA 02210
(617) 338-1773 E-mail:spford@historictours.com
Location: The museum is located at the Congress Street Bridge on Harbor Walk, south side of Boston's downtown area.
Highlights: *Beaver II* (brig), *Tea Times* (Newsletter), Gift shop
Website: www.bostonteapartyship.com/
General Information: On the night of December 16, 1773, a small band of Bostonians climbed aboard three vessels moored at Griffin's Wharf and destroyed 340-chests of dutied tea by dumping them into the harbor. (Rally Mohawks / Bring out your axes! / And tell King George / We'll pay no taxes!") This violent protest to Parliament's tax on tea — the Boston Tea Party — shattered a three-year period of relative calm between Great Britain and her colonies. It led, almost without interruption, to the outbreak of war at Lexington and Concord.

The Boston Tea Party Ship and Museum dramatically re-creates the notorious 1773 protest in the museum exhibits and aboard the full-scale working replica of one of the original tea party ships, the brig *Beaver II*. This 110-foot brigantine sailed across the Atlantic with a cargo of tea and is now moored at the Tea Party Site. (When your tour ends you will be in the Protest Room. "Take a stand" and voice or write your protest. Everyone does!)

Activities: Activities include viewing an audiovisual presentation on the ship's voyage and the taxing of the tea, tossing tea chests overboard and talking with colonial guides. Complimentary tea is served.

Admission: **REOPENING SUMMER 2012**

BOSTON, MASSACHUSETTS
Museum of Science
1 Science Park
Boston, MA 02114-1099
(617) 723-2500   E-mail: information@mos.org
Location: The Museum is located at the Charles River Dam, McGrath and Leverett Circle in Cambridge, adjacent to downtown Boston.
Highlights: Ship models,
Website: www.mos.org/
General Information: The Museum of Science offers several small exhibits to quench your nautical thirst. Visitors can view ship models on the basement level of blue wing in the Museum. There is also a replica of the E.B. McKay shipyard

where the famed *Flying Cloud* clipper ship was
built. It's located in the Museum's Big Dig
exhibit. Ship models, ranging from ancient
Egyptian sailing craft to modern power vessels,
will be found on the Museum's second floor.

Another exhibit that visitors can see is a model
of the yacht *Hi-Esmaro* located on the 3rd floor of
the Museum. The first floor contains a full-size
replica of a ship's bridge. Visitors can visualize
steering their vessel through dangerous waters.
And through the window you'll glimpse three
typical harbor buoys, once having done service at
sea. They are now floating in the Charles River
basin. A plaque describes their original uses.

Admission: Entry fee. The Museum is open
Saturday through Thursday, 9 A.M. – 5 P.M.;
Fridays, 9 A.M. – 9 P.M.

BOSTON, MASSACHUSETTS
The Old State House—The Bostonian Society
206 Washington Street
Boston, MA 02109-1713
(617) 720-1713
E-mail: ashley@bostonhistory.org
Location: The Old State House is in downtown
Boston on the Freedom Trail.
Highlights: Ship models, Marine paintings,
Maritime wood sculpture, Scrimshaw, Extensive
research library (6,000-volumes), Gift shop.
Website: www.bostonhistory.org/
General Information: The Old State House,
built in 1713, was the site of many events leading
to the American Revolution, such as James Otis'
speech protesting the Writs of Assistance, the
Stamp Act Debates, and the Boston Massacre.

From its balcony, the Declaration of
Independence was first read to Bostonians in 1776.
The building contains a museum maintained by The
Bostonian Society, which was founded in 1881 to
preserve the Old State House from demolition. The
museum's exhibits, including a fine collection of
maritime artifacts, illustrate the history of the city
of Boston. Among these are: seascapes, ship
portraits, and views of Boston Harbor; a life-size
female figurehead carved by Isaac Fowle;
navigational instruments; and scrimshaw.

The non-circulating library contains over 6,000
books, maps, documents, and broadsides related
to Boston history. A reading area is available for
researchers. The museum's gift shop sells
guidebooks, books on Boston history and marine
subjects, reproductions of American Colonial and
maritime objects and a wide variety of souvenirs.
Activities: Lectures, gallery talks, and guided
tours available by appointment
Admission: Entry fee. Open daily, 9 A.M.-5
P.M. Closed Thanksgiving, Christmas, New Year's
Day. Library open Wednesday-Friday, 9:30 A.M.-

4:30 P.M., Saturday, 10 A.M. – 3 P.M. with
admission free for non-members.

BUZZARDS BAY, MASSACHUSETTS
Capt. Charles H. Hurley Library
101 Academy Drive
Buzzards Bay, MA 02532
(508) 830-5000 E-mail: sberteaux@maritime.edu
Location: At beginning of Cape Cod, Buzzards
Bay is sixty miles southeast of Boston off I-495.
Exit onto Rte. 6, heading east four miles. The Capt.
Charles H. Hurley Library is located on the campus
of The Massachusetts Maritime Academy.
Highlights: Scale models, library (52,000 volumes
on transportation and engineering),
Website: http://library.maritime.edu/
General Information: Capt. Charles H. Hurley
Library, founded 1980, has collections, archives,
and ninety-five scale models set in a base
representing the sea and panoramic background.
The Library features books primarily on maritime
transportation and engineering. They are available
for in-house or inter-library loan. Reading rooms
are likewise available.
Activities: Guided tours, lectures, education
programs, and library.
Admission: No entry fee. Open daily: Monday-
Thursday, 7 A.M.-11 P.M., Friday, 7 A.M.-5 P.M.;
Saturday, 12 Noon-6 P.M.; Sunday, 3:30 P.M.-
11 P.M.

CAMBRIDGE, MASSACHUSETTS
Hart Nautical Collections
M.I.T. Museum, Hart Nautical Gallery
265 Massachusetts Avenue
Cambridge, MA 02139
(617) 253-5927 Fax: (617) 258-8994
E-mail: kurt@mit.edu
Location: Across the Charles River from Boston in
Cambridge, these collections are reached by
entering the lobby at 77 Massachusetts Avenue,
then turning right down the hall heading in the
direction of the Charles River.
Highlights: Ship models, major collections of
working drawings,
Website: http://web.mit.edu/museum/collections/
nautical.html
General Information: The Francis Russell Hart
Nautical Museum (now the Hart Nautical
Collections) was founded in 1921 as a part of the
Department of Naval Architecture and Marine
Engineering at MIT. In 1940 the collection was
officially named in honor of Francis R. Hart,
former President of the United Fruit Company and
Class of 1889, who had worked with the Museum
from its founding until his death in 1938.

In 1982, the Hart Nautical Collections joined
with the Massachusetts Institute of Technology in
Cambridge (MIT). The MIT Museum continues the

original commitment of the Hart Nautical Museum by preserving and interpreting the history of one of the oldest engineering fields; namely, marine engineering, ship design and construction. Exhibits include exquisitely crafted model ships built to scale, descriptively labeled so you can wander about on your own. Models range from simple a tiny, plain Norwegian pram to a complex four-foot reproduction of the US frigate *President*, fully rigged, complete with coiled lines, lifeboats, and brass fittings.

For exotica, a Korean warship *Turtle* has a spiked cover to shelter its gunners and crew. The sixteenth-century real ship spouted sulfuric fumes from the *Turtle's* mouth to frighten its superstitious foe and to provide a smoke screen.

Major Collections:
• Captain Arthur H. Clark Collections — paintings, photographs, prints, plans of vessels, half-models, books
• Allan Forbes Collection — paintings/prints on whales.
• C. H. W. Foster Collection—yachting photographs (1885-1930)
• Haffenreffer-Herreshoff Collection —working drawings
• McInnis-Lawley Collection—working drawings
• Gordon Munro Collection—working drawings and models (1915-1940)
• George Owen Collection—working drawings/models (1902-1958)
• Frank C. Paine Collection—working drawings, models, photographs (1923-39)
• Bethlehem Steel Collection—working drawings and photographs (1851-1940)
Admission: No entry fee. 0900-1900 daily except holidays. Research by appointment only at 265 Massachusetts Avenue.

CHARLESTOWN, MASSACHUSETTS
Charlestown Navy Yard
Attn.: Superintendent
Boston National Historic Park
Charlestown Navy Yard
Boston, MA 02129-4543
(617) 242-5601 Fax: 617-241-0884
E-mail on Web site
Location: FROM POINTS SOUTH; Interstate 93 North:- I-93 North to exit 28 (Sullivan Square). Turn RIGHT at the end of the ramp (Cambridge St.) to the first traffic light. Enter traffic circle and take first right onto Rutherford Ave. Move left and at City Square, just before bridge, turn left onto Chelsea St. Follow directions for All (below)
FROM POINTS NORTH Massachusetts Turnpike: - Take Massachusetts Turnpike to its end in downtown Boston. - Get on I-93 North and

follow directions above. Downtown Boston: Take North Washington St. to Charlestown Bridge.- Turn RIGHT at traffic light on Charlestown side of the bridge, onto Chelsea St. Follow directions FOR ALL: At first traffic light, turn right onto Warren Street, then take first left onto Constitution Road. Visitor Center/Bunker Hill Pavilion is on Constitution Road on your right. **Website**:www.nps.gov/bost/Charlestown_Navy_ Yard.htm
General Information: The "Yard" has one of the oldest dry-docks in the country and a historic ropewalk which exists side-by-side with forge shops, a marine railway, officers' quarters, and the Commandant's quarters. "Old Ironsides," the oldest fully commissioned warship in the world (launched in 1798), was the first ship to use the dry-dock.
Activities: Self-guided and guided tours
Admission: No entry fee. Open daily, 9 A.M.-5 P.M., year-round. Public docking is available at Pier 4 and nearby marinas.

CHARLESTOWN, MASSACHUSETTS
USS *Cassin Young (DD-793)*
Charlestown Navy Yard
Charlestown, MA 02129-2308
(617) 426-1812 Fax: (617) 242-0496
E-mail: constitution.faq@navy.mil
Location: Across the wharf from the USS *Constitution* Museum and the USS *Constitution,* the USS *Cassin Young* is docked at the Charlestown Navy Yard National Park. Follow signs along I-93 to Rte. 1, and then turn immediately off onto Constitution Road to the yard, just north of downtown Boston.
Highlights: The USS *Cassin Young*
Web site: www.hnsa.org/ships/young.htm
General Information: The USS *Cassin Young*, commissioned on December 31, 1943 at San Pedro, CA. In October 1944, she participated in the Battle for Leyte Gulf where she rescued over 120 men from the carrier *Princeton* when the ship sank on October 24 and participated in the Battle of Cape Engano the next day when four Japanese carriers were sunk by the American carriers that Cassin Young was helping to escort.

In the 1950s, the *Cassin Young* was recommissioned on September 7, 1951 and initially served in Atlantic and Mediterranean waters.

Today, the ship has a new mission. Maintained and staffed by the National Park Service and volunteers, *Cassin Young* is an example of the type of ship built, repaired, and modernized in the Charlestown Navy Yard. She provides a contrast to USS Constitution and is a memorial to destroyer men and the ships they served on. She has been

open to the public since 1981 and is basically restored to her late 1950s appearance.
Admission: No charge. Open Tuesday through Sunday, 10 A.M. to 3: 50 P.M.

CHARLESTOWN, MASSACHUSETTS
USS *Constitution*
Charlestown Navy Yard Pier 1– Thompson Sqr.
Charlestown, MA 02129-2308
(617) 426-1812 Fax: (617) 242-0496
E-mail: constitution.admin@navy.mil
Location: Across the wharf from the USS *Constitution* Museum, the USS *Constitution* is docked at the Charlestown Navy Yard National Park. Follow signs along I-93 to Rte. 1, then turn immediately off onto Constitution Road to the yard, just north of downtown Boston.
Highlights: The USS *Constitution* ("Old Ironsides"),
Website: www.ussconstitution.navy.mil/index.htm
General Information: The USS *Constitution*, launched in 1797, is the oldest commissioned warship afloat in the world. The *Constitution* is one of six ships ordered by President George Washington for construction to protect America's growing maritime interests in the 1790s.

Constitution soon earned widespread renown for her ability to punish French privateers in the Caribbean and thwart Barbary pirates in the Mediterranean. The ship's greatest glory came during the War of 1812 when she defeated four British frigates. During the battle against HMS *Guerriere* in 1812, seamen watched British cannon balls glance off her twenty-one-inch-thick oak hull, and gave her the famous nickname, "Old Ironsides."

In the 1830s, the ship was slated to be broken up, but a public outcry, sparked by a poem by Oliver Wendell Holmes, saved her. Over the following century, the ship undertook many military assignments, including circumnavigating the world and acting as both a barracks and training ship. She was restored in 1927 with contributions from the nation's school children.

After a final tour during which she was towed coast-to-coast, in 1934 she was moored in her homeport, the Charlestown Navy Yard. She was again completely restored in 1997 and sailed unassisted for the first time in over 100 years—a remarkable vessel and still fully commissioned in the United States Navy.

As a salute to the nation, every Fourth of July and several other times a year, she is maneuvered into Boston Harbor for an underway sail demonstration. On Independence Day, a twenty-one-gun salute in honor of the Nation's Birthday is presented. Although she has been repaired several times, her basic lines have not been altered nor the ship's symbolic value reduced, and she accurately depicts a U.S. navy ship of the War of 1812, the period of greatest renown for *Constitution*. Nearby, the *Constitution* Museum and the World War II destroyer *Cassin Young*, (operated by the National Park Service), are also open to the public.
USS *Constitution*:
Rig: three masted, forty-four-gun frigates.
Specifications: Sparred length: 308',
Length overall: 204', beam: 43'6", draft: 22'6", rig height: 185'
Armament:
Thirty-two: 24-pounder long guns
    (crew, 9-14 men)
Twenty: 32-pounder Carronades
    (crew, 4-9 men)
Two: 24-pounder Bow Chasers
Crew: 450 Sailors, 44 Marines, and 30 Boys
Activities: The *Constitution* is open year-round, rain or shine, for free public tours guided by U.S. Sailors in historic 1813 uniforms. The visitor center staff will direct you to the self-guided tours.
Admission: No charge. Open Tuesday through Sunday, 10 A.M. to 3: 50 P.M.

CHARLESTOWN, MASSACHUSETTS
USS *Constitution* **Museum**
Boston National Historical Park
Charlestown Navy Yard – Building 22
P. O. Box 1812
Boston, MA 02129
(617) 426-1812 Fax: (617) 242-0496
E-mail: giftshop@ussconstitutionmuseum.org
Location: Across the wharf from the USS *Constitution* at the Charlestown Navy Yard in Boston is the USS *Constitution* Museum.
Highlights: Computer and hands-on exhibits, video presentation, *Constitution Chronicle* (newsletter), research library, ship models,
Website: www.ussconstitutionmuseum.org/
General Information: USS *Constitution* Museum, founded in 1972, houses objects related to life aboard ship, objects removed during restorations of *Constitution*, examples of sailors' arts, historic memorabilia, and decorative arts related to *Constitution* and the early sailing Navy. Hands-on exhibits examine the construction of "Old Ironsides," her history and preservation, and the lives of her sailors. Replicas of such components as her keel, yardarms, and sickbay evoke a sense of the complexity of the Ship's design.

Visitors of all ages can fire a cannon, swing in the hammocks, and build a ship model. Two videos include a 10-minute one, which will take you on a tour of the Ship, which will allow the visitor to see parts of the ship, not open to the public. The second video "All Hands on Deck," is a 19-minute video that is part of the Museum's award-winning curriculum. The video follows a 14-year old girl on the day the Ship sailed in 1997 and she meets heroes and heroines from *Constitution's* past.

Visitors can step into the shoes of Captain, Lieutenant, Able-bodied Seaman, Marine, or nine-year-old "Powder Monkey" by playing at the computer exhibit. See what kind of judgment decisions you would make "The Great Chase" when *Constitution* escaped from five British frigates during the first encounter with the British in the War of 1812.

The entry ramp from the original Museum building to the new wing gives the appearance of shops lining a street in Boston in the 1790s. Looking into the shop windows, the visitor learns about the craftsmen like Benjamin Seward, who supplied small arms of the *Constitution*, Paul Revere who supplied the copper sheathing, and William Bradford, the tailor, who made the crew's uniforms. The second-floor expansion continues the story of her most recent refit (1996).

The newly expanded Samuel Eliot Morison research library, access to which is available by appointment only, contains research materials related to naval and maritime history, originals and microfilm copies of ship logs, personal journals and letters, and plans of the *Constitution*.

Activities: Special programs for school groups by reservation, audiovisual programs, gun drills and performances by the Volunteer Marine Corps Detachment of 1797, and maritime artisan workshops and demonstrations are scheduled periodically.

Admission: No entry fee. Memberships are available. Open daily 9 A.M.- 6 P.M. May-October; 10 A.M.-5 P.M. November-April; Closed Thanksgiving, Christmas, and New Year's Day. The Museum is wheelchair accessible.

COHASSET, MASSACHUSETTS
Cohasset Maritime Museum
Cohasset Historical Society
301 Driftway   P.O. Box 627
Cohasset, MA 02066-1904
(781) 545-5565
E-mail: cohassethistory@yahoo.com
Location: Cohasset is a suburb of Boston, fifteen-miles to the south and east. Head south on Rte. 3 to Rte 228 toward Hingham. Turn south on Rte. 3A and turn left on Sohier Street to Cohasset center where the museum is located midtown in the village. On street parking.
Highlights: Ship models, 1760 ship chandlery
Website: www.cohassethistoricalsociety.org

General Information: Cohasset Maritime Museum was established in 1957 by the Cohasset Historical Society, which also maintains two other historical buildings. Its collections relate to the town's seafaring history: shipwreck relics; lifesaving equipment; nineteenth-century maritime artifacts; sailing ship models; paintings; early tools; Indian stone artifacts; and general historical artifact collections of local origin. (Cohasset was settled around 1670, as the east part of Hingham. Captain John Smith visited here briefly in 1614 to trade with Quonshasset Indians.)
Activities: Guided tours and summer walking tours of Cohasset
Admission: No entry fee. Memberships are available. Open Tuesday-Sunday 1:30 P.M.-4 P.M., mid June-late September.

EASTHAM, MASSACHUSETTS
Salt Pond Visitor Center
National Park Service Visitor Center
50 Doane Road
Eastham, MA 02642
(508) 255--3421
Location: Eastham, on Cape Cod, is 40 miles from Borne Bridges to the Visitor Center.
Highlights: Local maritime historical displays,
Website:
www.nps.gov/caco/places/saltpondvc.html
General Information: The National Park Service has developed a fine exhibition space in the Visitor Center, where the curator has collected maritime artifacts along with an excellent collection of local flora and fauna, stuffed birds, and other important items, leading the visitor through the past where our forefathers first landed to establish settlements on the coast of Massachusetts.

When visiting here be sure to see the excellent video presentation on the environmental development of Cape Cod. The Cape is a glacial deposit that is constantly undergoing natural changes as winds and water move sand along the shorelines, tearing away one place and building up another.
Admission: No entry fee. Open year-round, daily 9 A.M.-4:30 P.M., Columbus Day-Memorial Day. **NOTE:** Under restoration – call for hours.

EDGARTOWN, MASSACHUSETTS
Martha's Vineyard Historical Society and Museum
59 School Street P.O. Box 1310
Edgartown, MA 02539
(508) 627-4441 x-122 Fax: 508-627-4436
E-mail: dnathans@mvmuseum.org
Location: Edgartown, on Martha's Vineyard, is six miles form the ferry dock in Vineyard Haven or Oak Bluffs. Corner of Cooke & School St. 59 School St. (Pease House)

Highlights: Lighthouse Fresnel lens, whaleboat, Norman's Land double-ender, whaling information, research library (Francis Foster Museum)

Website: www.marthasvineyardhistory.org

General Information: The Society was founded to preserve the history of Martha's Vineyard and the Elizabeth Islands through Museum's libraries, publications, and educational programs. The main maritime informational collection is housed at the Francis Foster Museum, which includes a research library containing many whaling logs, coastal vessel records, and customs records.

Admission: Entry fee. Open summer, Tuesday-Saturday, 10 A.M. – 4:30 P.M.; rest of the year, Wednesday-Friday 1 P.M. – 4 P.M., Saturday 10 A.M. – 4 P.M.

ESSEX, MASSACHUSETTS
Essex Shipbuilding Museum
66 Main Street
P.O. Box 277
Essex, MA 01929-1343
(978) 768-7541 Fax: (978) 768-2541
E-mail:
maineoffice@@essexshipbuildingmuseum.org

Location: Travel I-95 north from Boston to Rte. 128 north to Gloucester. Take Exit 15 (School Street, Essex-Manchester) and go 3.2 miles to Essex. At a "T" Intersection with Rte. 133, turn left, north toward Ipswich. Look for the Museum and shipyard on the right on Rte. 133. 66 Main Street is Museum entrance and Gift Shop; one and one-half blocks north are the exhibits at 28 Main.

Highlights: Hands-on exhibits of building tools, fully rigged ship models and half-models, photographs and videotape of the *Ste. Rosalie's* (dragger 1947), construction, and schooner *Evelina M. Goulart*, Waterline Center,

Website: www.essexshipbuildingmuseum.org

General Information: Essex Shipbuilding Museum, founded in 1976, honors the shipbuilders of Essex who built more two-masted vessels than anywhere else in the Western World — over 4,000 two-masted schooners. Museum exhibits at the 1835 schoolhouse, at 28 Main Street, portray the evolution of the American fishing schooner from the Chebacco boat to Schooner *Gertrude L. Thebaud.*

Many shipbuilders are buried in the Ancient Burying Ground adjacent to the schoolhouse. The shipyard site on the scenic Essex River is now the site of small craft activity, including sea kayaking and boat building, as well as the Waterline Center of the Museum where education programs are often in progress.

The Museum maintains an excellent archive of ships' plans, photographs, and original documents of the shipbuilding industry of interest to model builders, historians, and writers. The Museum welcomes those involved in research, restoration, and relaxation.

Admission: Entry fee. Open Summer Hours: Wednesday through Sunday, 12:00 thru 4 P.M.

FALL RIVER, MASSACHUSETTS
Battleship Cove
5 Water Street
PO Box 111
Fall River, MA 02721-1540
(508) 678-1100 Fax: (508) 674-5597
(800) 533-3194 (New England only)
E-mail: battleship@battleshipcove.org

Location: Battleship Cove is located off Route I-95 (Exit 5) and Route 24 (Exit 7). Follow the signs to Battleship Cove.

Highlights: Five National Historic Landmarks including: North Dakota Class battleship USS *Massachusetts*, (BB-59), Gearing Class destroyer USS *Joseph P. Kennedy, Jr.* (DD-850), Balao Class submarine USS *Lionfish* SS-298), and PT Boats 796 & 617. In addition, Russian Missile Corvette *Hiddensee*. The world's largest PT Boat Museum and Library, and the Admiral Arleigh A. Burke National Destroyer men's Museum.

Website: www.battleshipcove.org

General Information: Battleship Cove is home to the world's largest fleet of Historic Naval Ships. Battleship Cove is a popular destination for Overnight Camping and school group visits. Offering a wide range of special programs including reunions, memorial services, banquets. birthday parties, facilities for business meetings, and a sailing program.

Five of the vessels are National Historic Landmarks open to visitors to educate the public and promote duty, honor and country. For the kid in everyone, there is a restored Carousel housed in a modern, Victorian-style pavilion is open seasonally. Gift shop. Snack Bar. Free Parking

Activities: Overnight Camping Program and Educational Programs.

Admission: Entry fee. Group rates are offered with reservation, contact for more information. Memberships are available. Ships and Museum open at 9 A,M. everyday except Thanksgiving, Christmas and New Year's Day.

FALL RIVER, MASSACHUSETTS
Marine Museum at Fall River
70 Water Streets
Fall River, MA 02721-1598
(508) 674-3533 E-mail: museumfr@aol.com
Location: The museum is housed in an old mill
structure on the waterfront in Battleship Cove just
a short walk from the battleship USS
Massachusetts (BB 59), the Heritage State Park,
the sail training vessel HMS *Bounty*, and a
restored vintage carousel; at the junction of I-195
and Rte 138.
Highlights: The *Titanic* exhibit, Ship models, *Fall
River Line Journal* (quarterly newsletter), Library
and archives (2,000 volumes), Gift shop
    General Information: The Marine Museum at
Fall River, Inc., was founded in 1968 as a
repository for the memorabilia of the Fall River
Steamship Company's famous Fall River Line
(1847-1937), which used Fall River as the New
England terminus for its New York to New
England run. The Line is a particular concern of
the museum in the broader context of the
development of steam navigation and coastal blue
water shipping. Other special interests include
marine archaeology and underwater exploration;
the local history of Narragansett Bay and its ports,
tributaries and adjacent waters; and the maritime
background of the various ethnic groups in the
community.
    A centerpiece of the Museum is a one-ton
twenty-eight-foot-long model of the RMS *Titanic*,
created in exact detail by 20th Century Fox Studios
for the 1953 movie of the same name starring
Barbara Stanwyck, Clifton Webb, and Robert
Wagner. Original *Titanic* newspapers and
photographs compliment the exhibit.
    A growing collection of china and silver and
other artifacts recovered from the wreck of the
Andrea Doria form a new special exhibit, with
accurate scale models of both the *Andrea Doria*
and the *Stockholm*, the ship that she collided with.
The gift shop features books and prints on the
Titanic and the old Fall River Line paddle wheel
steamers.
    The gift shop features books and prints on the
Titanic and the old Fall River Line paddle wheel
steamers. The library and archives feature:
•The William King Covel Collection, the museum's
first major acquisition, was purchased from this
Newport, Rhode Island native in the mid 1960s. It
consists of photographic prints, negatives, glass
slides and paintings, relating primarily to the Fall
River Steamship Co.'s great "white palaces" that
sail Long Island sound carrying passengers, raw
cotton bales, and finished cotton;
•The John A Breynaert Collection of 1000+
volumes, accumulated by the late Mr. Breynaert,
and executive of General Dynamics Fore River
Shipyard of Quincy, Massachusetts;
•The United Fruit Company Collection comprises
ship models, logs, journals, books and photographs

relating to the company's steamships operating
between New England and it's Caribbean banana
plantation holdings;
•Other ship models form Seamen's Church Institute
of New York and Philadelphia; German prisoner-
of-war models *von Tirpitz* and *Admiral Hipper*.
    Activities: Museum facilities are available for
meetings, lectures; the library contains books on
maritime history that are available on premises.
    Admission: Entry fee.
Monday through Friday 9:00 AM to 5:00 PM
Saturday 12:00 Noon to 5:00 PM
Sunday 12:00 Noon to 4:00 PM

FALL RIVER, MASSACHUSETTS
The PT Boat Museum and Library
Battleship Cove
5 Water Street, P.O. Box 111
Fall River, MA 02722-0111
(508) 678-1100 Fax: (508) 674-5597
E-mail: battleship@battleshipcove.org
(For Photo and Archives, Contact:
PT Boats, Inc.
1384 Cordova Road, Suite 2
Germantown, TN 38138)
Location: The Museum and Library are located at
Battleship Cove in Fall River, off I-195, at exit 5.
Highlights: World War II PT boats 617 (The only
80-foot Elco Boat on display in the world) and 796,
PT Memorial and a 200 volume library, Newsletter:
The PT Boater,
Website: www.battleshipcove.org/pt109.htm
    General Information: The collections at the PT
Boat Museum include books, diaries, insignia,
memorabilia of forty-three operating squadrons of
World War II P.T. boats, tenders, and bases, films,
photographs, and plans. Also on display is a one-
man Japanese suicide demolition boat. See also the
listing in Germantown, Tennessee for PT Boats,
Inc. Headquarters.
    Admission: Entry fee. Memberships are
available. Open daily, 9 A.M.- 5 P.M., year-round.

FALMOUTH, MASSACHUSETTS
Falmouth Historical Society Museums
Falmouth Historical Society
55-65 Palmer Avenue, P.O. Box 174
Falmouth, MA 02541
(508) 548-4857 E-mail: fhs@cape.com
Location: From Boston travel south on I-495. Turn
onto SR-25 east for five miles to the junction of
SR-28. Falmouth is seventeen miles south on
SR-28; the Museums are on the north side of
Village Green at Falmouth Center.
Highlights: Whaling era memorabilia,
Website: www.falmouthhistoricalsociety.org/
    General Information: Falmouth was settled in
1661 and was a center for whaling and
shipbuilding. In the former home of a sea captain,
the Falmouth Historical Society's Museums
(founded in 1900) maintain a small maritime
collection with memorabilia from the whaling era.

Activities: Summer guided tours of a 1790 home (the Julia Wood House), a "museum" building, and a barn with farm equipment.
Admission: Entry fee. Open: Summer hours, Tuesday - Saturday - 10 A.M. – 4 P.M.; Fall Museum Hours, Satu.y & Sun.- 1 P.M. - 4 P.M.

GLOUCESTER, MASSACHUSETTS
Cape Ann Historical Museum
27 Pleasant Street
Gloucester, MA 01930
(987) 283-0455 Fax: (987) 283-4141 E-mail: rondafaloon@capeannhistoricalmuseum.org
Location: The museum is located in the heart of downtown Gloucester, one block north from Main Street and one short block east of City Hall and the Sawyer Free Library. **Web site:** www.capeannhistoricalmuseum.org/
Highlights: Permanent exhibition which explores Cape Ann's fisheries and maritime history; Vessels: Howard Blackburn's *Great Republic* and Alfred Johnson's *Centennial*, Nation's largest collection of paintings and drawings by marine artist Fitz Hugh Lane (1804-1865), Gloucester Fishermen's Museum collections, Library/ archives/photograph collections, Museum shop, 1890 Fresnel bulls-eye lens,
Website: www.capeannhistoricalmuseum.org/
General Information: The Cape Ann Historical Museum, founded in 1875, celebrates the area's proud fishing and maritime heritage with permanent exhibitions of artifacts and photographs from the continent's most productive nineteenth-century fishing port. Exhibits feature displays of fine arts, American decorative arts and furnishings, and guided tours of the furnished home of Captain Elias Davis built in 1804 for one of Gloucester's enterprising merchant sea captains. In July 1993, the Gloucester Fisherman's Museum entire collection was transferred to the Cape Ann Historical Museum.

The museum exhibits the nation's largest collection of paintings and drawings by Fitz Hugh Lane (1804-1865). A native of Gloucester, Lane is now recognized as one of America's most important nineteenth-century artists.

The museum's Gloucester 1892 room displays a large model of the Gloucester waterfront with a variety of fishing related trades and businesses. Here you will find a fully equipped Grand Banks dory, sail makers bench and tools, schooner half hulls and other exhibits with the fisheries focus.
Activities: Special exhibitions of American artists of the first rank who have worked on Cape Ann, including Marsden Hartley, Frank Duveneck, Walter Hancock, and Milton Avery, and Fitz Hugh Lane.

The Cape Ann accepted the Gloucester Fishermen's Museum collections Historical Museum and have become a permanent part of that museum's collections.

Admission: Entry fee. Open Tuesday-Saturday, 10 A.M.-5 P.M., Sunday 1 P.M. – 4 P.M. year-round except February. Memberships are available. Group tours arranged by reservation: (508) 283-0455.

GLOUCESTER, MASSACHUSETTS
The Gloucester *Adventure*
4 Harbor Loop
Gloucester, MA 01930-1306
(978) 281-0470 Fax: (978) 281-2393
E-mail: info@schooner-adventure.org
Location: Located at Harbor Loop off Rogers Street next to the Coast Guard Station. *Highlights:* *Adventure* (sailing fishing schooner), Ship's Store, **Website:** www.schooner-adventure.org
General Information: The society was established in 1988 to preserve the historic Gloucester fishing schooner 121.5-foot *Adventure*. Built in 1926, she is the last American Grand Banks fishing schooner to fish and one of a handful still sailing. She is listed on the National Register of Historic Places and has a permanent place in our national maritime heritage. The Adventure is currently undergoing restoration, and is not sailing but is open to the public for tours and events.

Bowsprintless, the "knockabout," 121-foot *Adventure* was built in nearby Essex. In twenty-seven years of fishing, she consistently brought in great quantities of codfish and haddock (capacity of 160,000 pounds). Later in her career she carried passengers on pleasure cruises along the Maine Coast. Now she is a monument to Gloucester's history, and used for education and the pleasure of the public.
Admission: Donations accepted. Open year round, Thursday-Sunday, and Saturdays in the winter.

GLOUCESTER, MASSACHUSETTS
Gloucester Maritime Heritage Center
23 Harbor Loop
Gloucester, MA 01930
(978) 281-0470 Fax: (978) 281-0327
e-mail: hwebster@gloucestermaritimecenter.org
Location: The Center can be easily reached by Rtes. 127, 128, or 133. If on 128, exit at the Grant Circle Rotary, or at the end of Rte. 128 (Eastern Ave. lights), and head to Harbor Loop and the Center.
Highlights: Burnham Brothers (marine) Railway, Schooner *Adventure*, Visitor Center & Gift Shop.
Web site: www.gloucestermaritimecenter.org
General Information: The Gloucester Maritime Heritage Center features the oldest continuously operating marine railway in the country. The Burnham Brothers Railway, the first rail was built in 1849 by brothers Parker, Joseph, and Elias Burnham, who recognized the nee4d for a facility

that could haul boats out of the water for repairs. A second rail was added in 1856. Originally powered by steam engine, the single rail still in operation today now runs on electricity.

The Center's mission is to "champion the preservation of Gloucester's maritime industrial history and tradition" and "to serve as a resource for the study of maritime history, industry, and ecology."

Activities: Guided tours, Youth Rowing, Community Rowing Days, Marine Science Internships, Gloucester Gig Rows, After-School Programs, School & Camp Field Trips, and Boatbuilding & Seamanship Courses.

Admission: Guided tours or self-guided site visits are free but donations gladly accepted. Entry fee for Sea Pocket Lab. Open: Mem/Day – Lab/Day, daily 10 A.M. – 5 p.m. Off season: Weekends 10 A.M. – 5:30 P.M.

HULL, MASSACHUSETTS
Hull Life-Saving Museum
1117 Nantasket Avenue
P. O. Box 221
Hull, MA 02045-1310
(781) 925-5433 Fax: (781) 925-0992
E-mail: lifesavingmuseum@comcast.net
Location: By land, take Rte 3A to Nantasket Beach, or Rte. 3 to Rte. 228 to Nantasket Beach. Follow signs to Museum once in Hull. By sea, take Nantasket Ferry from Boston's Long Wharf. When boarding, request stop at Pemberton Pier.
Highlights: Lifeboat and lifesaving cart and equipment
Website: www.lifesavingmuseum.org
General Information: The Hull Lifesaving Museum, the museum of Boston Harbor heritage, is situated dramatically at the mouth of Boston Harbor, with breathtaking views of Boston Light. The restored Point Allerton Lifesaving Station (c. 1889) was the home of Joshua James and his crew, the most celebrated lifesavers of their day.

The Orientation Room traces the history of organized lifesaving from its roots in the 18th century through today's modern Coast Guard. In other galleries, visitors learn about lighthouses, storms, shipwrecks, and the rescues. In the Navigation Loft, a special play attic is set up for children, with dress-ups, games, and a climb-on, rigged boat; stairs lead to the Observation Cupola, where you can scan stunning views of Boston Harbor and Islands, like surfmen of old.

From the door of the Museum, you can see for miles out to sea, and photograph Boston Light, the oldest lighthouse in the nation. Nearby, you can look out from Fort Revere's Observation Tower on Telegraph Hill to recognize why this site was chosen to scan Boston Harbor. Walk through Hull

village to see the buildings Joshua James grew up among, well marked to tell their role during his life.
Activities: Lecture series, boat-building workshops, school-vacation programs, art shows, group tours; the museum's award-winning open-water rowing program operates year-round in Boston Harbor from a fleet of 14 big, traditional — most built by the rowers themselves. Youth and adult programs conducted to boathouses in Hull downtown Boston's Seaport District.
Admission: Entry fee. Open year round: September - June: 10 A.M. to 4 P.M., Wed. to Sun., school vacations, and by appointment. June - August: Open Wednesday-Sunday 10 A.M. to 4 P.M.

HYANNIS, MASSACHUSETTS
Cape Cod Maritime Museum
135 South Street, P.O. Box 443
Hyannis, MA, 02601-4014
(508) 775-1723 Fax: (508) 775.1706
E-mail: maritime@capecodmaritimemuseum.org
Location: The Museum is located on the Hyannis waterfront harbor in the heart of Hyannis, within walking distance of Main Street and island ferries
Highlights: 1930s Surfboat, Gift Shop
General Information: Cape Code Maritime Museum opened the doors November 5, 2005 to it's newest gallery exhibit "For Those in Peril On the Sea." Tis exciting interactive show, designed and installed by Director/Curator Mark Wilkiins, explores local shipwrecks and traces the development of lighthouses on Cape Cod.

Tales of tragedy, heroism and inspiration are depicted in displays tat include: artifacts from the lost vessels Sparrow-Hawk, Jason and Portland; items from the US Lifesaving Service; video re-enactments of beach rescue drills; and reproductions of paintings by Edward hopper, Winslow Homer and other great American artists. A fully restored 1930s Surfboat forms the centerpiece of this exhibit.
Activities: video re-enactments of beach rescue dirlls; A specially designated Children's Corner has plenty of hands-on activities including an art station, quizzes, scavenger hunts and Mystery Objects.
Admission: Entry fee: Open Tues-Saturday 10 a.m. to 4 p.m. Sunday 12 Noon – 4 p.m.

MARBLEHEAD, MASSACHUSETTS
Jeremiah Lee Mansion (1768)
(Marblehead Historical Society)
170 Washington Street
Marblehead, MA 01945
(781) 631-1768
E-mail: info@mrbleheadmuseum.org
Location: From Boston north on I-95 to 128 North.
Exit 25A, Rte. 114 East-10 miles to Marblehead.
Highlights: Home of Col. Lee with abundant
artifacts. **Web Site:**
www.marbleheadmuseum.org/LeeMansion.htm
    General Information: Opulent home of Colonel
Jeremiah Lee, a wealthy merchant and ship-owner
who supported the Revolution in risky undercover
capacities. In the home you will find Ceramics and
other artifacts from maritime trade (18th and 19th
century), fishing history. Architecture (18th
century), furnishings, (18th and early 19th century),
rare original hand-painted English wallpaper, rich
mahogany woodwork, caved rococo interiors. Also
be seen are Portraits of sea captains, ships, and
foreign ports.
    Admission: Entry fee. Mansion open Tuesday-
Saturday, 10 A.M. - 4 P.M., Sunday, 1 P.M.-4
P.M., June through October.

MARBLEHEAD, MASSACHUSETTS
Marblehead Museum and Historical Society
170 Washington Street
Marblehead, MA 01945-3340
(781) 631-1768(Adm. offices) (781) 631-1069
E-mail: info@marbleheadmuseum.org
Location: From Boston north on I-95 to 128 North.
Exit 25A, Rte. 114 East-10 miles to Marblehead.
Highlights: Maritime folk art paintings and
models (19th and 20th century), maritime trade
(18th and 19th century), fishing history, Gift &
Book Shop,
Website: www.marbleheadmuseum.org
    General Information: The Marblehead
Society's collections include ships' logs, marine
artifacts, sextants, paintings, and early fishing
equipment. Permanent and annual changing
exhibits. Gift and Book Shop, including prints of
maritime folk art paintings and framed
reproductions of watercolor illustrations from an
18th century diary (Ashley Bowen) for sale.
    Admission: No entry fee but donations
welcome. Galleries open Tuesday-Saturday,
10 A.M. - 4 P.M., Sunday, 1 P.M. - 4 P.M year
round. Museum rooms in Lee Mansion open June
1-October 15. Office and archives open Tuesday-
Friday, 10 A.M. - 4 P.M. Appointments
appreciated.

MARION, MASSACHUSETTS
Mary Celeste **Museum**
c/o Sippican Historical Society
Front and Main Streets
Marion, MA 02738
Location: Center of Marion

Highlights: *Mary Celeste* history,
Website: www.fortogden.com/maryceleste.html
    General Information: The Sippican Historical
Society maintains the *Mary Celeste* Museum in
honor of the memory of Captain Benjamin Briggs,
skipper of the famous ship *Mary Celeste* of 1872.
He was a native of Marion where the museum
contains many items of interest concerning the
mysterious vessel.
    The Atlantic Financial Insurance Company of
Madison, New Jersey paid the original insurance
claim on the lose of the *Mary Celeste* and maintains
the records in their offices.
    Admission: No entry fee. Open Saturdays
during June, July, and August.

MEDFORD, MASSACHUSETTS
Medford Historical Society Museum
10 Governors Avenue
Medford, MA 02155-4513
(781) 391-8739
Medford, MA 02155
Location: The Museum is on Governors Avenue
just off High Street. Take Exit 32; (Medford Exit)
off Rte. 93, then Rte. 60 to Governors Avenue.
The Museum is on the left.
Highlights: Ship models, Civil War prints, Peter
Tufts house. **Web site:**
www.medfordhistorical.org/remembrance.php
    General Information: The Medford Historical
Society Museum houses a wide variety of artifacts
and records about the city. Even Medford's city
seal depicts a ship under construction. From 1803-
1873 Medford built 568 ships — her merchant
ships and clippers sailed around the globe.
    The Museum contains a number of ship models
(both full and half-hull), as well as shipbuilding
tools. L A diorama of the city just before the Civil
War affords visitors an excellent idea of how city
might have looked in its shipbuilding days.
Medford was also the terminus of the Middlesex
Canal (see separate listing) and an important
distillery center in the Triangle Trade in rum and
slaves. The Museum also holds one of the largest
collections of Civil War prints available. The
Society also operates the Pewter Tufts house,
which is one of the oldest brick houses in the
country.
    Activities: The MHS has memberships in several
categories. The Society presents programs for its
members and the public. L It provides educational
programs for local schools. The Society works to
conserve the many documents and objects in its
collections.
    Admission: No entry fee. Open Sundays
2 P.M. – 4 P.M.

Smith's Guide to Maritime Museums of North America

MILTON, MASSACHUSETTS
Captain Robert Bennet Forbes House
215 Adams Street
Milton, MA 02186
(617) 696-1815 Fax: 617-696-1907
E-mail: info@forbeshousemuseum.org
Location: Milton is six miles south of Boston.
The museum, on top of Milton Hill, has a
commanding view of the Neponset River and
Boston Harbor.
Highlights: Ship models, China trade
memorabilia, *Forbes House Jottings* (newsletter),
Forbes House Museum Shop,
Website: www.forbeshousemuseum.org/
General Information: The museum, established
in 1984, is a historic house restored to its 1870s
condition. It commemorates Captain Robert Bennet
Forbes displaying ship models, shipboard furniture,
marine art prints, drawings and paintings. The
furnishings include Chinese export porcelain and
furniture.
Admission: Entry fee. Open Sundays- and
Tues - Thurs, 1 P.M.-4 P.M. and by appointment.
Closed holidays.

NANTUCKET ISLAND, MASSACHUSETTS
Egan Institute of Maritime Studies
The Coffin School
4 Winter Street
Nantucket, MA 02554-3638
(508) 228-2505 Fax: (508) 228-7069
E-mail: egan@eganmaritime.org
Location: On Nantucket Island
Highlights: Nantucket history, art, literature and
maritime traditions,
Website: www.eganinstitute.org/
General information: The Egan Institute of
Maritime Studies is housed in the historic Coffin
School, a brick Greek revival style building built
in 1854. The school was founded by Sir Admiral Isaac Coffin in 1827,
American, born Sir Admiral Isaac Coffin in 1827,
to benefit his island kin and serve as a memorial.
The Egan Institute was founded in 1996 to
advance the scholarly study and appreciation of the
history, literature, art and maritime traditions of
Nantucket Island.
"In addition to sponsoring research, educational
programs, the Egan Institute seeks to perpetuate
the legacy of the school's founder, Admiral
Coffin, through its support of nautical training for
the youth of Nantucket. Nantucket Island
Community Sailing is housed in the lower level of
the Institute.
Activities: Lectures and other educational
programs are offered throughout the year along
with special exhibitions, and a lecture series. Also,
Mill Hill Press, an arm of the Institute, publishes
books on topics relating to Nantucket history.

Admission: Entry fee - modest. Open daily from
late May through early October, 1 P.M. to
5 P.M.

NANTUCKET ISLAND, MASSACHUSETTS
Nantucket Lifesaving Museum
158 Polpis Road
Nantucket, MA 02554-2320
(508) 228-1885
E-mail: Uslssack@aol.com
Location: The Museum is located 2.4 miles from
the Rotary or 2.4 miles from the junction of the
Sconset and Polpis Road until you come to Folger's
Marsh at 158 Polpis Road, a short distance from
the town's center. Look for the white rocks with
lettering and turn in to ample parking.
Highlights: H. H. Kynett Library and Research
Center, two fully restored and operable Beachcarts,
with Lyle and Hunt guns, Breeches Buoy and
Francis Life Car, Fresnel lighthouse lenses from
Brant Point Light (1856) and Great Point Light
(1857), *Andrea Doria* artifacts,
Website:www.nantucketlifesavingmuseum.com/
General Information: The Nantucket Life
Saving Museum, located at Folger's Marsh on
Polpis Road, was established in 1972. It is an
authentic re-creation of the original Station on
Nantucket Island that was built by the United States
Life Saving Service in 1874. The Museum is
dedicated to the drama of human efforts against the
relentless sea. It focuses on the heroic deeds of the
U.S. Life Saving Service, U.S. Revenue Cutter
Service founded by Alexander Hamilton, U.S.
Lighthouse Service, U.S. Coast Guard, and the
Massachusetts Humane Society, whose members
all risked their lives — and in some cases lost their
lives — rescuing shipwrecked sailors on the shores
and shoals of Nantucket. *"You have to go out, but
you don't have to come back."*
Also displayed are artifacts from recent wrecks,
such as the Italian liner *Andrea Doria*, and
memorabilia from the U.S. Coast Guard's heroic
contribution to the Battle of the Atlantic.
Seasonally, the local Coast Guard Station, in
cooperation with the Museum, demonstrates the
operation of the fully restored Beachcart and its
equipment, plus demonstrating the operation of
one of the life boats on the waters of Nantucket
Harbor. Books on lifesaving, replica buttons,
surfman's devices, shirts, hats, and other
memorabilia are for sale in the Museum. You are
invited to become a member/supporter.
Admission: Entry fee. Memberships are
available. Open June 15 to Columbus Day,
9:30 A.M. - 4:00 P.M. Open for group tours and
members at other times by special arrangement.

70

NANTUCKET ISLAND, MASSACHUSETTS
Whaling Museum
Nantucket Historical Association
11 Broad Street, P.O. Box 1016
Nantucket Island, MA 02554-1016
(508) 228-1894 Fax: (508) 228-5618
E-mail: info@nha.org
Location: Ferry to Nantucket Island from Hyannis.
The Museum is at Broad Street at the
head of Steamboat Wharf.
Highlights: A finback whale skeleton (forty-three
feet long), a lighthouse lens (sixteen feet tall),
scrimshaw, library, whaling tools and harpoons
Website: www.nha.org
   General Information: The Whaling Museum,
established in 1846, was built as a candle factory to
refine spermaceti oil—a wax like substance
taken from the oil in the head of a sperm whale
used to make candles. The building now houses
extensive collections of whaling implements used
in the pursuit and processing of sperm whales. The
huge press, used to extract the wax from the oil,
spans the building where a full-size tryworks (large
iron cooking pots where whale blubber is
rendered), a whaleboat from the bark *Sunbeam*,and
an unparalleled collection of scrimshaw is
displayed.
   The skeleton of a forty-three-foot finback whale
is exhibited, and the original sixteen-foot-tall lens
from the Sankaty Lighthouse highlights an area
devoted to navigation and exploration. Also
displayed are paintings and portraits of those who
made Nantucket the third-largest port in the United
States.
   The Research Center, located on Fair Street,
contains 450 rare books, 363 logbooks and
journals, 477 account books, 400 manuscript
collections, and 45,000 photographs for use by
students, historians, and genealogists.
   Activities: Guided tours of twelve historic
Nantucket buildings
   Admission: Entry fee. Open Mon-Sat, 10
A.M.-5 P.M., May 16-October 16; Thurs 10 A.M. –
8 P.M. (until Labor Day); Sunday, 12 Noon –
5 P.M., The Research Center is open Monday-
Friday, 9 A.M.-4 P.M. Closed Christmas.

NEW BEDFORD, MASSACHUSETTS
Lightship *New Bedford* LV 114/WAL 536
c/o Harbor Development Commission
Pier 3
New Bedford, MA 02740
(580) 993-1770
Location: Located near the State Pier in New
Bedford where you will find the lightship is close
to the New Bedford Whaling National Historic
Park District in New Bedford. From Route 6, on the
western side of the Acushnet River, go south on
Route 18 for just 0.2 miles, and the State Pier will
be on your left.
Highlights: The Lightship *New Bedford*
   General Information: The 133-foot steel-hulled

lightship, built in 1930, and designated as No. 114,
is berthed at the town landing and currently
undergoing restoration. It was among the last built
before the U.S. Lighthouse service became a part of
the Coast Guard in 1939. From 1930 to 1942, it
was anchored off Fire Island. She guided mariners
to New York Harbor and then to Cape Hatteras
from 1945-1947 where she replaced a lightship
sunk by a German U-boat during the war. Finally
retired in 1971, she was rescued in 1985 and
restored to become a floating exhibit.
   Admission: Entry Fee. Open daily 9 A.M. –
5 P.M. and until 9 P.M. Thursdays in Summer.
Closed Thanksgiving, Christmas & New Year's.

NEW BEDFORD, MASSACHUSETTS
New Bedford Free Public Library
613 Pleasant Street
New Bedford, MA 02740-6203
(508) 991-6275 Fax: (508) 991-6368
E-mail: nbmref@sailsinc.org
Location: New Bedford is seventy miles south of
Boston on I-195. The library is located at 613
Pleasant Street in center of city.
Highlights: History on whaling, New Bedford
Customs House records, **Web site:**
www.newbedford-ma.gov/Library/Library.html
   General Information: The New Bedford Free
Public Library, founded in 1852, contains
collections of Custom House records for the Port of
New Bedford 1796-1920, 526 whaling logbooks
(and several merchant) for 526 voyages, whaling
agent records including those of C.W. Morgan,
William Rotch, George Hussey, C.R. Tucker, and J
& W.R. Wing. Also a complete run of the
Whalemen's Shipping List and Merchant
Transcript newspaper edited by Lindsey beginning
in 1843, and extensive rare printed book collection
on Whaling and Maritime History.
   The library has undertaken it's most recent
State grant funded project to create a
comprehensive automated database of the
Whaling Crew Lists from the earliest to 1850.
The resulting database will be searchable on 10
fields and be made available for searching free of
charge through the City of New Bedford - New
Bedford Free Public Library Homepage.
   Admission: No entry fee.
Monday -Thursday 9 A.M. – 9 P.M. Friday &
Saturday 9 A.M. – 5 P.M. Closed Sunday &
Holidays Handicapped Accessible

NEW BEDFORD, MASSACHUSETTS
New Bedford Whaling Museum
18 Johnny Cake Hill
New Bedford, MA 02740-6398
(508) 996-7800 Library Fax: (508) 997-0118
E-mail: abrengle@walingmuseum.org
Location: The Museum is nestled in New
Bedford's historic district on Johnny Cake Hill (a
road).

Highlights: Half-size (eighty-nine-foot) model of whaling bark *Lagoda*, ship models, scrimshaw, The Bulletin from Johnny Cake Hill (quarterly newsletter), library (20,000 volumes), 66-foot skeleton of a juvenile blue whale,
Website: www.whalingmuseum.org/
General Information: Under the sponsorship of the Old Dartmouth Historical Society, the New Bedford Whaling Museum was established in 1907 for the purpose of collecting, exhibiting, interpreting, and preserving the history of American whaling and the local area. The Museum is one of the largest museums in America devoted to local history. During the whaling era, New Bedford's local history was world history, and that fact is reflected in its collections as the far-flung whaleships made the city known in every ocean on the globe.

The principal whaling exhibition consists of: the full-rigged half-scale 89-foot model of the New Bedford whaling bark *Lagoda*, which may be boarded; the 100-foot Richard Ellis mural of sperm whales; whaling industry tools and artifacts; and exhibits of waterfront trades that supported the whaling industry; plus interactive exhibits on whales and whale conservation.

The exhibit galleries contain examples from the permanent collections of scrimshaw, painting, prints, ship models; exhibits pertaining to life in New Bedford and Old Dartmouth; "The World of the Whaleman," featuring two sections of the 1848 Russell-Purrington "Panorama of a Whaling Voyage Round the World"; and changing exhibitions of varied nature.

The library contains a permanent collection of well over 15,000 books, pamphlets, maps, charts, broadsides, and periodicals as well as 1800 reels of microfilm and access to 15,000 photographic negatives. There are 750 feet of manuscripts, including over 1,100 logbooks and journals. (Library users may wish to call in advance of visit.)

During the 1820s, when the whaling industry in New Bedford was rising, local citizens organized the Seamen's Bethel dedicated to the moral and religious improvement of seamen. It is right across the street from the Whaling Museum.

Activities: guided tours, lectures, films, gallery talks, and education programs. A whaling film is shown daily in a large theatre.
Admission: Entry fee. Open daily 9 A.M. – 5 P.M., and until 9 p.m. on the second Thursday of the month. Closed Thanksgiving, Christmas, and New Year's Day.

NEW BEDFORD, MASSACHUSETTS
Schooner *Ernestina/Morrissey*
89 North Water Street, P.O. Box 2995
New Bedford, MA 02741-2010
(508) 992-4900 Fax: (508) 984-7719
E-mail: office@ernestina.org
Location: New Bedford is forty miles south of Boston. Schooner at New Bedford State Pier
Highlights: Schooner *Ernestina Morrissey*
Website: www.ernestina.org
General Information: Launched in Essex, MA in 1894, as the 156-foot *Effie M. Morrissey*, she served three long, distinguished careers as a Grand Banks fishing schooner, U.S. Navy survey and supply vessel in World War II, and finally, as an immigrant packet sailing out of Cape Verde, a West African Republic, where she was renamed *Ernestina* in 1948. A small museum contains research materials on nineteenth-century fishing schooners; Arctic expeditions; World War II; Republic of Cape Verde and Portugal Atlantic packet ships; historic restoration, and information on the African-American contribution to American maritime heritage.
Admission: Entry fee. Open Monday-Friday, 10 A.M. - 3 P.M., year-round.

NEWBURYPORT, MASSACHUSETTS
Custom House Maritime Museum
25 Water Street
Newburyport, MA 01950-2754
(978) 462-8681 Fax: (978) 462-8740
Location: Newburyport is situated forty miles north of Boston on the south bank of the Merrimack River. Take I-95 to exit 57. Head east on Rte. 113, which becomes High Street. 2 1/4 miles from the Interstate, at a yellow blinker, turn left onto Green Street. Go three blocks to the foot of Green Street, and turn right on Merrimack Street. In one block this becomes Water Street. One block further on the left is the grey granite Custom House Maritime Museum.
Highlights: Exhibits, programs, tide-pool touch tank, research library (200 volumes), The Maritime Museum Shop,
Website: www.themaritimesociety.org
General Information: At the northeastern corner of Massachusetts, five miles south of the New Hampshire border, the Custom House Maritime Museum of Newburyport, founded in 1969, is located in a Greek revival custom house built in 1835 by the government architect Robert Mills (also architect of the US Treasury, to which the Custom Services reported, and of the Washington Monument).

Museum collections, spanning a period of 300 years, include: local maritime, nautical, and fishing artifacts, half-hull models (a form believed

72

to have been invented in Newburyport), ship models; sea captains' souvenirs of their travels to Asia, Europe, and the South Seas; shipbuilding and navigation tools and instruments, and Coast Guard artifacts.

Newburyport is the traditional birthplace of the U.S. Revenue Service, which evolved into the modern Coast Guard. The first Revenue Cutter, the *Massachusetts*, was built here.

The library contains books on maritime history, ship types and shipbuilding, the lighthouse service, the Coast Guard, and Newburyport history. Manuscripts include captain's journals, business papers, navigation charts, and local ephemera. Library and manuscripts are available for use on the premises by appointment.

Activities: Tours, lectures, youth programs.

Admission: Nominal. Memberships are available. Open Tuesday - Sunday, 11 A.M. – 4 P.M.,

NORTH BILLERICA, MASSACHUSETTS
Middlesex Canal Museum & Visitor Center
at the Faulkner Mills
71 Faulkner Street
North Billerica, MA 01862
(978) 670-2740   E-mail:
middlesexcanalcomm.jreardon@juno.com
Location: The Museum lies approximately 20 miles north of Boston, MA or 5 miles south of Lowell, MA at the Concord River Millpond where the canal began.
Highlights: Middlesex Canal, *Canal Routes* (quarterly newsletter)
Websites: www.middlesexcanal.org
General Information: The Middlesex Canal Museum, opened in July 2001, contains some archives of the Middlesex Canal Association and its exhibit artifacts. The Millpond was the highest point in the 27-mile Middlesex Canal, and so was its primary source of water. It is a great setting.
Admission: No entry fee. Open Saturdays 12 Noon - 4:00 PM and Sundays 12:00- 4:00 from April through September.
(See also: Medford Historical Society Museum)

NORTH TRURO, MASSACHUSETTS
Truro Historical Society Museum
27 Highland Road, P.O. Box 486
North Truro, MA 02666   (508) 487-3397
E-mail: curator@trurohistorical.org
Location: From Boston, take SR-3 south forty-one miles to Rte. 6. Head east to Cape Cod, traveling sixty miles to north tip of Cape Cod.
Highlights: Highland Lighthouse, Cape Cod maritime history ship models, **Website:** www.trurohistorical.org/moremuseum.htm

General Information: Truro Historical Society Museum is now the operator of the Cape Cod/Highland Lighthouse, which is located some 500 feet from the Museum. In 1996 the lighthouse was moved back from the high bluff overlooking the Atlantic due to continued sloughing off of the bluff into the sea. The attached keeper's cottage is the shop where items sold generate funds to "keep the Cape Cod Lighthouse" in good condition.

It was here that Captain Miles Standish and party stayed their second night ashore in a strange land and where Indian corn was discovered and used for the Pilgrims' survival.

The Highland House, a classic turn-of-the-century summer hotel through the late 1960s, now houses the Museum where Henry David Thoreau stayed on his visits to the Cape. The Courtney Allen Room, dedicated as a memorial to the artist by his friends and neighbors, contains fine examples of his masterful woodcarvings, paintings, and models.

The Museum has an exciting collection of artifacts from the town's historical past, including shipwreck mementos, whaling gear, ship models, seventeenth-century firearms, pirate's chest and period rooms, and fine art works.

Activities: Lighthouse is open to the public for tour. Children must be 51-inches high to tour the lighthouse.

Admission: No entry fee. Open Monday-Saturday, 10 A.M.- 4:30 P.M., Sunday 1 P.M. – 4:30 P.M. June to September. Entry fee for lighthouse.

OSTERVILLE, MASSACHUSETTS
Osterville Historical Society and Museum
155 West Bay Roads
Osterville, Cape Cod, MA 02655-2427
508-428-5861 Fax: 508-428-2241
E-mail: OHS@ostervillemuseum.org
Location: Take Hwy. 6, Exit 5 going south 10 miles to Osterville. *Highlights:* Cape Cod history
Website: www.ostervilleMuseum.org/
General Information: The Osterville Historical Society was first formed in 1931, its collection of historical memorabilia was small and very little space was required to house and display the items. The Society was able to use the old Osterville Community Center Building, formerly "Dry Swamp Academy," the school for Osterville children.

By 1960, the Society's collection had outgrown the available space and an appeal went out to find a new location. The appeal was soon answered. Through the generosity of Mrs. Gladys Brooks Thayer of Oyster Harbors and New York, the Society was able to acquire its present building, the Captain Jonathan Parker House, at the corner of West Bay and Parker Roads. This historic sea captain's home was built by Parker in 1824 and is one of the oldest houses in Osterville. Little of the original three-room house is visible, as rooms, porches and dormers have been added to its basic Cape Cod "half house" form.

Admission: No entry fee. Open June to September, Thurs -Sunday 1:30 P.M. to 4:30 P.M.

PLYMOUTH, MASSACHUSETTS
Pilgrim Hall Museum
75 Court Street (Route 3A)
Plymouth, MA 02360-3891
(508) 746-1620 E-mail: director@pilgrimhall.org
Location: The Museum is at 75 Court Street (Rte. 3A) at Chilton Street, two blocks up the hill west of Water Street.
Highlights: Hull of the *Sparrowhawk*, museum shop, **Website:** www.pilgrimhall.org/
General Information: Built in 1824 by the Pilgrim Society of Plymouth, the Museum exhibits and interprets the history of the Pilgrims and the town they founded. Pilgrim Hall is one of the oldest museums in continuous operation in the United States Maritime. A maritime exhibit is in the recovered and preserved lower half of the hull and frame of the *Sparrowhawk*, an ocean-going vessel sunk off Cape Cod in 1626. *Sparrowhawk* was found in May 1863; the timbers were excavated from marsh-mud and sand. P. T. Barnum even took her on tour. Now, *Sparrowhawk* is displayed in the main hall. Also, see the painting of Edward Winslow — the only portrait of a Pilgrim painted from life.
Admission: Entry fee. Open daily, 9:30 A.M.-4:30 P.M., March-November. *Mayflower II* and dockside exhibits are open from 9:00 A.M. to 5:00 P.M.

PLYMOUTH, MASSACHUSETTS
Plimoth Plantation
137 Warren Avenue, P.O. Box 1620
P. O. Box 1620
Plymouth, MA 02362
(508) 746-1622 Fax: (508) 746-4978
E-mail: kcurtin@plimoth.org
Location: From Boston, take SR-3 forty-one miles southeast to Plymouth. Follow Rte. 3A to Plimoth Plantation at Mayflower.
Highlights: The living museum of seventeenth-century Plymouth, The *Mayflower II* (replica ship), library (4,000 volumes),
Website: www.plimoth.org/
General Information: Featured are a reproduction of a 1627 Pilgrim Village and Wampanoag Indian Homesite. Village and homesite feature costumed personnel, who re-create life in seventeenth-century Plymouth. Collections include: archaeology with seventeenth-

century English and Native American artifacts; house furnishings; tools; arms and armor.

Also located near Plimoth Plantation is the recreation Mayflower *II*, typical of ships that brought the Pilgrims to the New World in 1620. Costumed interpreters and modern guides describe life aboard the ship in 1620 and the 1957 voyage of the *Mayflower II*. Exhibits recount the history of the *Mayflower*.

Activities: The library contains imprints and manuscripts available for use by appointment. Additionally, theatre, picnic area, lectures, demonstrations, recreation, and first-person interpretation of daily life in seventeenth-century Plymouth are presented. Education programs are available. Visitor Center, cafeteria and museum shops are on-site.

Admission: Entry fee and memberships are available. Open daily, March 27-November 28, 9 A.M.-5 P.M.; *Mayflower II* and dockside exhibits are open from 9:00 A.M. to 5:00 P.M.

PROVINCETOWN, MASSACHUSETTS
Expedition *Whydah*
Sea Lab and Learning Center
16 MacMillan Wharf, P.O. Box 493
Provincetown, MA 02657
(508) 487-8899
Location: The Center is at the seaward end on MacMillan Wharf in Provincetown
Highlights: The Treasure of the Pirate Ship *Whydah*, **Website:** www.whydah.com/
General Information: Swashbuckling sea wolves hold our imagination in an iron grip. In 1984, treasure-hunter Barry Clifford led a team that discovered one of the world's unique archaeological sites off the east coast of Cape Cod at Wellfleet—the shipwreck of the *Whydah*.

Commanded by the pirate Sam Bellamy, the *Whydah* (pn. WID—ah) was driven to her grave by a savage storm in 1717. Nearly 280 years later, the world's first sunken pirate treasure — together with such personal remains as clothing, weapons, and jewelry — showcase both the history of the ship and the legendary love story of "Black Sam" and a Cape Cod girl.

The *Whydah* went down with picked booty of over fifty other vessels, thus giving scholars an unprecedented cross-cultural window into the 18th-century. Aside from a sampling of the *Whydah* Collection, the exhibit tells the story of the *Whydah*, together with Barry Clifford's discovery of her treasures. The visitor learns first-hand how these treasures are recovered and preserved

Described as "a model for private archaeology," this exhibition is a once- in-a-lifetime educational experience: Learn how pieces of eight are wrested from the ocean floor. See for yourself how pirates lived — and died. Speak with our scientists as they unlock "time-capsules" to reveal the mysterious relics hidden within...Explore a sealed cannon with a fiber-optic camera...Help us decipher the pirates' secret riddles...Watch for still-dripping treasures come ashore from our salvage ship as the quest continues for the *Whydah's* untold hoard! And see the videos with Walter Cronkite and the National Geographic Society.

Admission: Entry fee. Open daily: 10 A.M. – 4 P.M.

QUINCY, MASSACHUSETTS

United States Naval Shipbuilding Museum
739 Washington Street (Wharf Street)
Quincy, MA 02169-7330
(617) 479-7900 Fax: (617) 479-8792
E-mail: webteam@uss-salem.org
Location: The shipyard and Museum are located at Fore River Yard on Wharf Street just off Rte. 3A. Also, the Harbor Express Boat from Logan Airport or Long Wharf Pier in Boston, right to the USS *Salem*.
Highlights: USS *Salem* (CA 139) (heavy cruiser), archives and historical collection,
Website: www.uss-salem.org

General Information: The first recorded local vessel constructed at Ship Cove in 1696 was the ketch *Unity*. Shipbuilding continued and surged during the Spanish-American War when Congress authorized Quincy to build the *Lawrence* and *MacDonough* (torpedo boat destroyers) and the armed cruiser *Des Moines*. The 1920s and 1930s saw the USS *Lexington* converted from a battle cruiser to the Navy's first true aircraft carrier. She was sunk in May of 1942 in the Coral Sea.

On September 23, 1941, the battleship *Massachusetts* was launched and delivered some fifteen months ahead of schedule at the yard and served meritoriously in Northern Africa. The USS *Salem's* keel was laid on July 4, 1945 and she was launched on March 27, 1947 and commissioned two years later, May 14, 1949. The cruiser *St. Paul*, launched here, will be memorialized in a special space on the *Salem*. Other spaces will include a special exhibit on Cruiser Sailors, a model room with museum-quality ship models some from the U.S. Navy's vast collection, and a space dedicated to the history of naval small arms, historical correspondence, and artifacts from the land warfare in France in WW I.

The shipyard, called the "greatest shipyard of World War II," is having a new life with the Des Moines class heavy-cruiser *Salem*, one of its fine products to be maintained by the Museum's crew for all to tour and see.

Activities: Guided tours 10 A.M.-6 P.M., overnight camping programs.

Admission: Entry fee. Open daily 10 A.M.- 4 P.M

ROCKPORT, MASSACHUSETTS

Sandy Bay Historical Society and Museums
40 King St. P.O. Box 63
Rockport, MA 01966
(978) 546-9533
E-mail: info@sandybayhistorical.org
Location: From I-95 (north or south) some fifteen miles north of Boston, exit onto Rte. 128, then east twenty-two miles to county Rte. 127 four miles to Rockport.
Highlights: Ship models, Rockport history,
Website: www. sandybayhistorical.org/
General Information: The Sandy Bay Historical Society and Museums, Inc. maintains two historic houses as its museums; The "Old Castle" (1715) in Pigeon Cove and the Sewall-Scripture House (1832) at 40 King Street. Collected and exhibited are materials about the town of Rockport and its people. Included in the exhibits are ship models, artifacts, and paintings pertaining to local fishing and coastal trade.

Admission: Entry fee and contributions welcome. Open daily, 2:00 P.M.-5:00 P.M. Mon/Sat, June 30-Labor Day. Research Library, 9 A.M. – 1 P.M. Mondays year round

SALEM, MASSACHUSETTS

New England Pirate Museum
274 Derby Street
Salem, MA 01970-3635
(978) 741-2800 Fax: (978) 741-2902
E-mail: info@piratemuseum.com
Location: Salem is located 16 miles north of Boston, and is a convenient 30-minute drive. Take Rte. 128 North, Exit 25A and follow Rte. 114 East. In Salem, follow signs to Waterfront, and The New England Pirate Museum, which is next to the Salem Beer Works, across from Pickering Wharf, and a 5 Minute Walk from Salem Train Depot.
Highlights: Pirate history,
Website: www.piratemuseum.com/
General Information: The New England Pirate Museum features exhibits recounting the history of marauding pirates who once plundered merchant ships off the New England Coast. The Museum re-creates a colonial seaport, pirate ship, and treasure-laden cave.
Activities: Guided tours
Admission: Entry fee. Open daily May-October, 10 A.M.- 5 P.M. Weekends in November, Saturday and Sunday, 10 A.M.- 5 P.M.

SALEM, MASSACHUSETTS
Peabody Essex Museum
East India Square (161 Essex Street)
Salem, MA 01970- 3783
1-866-745-1876, (978) 740- 9500
E-mail: pem@pem.org
Location: Salem is only nineteen miles northeast of Boston on Rte. 95. The Museum is in the heart of downtown Salem.
Highlights: Maritime paintings and prints, ship models, figureheads, objects related to Nathaniel Bowditch, scrimshaw, recreated interior of early-nineteenth-century yacht, Phillips Library,
Website: www.pem.org/homepage/
    General Information: In 1799 Salem's sea captains and merchants of the East India Marine Society founded Peabody Essex Museum, our country's oldest continuing museum. One can study early methods of navigation and the development of navigational instruments, focusing on Nathaniel Bowditch, Salem resident and author of the *American Practical Navigator.*
    One of the largest museums in Massachusetts, the Peabody Essex Museum is home to renowned collections of maritime art and history, Asian export art, art from China, Japan, India, and Korea; Oceanic art, Native American art, American decorative art, folk art, costumes, and textiles, and art from Africa. Spread over two cityblocks and several off-campus sites, the museum also includes one of the nation's premier ensembles of early American architecture.
    The Museum showcases the maritime history of New England, including marine paintings, ship models, figureheads, scrimshaw, nautical tools, and instruments, and an exhibit on an early nineteenth century yacht.
    The museum's Phillips Library contains maritime history, cultural history of Asia and Oceania, photographs, natural history of Essex County, paintings, prints, ship models, charts, and arts and crafts.
    Activities: Changing exhibitions, music, film, guided tours, lectures, gallery talks, and education programs.
    Admission: Entry fee. Memberships available. Open daily 10 A.M.-5 P.M. Closed Thanksgiving, Christmas, and New Year's Day

SALEM, MASSACHUSETTS
Salem Maritime National Historic Site
Custom House
160 Derby Street
Salem, MA 01970
(978) 740-1650 Fax: (978) 740-1685
Location: Salem is nineteen miles northeast of Boston on Rte. 1A.
Highlights: Historical waterfront commercial district which includes: Derby, Central, and Hatch's Wharves, Warehouses, the Custom House, the Scale House, the West India Goods Store, Derby House, Hawkes House, Narbonne-Hale House, and

the Lighthouse. Gift shop nearby.
Website: www.nps.gov/sama
    General Information: Salem Maritime National Historic Site, established in 1938, extends over 9.2 acres from the historic waterfront back into downtown Salem. There are two visitor centers: Downtown Visitor Center is located on the corner of New Liberty and Essex Streets;Orientation Center is on Derby Street. The National Park Service operates the site.
    It includes: Derby Wharf — once center of Salem shipping; Derby House — home of Elias Hasket Derby, a Salem merchant and the first U.S. millionaire; U.S. Custom House; and a commercial and residential village from the days when Salem was a seaport rivaling Boston and New York. A full-scale replica of a 1797 Salem merchant vessel, *Friendship*, is under construction.
    The wharves at Salem Maritime National Historic Site stretch out into the salt waters of Salem Harbor, testifying to the city's former dependence on the sea. The once-busy wharves and the buildings facing the harbor are remnants of the shipping industry that prospered in Massachusetts Bay's oldest seaport well into the nineteenth century. In its prime there were fifteen buildings on Derby Wharf.
    Admission: No entry fee; fee for tours of buildings. Open daily, 9 A.M. to 5 P.M.; closed January 1, Thanksgiving Day, and December 25.

SCITUATE, MASSACHUSETTS
The Maritime & Irish Mossing Museum
301 Driftway
Scituate, MA 02066
(781) 545-1083 Fax: (781) 544-1249
E-mail: director@scituatehistoricalsociety.org
Location: Scituate is located about 30 miles south of Boston. Take Rte. 3 to East 13 and head east 1/4 mile. Turn right on Ret. 1234 and go several miles through Norwell to Rte 3A. Cross 3A and bear right at fork, following sign to Scituate Harbor. Museum is on the right hand side just past the nursing home.
Highlights: Shipwrecks, shipbuilding, Irish Mossing, museum store, **Website:** www.scituatehistoricalsociety.org/sites_maritime.ht ml
    General Information: The Maritime & Irish Mossing Museum is housed in the 1739 home of Captain Benjamin James, which contains six exhibit rooms. The Shipwreck Room focuses on four maritime disasters that took place off Scituate including the *Fairfax-Pinthis* collision (1930), and *Etrusco* (1956). The Life-Saving Room remembers the deeds of the lifesavers of the Massachusetts Humane Society, U.S. Life-Saving Service and the U.S. Coast guard, as well as the stories of Scituate and Minot's Lighthouses. A Fourth Order Fresnel lens was recently added to the collection. The Shipbuilding Room traces the 250-year history of this industry on the North River.

The Captain's Room presents a glimpse into a sea captain's room in the mid-nineteenth century. The Irish Mossing Room is perhaps the only exhibit of its kind in America. Irish Moss, also known as carageen, is a non-edible North Atlantic seaweed (Chondrus crispus) that yields a mucilaginous substance used medicinally and as an emulsifier in several food products. The Reception Room contains changing exhibits and an orientation video. The museum store has many items of local and historical interest. Nearby are Scituate Lighthouse, Lawson's Tower, the Stockbridge Grist Mill, and other seacoast attractions.

Admission: Entry fee. Open July through Labor Day, Saturday and Sunday 1 P.M. – 5 P.M. Group tours by appointment. Call (781) 545-1083. Please contact the Scituate Historical Society for winter hours.

SCITUATE, MASSACHUSETTS
Scituate Lighthouse
43 Cudworth Road
P.O. Box 276
Scituate, MA 02066
(781) 545-1083
E-mail: director@scituatehistoricalsociety.org
Location: Scituate is south of Boston and south of Cohasset on the Atlantic coast and is accessible from Rte-3A. Go to the harbor, and then take Jericho Road north to Lighthouse Road.
Highlights: Lighthouse, historic structures, library (300 volumes),
Website:
www.scituatehistoricalsociety.org/sites_lighthouse.html
General Information: Illuminated in 1811, Scituate Lighthouse is the sixth oldest active aid to navigation in New England, and the ninth oldest in the United States. It features the story of Abigal and Rebecca Bates, daughters of the keeper, who took up a fife and a drum and frightened away British sailors intent on ransacking the town of Scituate during the War of 1812. The fife is on display during tours.

The Lighthouse now features twenty-five new graphic panels inside the runway between the tower and the keeper's house that detail different aspects of the science and history of American lighthouses. The tower is open to the public four times per year; group tours can be arranged by request. The lighthouse is less than two miles from the Scituate Maritime and Irish Mossing Museum, also operated by the Scituate Historical Society.
Admission: Entry fee. Call for group rates.

WELLFLEET, MASSACHUSETTS
Old Harbor Life-Saving Station
c/o Cape Cod National Seashore
National Park Service
99 Marconi Site Road
Wellfleet, MA 02663
(508) 349-3785
Location: From Boston, south on Rte. 3. Exit on Rte. 6 east seventy-three miles to Provincetown. Turn right at first traffic light (Race Point Road), then three miles to the end of Race Point Beach. Take boardwalk past the shower/lavatory building to museum. *Highlights:* Life-saving equipment,
Website:
www.cr.nps.gov/maritime/park/oldhbrls.htm
General Information: "You have to go, but you don't have to come back." That was the life-savers' motto, and their work earned them the title, "Guardians of the Ocean Graveyard." Life-Savers were stationed on Cape Cod between 1872 and 1915. The Old Harbor Life-Saving Station, under the auspices of the National Park Service, contains exhibits from the U.S. Life-Saving Service with the historical perspective of those who risked their lives helping those in storm-tossed seas. The Salt Pond Visitor Center, about halfway up the Cape, on Rte. 6 in Eastham, also exhibits Life-Saving Service artifacts.

The Province Lands Visitor Center (508/487-1256) is located one mile from the station and provides orientation to the Provincetown area.
Activities: Every Thursday in summer, re-enactment of Breeches Buoy ship-to-shore rescue; 6 P.M. at station.
Admission: No entry fee but beach-parking fee. Station open daily in the summer months only 3 P.M.- 4 P.M., variable hours spring and fall — call ahead.

WELLFLEET, MASSACHUSETTS
Wellfleet Historical Society Museum
266 Main Street, P.O. Box 58
Wellfleet, MA 02667
(508) 349-9157
E-mail: info@wellfleethistoricalsociety.org
Location: From Boston take SR-3 south to Rte. 6 (41-miles). Travel east to Cape Cod, then an additional forty-one-miles to Wellfleet Harbor at Cape Cod's northern tip.
Highlights: Old Cape Cod history, ship models
Website: www.wellfleethistoricalsociety.com
General Information: The Wellfleet Historical Society Museum has marine items, whaling tools, Maraconi (radio) memorabilia, needlecraft and photograph collection. Nearby Rider House is restored and depicts life on Old Cape Cod through displays of early farming, carpentry tools and a herb garden.

Admission: No entry fee. Open June 22 - September 4, 2004, Wednesday, Thursday & Saturday – 1 – 4 P.M. Tuesday & Friday, 10 A.M. – 4 P.M.

WOODS HOLE, MASSACHUSETTS
Woods Hole Historical Collection
Woods Hole Historical Museum
573 Woods Hole Road, P.O. Box 185
Falmouth, MA 02543-1041
(508) 548-7270 Fax: 508-548-7270
E-mail: woods_hole_historical@hotmail.com
Location: Woods Hole is on the southwest tip of Cape Cod where the ferries are boarded for Martha's Vineyard and Nantucket. The collection archives and exhibit galleries are located in Bradley House (circa 1800), next to the Woods Hole Library and the Woods Hole Small Craft Exhibit building. There is very limited parking.
Highlights: Historical restored small craft, Small Craft Museum, Woods Hole spiritsail boat, a Cape Cod Knockabout, and a Herreshoff twelve and one-half, restored; scale model of Woods Hole in 1890s, exhibits, library and archives with photographs, oral history collection, gift shop,
Website: http://woodsholemuseum.org
General Information: The Woods Hole Historical Collection was founded in 1973 as an adjunct of the Woods Hole Library, to establish and preserve a collection of objects and materials of cultural, historical, and artistic value illustrating the history of Woods Hole and to keep the story of its heritage alive.

The Small Boat Museum, opened in 1996, exhibits local small-craft in the Swift Barn, built in 1877. It cost $80.71, labor and materials. Numerous models, other maritime artifacts, and illustrations are displayed. Other exhibits include 1890s Woods Hole spirit sailboat *SPY*, built by the same Mr. Swift who built the barn. Also displayed: the Herreshoff 12 Cod Knock-about *IMP*, a two time national champion. All these sailing craft were raced in local waters. The workshop exhibits the talents, tools, and hobbies of a late-nineteenth-century physician: etching, constructing fishing rods, and tying flies. Other galleries have changing exhibits.

The Small Boat Collection includes a Chamberlain Dory made entirely of local wood and a 1922 Old Town canoe, which was the preferred pleasure craft of summer scientists here in the 1920s and 1930s. Also in the barn are boat models. A new shed addition houses the Knock-about Penguin, allowing children to climb aboard and sail away with their imaginations.

The archives contains local business records and personal correspondence, household receipts, postcards, newspaper articles, diaries, ships' logs,

maps, and a large photograph collection including photos by Baldwin Coolidge of Woods Hole at the turn of the century. The library contains about one hundred volumes devoted primarily to maritime and Cape Cod History. The artifact collection includes paintings, memorabilia, and tools.

Activities: Semi-annual journal *Spiritsail*, newsletter, lunch-time talks (ten a year); walking tours of the Woods Hold Village (on Tuesday afternoons in July and August), an on-going boat restoration program, special events
Admission: No entry fee. Memberships are available. Open Tuesday-Saturday, 10 A.M.-4 P.M., Mid-June – Mid-October.

YARMOUTH PORT, MASSACHUSETTS
Historical Society of Old Yarmouth
Strawberry Lane
P.O. Box 11
Yarmouth Port, MA 02675
(508) 362-3021 E-mail: hsoy@comcast.net
Location: Located on the Strawberry Lane Common, just off Route 6A in Yarmouth Port. From Route 6 take exit 7. Right on Willow street to Route 6A. Right on 6A about a mile, past the Yarmouth Port Post Office. Turn right onto Strawberry Lane (the Common). The Bangs Hallet House is the second house on the right.
Highlights: Maritime local history, bookstore.
Website: /www.hsoy.org/
General Information: The Historical Society of Old Yarmouth was founded in 1953 to develop community interest in and preserve the history of Yarmouth. To achieve this goal, the Society owns and maintains the Captain Bangs Hallet House, Kelley Chapel, and adjoining conservation lands and buildings. It also sponsors special programs throughout the year.

The lovely Greek revival style home, built in the 1840s, was donated to the Society by the Thacher family in 1956. Through the efforts of friends and members of the Society, the house was refurbished and furnished and is today arranged in a manner reminiscent of the lifestyle of a prosperous, nineteenth-century sea captain.

Admission: Entry fee. Open June 1 through mid-October, Thursday, Friday, Saturday, and Sunday. Tours at 1 P.M., 2 P.M., and 3 P.M.

MICHIGAN

ALPENA, MICHIGAN

Jesse Besser Museum
491 Johnson Street
Alpena, MI 49707
(989) 356-2202   Fax: (939) 356-3303
E-mail: adozier@bessermuseum.org
Location: Alpena is located on the Sunrise Side of
Michigan at the junction of M-32 and U.S. 23 on
the shores of Thunder Bay.
Website: www.bessermuseum.org/
Highlights: Shipwrecks in Thunder Bay, lumber
and agricultural exhibits, Gallery of Early Man,
    General Information: The Jesse Besser
Museum is a regional center for art, history, and the
natural sciences. The Museum contains
galleries devoted to changing art exhibits, Great
Lakes marine photographs, some ship models,
Early Man, lumber and agricultural exhibits, and
planetarium. Period shops line a re-created 1890s
street. Restored nineteenth-century historic
buildings on the Museum grounds include a 1928
fish tug, homesteader's cabin, a log house, the
Maltz Exchange Bank, a church and a one-room
school.
    Activities: Sky Theatre Planetarium shows
    Admission: Entry fee. Open year round,
Tuesday through Saturday, 10 A.M.- 5 P.M.;
Sunday, 12 P.M. - 4 P.M.

ALPENA, MICHIGAN

**Thunder Bay National Marine Sanctuary
    and Underwater Preserve**
500 W. Fletcher
Alpena, MI 49707
(989) 356-8805   (800) 4-ALPENA
E-mail: thunderbay@noaa.gov
Location: Alpena is located on the Sunrise Side of
Michigan at the junction of M-32 and U.S. 23 on
the shores of Thunder Bay. near Alpena, Michigan
Highlights: An underwater Sanctuary with
estimated 118 shipwrecks, Diving for shipwreck
viewing for beginners and advanced divers,
Website: www.thunderbay.noaa.gov
    General Information: 448 square miles of
Thunder Bay were established as the Thunder Bay
National Marine Sanctuary on October 7, 2000.
This incredible underwater "museum" —
Shipwreck Alley — and sanctuary protect
approximately 118 historically significant
shipwrecks — approximately 80 per square mile.
The vessels, preserved in time within the fresh,
cold waters of Lake Huron, still has stories to tell
of U.S. maritime history and commerce.
    The Sanctuary runs between South Point and
Middle Island and includes all bottomland and
water marks along the shoreline and out to the 150-
foot-depth contour. The Thunder Bay Sanctuary is
one of the few preserves that have dives for the
beginning diver. The local dive club for offshore

diving has buoyed some diving sites, while dive
boat charter service is available to others.
    Admission: No admission charge to diving area
(public waters). Mon-Sat 10 A.M. to 5 P.M.
and Sun 11 A.M. to 4 P.M. Information center at
Marathon Station (M-32) and Dunkin' Donuts
(U.S.-23) (**See also in this area:** Old Lighthouse at
Presque Isle and Sturgeon Bay Lighthouse.)

BAY CITY, MICHIGAN

Historical Museum of Bay County
321 Washington Avenue
Bay City, MI 48708-5837
(989) 893-5733   Fax: (989) 893-5741
E-Mail: info@bchsmuseum.org
Location: Bay City is approximately 100 miles
north of Detroit offI-75 at the southern end of
Saginaw Bay. The Museum is one block south of
Rte. 25 on Washington Street.
Highlights: Ship models, local shipbuilding,
photograph collection, research library, Museum
store (offers wide selection of maritime
publications and other items),
Website: www.bchsmuseum.org/
    General Information: The Historical Museum
of Bay County focuses on early local history and
on shipbuilding in Bay City, which helped in the
rapid development of the lower Saginaw Valley.
First lumbering occurred in the 1860s to 1880s —
the precursor to the development of the lumber
industry and then, early shipbuilding.
    Shipbuilding first came with the
development of the James Davidson Shipyard in
1870, then Chesley and Frank W. Wheeler
Shipyard in 1873-1914, then Defoe Shipbuilding
Company in 1905. Defoe first built kit boats,
then, during W.W.II, developed the unique
upside-down hull construction used to build
patrol craft for the U.S. Navy. The yard also built
mine sweepers and destroyers. The Wheeler
yard's vessels were wooden, but in 1914 it
switched to steel — the first in Bay City to do so.
Associated material is displayed in the new
Kantzler Maritime Gallery.
    The Museum maintains a modest, but important,
collection of archive materials for use only in the
research library. The collections include history
magazines, shipbuilding encyclopedias, maps,
atlases, plats, and a small number of local-water
navigational charts. The Museum maintains a
photograph collection on local ships and shipping.
Also included are twenty wooden boat models
made by local residents and the Cathy Baker
collection of Michigan ships and local ships.
    Admission: No entry fee. Open Monday-Friday,
10 A.M. 5 P.M., Saturday-Sunday, 12 Noon –
4 P.M. Research is library open Tuesday-Thursday,
1 P.M.- 5 P.M.

BRIMLEY, MICHIGAN
Point Iroquois Lighthouse & Maritime Museum   Hiawatha National Forest
6 Mile Road (Lakeshore Drive)
Brimley, MI 49715
Phone: (906) 437-5272 (906) 635-5311
E-mail: ninelakes@yahoo.com
Location: The lighthouse museum is located near Brimley. From I-75, go west 7 mi. on M-28, take M-221 north to where it dead ends at Lake Superior, turn left onto 6 Mile Rd. (called Lakeshore Dr. near lighthouse) then 7.5 miles.
Highlights: Point Iroquois Lighthouse, Museum Shop   **Website:**
http://www.exploringthenorth.com/ptiroquois/uriq uois.html
General Information: Point Iroquois Lighthouse & Maritime Museum shows its light where Lake Superior begins its treacherous rush into the St. Mary's River. In 1662, a war raged between the Ojibwa Indians who massacred members of the invading Iroquois warriors at the lighthouse site. The area became significant when the St. Mary's Falls Ship Canal opened in 1855 where ships passing from Lake Superior into the canal came close to Point Iroquois, through a narrow passage between the sandy shores on the American side and the reefs on the Canadian side.
Activities: The 65-foot tower is open to the public.
Admission: Call for fees. Open from May 15th - October 15. Hours are 9 a.m. to 5 p.m., daily. Hours may vary, so call (906) 437-5272 for a current schedule.

CEDARVILLE, MICHIGAN
Les Cheneaux Maritime Museum
Les Cheneaux Historical Association
Hwy. M-134 & Lake Street
Cedarville, MI 49719
(906) 484-3354 E-mail: lcha@ichistorical.org
Location: Cedarville is located at the northern tip of Lake Huron on the southern shore of Michigan's Upper Peninsula and is reached from Exit 359 off I-75. Travel east on M-134, to 4 blocks east of the intersection of M-134 and M-129. *Highlights:* Boating and fishing history, ship models, wooden boat building shop, logging, range light,
Website: www.lchistorical.org/marimus.html
General Information: The Les Cheneaux Maritime Museum of Cedarville in the Les Cheneaux Islands area of Hessel and Cedarville. The area was once on the path of early exploration, a shelter for Voyageurs, a harbor for the lumber shipping, the fishing and tourism industries, and the communities developed "from the water." The Museum is housed in the 1920s O.M. Reif Boathouse and its extensive addition, where artifacts, photos, and vintage boats from the wooden boat era are on display.
Of particular interest are the Rudd Johnson

Outboard Motor Collection of Lee Rudd and a replica Mackinac boat of the type used by Native Americans and adapted by French explorers. The Archie Visow display features his Cedar Craft small hydroplanes whose ten-horsepower outboard motors drove the beautiful craft at 60 miles per hour.
Activities: Wooden boat building, annual Hessel Antique Wooden Boat Show, held on the second Saturday of August in Hessel.
Admission: Entry free. Open July-August, weekdays 10 A.M.- 4 P.M., Sundays 1 P.M.- 4:30 P.M. and Sept. weekends.

COPPER HARBOR, MICHIGAN
Copper Harbor Lighthouse Museum
14447 State Highway M 26
Copper Harbor Marina, MI 49918
(906) 337-2310   (906) 289-4966
E-mail: info@copperharborlighthouse.com
Location: Copper Harbor is in Michigan's northernmost peninsula (Keweenaw) jutting into Lake Superior. Bear north on Rte. 41 at Covington (fifty-four miles west of Marquette). The lighthouse is accessible only by a 16-minute boat ride from Copper Harbor Marina.
Highlights: Lighthouse, Great Lakes shipping displays,
Website: www.copperharborlighthouse.com/
General Information: The Copper Harbor Lighthouse Museum (1848) and Fort Wilkins (1844), both a part of the Fort Wilkins State Park, were linked to Upper Michigan's copper rush of the 1840s and the increased traffic it brought. The 15-acre site includes the original 1848 dwelling, the 1866 combined tower and dwelling, and the still operating 1933 steel tower.
The original 1848 Lighthouse is one of the two oldest on Lake Superior, along with Whitefish Point, built the same year. The 1866 building, which replaced it, contains period-room displays showing life of a light keeper in the 1910s. And the original 1848 dwelling is now open with interpretive panels and interactive exhibits doubling the display areas. The light was automated in 1919, site purchased by State of Michigan in 1957, and opened for tours in 1975.
Activities: On site is a new interpretive foot-trail taking visitors to the location of the chrysacola copper vein and the 1844 Pittsburgh and Boston Copper Harbor Mining Company copper mine shafts. The trail deals with Dr. Douglass Houghton, his early exploration of the area and the promotion of copper, and ends with the mine site— the earliest commercial copper mine in Michigan. One-hour tours at 10 A.M., 12 Noon, 2 P.M. and 4 P.M. during June and September; every hour 10 A.M.-5 P.M. and a sunset tour in July and August there, hiking trails on fifteen-acre peninsula, and especially interesting are the underwater sightings

80

of chrysacola crystals which are beautiful and evidence the copper ore deposits of the Michigan Upper Peninsula

Admission: No entry fee but charge for ferry. Lighthouse Ferry Service (906) 289-4966 (winter) (906) 337-2310

DeTOUR VILLAGE, MICHIGAN
DeTour Passage Historical Museum
104 Elizabeth Street, P.O. Box 111
DeTour Village, MI 49725
(906) 297-3404 Toll Free: 800-649-3777
Location: The Museum is located next to the Drummond Island Ferry Dock in DeTour Village at the eastern tip of the Upper Peninsula. From Sault Ste. Marie, drive south on Rte. 129, 35 miles to Cedarville, then east 24 miles on Rte. 134 to the Village. From St. Ignace, drive north 15 miles on I-75 to Rte. 134 then east 41 miles to DeTour.
Highlights: Fresnel lens, local small craft, unique range light (**See:** Les Cheneaux Maritime Museum for the matched range light), **Website:** http://history.eup.k12.mi.us/History/6.html

General Information: The DeTour Passage Historical Museum, opened in 1992 as a small historical museum, includes exhibits of maritime interest, including several small craft displayed in the exterior of the Museum. Many of the Museum's artifacts, like so many other museums, have been contributed from local families.

Exhibits include artifacts relating to marine operations of the past; pioneer families of the area, Indian history; churches, schools, businesses, social and governmental activities; and life in general of the early years of the DeTour area. Traveling exhibits are occasionally displayed.

Prominent among the exhibits is a rare third-order Fresnel lens, which was removed from the DeTour Lighthouse in 1988 when a new system was installed.

Admission: No entry fee, but donations accepted. Memberships available. Open Memorial Day during summer, Sunday through Friday 1 P.M.-5 P.M., Saturday 10 A.M.-5 P.M.

DETROIT, MICHIGAN
Dossin Great Lakes Museum
100 Strand Drive on Belle Isle
Detroit, MI 48207
(313) 833-5538 Fax: (313) 822-4610
Location: The Museum is on the south side of Belle Isle in the heavily trafficked Detroit River. In Detroit go to Jefferson Street and east from downtown to Grand Boulevard East, turn south across Douglas MacArthur Bridge to Belle Isle.
Highlights: Pilot house from the *William Clay Ford*, topographical model of the Great Lakes, submarine periscope, ship models, *Telescope* (bi-monthly magazine), library (700 volumes),

Website: www.glmi.org/directions.htm
General Information: Dossin Great Lakes Museum, founded in 1948. Exhibitions in the Museum's 16,000 square foot building focus on the permanent exhibitions include: the S.S. *William Clay Ford* Pilot House; the Gothic Room from the *City of Detroit III*; the *Miss Pepsi* hydroplane; the anchor from the S.S. *Edmund Fitzgerald* and many changing exhibitions.

Visitors can view the paintings and models and the artifacts that recall the fleet of magnificent side-wheelers that once steamed up and down the river that dominated the waterfront like a flotilla of waterborne palaces.

When you take the helm of the working pilothouse from the steamer *William Clay Ford* while looking out over the Detroit River, you will feel as if you are really out on the Great Lakes — ore boats down-bound passing right in front of your eyes!

The Museum's staff works with such groups as the Great Lakes Maritime Institute, the Detroit Historical Society, the Mariner's Church of Detroit, the Greater Michigan Boat and Fishing Show, and the American Powerboat Association — all helping to stimulate and provide interest in the lore of the lakes.

Activities: Guided tours, lectures, and, films.
Admission: Entry fee. Open Saturday and Sunday from 11 A.M. to 5 P.M.

DOUGLAS, MICHIGAN
***Keewatin* Maritime Museum**
219 N. Union Street
P.O. Box 638
Douglas, MI 49406
(269) 857-2464 (In season) (269) 857-2107
E-mail: info@keewatinmaritimemuseum.com
Location: Take I-196/Rte. 31 thirty-six miles southwest of Grand Rapids to Douglas. The Keewatin is moored off County Rte. A-2, south of Saugatuck/Douglas Bridge.
Highlights: Steamship *Keewatin*, *Reiss* (steam tug)
Website: www.keewatinmritimemuseum.com/#
General Information: The Steamship *Keewatin* became a museum in 1968. The *Keewatin* was built by the Fairfield Shipbuilding and Engineering Co., Ltd., Govan, Glasgow, Scotland, in Scotland for the Canadian Pacific Railway. Delivered to the Great Lakes in 1907, this lovely steamer was destined to make history. For over 50 years she served as a railway link, connecting the Georgian Bay and Upper Lake Superior railheads, for 57 years and retired in 1965. Known for her refined accommodations and speed, she sailed her entire life under the Canadian Pacific Railway flag with homeport of Montreal.

Step aboard and be transported back in time as

81

you tour a ship of a by-gone era of Great Lakes coal-burning overnight passenger steamships. The main entry area of the ship has been transformed into a modest but important maritime museum. Collections include old ships of the Greats Lakes. She is the last of the Classic Great Lakes passenger steamships still afloat.

Activities: Guided tours on the 350-foot coal-burning vessel.

Admission: Entry fee. Open 10:30 A.M. – 5 P.M. Memorial day-Labor Day.

EAGLE HARBOR, MICHIGAN
Eagle Harbor Lighthouse and Museum
Keweenaw County Historical Society
HC-1, Box 265L
Eagle Harbor, MI 49950
(906) 289-4990
E-mail: ninelakes@yahoo.com
Location: Located on the shore at Eagle Harbor Michigan Complex on the Keweenaw Peninsula
Highlights: Lighthouse; Maritime, Commercial Fishing, and Kewanaw history museums, **Website:** www.exploringthenorth.com/eagleharbor/eaglehar bor.html

General Information: Eagle Harbor Lighthouse first opened in 1851, was replaced in 1871 by the present red brick structure, and supported a fourth-order Fresnel lens illuminated by a sperm whale lamp. The U.S. Coast Guard continues to operate the light at the top of the tower, now a rotating beacon.

The U.S. Life-Saving Service installed the Eagle Harbor Station in 1912 where brave seamen risked their lives manning open surfboats on behalf of faltering ships off Keweenaw.

The Keweenaw County Historical Society became the 22nd "keeper of the light" in 1982 and through museum exhibits, local photographs, period furnishings, and interpretive devices describes the proud history of Eagle Harbor's most prominent structure brought back into sharp focus. A number of interesting museums from the area's past surround the lighthouse, and a fine view station overlooks the lake.

Admission: Entry fee, children free. Memberships are available. Open mid-June-early October, daily, 10 A.M.-5:00 P.M.

EMPIRE, MICHIGAN
Sleeping Bear Point Life-Saving Station
Maritime Museum
National Park Service
9922 Front Street (Hwy M-72)
Empire, MI 49630
(231) 326-5134
E-mail: SLBE_Interpretation@nps.gov
Location: From Detroit take I-75 northwest 212

miles to Grayling. Exit west on SR-72, traveling seventy-five miles to Empire on the Lake Michigan shore. The Museum is in the Sleeping Bear National Lakeshore seven miles north from the Visitor Center.
Highlights: Life-Saving Service boathouse, fully equipped ship's pilothouse on second floor of station residence,
Website:
www.cr.nps.gov/maritime/park/slbelss.htm

General Information: On the northwestern shore of Michigan's lower peninsula lies Sleeping Bear Dunes National Lakeshore, a beautiful hilly region fringed with massive coastal sand dunes and dotted with clear lakes. On the north, in the National Lakeshore, is the Sleeping Bear Point Life-Saving Station Maritime Museum, founded in 1984. The dynamic story of the Life-Saving Service is told in the excellently restored Life-Saving Station, where displays exhibit and depict how the Service and Coast Guard have played, and continue to play, an important humanitarian role in saving lives by rescuing passengers and crews from ships in trouble in the stormy waters in the early years off the Sleeping Bear Dunes and Lake Michigan's Manitou Islands.

An important part of the complex is the completely restored and equipped boathouse containing all the rescue equipment — surfboats, line-throwing cannon (Lyle Gun), a unique line-cutting device, and all the other equipment a 1901 lifesaver would need to make a rescue. The main Museum is housed in the old station residence and contains many interesting exhibits on the area's maritime history. There is even a mock-up of a ship's pilothouse and a restored Life-Saving Service crew's bunkroom.

Activities: Guided tours, lectures, films, and education programs
Admission: National Park entry fee. Open daily Memorial Day to Labor Day, 10 A.M. – 5 P.M.

ESCANABA, MICHIGAN
Sand Point Lighthouse
Delta County Historical Society - Ludington Park
16 Water Plant Road   P.O. Box 484
Escanaba, MI 49829
(906) 789-3763 E-mail: clara@mosenfelder.net
Location: On the Upper Peninsula of Michigan, Escanaba is 10 miles east from junction of US 41 US 2. Turn east on Ludington Street to Sand Point Lighthouse and museum.
Highlights: Delta County Historical Museum, Sand Point Lighthouse, Fresnel (fourth-order lens), **Website**:
www.exploringthenorth.com/sandpoint/light.html

General Information: Sand Point Lighthouse, erected originally in 1867 and founded as a

1868. The Lighthouse served mariners continuously from 1868 until 1939, warning the ships — first schooners and later steamers and whalebacks carrying iron ore and lumber — off Sand Point and the sand reef which reached out into the Bay. Displayed are maps, charts, pictures, and a lantern room with a fourth-order Fresnel lens. Adjacent to the Lighthouse is the Delta County Historical Museum containing a variety of written and pictorial material about the maritime history of the Great Lakes.

Admission: Entry fee. Open daily, 9 P.M.-5 P.M., June 1-September 1. Other times by appointment.

GRAND HAVEN, MICHIGAN
Tri-Cities Historical Museum
200 Washington Avenue
P.O. Box 234
Grand Haven, MI 49417
(616) 842-0700
E-mail: dswartout@tri-citiesmuseum.org
Location: Grand Haven is west of Grand Rapids. Take I-96 seven miles exiting at Spring Lake on Rte. 104. The Museum is situated on the banks of the Grand River adjacent to the world's largest musical fountain.
Highlights: "Coast Guard City, USA," ship models and Maritime Gallery, Victorian Vignette Rooms, lumbering, rocks and mineral display, textile and weaving display, library, Grand Trunk Depot (museum), gift shop, **Web Site:** www.tri-citiesmuseum.org/staff.php

General Information: The Museum, founded in 1972, is housed in the 1870 Grand Trunk Depot constructed in 1870. The first historical fact relates to the Museum itself. The depot was constructed as the western terminus of the Detroit, Grand Haven, and Milwaukee Railroad. The station served Grand Haven as a passenger depot until the Grand Haven ended in 1955. In 1967, the city purchased the property and leased the depot to the Tri-Cities Historical Society.

Collections and exhibits include: Coast Guard items; shipping items; medical, agriculture, photographs, lumbering, and railroad items. The Coast Guard Room tells this story and proudly exhibits locally crafted scale models of Coast Guard ships and other Great Lakes and Grand River vessels. Of major interest to the community was the Coast Guard ship *Escanaba,* which blew up during WW II with a crew almost entirely made up of residents of Grand Haven. As a memorial, the citizenry raised enough funds to build the second *Escanaba* and presented it to the Coast Guard.

Admission: No entry fee, but donations accepted. Summer hours: Open Tuesday-Friday, 9:30 A.M.-7:30 P.M., Sat/Sun, 12:30 P.M. -9:30 P.M. Memorial Day-Labor Day. Winter hours: Tuesday-Friday, 9:30 A.M.-5 P.M., Sat/Sun 12:30 P.M. – 5 P.M. Labor Day-Memorial Day.

GRAND MARAIS, MICHIGAN
Grand Marais Maritime Museum
Picture Rocks National Lakeshore
P.O. Box 40
Munising, MI 49862
(906) 494-2669 Fax: (906) 494-2269
Location: The Museum is at Grand Marais some ninety-two miles northeast from Marquette.
Highlights: Life-saving service and fishing memorabilia, bookshop, lifeboat station, **Website:** www.michiganlights.com/GrandmaraisLSS.htm
General Information: The Grand Marais Maritime Museum, housed in a former Coast Guard building, relates the late nineteenth- and twentieth-century maritime history of the south shore of Lake Superior. Exhibits focus on the Grand Marais fishing industry, which thrived in the 1920s, as well as the heroic lifesaving efforts of local U.S. Life-Saving Servicemen and fishermen called to the aid of sailors shipwrecked near the Grand Marais Harbor.

Exhibits on breeches buoy deployment and artifacts from steamers and lumber hookers. The Museum, made possible through private gifts and loans from local residents, features a National Park Service cooperating bookstore.

Admission: No entry fee. Open five days a week, July-Labor Day, staffing permitting. Closed winter.

GULLIVER, MICHIGAN
Seul Choix Point Lighthouse
672 N. West Gulliver Lk.
Gulliver, MI 49840
(906) 283-3183   E-mail: seulchoix@reiters.net
Location: The Lighthouse is located in the Upper Peninsula of Michigan's Gulliver area on Rte. 2, on the south side of the Peninsula. It is 74 miles west of the Mackinac Bridge and 67 miles east of Escanaba, Michigan—14 miles east of Manistique, Michigan
Highlights: Lighthouse, gift shop,
Website: www.greatlakelighthouse.com/
General Information: The Seul Choix Point Lighthouse, located in the Upper Peninsula of Michigan's Gulliver area. The Gulliver Historical Society, in cooperation with the Department of Natural Resources, operates it. Several hundred years ago French sailors were caught in a storm and found refuge in a small harbor, which they named "Seul Choix" (pronounced Sis-Shwa), and

means "only choice." In 1892, the lighthouse became operable.

Representations of all aspects of the area's history are on view in the Fog Signal building. Exhibits include a well-preserved dugout canoe, one of the rarest finds to be uncovered in the Midwest. You can stroll through the light keeper's living quarters where rooms have been decorated, as they would have appeared in the 1900-1930 period. A rare find, the uniform of R. Rosie, light keeper in 1941, is displayed next to a table setting of original china and stemware used by his family.

Admission: No entry fee. Open Memorial Day-mid September 10 A.M. - 6 P.M. Seven days a week (depending upon availability of volunteer tour guides). Off-season hours may vary. Private group tours upon request.

HARRISVILLE, MICHIGAN
Sturgeon Point Lighthouse and Museum
Alcanon Historical Society
6071 E. Point Road
Harrisville, MI 48740
(989) 727-4703 E-Mail: iklemens@mail.com
Location: The Lighthouse is four miles north of Harrisville off Rte. 23 onto Lake Shore Drive, then east on Sturgeon Point Drive to Lighthouse.
Highlights: Lighthouse, local maritime artifacts/history, gift shop, **Website:** www.alconahistoricalsociet.co/
General Information: The Sturgeon Point Lighthouse and Museum, located on the shore of Lake Huron on Michigan's east side, was originally built in 1869 and has been maintained ever since. A small amount of maritime artifacts are shown along with other memorabilia. The Museum provides a gift shop.
Admission: No entry fee, but donations accepted. Open seven days a week from 10 A.M. - 4 P.M., mid-May-mid-October.

HOUGHTON, MICHIGAN
Isle Royale National Park
800 East Lakeshore Drive
Houghton, MI 49931-1869
(906) 482-0984 E-mail: ISRO_ParkInfo@nps.gov
Location: Isle Royale National Park is located at the middle-northern side of Lake Superior closest to Thunder Bay on the Canadian Shore in the Province of Ontario. Park headquarters is in Houghton, Michigan. Isle Royal is reached via water transportation from Houghton, MI (6 hours), Copper Harbor, MI (4.5 hours), and Grand Portage, MN 2 - 3 hours). Seaplane service is available from Houghton, MI.
Highlights: Maritime history exhibit in the Rock Harbor Lighthouse, 2nd order Fresnel lighthouse

lens on display in the Windigo visitor center, commercial fishery equipment at the Edisen Fishery. Isle Royale history, wilderness exploration, library (1,000 volumes), **Website:** www.nps.gov/isro
General Information: Isle Royale National Park, founded in 1931, also maintains a variety of museum collections at the Park headquarters in Houghton, including shipwreck artifacts and photographs. On the Island at the Mott headquarters are a library (1000 volumes) and an oral history collection for research. Also displayed are commercial fishery equipment and a 1928-1931 photographic collection of Isle Royale. Library for research.
Admission: Museum collection open by appointment only. No entry fee for Rock Harbor Lighthouse, Windigo visitor center, or Edisen fishery, although there is a $4 per day user fee for visiting the island. Island facilities open every day from 8 A.M.- 6 P.M., June-August and closed in the winter.

LANSING, MICHIGAN
Michigan Historical Museum
Bureau of History
702 West Kalamazoo Street, P.O. Box 30740
Lansing, MI 48909-8238
(517) 373-3559 Fax: (517) 373-0581
E-mail: museuminfo@michigan.gov
Location: Lansing is in the south-central part of the state on I-96 some eighty miles west of Detroit.
Highlights: Shipwreck history, library, general Michigan history,
Website: www. michigan.gov/museum
General Information: Michigan Historical Museum, founded in 1879, maintains exhibits on lighthouses, 3rd order Fresnel lighthouse lens, underwater archaeology, and regional shipping. The collection includes a Native American dugout canoe and Ausable River guide boat. Archives include photographs, drawings, and documents that cover many Great Lakes subjects.
Admission: No entry fee. Open Monday-Friday, 10 A.M.- 5 P.M., Saturday 10 A.M.-4 P.M., Sunday 1 P.M.-5 P.M. Closed Christmas, New Year's Day, and State holidays.

LUDINGTON, MICHIGAN
White Pine Village
1687 S. Lakeshore Drive
Ludington, MI 49431
(231) 843-4808 Fax: (231) 843-7089
E-mail: info@historicwhitepinevillage.org
Location: Follow signs two miles south on Old US 31 (Pere Marquette Hwy) from Ludington to Iris Road turning west, then 1.5 miles to South Lakeshore Drive and north to White Pine Village

Smith's Guide to Maritime Museums of North America

on the historic Buttersville peninsula. Watch for highway signs south of Ludington Exit from US 31 expressway, three miles south of Ludington. **Highlights:** Third- and fourth-order Fresnel lighthouse lenses, library and archives, gift shop, **Website:** www.historicwhitepinevillage.org

General Information: The White Pine Village, founded in 1976, is a grand historic village — a community of 21 historic buildings located on a bluff overlooking Lake Michigan. The Village, providing a fascinating look into the history of Mason County, features the Rose Hawley Museum, maritime and lumbering museums, Time and Museum of Music.

Through extensive archives and collections, the museum exhibits local history of lumber camps, farms, Great Lakes ships, and trains. A separate building now houses the museum's maritime collection, which evidences the Ludington area as an important port, even today. A wide variety of historical or genealogical research is available on maritime, business and industry, Michigan history, and much more.

Admission: Entry fee. Open Tuesday-Saturday, 10 A.M. - 5 P.M., Apr-Oct; 11 A.M.- 4 P.M., November-March.

MACKINAW CITY, MICHIGAN
Old Mackinac Point Lighthouse Museum
426 N. Huron Avenue
Mackinaw City, MI 49701
Phone: (231) 436-4100
Email: mackinacparks@michigan.gov
Location: The lighthouse is just east of the Colonial Michilimackinac Visitor's Center in Mackinaw City near the south end of the Mackinac Bridge. Take Exit 339 off northbound I-75, turn left at Nicolet and right on Huron.
Highlights: The Old Mackinac Point Lighthouse, Lighthouse Information Center/bookshop, **Website:** www.historicwhitepinevillage.org/net/
General Information: Old Mackinac Point Lighthouse opened to public tours in June of 2004 as a restoration in progress. Just a few hundred feet east of the Mackinac Bridge in Mackinaw City, the castle-like structure guided ships through the Straits of Mackinac from 1892 to 1957. Visitors will see the ongoing restoration, and also exhibits, period settings, and historic interpreters in costume.
Activities: Tours to the top of the lighthouse tower are available. The climb is about 4 stories via 51 steps and an 11-rung, vertical ladder through a narrow access opening. You should be over 4 feet tall and wear shoes that have no chance of falling off your feet while climbing the stairs and ladder (no bare feet or flip-flops).
Admission: Entry fee. Open June 10 – Aug.20, 9 a.m. to 5 p.m. Call for additional hours.

MANISTEE, MICHIGAN
Manistee County Historical Museum
425 River Street
Manistee, MI 49660-1522
(231) 723-5531
Location: Manistee is 120 miles northwest of Grand Rapids on US 31. The Museum is on River Street several blocks west of US 31, on the south side of the Manistee River.
Highlights: Local maritime history, library (500 volumes), ship models, **Website:** www.rootsweb.com/~mimanist/Page63.html
General Information: Manistee County Historical Museum, founded in 1953, is housed in the 1883 A. H. Lyman Drug Company building. Over the years, the Museum's supporters have contributed a wealth of information and artifacts reflecting the lumbering industry and the significant maritime presence in Manistee. A local model maker provides, from time to time, excellent models of ore boats and other vessels of historical interest and recently added 15 more ship models.

Manistee was one of the busiest maritime ports in Michigan; over 3000 port calls were made in one year. And 50 vessels called Manistee home port. Exhibits include information on Great Lakes shipping and passenger boats, a Civil War collection, and numerous historical photos. The Museum's primary focus is on local history with displays that include the Lyman Drug Store, period rooms, and one of the most extensive collections of Victorian antiques and photographs in the state.

Admission: Entry fee. Open Tuesday - Saturday,10 A.M.-5 P.M., June-September; Tuesday-Saturday, 10 A.M.-5 P.M., October-May. Closed Mondays.

MANISTEE, MICHIGAN
SS *City of Milwaukee* (Car Ferry)
National Historic Landmark
99 Arthur Street (US-31 North)
Manistee, MI 49660
(231) 723-3587 E-mail: lspencer@carferry.com
E-mail: carferry@carferry.com
Location: The ship is located at the northwest end of Manistee Lake. It is directly next to the US-31 Highway half of a mile north of downtown Manistee.
Highlights: S.S. *City of Milwaukee* museum ship, 50 slip marina, shipboard bed &breakfast, 25-room motel. **Website:** www.carferry.com
General Information: The S.S. *City of Milwaukee* is the last traditional Great Lakes railroad car ferry. For over a century these hearty car ferries carried passengers and entire freight trains across the treacherous and ice covered waters of the Great Lakes. Built in 1931 it served the Grand Trunk and Ann Arbor railroads and now serves as a National Historic Landmark museum

for the public to enjoy.

The ship features two triple-expansion steam engines and four scotch fire tube boilers. The sturdy ice breaking riveted steel hull is complimented by varnished oak and brass interiors done in the craftsman style. The cavernous car deck of the ship houses 5 boxcars that serve as the gift shop, theater and exhibit spaces.

Also on site is a motel and marina with fishing and picnic areas. The ship and other facilities are available for special events and private party rentals.

Activities: Guided tours, educational programs, special events, membership and volunteer opportunities. Shipboard Bed & Breakfast: June to September. Please contact for more information.

Admission: Fee for tours. May, Fridays - Sundays 11 A.M. - 6 P.M.; June & September, Wednesdays – Sundays 11 A.M. - 6 P.M.; July & August, daily 11 A.M. - 6 P.M. (Dates & hours subject to change. Please call or e-mail ahead of time to confirm.)

MARINE CITY, MICHIGAN
Pride & Heritage Museum and
Peche Island Lighthouse
405 Main Street
Marine City, MI 48039
(810) 765-5446
E-mail: lighthousefriends@marinecitymich.org
Location: Marine City is twenty-eight miles north from Detroit or twenty-eight miles south from Port Huron via I-94 to Rte. 29. The Museum is three blocks west of the St. Clair River on Main Street, which parallels the river.
Highlights: Ship models, local maritime history,
Website: marinecitymich.org/LightHouse.htm
General Information: The Pride & Heritage Museum, founded in 1984, is located near the shore of the St. Clair River in a former school building, most recently a library. The town is a gateway to Canada —the Museum's theme is "preservation of local and nautical history."

Marine City was once the home of the five Belle River Shipbuilding Yards that built over 250 large ships depicted in a new 1890 era diorama. Much of the Museum is devoted to this phase of the city's history and displays ship models, paintings, a steering controller from the lake freighter *Walter Sterling*, and other nautical artifacts, some from diving explorations in theGreat Lakes. The Peche Island Lighthouse is a few blocks away on the St. Clair River shoreline.

Admission: No entry fee. Open Saturday and Sunday, 1 P.M.- 4 P.M., April-October.

MARQUETTE, MICHIGAN
Marquette Maritime Museum
300 Lakeshore Drive, P. O. Box 1096
Marquette, MI 49855
(906) 226-2006
E-mail: mqtmaritimemuseum.com/
Location: Marquette is approximately 170 miles west of Sault Ste. Marie off Rtes. 41 and M-28 on the upper peninsula of Michigan. The Museum is on the corner of East Ridge and Lakeshore Boulevard immediately northeast of the downtown area.
Highlights: The *Double Nickel Deuce* (Coast Guard vessel), ship models, 2nd-order Fresnel lens from Lake Superior's Stannards Rock Light, the largest Fresnel lens on the Great Lakes, 3rd-order Fresnel lens from Big Bay Light, Lake Superior, gift shop,
Website: http://mqtmaritimemuseum.com/
General Information: The Marquette Maritime Museum, founded in 1984 to preserve and promote the rich, rewarding maritime history of Marquette and its relationship to the Great Lakes.

The Museum is housed in the Old Water Works building and exhibits a restored dispro (disappearing propeller) boat, birchbark canoes, photos of sail, steam, freighting, fishing, the Lifesaving Service, and shipwrecks. Also displayed are the house flags of Great Lake ships along with replicas of the dockside offices of the first fishing company and first freight passenger company.

Also exhibited are the forty-foot Coast Guard vessel *Double Nickel Deuce*, retired in the early 1980s after forty years of service on the Great Lakes, and a thirty-six foot Coast Guard vessel #36392.

Activities: Self-guided tours and an excellent video of Marquette maritime history
Admission: Entry fee. Open May 14 – October 22, 10 A.M.-7 P.M., Monday – Sunday, 10 A.M. - 5 P.M.

MUSKEGON, MICHIGAN
Great Lakes Naval Memorial & Museum
1346 Bluff Street
Muskegon, MI 49441-1089
(231) 755-1230 Fax: (231) 755-5883
E-mail: contactus@ginmm.org
Location: Muskegon is thirty-three miles northwest of Grand Rapids off I-96. The Museum is located at the far west end of Muskegon at Père Marquette Park on the south entry channel wall.
Highlights: USS *Silversides* (SS-236) Submarine, The USCGC *McLane WMEC*, and USS LST-393, gift shop, **Website:** www.glnmm.org/
General Information: The Great Lakes Naval Memorial & Museum was founded in 1972 to save

and restore the 311-foot submarine *Silversides*. She was launched at Mare Island, Vallejo, California, and was launched just eight days after the December 7, 1941, attack on Pearl Harbor. She left for the first of her fourteen war patrols on April 30, 1942. She sank a total of 23 ships. Amazingly, only one crewmember was killed in her entire career.

The Coast Guard Cutter *McLane* was authorized under President Calvin Coolidge's administration in 1927 for use during Prohibition as one of a class of 33 "Rum Chasers." The LST-393 was acquired by the Museum in 2000. It is the first LST to go on display as a museum vessel in the U.S.

On shore is a fine exhibition of submarine training equipment and displays of the *Silversides* artifacts.

Activities: Guided tours, lectures, films, radio programs, and education programs; overnight camping program for groups of 20 or more.

Admission: Entry fee. Memberships are available. USS *Silversides* open April, Sat/Sun, 10 A.M.-5:30 P.M.; May, Sat/Sun, 10 A.M.-5:30 P.M., Weekdays, 1 P.M. – 5:30 P.M.; Jun/Aug, every day 10 A.M.-5:30 P.M.; September, Sat/Sun, 10 A.M.-5:30 P.M., weekdays, 1 P.M.-5:30 P.M.; October, Saturday and Sunday, 10 A.M.-5:30 P.M.

MUSKEGON, MICHIGAN
SS *Milwaukee Clipper* (passenger steamer)
SS *Milwaukee* Clipper Preservation, Inc.
2098 Lakeshore Drive, P.O. Box 1370
Muskegon, MI 49443-1370
(231) 755-0990 Fax: (231) 722-3533
E-mail: res035d8@gte.net
Location: The ship is in Muskegon, MI at
Highlights: *Milwaukee Clipper* (retired 1905 Great Lakes passenger steamer), Bed and Breakfast,
Website: www.milwaukeeclipper.com/
General Information: The National Trust Guide characterizes the *Milwaukee Clipper* as "The oldest American passenger steamship on the Great Lakes, (originally) built as the *Juniata* by the American Shipbuilding Company to carry passengers and freight for the Anchor Line of the Erie and Western Transportation Company, a subsidiary of the Pennsylvania Railroad." This splendid 361-foot vessel with six stories filled with historic charm is a museum and painstakingly being restored to her former glory. Winter runs with new automobiles kept the steamer profitable while other cruise ships ceased operation.

Finally, in 1970, she was retired and then restored as a floating exhibit in 1993. Of special note is the quadruple-expansion steam engine installed in 1905, one of the few surviving examples of such a power plant.

Activities: Learning center for passenger trade history on the Great Lakes.
Admission: Entry fee. Open daily 10 A.M.-5 P.M.

NORTHPORT, MICHIGAN
Grand Traverse Lighthouse Museum
15500 North Lighthouse Point Rd.. P.O. Box 43
Northport, MI 49670
Phone/Fax: (231) 386-7195
E-mail: gtlthse@triton.net
Location: Northport is 26 miles north of Traverse City on Rte. 22.
Highlights: Lighthouse,
Website: www.grandtraverselighthouse.com/
General Information: The Grand Traverse Lighthouse, locally called Northport Light, was ordered built by President Millard Fillmore in July of 1850. A brick tower with separate keeper's quarters was constructed at a site east of the present Lighthouse in the state park campground.

The house and tower were deemed inadequate and razed in 1858 when the present structure was built of Milwaukee yellow brick with its roof top tower and cupola sheathed in copper. In 1901 the house was converted to separate quarters for two families. A kitchen was added to one of the apartments in 1916. Still visible is a portion of the lighthouse foundation and the original tower site which was recently located in 1999.

The new site chosen on Lighthouse Point made the light visible from all waterways. A fourth-order Fresnel lens, replacing a smaller, 5th-order lens, was installed in the tower in 1870. At 47 feet above lake level, its magnified light approximated 15,000 candles, and was visible for 12 to 17 miles out on the lake. Whale oil and kerosene powered the light until electrification in 1953. Beginning in 1941 the lighthouse was occupied by U.S. Coast Guard personnel until it was closed in 1972. In that same year, the U.S. Coast Guard replaced the tower light with an automated beacon mounted on a steel skeletal tower. Orange diamond-shaped markers on the steel tower are aids to daytime navigation and are visible six to seven miles out on the lake.

Admission:: Admission fee for Park. Open May 1-October. May: 12 Noon-4 P.M. daily; June-Labor Day, 10 A.M.-7 P.M. daily; Labor Day-October, 12 Noon-4 P.M.

PARADISE, MICHIGAN
Great Lakes Shipwreck Museum
18335 N. Whitefish Point Road
Paradise, MI 49768
1-888-635-1742 (906) 635-1742
(906) 492-3747 Fax: (906) 492-3383
Location: The Museum is located on the Upper Peninsula of Michigan, north of Paradise at

Whitefish Point off M-123 on Whitefish Point Road. It is twenty miles from the famous Tahquamenon Falls.

Highlights: Whitefish Shoal Lighthouse lens, Lake Superior shipwrecks, Whitefish Point Bird Observatory, The Shipwreck Coast Museum Store,

Website: www.shipwreckmuseum.com/

General Information: "From the wreck of the schooner *Invincible* in 1816 to the wreck of the *Edmund Fitzgerald* in 1975, Lake Superior has shown it can be dangerous and unpredictable." The wall-plaque description goes on to say: "Underwater investigation and exploration progressed through the years, but it, too, can be dangerous as some vessels lie in hundreds of feet of water." Violent storms, poor visibility combined with congested shipping lanes at the Point have exacted a heavy toll on ships and lives. The Museum's main display hall and its exhibits are excellent.

A wide variety of exhibits depict 170 years of shipwreck history along with a fascinating diorama display, Lake Superior shipwrecks, artifacts, interpretive signage featured in Museum exhibits, and video documentary (Emmy Award). The Museum is the site of the retrieved *Edmund Fitzgerald* bell. The fully restored Whitefish Point Light Station, established in 1849, is also open for tours.

Admission: Entry Fee. Open daily, 8 A.M.-6 P.M., May 15-October 15. Group travelers' welcome. Administrative office, 111 Ashmus, Sault Ste. Marie, MI 49783, (906) 635-1742.

PORT AUSTIN, MICHIGAN
Huron City Museums
7995 Pioneer Drive
Port Austin, MI 48467-9400
(989) 428-4123 (877) 428-4123
E-mail: info@huroncitymuseums.com
Location: Port Austin is 100 miles due north from Detroit. The small village known as "Huron City" is eight miles east of Port Austin on Rte. 25.
Highlights: U.S. Life-Saving Station, library (10,000 vol), unique life-saving line-cutting tool.
Website: http://huroncitymuseums.com/
General Information: "Huron City" was founded by lumberman Langdon Hubbard in the mid-1850s, and was once the largest village in the "Thumb" of Michigan. When the great fires of 1871 and 1881 devastated the region, it became a farming community. The village, saved by Hubbard's descendants and the William Lyon Phelps Foundation, contains some ten buildings, including the life-saving structure originally built on the Pointe Aux Barques Lighthouse property and moved to this site in the 1960s.

The Point Aux Barques Life-Saving Station

(USLSS), commissioned with the USLSS station at Whitefish Point in 1876, are the three such stations in Michigan. And this station is one of only two in the state open to the public. The Life-Saving Service was the predecessor of today's Coast Guard.

The USLSS building is fully furnished as it might have been during the tenure of the several captains who lived in it. And the adjacent room, originally the boathouse, contains many interesting and important USLSS artifacts, including a Francis Life Car, Breeches Buoy, Lyle Gun, and line projectiles.

On April 12, 1880, the worst disaster in the records of the USLSS occurred affecting Captain Kiah of Point Aux Barques Station in particular. After valiant life-saving attempts by the USLSS crew, their boat turned over on the final return trip from Lake Huron, and one-by-one six of the seven crew slipped under the cold lake water, leaving only Captain Kiah to survive.

Admission: Entry fee. Open July-Labor Day, Wednesday-Monday, 10 A.M.- 5 P.M.

PORT HOPE, MICHIGAN
Lighthouse Park Museum
Lighthouse County Park
7320 Lighthouse Road
Port Hope, MI 48468-9759
(989) 428-4749 Toll Free: 1-877-404-4447
E-mail: huronpks@avci.net
Location: The Museum on Lighthouse road, just off M-25, 5 miles N. of Port Hope.
Highlights: Dive Museum and Thumb Area Diving Information Center.
General Information: Huron City is a museum village where the Life-Saving Station was located after being removed from the nearby shoreline. Lighthouse Park Museum is a short distance from the charming village of Huron City.

During summer months, tours of the Pte. Aux Barques Lighthouse Museum, located on the park grounds, are offered. Artifacts salvaged from shipwrecks along Lake Huron's shoreline may be viewed and lore of the lakes tales are told.
Admission: No entry fee. Open Memorial Day through Labor Day on weekends noon-4 P.M. or by appointment.

PORT HURON, MICHIGAN
Coast Guard Cutter *Bramble*
2336 Military Street
Port Huron, MI 48060
(810) 982-0891 Fax: (810) 982-0053
E-mail: info@phmuseum.org
Location: The *Bramble* is at the Acheson Ventures Port Huron Seaway Terminal on Military Street near Beard Street S. of downtown

Highlights: The *Port Huron* (lightship), gift shop, **Website:** www.phmuseum.org/bramble.html

General Information: The Coast Guard Cutter *Bramble* was commissioned in 1944. Following World War II, the *Bramble* participated in "Operation Crossroads," the first test of an atomic bomb's effect on surface ships, at Bikini Island. In 1957, along with the cutters *Spar* and *Storis*, she headed for the Northwest Passage, traveling through the Bearing Straits and Arctic Ocean. Traveling for 64 days through 4500 miles of partially uncharted waters, the vessels finally reached the Atlantic Ocean. These three surface vessels were the first to circumnavigate the North American Continent, an ambition mariners have had for more than 400 years.

In 1962, the *Bramble* transferred to Detroit to perform the missions of search and rescue, icebreaking, and law enforcement throughout the Great Lakes, in addition to aids to navigation. In 1975, the *Bramble* reported to Port Huron. After Great Lakes service, she was decommissioned in 2003 to be used as a museum.

Activities: Tour the *Bramble*.

Admission: Entry fee: Open 7 days, Memorial Day to Labor Day – 11A.M. to 5 P.M., September through December, Thursday through Monday, April through May, Thursday through Monday. closed January through March.

PORT HURON, MICHIGAN
Port Huron **Lightship Museum**
Pine Grove Park
1115 6th Street
Port Huron, MI 48060-5346
(810) 982-0891 Fax: (810) 982-0053
E-mail: lightship@phmuseum.org
Location: The Museum is on Business Loop 69, one-half mile south of the Blue Water International Bridge at Pine Grove Park.
Highlights: The *Port Huron* (lightship), gift shop, **Website:** www.phmuseum.org
General Information: Acquired by the city of Port Huron, the ninety-foot *Huron* Lightship is located on the beautiful St. Clair River— the main shipping channel from Lake Huron to Lake Erie — at Pine Grove Park as a tribute to her vigilance.

The Huron Lightship Museum is operated by the Port Huron Museum Lightships were floating lighthouses anchored in areas where it was too deep, expensive, or impractical to construct a lighthouse. The *Huron* is the smallest type of lightship. Lightships displayed a light at the top of a mast for maximum sighting distance. Also, fog signals were on board to help in times of limited visibility. The *Huron* was affectionately known as "Old B.O." because of the familiar sound her horn made.

Built in 1920, *Huron* was designated as Lightship 103 but later re-named U.S. Coast Guard WLV 526. She was stationed at various shoals on Lake Michigan until 1935, and then transferred to Corsica Shoals in Lake Huron. There, for the next thirty-six years, she guided mariners into the narrow dredged channel of lower Lake Huron leading to the St. Clair River. She was retired from active service in 1971.

Admission: Entry fee. Memberships available. Open Apr – Mid-September Other times by appointment.

PORT HURON, MICHIGAN
Port Huron Museum
1115 6th Street
Port Huron, MI 48060-5346
(810) 982-0891 Fax: (810) 982-0053
E-mail: info@phmuseum.org
Location: The Museum is on Sixth Street between Wall and Court Streets downtown one block west of Rte. 29 and Business Loop 69.
Highlights: Pilot house of Great Lakes steamer, 300 years of local history, ship models, diving gear, gift shop, **Website:** www.phmuseum.org
General Information: The Port Huron Museum opened in 1968 in the old Port Huron 1904 Andrew Carnegie Library building. The Museum displays, in its Marine Gallery, a wide variety of maritime historical items, including models of tugs, St. Clair River steamers, Great Lakes steamers and ore ships, a pioneer log, and exhibits of fine art. Also displayed are many items related to Thomas A. Edison from his nine-year residence in Port Huron during his youth.

The Museum traces 300 years of local history with a gallery dedicated to "Blue Water History." A pilothouse in excellent condition containing equipment from a variety of Great Lakes steamers is in the Museum, where you can turn the wheel, ring the bell, and feel the excitement of the Great Lakes ships.

The Museum also maintains two vessels: the *Huron* Lightship Museum, (see separate entry) located on the St. Clair River adjacent to Pine Grove Park; and the CG Cutter *Bramble* at the Port Huron Seaway Terminal on the St. Clair River, open daily Mem. Day-Labor Day, 11 A.M. – 5 P.M. and then to Dec. Thurs – Mon.

Activities: Local volunteer groups include the Lake Huron Lore Marine Society and 10 other support groups.

Admission: Entry fee. Open Wednesday-Sunday, 1 P.M. -5 P.M., year-round. Closed holidays.

PORT SANILAC, MICHIGAN
Sanilac County Historical Village and Museum
228 So. Ridge Street, P. O. Box 158
Port Sanilac, MI 48469-9704
810-622-9946 E-M: sanilacmuseum@gmail.com
Location: Port Sanilac is about 100 miles north of
Detroit. From Detroit take I-94 northeast fifty-
eight miles to Port Huron. Exit onto Rte. M-25
north and travel thirty-three miles to Port Sanilac,
in the "Thumb" of Michigan along Lake Huron.
The Museum is at the south entrance to Port
Sanilac.
Highlights: Ship models, artifacts taken off the
shipwreck *Regina*, Navigational instruments,
marine artifacts,
Website: www.sanilaccountymuseum.org/
    General Information: Sanilac Historical
Museum was founded in 1964 as a countywide
institution for the study and preservation of local
history. Sanilac was one of the many shipping ports
for early lake transportation in the early 1800s.
Included in the village is the Port Sanilac
Lighthouse (c. 1886). The village now supports
the first Harbor of Refuge along the Great Lakes
for pleasure craft.
    The Museum's displays depict early shipping,
bringing passengers and freight out of Detroit, and
one room is devoted to marine artifacts — some
from the shipwrecks along the shore.
    Activities: Tour a 20-room Victorian mansion
with contents of mansion all original from 1875
(all furnishings), log cabin, general store with
giftshop, dairy museum, one-room schoolhouse,
carriage barn: all with interesting displays.
    Admission: Entry Fee. Open mid-June-
September, Wednesday through Saturday,
11 A.M.- 4:30 P.M.; Sunday, Noon - 4:30 P.M.
Closed Monday and Tuesday.

PRESQUE ISLE, MICHIGAN
Presque Isle Lighthouse and Museum
4500 East Grand Lake Road
Presque Isle, MI 49777
(989) 595-5419
E-mail: neilsbungalow@yahoo.com
Location: Presque Isle is twenty-three miles is
twenty-three miles north of Alpena and twenty
miles south of Rogers City, east off US 23 on
Grand Lake Road.
Highlights: Old Presque Lighthouse and New
Presque Lighthouse, Ship models, Fresnel
lighthouse lens, gift shop,
Website: www.keepershouse.org/
    General Information: The Old Presque Isle
Lighthouse and Museum, on the eastern shoreline
of Lake Huron, operated for 30 years and is still
maintained in excellent condition. Then a new,
taller lighthouse was built in 1870 just a mile away.
    Presque Isle was the finest port open to Great
Lakes mariners in the mid-nineteenth century. And
in 1914, previously discovered limestone, an
important ingredient in the making of steel, was

mined here and created the development of a major
port and the establishment of a Great Lakes
shipping line of ore ships.
    Collection includes antiques focusing on
nineteenth- century lighthouse service and
seafaring life. Also included are a variety of
antique nautical instruments and tools, foghorns,
capstans, and ship models. Also shown is a Fresnel
lighthouse lens made in France and the type used in
Great Lakes lighthouses. And the old courthouse
bell — over 3000 pounds — is on the site. There is
even a ghost story a mystery light that has been
seen by many.
    Admission: Entry fee. Open daily
May 15-October 15, 9 A.M.-6 P.M.

ROGERS CITY, MICHIGAN
Presque Isle County Historical Museum
176 West Michigan Avenue
P.O. Box 175
Rogers City, MI 49779
989-734-4121 EM: bradleymuseum@yahoo.com
Location: Presque Isle County is fifty miles
southeast of Mackinaw City on US 23. The
Museum is one block west of business Rte. 23 on
West Michigan Avenue in Rogers City.
Highlights: Great Lakes shipping history, ship
models
    General Information: The Presque Isle
County Historical Museum is in the former home
of Calcite President Carl D. Bradley. The Museum
displays Indian artifacts, 1890s general store,
Victorian music room, lumbering, farming, and
shipping industries items.
    Focusing on Great Lakes shipping history, the
Museum's archives include ship's logs and an
original ship's model of the *Carl D. Bradley*, which
sank November 18, 1958, off Beaver Island in
Lake Michigan. Also displayed is an original
Ship's model of the *John G. Munson* out of Port of
Calcite. Calcite is limestone, an important
ingredient in steel making and mined at Rogers
City in the world's largest limestone mine.
    Admission: No entry fee, but suggested
donations. Open Monday-Friday, 12 noon-4 P.M.,
June-October. Open Monday-Saturday, 12 noon -4
P.M., June - October.

SAGINAW, MICHIGAN
Castle Museum of Saginaw County
Historical Society of Saginaw County History
500 Federal Avenue
Saginaw, MI 48607
(989) 752-2861 Fax: (989) 752-1533
Email: info@castlemuseum.org
Location: Saginaw is eighty miles northwest from
Detroit on the Saginaw River and ten miles south
of Saginaw Bay on Lake Huron.
Highlights: Saginaw gig (from 1870), Voyageur
freight canoe, identification items from USS
Saginaw (LST-1188),
Website: www.castlemuseum.org/

General Information: The Castle Museum of Saginaw County History is in the renovated 1897 "French chateau" post office building. The Museum is home to the Saginaw Voyageurs and the Saginaw Archaeological Commission. It traces the industrial and social development of Saginaw Valley.

Admission: Entry fee. Open Tuesday -Saturday, 10 A.M.-4:30 P.M., Sunday, 1 P.M.-4:30 P.M. Closed holidays.

ST. JAMES, MICHIGAN
Marine Museum
Beaver Island Historical Society
26275 Main Street, P.O. Box 263
St. James, MI 49782
(231) 448-2254 or 2106
E-mail: Phyllis@beaverisland.k12.mi.us
Location: Beaver Island is some thirty miles from the mainland in Lake Michigan and can be reached only by boat or airplane. Island Airways flies from Charlevoix Airport several times a day — a fifteen-minute ride. By boat, a two- and one-quarter-hour trip one to three times a day. Charlevoix is 267 miles north of Detroit.
Highlights: Local shipping history, library, restored commercial fishing vessels,
Website: www.beaverisland.net/history
General Information: Memories of disasters, which overtook men, and ships of the area and the efforts of the Coast Guard and Lighthouse Services are part of the local history. Archives include photographs and material relevant to local vessels. The files are housed at the Print Shop office as well as at the marine museum. Exhibits include material on commercial fishing, ships of local interest, lighthouses and life-saving in the area, lumbering, the history of other islands in the Beaver archipelago, shipwrecks, and shipbuilding. Exhibits illustrate also the methods of gill net, pound-net, and trap-net fishing.

The Society is engaged in the restoration and preservation of two 1930s vessels — one a gill-net fishing boat and the other a trap-net boat. Both wooden vessels will be open for public inspection.

Admission: Entry fee. Open Monday-Saturday, 11 A.M.-5 P.M., Sunday Noon-3 P.M., mid-June through Labor day, and off-season by appointment.

SAULT STE. MARIE, MICHIGAN
Museum Ship *Valley Camp*
Le Sault de Ste. Marie Historical Sites, Inc.
501 East Water Street
Sault Ste. Marie, MI 49783 Toll-free: 1- 888-744-7867 (906) 632-3658
Fax: 906/632-9344
E-mail: On web site

Location: Sault Ste. Marie is on Michigan's Upper Peninsula on I-75 (fifty-five miles north of Mackinaw City). The Museum ship is located five blocks east of the Soo locks on the corner of Johnson and Portage on the St. Marys River.
Highlights: Museum Ship *Valley Camp* (listed on National Register of Historic Places), ship models, Great Lakes Hall of Fame, Ship's Store, **Website:** www.thevalleycamp.com/
General Information: Museum Ship *Valley Camp* is a straight-deck 550-foot Great Lakes bulk freighter built in 1917 and taken out of service in 1966. The maritime museum is in holds 2 and 3, where information on the shipwrecked *Edmund Fitzgerald*, a freighter that sank in over 500 feet of water in Lake Superior in 1975, is shown, including two lifeboats recovered from the *Fitzgerald*.

Walk-in tours of the *Valley Camp* include the pilothouse, captain's quarters, the Marine Museum, and an aquarium. Other maritime exhibits in the cargo holds include displays on lifeboats, ship models, photographs, the Kemp Marina, picnic areas — all of these on the St. Marys River Front Park.
Activities: Tour of the Great Lakes freighter
Admission: Entry fee. Open daily, 10 A.M.-7 P.M., July and August (last ticket sold 8 P.M.). Sept. 1-Oct. 15 (last ticket sold 5 P.M.); daily, 9 A.M.-9 P.M.,

SAULT STE. MARIE, MICHIGAN
Soo Locks Information Center
300 W. Portage Ave., P.O. Box 666
Sault Ste. Marie, MI 49783
1-800-MI-SAULT (906) 253-9101
E-mail: ninelakes@yahoo.com
Location: Sault Ste. Marie is on the Upper Peninsula of Michigan and adjacent to Sault Ste. Marie, Ontario. *Highlights:* Canal locks history, **Website:** www. soolocksvisitorscenter.com/SLVCA/center.html
General Information: The St. Marys River is the only water connection between Lake Superior and the other Great Lakes. On May 31, 1855, the newly constructed locks were turned over to the state, and in 1881 the locks were transferred to the United States Government. Since that time, the Corps of Engineers has taken many steps to enhance the beauty of the Soo Locks and to make the locks, in addition to their importance to commerce, one of the finest tourist attractions in the United States.

The Soo Locks are, in fact, four locks — MacArthur, Poe, Davis, and Sabin — lowering or raising deep-draft international vessels twenty-one feet. Two of the locks will be converted to one large lock (similar to the Poe) upon Congressional appropriation. The Center contains a working model of a lock, which illustrates the entire operation on how our vast fleet of ore, coal, grain (and other freight) carriers, can move easily from one lake to another. A motion picture theatre features a film on the history and operation of the locks. And a crew of knowledgeable receptionists staff the Visitor's Center during the season. As ships transit the locks, such general information as size, destination, kind of cargo, tonnage, and nationality is provided through the public address system to visitors.

Admission: Open mid-May-November, 8 A.M. – 8 P.M. Also, a raised out-door ship-viewing area is next door along the canal lock.

SOUTH HAVEN, MICHIGAN

Michigan Maritime Museum
260 Dyckman Avenue at the Bridge
South Haven, MI 49090-1065
1-800-747-3810 (269) 637-8078
Fax: (616) 637-1594
E-mail: info@michiganmaritimemuseum.org
Location: South Haven is 180 miles due west of Detroit and just north of I-94. Take I-196 north at Benton Harbor to Exit 20 (Phoenix Street) west into South Haven. Turn north on Broadway across the small bridge and turn left at Black River Street into parking lot.
Highlights: Historic restored vessels, US Life-Saving and Coast Guard exhibits, *Ship's Lamp* (newsletter), library (1,000 volumes), museum store,
Website: www.michiganmaritimemuseum.org/
General Information: Michigan Maritime Museum, founded in 1976, contains collections of historically restored vessels; archival materials; photos; ship and small-craft models; marine art; tools and technological implements; personal possessions, all of which pertain to the Great Lakes regional maritime history.

Explore the Museum's exhibits and discover how people used schooners and steamers on Michigan's Great Lakes. And learn about the boat builders, too. Visitors can examine U.S. Life-Saving rescue boats and the Life-Saving Stations in an on-site U.S. Life-Saving Station with crew's quarters (c. 1900), where they were stationed. Other displays include marine art and a mapping exhibit.

The Museum's center building contains two exhibit galleries and the Marialyce Canonie Great Lakes Research Library. Additional facilities include a 500-foot waterfront boardwalk, a boatbuilding workshop, historical commercial fishtug, three U.S. Coast Guard boats, and the marine motor boat collection.

Activities: Guided tours, lectures, films, gallery talks, hobby workshops, and educational programs.
Admission: Entry fee. Memberships are available. Open Summer Monday-Saturday, 10 A.M.- 5 P.M., Sunday, 12 Noon-5 P.M. For Winter hours, call (616) 637-8078. Closed major holidays.

TRAVERSE CITY, MICHIGAN

Madeline (replica schooner)
Maritime Heritage Alliance
322 Sixth Street
P.O. Box 1108
Traverse City, MI 49684
(231) 946-2647
E-mail: Kelly@maritimeheritageallince.org
Location: Traverse City is off US-31. Upon arrival at the bottom of Traverse Bay, turn east to Clinch Park Marina at the bayfront and end of Union Street. The ship is at the marina.
Highlights: Madeline (92-foot replica schooner), small-craft collection, **Website:** www.mhatc.net
General Information: The Topsail Schooner *Madeline*, launched on June 24, 1990, after a five-year construction period, is docked and open for tours at the breakwall at Clinch Park Marina just one block from historic downtown Traverse City.

Madeline's soaring white pine masts provide a beautiful centerpiece for the scenic West Grand Traverse Bay waterfront. The original *Madeline* was a merchant schooner built at Fairport, Ohio in 1845. In 1850, her crew anchored for the winter in West Bay where William, Michael, and John Fitzgerald learned from teacher S. E. Wait. *Madeline*, therefore, is recorded as the first public school in Traverse City. These three brothers all became Great Lakes ship captains. John Fitzgerald's grandson, Edmund Fitzgerald became Chairman of Northwestern Mutual Life Insurance Company in Milwaukee and the ill-fated *Edmund Fitzgerald* was named for him.

The present-day *Madeline* continues this educational tradition, regularly hosting school groups for historic tours, and sailing to ports throughout the Great Lakes as an ambassador of the grand Traverse area's maritime heritage.

The Maritime Heritage Alliance (MHA) of Northern Lake Michigan, organized in 1982, has collected a fleet of nearly thirty vessels. These includes two Mackinaw boats, the *Gracie L* and *Estella*, an original 1890s pulling boat; *Witchcraft*, a 33-foot sloop; a turn-of-the-century steel-hulled East Jordan skiff; and an original Star Olympic- class-racing sloop.
Admission: No entry fee, but donations accepted. *Madeline* is open for tours daily 10 A.M.-6 P.M., May-September. Large groups by appointment. Each port-of-call will be publicized as "Schooner Days" with displays of ship handling,

nautical skills, and historical artifacts. Call for times.

WHITEHALL, MICHIGAN
White River Light Station Museum
6199 Murray Road
Whitehall, MI 49461
(231) 894-8265 Fax: (231) 766-3027
E-mail: curator@whiteriverlightstation.org
Location: Whitehall is on the western shoreline of Michigan, nineteen miles north of Muskegon off US 31 White Lake Drive Exit, turn right heading west to road ends at White Lake, go left on South Shore Drive and follow to next stop sign, turn right continuing on South Shore Drive to end at 4-way stop. To straight through and now you are on Murray Road. Go 1 mile to Museum.
Highlights: White River lighthouse, Fresnel 4th-order lens,
Website: www.whiteriverlightstation.org/
General Information: Lumbering made Muskegon/White Lake the "The Lumber Queen of the World," with shipping over the Great Lakes the primary transportation route. Lighthouses played a central role in Great Lakes commerce as essential guides in these "Inland Seas."

The 1875 lighthouse, purchased by the Township and now a museum, depicts the bustling enterprises of shipping, logging, the Lighthouse Service, the fishing industry, and the resort center activities through a variety of displays, which include ship artifacts and navigational devices. Climb a spiraling wrought-iron staircase for a breathtaking view of Lake Michigan and its sand dunes.
Admission: Entry fee. Open June-August.; Tuesday-Friday, 11 A.M.-5 P.M., Saturday and Sunday, noon-5 P.M., September, weekends noon - 5 P.M. Closed on Mondays.

MINNESOTA

ALEXANDRIA, MINNESOTA
Minnesota Lakes Maritime Museum
203 – 3rd Avenue W, P.O. Box 1216
Alexandria, MN 56308
320-759-1114 Fax: 320-759-1101
E-mail: boat@mnlakesmaritime.org
Location: The museum is 61-miles northwest from St. Cloud on I-94.
Highlights: Chain of Lakes Classic Boat Show Marine art, Museum Store
Web Site: http://www.mnlakesmaritime.org/
General Information: The Minnesota Lakes Maritime Museum is dedicated to the preservation of antique and classic watercraft, resort memorabilia and sporting equipment used on the Minnesota lakes. From handcrafted wood boats to grand hotels and private fishing clubs, the Minnesota lakes have a rich and colorful maritime and resorting tradition reaching back nearly a century and a half.

Of special interest is an overview presented of the resort hotel industry on Lake Minnetonka, and local resort history. Featured is Bedman's Beach Resort, one of the state's oldest resorts dating back to the late 1800's. In addition, The Pete and Mado Peterson Gallery includes the history of these Alexandria area grand hotels: The Letson House, Blakes Hotel, Geneva Hotel, Dickinson Inn and the others.

Four other galleries include the Mahan-Zimmerman Gallery, Peterson Gallery, the Mammel Foundation Exhibit Hall, and Fishing Gallery.
Activities: Group tours, boat show
Admission: Entry fee. Mid-May to Mid-October. Museum Hours: Monday through Friday 9 a.m. – 5 p.m. Saturday 10 a.m. -5 p. m. Sunday closed.

DULUTH, MINNESOTA
Lake Superior Maritime Visitor Center
Detroit District, US Army/Engineers
600 Lake Avenue South
P.O. Box 177
Duluth, MN 55801-0177
Phone: (218) 727-2497 FAX: (218) 720-5270
E-mail: info@lsmma.com
Reference Collection: (715) 394-8359,
Location: In Duluth, the Museum sits on shore of Lake Superior alongside primary entry for Duluth-Superior harbor; foot of Canal Park Drive near Aerial Lift Bridge.
Highlights: Two-story fore- and aft-steam engine, ship models (over forty), Corps of Engineers History Exhibit, *The Nor'Easter* (newsletter), replica pilothouse and ship cabins, Archival collections, **Website:** www.lsmma.com
General Information: Lake Superior Maritime Visitor Center was founded in 1973 by U.S. Army Corps of Engineers. The Corps and the Lake Superior Marine Museum Association have developed a fine maritime collection with shipwreck relics, full-sized replica pilothouse and ship cabins, hardhat diving gear, photographs, charts, marine engines, and numerous ship models. Colorful exhibits explore such subjects as the anatomy of an ore boat, Lake Superior shipwrecks, harbor dredging operations, mining, lumbering, and the grain trade.

The Museum is uniquely situated on the shore of Lake Superior adjacent to the Duluth-Superior "Twin Ports" Harbor entrance channel, where 1,100 commercial ships pass by annually and where crowds often gather to watch. TV monitors note the arrival of ships with names, tonnage, and cargo. Lively audiovisual programs, operating radar, and ship-to-shore radio keep visitors

informed and interested in current harbor activity. Archival collections are also maintained at the nearby University of Wisconsin-Superior Hill Library for use byscholars and steamboat fans.
Admission: No entry fee. Memberships are available. Spring Hours: March 17, Sunday – Thursday10 AM - 4:30 PM; Friday and Saturday 10:00 AM - 6:00 PM.; Summer Hours- May 26, daily 10 AM - 9:00 PM.

DULUTH, MINNESOTA
Leif Erikson **Viking Ship Restoration Project**
P.O. Box 411
Duluth, MN 55801
(218) 727-4767   Fax: (218) 727) 4776
E-mail: duluthvikingship@gmail.com
Location: The ship is in Leif Erikson Park.
Highlights: Viking ship replica* and photo exhibit.
Website: www.leiferiksonvikingship.com/
General Information: Leif Erikson Park is the *Location* of the forty-two-foot Viking ship replica, built in Bergen, Norway, which sailed to Boston, then to Duluth in 1926—arrived June 23, 1927. Plans for the restored ship includes a building and permanent roof structure under which is displayed a photo exhibit alongside.
Admission: No entry fee. Open daily, 6 A.M. - 10 P.M., year-round.   * See also Heritage *Hjemkomst* Interpretive Center and Longship Company, Ltd.

DULUTH, MINNESOTA
SS *William A. Irvin* **Ore Boat**
350 Harbor Drive
Duluth, MN 55802-2600
(218) 722-5573
Shipboard office: (218) 722-7876
Location: Ship is located next to on-waterfront Convention Center in downtown Duluth.
Highlights: The SS *William A. Irvin* (ore boat), gift shop (on board), Coast Guard Cutter, *Sundew*, and tug.
Website: www.williamairvin.com
General Information: The 1937 SS *William A. Irvin*, once the flagship of United States Steel's Great Lakes Fleet, journeyed the inland waters from 1938 to 1978. The *Irvin* transported loads of coal and iron ore — up to 14,000 tons at a time — from Duluth to the lower ports of the Great Lakes. The straight-decker iron ore carrier *Irvin* is berthed on the waterfront behind the Duluth Entertainment Convention Center, where she is open for tours with displays aboard.

Explore the decks and compartments of the 610-foot ship, including the intricate workings of the engine room, the elaborate guest staterooms

and galley, and the pilothouse. The great ship has been restored to its original grandeur and is kept in such fine shape that it could be returned to service quickly.
Admission: Entry fee. Open daily: Summer, Sun - Thurs 9 A.M.- 6 P.M.; Fri/Sat 9 A.M. – 8 P.M.

McGREGOR, MINNESOTA
Big Sandy Lake Lock and Dam
22205 531st Lane
McGregor, MN 55760-0192
(218) 426-3482 Fax: (218) 426-4815
E-mail: lake.sandy@mvp02.usace.army.mil
Location: Big Sandy Lake is forty miles west of Duluth and thirteen miles north of McGregor on Rte. 65 in the Big Sandy Lake Recreation Area.
Highlights: Lock and dam history,
Website: www.mvp.usace.army.mil/recreation/default.asp?pageid=148
General Information: The Big Sandy Lake Lock and Dam were originally built of wood in 1895, and in 1911 the structures were replaced by concrete. The purpose of the Lock was to transport timber from the Big Sandy Lake to the nearby Mississippi River. A museum has been established in the lock tender's home, where information on the lock and dam are located along with Indian artifacts and displays depicting the history of fur trading in the area.
Admission: No entry fee. Open daily, 7:30 A.M.-10 P.M., mid-May to mid-September.

MOORHEAD, MINNESOTA
Heritage *Hjemkomst* **Interpretive Center**
202 1st Avenue North
Moorhead, MN 56560
(218) 299-5515 Fax: 218/299-5518
E-mail: michelle.griffin@ci.moorhead.mn.us
Location: From Minneapolis take I-94 to Moorhead (just across from Fargo, North Dakota). Take the 8th Street north exit (Rte. 75) to the intersection of 1st Avenue North.
Highlights: The *Hjemkomst* (Viking ship reproduction), Heritage Gift Shop,
Website: www.hjemkomst-center.com
General Information: Heritage *Hjemkomst* Interpretive Center, was founded in 1983 to create a home for the reproduction of the Viking ship, *Hjemkomst* (pn. YEM-komst). At the Center, you can see how one man made a dream come true.

"A Dream Is a Dream" tells the story of the building of a Viking ship until the end of its incredible voyage on July 19, 1982, in Bergen, Norway, after sailing more than 6,100 miles from Duluth, Minnesota, across the Atlantic. The museum has much to offer with permanent and traveling displays and interpretive exhibits.

Activities: Audiovisual presentations about exhibits, documentary film on *Hjemkomst* (twenty-eight minutes).
Admission: Entry fee. Open Monday-Saturday, 9 A.M.-5 P.M., Sunday noon-5 P.M., year-round.

TWO HARBORS, MINNESOTA
Lighthouse Point and Harbor Museum
P.O. Box 128
Two Harbors, MN 55616
Toll free: 1-800-777-7384   (218) 834-4898
E-mail: thchamber@twoharborschamber.com
Location: Lighthouse Point is two blocks from the Lake County Historic Depot on Waterfront Drive and South Avenue.
Highlights: Local Two Harbors history, major iron ore shipping harbor, and Keeper's Quarters Bed and Breakfast, and tug *Edna G.* **Website:** www.twoharborschamber.com/lighthouse.htm
General Information: The Lighthouse Point and Harbor Museum is one of the few active lighthouses on Lake Superior. The Museum explores the development of Agate Bay, where the first shipment of iron ore left the state of Minnesota in 1884 with ore mined at Soudan Iron Mine. The lighthouse quickly became necessary.
The Lighthouse Station has a total of six structures on the site, the Fog Horn Building, the Oil house, the Boat House, the Assistant Keepers House, the lighthouse, and garage. Also on the site is a restored "pilot house" from a wrecked iron-ore boat — the *Frontenac* ore boat and a Great Lakes fishing boat.
Activities: Guided tours take you to the top of the light tower and into the restored, turn-of-the-century Assistant Keeper's House. The Keeper's Quarters have been turned into a Bed and Breakfast.
Activities: For divers, sunken ore boat *Ely*.
Admission: Entry fee. Open daily 9 A.M.-7 P.M., May 1 - October 31.

TWO HARBORS, MINNESOTA
Split Rock Lighthouse Historic Site
3713 Split Rock Lighthouse Road
Two Harbors, MN 55616
(218) 226-6372 Fax: 226-6373
E-mail: splitrock@mnhs.org
Location: From Minneapolis/St. Paul travel north on I-35 to Duluth. Then head northeast on Rte. 61 forty-six miles to Split Rock State Park, which is 20 miles north of Two Harbors.
Highlights: Split Rock Lighthouse, fog-signal building, restored light-keepers residence, gift shop, **Website:** www.mnhs.org/places/sites/srl/
General Information: The 1910 Split Rock Lighthouse was established as a museum in 1976

and became one of Minnesota's best-known landmarks almost as soon as it was opened. Today, restored to its pre-1924 appearance by the Minnesota Historical Society, it offers visitors a glimpse of lighthouse duty in the years when the isolated station could only be reached by water.
Split Rock Lighthouse owes its existence to the storms of 1905, especially to a record gale on November 28 that damaged nearly 30 ships on Lake Superior alone. The underpowered steel freighters, unable to cope with northeast winds in excess of 60 miles per hour that raged for more than half a day, were driven across the lake toward the rocky North Shore.
The Museum exhibits artifacts pertaining to the navigational and maritime history of the Great Lakes, the iron ore industry, and commercial fishing.
Activities: Visitors to the historic site may tour the Lighthouse, fog-signal building, and the restored keeper's dwelling; a visitor center and museum shop are adjacent to the Lighthouse. The center houses a 90-seat theatre which features the 22-minute film, "Split Rock Light: Tribute to the Age of Steel" and a twenty-two-minute documentary on the development of Split Rock Lighthouse.
Admission: Entry fee. Summer: Historic buildings, visitor center and grounds open daily May 15 through Oct. 15: 10 A.M. to 6 P.M. Winter: Jan. through May 14: Visitor Center only open Sat. and Sun., 11 A.M. to 4 P.M. No admission fee, but a State Park vehicle permit is required for parking. Closed Thanksgiving weekend, the month of December and Easter Sunday. School season may vary.

WARROAD, MINNESOTA
Warroad Heritage Center and Museum
202 Main Street NE,   P.O. Box 688
Warroad, MN 56763-2344
(218) 386-2500 E-mail: wcoc@wiktel.com
Location: Warroad is some 300-plus miles north of Minneapolis on Highway 11 on the south shore of the Big Traverse area of the Lake of the Woods— a lake that borders the U.S. and Canada. The Museum is located in the Heritage Center.
Highlights: Lake steamer era history
General Information: The Warroad Historical Society exhibits artifacts from the Warroad area: American Indian, commercial fishing, Northwest Angle, pioneer, military, lake boats, and other items from the steamer era of the Lake of the Woods trade, where, at one time, there were over 100 steamers on the lake. The *Na Ma Puk*, named for the Indian Chief of Warroad, was the first American steamer on the lake and was built by a local contractor in 1899.

Admission: No entry fee. Open: Monday-Saturday, 1 P.M. – 5 P.M.; Sunday 1 P.M. – 4 P.M

WINONA, MINNESOTA
Minnesota Marine Art Museum
800 Riverview Drive
Winona, MN 55987-2272
Toll free 1-866-940-6626
Fax: (507) 474-6625
lgorrell@minnesotamarineart.org
Location: The museum is along the Mississippi Riverfront in Winona
Highlights: William A. Thompson Dredge, Marine art, Museum Store,
Web Site: http://www.minnesotamarineart.org/
General Information: The Minnesota Marine Art Museum, opened July 27th, 2006, currently features four major art collections, making it a regional and national attraction. The collections include Burrichter-Kierlin Marine Art Collection, on loan to the museum, features oil paintings, watercolors and three-dimensional marine art objects from a variety of countries and periods created by many of the world's most important marine artists.

The Leo and Marilyn Smith Folk Art Collection consists of distinctive wood carved and hand painted sculptures that capture the spirit of small town river life. A rare collection of amazing photographs and maps by Henry Peter Bosse reflect 19th century Mississippi River life and landscapes.

Finally, U.S. Army Corps of Engineers' Dredge *William A. Thompson* will become a river history exhibit, docked adjacent to the museum once decommissioned in 2007 and open for display in 2008.
Activities: Mini-Camp for art making classes
Admission: Entry fee. Museum Hours: Tuesday-Saturday 10 a.m. -5 p. m. Sunday 11 a. m. -5 p. m. Closed Monday

MISSISSIPPI

BILOXI, MISSISSIPPI
Maritime Seafood Industry Museum
115 East 1st Street P.O. Box 1907
Biloxi, MS 39533-4703
(228) 435-6320 Fax: (228) 435-6309
E-mail: info@maritimemuseum.org
Location: From Mobile, Alabama, take I-10 southwest to exit 46 (I-110). Follow it south to Rte. 90 in Ocean Springs. Head east two miles, watching for Museum signs. Through the gates into Point Cadet Plaza, the Museum is on the right.
Highlights: The BILOXI SCHOONERS: *Glenn L. Swetman* and *Mike Sekul*, Coastal Geology,

seafood industry workboats, *The Mains'l* (newsletter), oystering history,
Website: www.maritimemuseum.org/
General Information: The Maritime Seafood Industry Museum, founded in 1983 and opened March 1986 in a renovated Coast Guard barracks. The Museum contains a wide variety of exhibits that include "Coastal Geology," explaining the development of the Mississippi Gulf Coast over a period of 100 years; "Biloxi's Early Fishermen and Colonial Dreams," describing the reasons for settlement during the period of 1699-1810; "Seafood Capital of the World," explaining the development of the fishing industry from 1881 to 1900; and "Boats of Biloxi," relating the history of working vessels. Collections contain photographs, objects, and implements that have been used during the industry's long and colorful history.

Also featured are nets for both commercial and recreational fishing and Biloxi's seafood workers, oystering, shrimping, and crabbing.

The schooner *Glenn L. Swetman,* a traditional topsail, two-masted wooden oyster schooner, was launched in 1989. The schooner *Mike Sekul* was launched in 1994 is used to revive the great Schooners offer two- and one-half-hour, half-day, full-day, and multi-day charters with professional captain and crew. Point Cadet Marina, Biloxi, is the homeport tradition of schooner racing.
Activities: The Biloxi Schooners offer two-and one-half hour, half-day, and multi-day charters with professional captain and crew. Point Cadet Marina, Biloxi, is the home port.
Admission: Entry fee. Open Monday-Saturday, 9 A.M.-4:30 P.M.

BILOXI, MISSISSIPPI
Old Lighthouse
Porter Avenue & US 90, P.O. Box 408
Biloxi, MS 39530
228-435-6244
Location: On Gulf of Mexico shoreline adjacent to public beaches.
Highlights: Lighthouse,
Website:
www.cr.nps.gov/maritime/light/biloxi.htm
General Information: The Old Lighthouse was built in 1847 in Baltimore, Maryland, and was shipped to Biloxi on a brig in 1848. Originally surrounded by water on three sides, the lighthouse now stands 100 yards north of the shoreline. It was painted black after the Civil War because of rust, not in commemoration of President Lincoln's death as was once thought. Today only a small band near the top is black.
Admission: Entry fee. Open Monday-Saturday, 10 A.M. year-round. Closed holidays.

PASCAGOULA, MISSISSIPPI
Scranton **Floating Museum**
City of Pascagoula
Drawer 908
Pascagoula, MS 39567
(601) 232-7073
Location: Pascagoula is twenty miles east of Biloxi in the southeast corner of the state. The Museum (the 70-foot-shrimp-boat *Scranton*) is on the water just north from Rte. 90 (west Pascagoula) at the Pascagoula River Park with entrance on access road west to Naval Repair Station.Signs show way.
Highlights: The *Scranton* (shrimp boat museum)
Website:
www.cityofpascagoula.com/recreation.htm
General Information: The *Scranton* Floating Museum is a shrimp boat converted to Museum and learning center. Enter the galley, go up to the wheelhouse, and investigate the rooms below. The boat Museum houses displays on seafood and maritime industry, aquaria, wetlands diorama, three 180-gallon aquariums, shrimp boat equipment, and art exhibits.
Activities: Picnic in the park, go crabbing and fishing at the pier.
Admission: No entry fee. Open daily, Tuesday-Saturday, 10 A.M.-5 P.M., Sunday, 1 P.M-5 P.M., year-round.

VICKSBURG, MISSISSIPPI
The Gray & Blue Naval Museum
1102 Washington Street
Vicksburg, MS 39183
(601) 638-6500 or FAX: (601) 638-7846
E-mail: grayblue@bellsouth.net
Location: The Museum is located at 1102 Washing Street in Vicksburg.
Highlights: Civil War gunboat, steamboat, and naval, vessel models.
General Information: The Gray & Blue Naval Museum, founded in 1993, was established to preserve the history of the Navies of the War Between of/the States. The Museum houses, at present, 84 models of the Civil War gunboats (43 Union and 41 Confederate). Our goal is to have 100 models of this period on display. Also displayed are paintings of the naval battles and some artifacts.
　　Two new exhibits have recently opened: "Life on the River," which features towboats and steamboat models, and the "The Mississippians," which features models of naval vessels with names connected to the State of Mississippi. The River Exhibit has 15 models on display. According to Navy records there have been more than 80 vessels with names connected to Mississippi.
　　The Mississippian Exhibit has on display

models representing 28 vessels and the Museum maintains a history of all models displayed. In addition, files on many of the vessels of the navies are also archived. The Museum also features a 250-square-foot diorama of The Battle of Vicksburg. The diorama contains 2500 miniature soldiers. Work is underway to add the City of Vicksburg and 1000 more figures to the diorama.
Admission: Monday - Saturday 9 A.M. to 5 P.M., Sunday 1 P.M. to 5 P.M.

VICKSBURG, MISSISSIPPI
USS *Cairo* Gunboat and Museum
Vicksburg National Military Park
3201 Clay Street
Vicksburg, MS 39183-3469
(601) 636- 2199 Fax: (601) 638-7329
E-mail: vick_interpretation@nps.gov
Location: Vicksburg lies on the Mississippi River forty-four miles west of Jackson on I-20. The Museum is within Vicksburg National Park.
Highlights: The USS *Cairo* Gunboat (partial restoration), library (600 volumes),
Website:
www.nps.gov/vick/cairo/gunboatcairo.htm
General Information: United States Ship *Cairo* Museum sits opposite the national cemetery within Vicksburg National Military Park, the site of the 1863 siege of the city of Vicksburg.
　　Founded in 1980, the Museum displays artifacts recovered from the Union ironclad *Cairo*, which was sunk in the Yazoo River north of Vicksburg in 1862. The vessel is believed to be the first sunk by an electrically detonated mine. A six- minute audiovisual program explains the sinking and salvage of the gunboat, which has been partially restored at the Museum.
Activities: Self-guided tours, Ranger guided activities, and audiovisual programs
Admission: Park entry fee. Open daily, 9:30 A.M.-6 P.M., April-October; open daily, 8:30 A.M.-5 P.M., Nov-March. Closed Christmas.

MISSOURI

HANNIBAL, MISSOURI
Mark Twain Home Foundation
120 North Main
Hannibal, MO 63401-3316
(573) 221-9010
E-mail: cindy.lovell@marktwainmuseum.org
Location: Hannibal is 100 miles north of St. Louis on the Mississippi River.
Highlights: Mark Twain River History, Steamboat models
Website: www.marktwainmuseum.org
General Information: The Mark Twain Home Foundation was established to perpetuate

the memory of Mark Twain. The Foundation operates seven buildings of Twain-related displays. One display in the New Mark Twain Museum focuses on Twain's book *Life on the Mississippi*. This includes a replica steamboat pilothouse and river displays including a few models of river steamboats, photographs of steamboats he piloted.

Admission: Entry fee. Open daily: June-August, 8 A.M. - 6 P.M.; September-October, 9 A.M. - 5 P.M.; November-February, 10 A.M. - 4 P.M., Sundays 12 Noon - 4 P.M.

HERMANN, MISSOURI
Historic Hermann Museum
312 Schiller Street, P.O. Box 105
Hermann, MO 65041
(573) 486-2389
E-mail: joyandcarol@centurytel.net
Location: Hermann is about forty miles east from Jefferson City, Missouri, on the Missouri River. The Museums are located in the Old German School (look for the Clock Tower).
Highlights: Steamboat models, photo archive, The River Room
Website: www.historichermann.com/
   General Information: The Historic Hermann Museums occupy the entire second floor of the 1871 Old German School where The River Room, a fine maritime museum, occupies the large west room of the Museum complex. The River Room houses a full pilothouse, a replica of the one from the steamer *Pin Oak*. Capt. Edward Heckmann built this replica, and it remains the focal point, the first view on entering The River Room. Hermann is noted locally as the shipbuilding site of thirty riverboats.
   The museum contains twelve or so riverboat models, which nicely depict the type of craft, built here and used on the river for many years. The photo collection is mounted on blade pages.
   Library material has been collected over the

Admission: Entry fee. Open Apr/Oct, Mon/Wed 10 A.M. to 4 P.M. Fri/Sat, 10 A.M. – 4 P.M., noon to 4 P.M. Sunday.

KANSAS CITY, MISSOURI
Arabia **Steamboat Museum**
400 Grand Boulevard
Kansas City, MO 64106
(816) 471-4030   Fax: (816) 471-1616
E-mail: david.hawley@1856.com
Location: The Museum is in the historic City Market area, which formerly housed produce wholesalers and is now renovated as part of the River Market redevelopment project near the Missouri River
Highlights: Items from the cargo of the 1856 sunken steamboat *Arabia*, gift shop,
Website: www.1856.com/
   General Information: The Great White *Arabia* was a 171-foot side-wheeler with three iron boilers capable of pushing more than 200 tons against the Missouri River current. Built in 1853, she was a veteran of the Missouri when she sank. The cargo hold was packed with 200 tons of crates containing the basic necessities of life in the 1850s. Hundreds of thousands of items, including hardware, dishes, glassware, clothing and footwear, building supplies, bottled fruit, liquor, perfume, and even Belgium rifles and brass powder flasks.
   The complete cargo was recovered in one of the most interesting excavations undertaken along the Missouri River in recent times. Examples of each of the items recovered are displayed in replica storefronts. And the main deck — in full-scale replica — is laid out on the main floor of the Museum, featuring a twenty-eight-foot reconstructed paddle wheels, original engines, boilers, and stern hull with rudder.
   Of the estimated 400 steamboats lost to the river, about 300 were "snagged". The *Arabia* was one of those victims.
   Admission: Entry fee. Open Mon-Sat, 10 A.M.- 6 P.M., Sunday, Noon – 5 P.M.

98

ST. LOUIS, MISSOURI
Golden Eagle **River Museum**
Bee Tree County Park
2701 Finestown Roads
St. Louis, MO 63129
(314) 846-9073
E-mail: info@mississippiriverinfo.com
Location: The Museum is in the Nims Mansion at
Bee Tree Park in southern St. Louis County. From
I-225 and I-270, travel south on Telegraph
Road 4.5-miles. Then take left fork on Becker
Road one and one-half miles to Finestown Road
and turn east to Bee Tree Park.
Highlights: River towboat models, The Parmely
Library
General Information: From atop a Mississippi
River bluff, where the *Golden Eagle* River
Museum, named after the steamer *Golden Eagle*,
occupies the Nims Mansion's Great Hall. You
can see the mighty river through the spokes of a
pilot wheel that once steered the steamer
Betsy Ann, an Ohio River boat made famous in
the book "The Log of the *Betsy Ann*."

Modern-day commerce is represented at the
Museum with house flags used by , towboat
models, towboat companies and other memorabilia and research material concerning today's
inland waterways. The Museum exhibits items
from the Steamer *Golden Eagle*, the last overnight
passenger boat running out of St. Louis, which
sank on May 18, 1947.

The Parmely Library is housed on the second
floor of the mansion. It contains a wide variety of
books on maritime history, navigation, and
fiction, as well as many pamphlets, maps,
newspaper clippings, and photographs about
steamboats, towboats, bridges, rivermen, and river
history.

The *Golden Eagle* —last St. Louis river packet
— sank in the Mississippi River, at Grand Tower
Island, May 18, 1947
Admission: No entry fee. Open: May 1 - Labor
Day, Friday through Sunday 1 –5 P.M.; Labor
Day - October 31 Saturday and Sunday

ST. LOUIS, MISSOURI
Herman T. Pott National Inland
Waterways Library
St. Louis Mercantile Library at the
University of Missouri, St. Louis
Thomas Jefferson Library Building
One University Blvd.
St. Louis, MO 63121-4400
(314) 516-7245/7247   Fax: (314) 516-7241
E-mail: jhover@umsl.edu
Location: The Library is on the North Campus of
the University of Missouri, St. Louis. For a map
see **website:** www.umsl.edu/ and type "map" in
search box

Highlights: Extensive inland waterways historical
materials,
Website: www.umsl.edu/pott/index.html
General Information: The Herman T. Pott
National Inland Waterways Library is a non-
circulation special collection of the St. Louis
Mercantile Library, founded in 1846. It is named
for Herman T. Pott, an industrialist and leading
figure in inland waterways barge transportation in
the twentieth century.

Its holdings comprise one of the most extensive
collections of inland waterways historical material
in the nation. They include approximately 8,000
books, 400 linear feet of manuscript material, and
10,000 photographs.

The book collections, dating from the early
1800s, cover all aspects of inland waterways
history. The history of the Mississippi-Missouri-
Ohio river system and its navigation and
development is a particular focus. Manuscript
collections include *The Waterways Journal*
Collection, containing the publisher's research and
photo files; the Federal Barge Line Papers,
containing documentation on the company,
including vessel plans, and the Ruth Ferris
Collection (partially available), with extensive
research files on inland river vessels, riverside
communities, and biographical data.

Extensive photographic holdings include
images of steam- and diesel-driven vessels in
passenger and freight service from the late 1800s
to the present.

Founder of Pott Industries, Inc., Herman T.
Pott was a dynamic and innovative waterways
leader in American shipbuilding. His first
shipyard was opened in 1933 and named the St.
Louis Shipbuilding and Steel Company. The yard
built barges, tank carriers, ocean-going tugs, and
during World War II, a variety of military craft.
Activities: Research appointments requested.
Photocopy, photographic, and interlibrary loan
services available. Book holdings catalogued on
OCLC, code SLM or SLMG. Hourly fee research
available.
Admission: No entry fee. Open Monday-
Thursday, 8 A.M.-10:30 P.M.; Friday, 8 A.M.-
5 P.M.; Saturday, 9 A.M.-5 P.M.; Sunday,
1 P.M.- 9 P.M.

ST. LOUIS, MISSOURI
Missouri Historical Society
5700 Lindell and DeBaliviere in Forest Park
P.O. Box 11940
St. Louis, MO 63112-0040
(314) 746-4599 E-mail: info@mohistory.org
Location: The Missouri History Museum is
located in the Jefferson Memorial Building, Forest
Park; north edge of park at corner of Lindell and
DeBaliviere; the Library and Collections are
located in the Library and Research Center at 225

S. Skinker, north edge of Forest Park in St. Louis.
Highlights: Maritime history archives, river steamboat documentation, gift shop,
Website:www.mohistory.org/content/HomePage/HomePage.aspx
    General Information: The Missouri Historical Society maintains a library, archival, photographic, and objects collections that document the history of St. Louis, the State of Missouri, and the Louisiana Purchase Territory.
    Collections document the history of the Missouri and Mississippi Rivers' travel and their role in the building of St. Louis, the Civil War, and in linking St. Louis to the West commercially. Particularly strong documentation on Missouri and Mississippi River steamboats.
    Admission: Museum: No entry fee. Open Mon/Thurs, 10 A.M. - 8 P.M., Fri/Sun 10 A.M. 6 P.M. Library/Research Center: No fees for research; photocopy services, and photographic reproduction services available; materials and use fees apply. Open: Wednesday –Monday, 10 AM.--6 P.M.; Tuesday, 10 A.M. – 8 P.M.

NEBRASKA

BROWNVILLE, NEBRASKA
Museum of Missouri River History
73088 646 Avenue P.O. Box 38
Brownville, NE 68321
(402) 825-3341
Location: Brownville is sixty miles south of Omaha on the Missouri River. Take I-29 south to the Rte. 136 exit, then head west into Brownville. (steamboat dredge)
    General Information: Founded in 1978, the Missouri River History Museum is housed aboard *Captain Meriwether Lewis*, a historic steam-powered, side-wheel steamboat dredges. The dredge is appropriately named for one of two men commissioned by Thomas Jefferson to look for the Northwest Passage. The 1804 Lewis and Clark exploration showed how the Missouri River could become one of the nation's important watercourses — which it did and is now the site of this important museum.
    The barge spent its entire working life (1932-1969) on the wild, unpredictable, and often dangerous Missouri River and is now designated as a national historic landmark. Visitors will see what role this massive floating dredge played in taming the Mighty Missouri.
    Giant steam engines and boilers, the wooden paddle-wheels, the dining halls, officers' sleeping quarters, and the popular pilot house along with its impressive brass fixtures and with its birds-eye view of the river, are waiting to be seen on the 268-foot *Lewis*.

Launched in December 1931, the *Lewis* has lived up to its name in its efforts to keep the Missouri River navigable.
    Activities: Guided tours
    Admission: Entry fee. Open daily, Mem/Day-Lab/Day, 12 Noon.-5 P.M.

OMAHA, NEBRASKA
Freedom Park, Inc.
2497 Freedom Park Road
Omaha, NE 68110-2745
(402) 402-345-1959
E-mail: info@freedomparknavy.org
Location: In Omaha, take Abbott Drive to 1600 North Abbott Drive or Seward Street. Turn east onto Seward Street. Then take an immediate left turn onto Freedom Park Road. Follow signs to where three museum vessels are berthed on the Missouri River.
    Highlights: USS *Hazard* (AM 240) (minesweeper), USS *Marlin* (ST2) (submarine), LSM-45 (Amphibious Landing Craft), and USS LSM 45 (amphibious landing vessel),
Website: www.freedomparkomaha.org/
    General Information: The 184-foot minesweeper *Hazard*, launched in 1944, and the 131-foot submarine *Marlin*, launched in 1953, are memorials to U.S. naval operations. All their compartments are open and accessible and contain original furnishings. The *Hazard* participated in the invasion of Okinawa during World War II.
    The *Marlin* was used primarily for postwar training. The LSM 45 served in the Pacific Theatre in WW II transporting personnel and vehicles between various ports. She later served in the Hellenic (Greek) Navy for 35 years.
    Admission: Entry fee. Open Monday-Saturday, 9 A.M.- 6 P.M., Sunday, 10 A.M. – 5 P.M. April-October.

NEW HAMPSHIRE

PORTSMOUTH, NEW HAMPSHIRE
John Paul Jones House (1758)
43 Middle Street   P.O. Box 728
Portsmouth, NH 03801
(603) 436-8420
E-mail: jpjhouse@seacoastny.com
Location: The home is located on the corner of State and Middle Streets.
Highlights: The John Paul Jones House
Website:
www.portsmouthhistory.org/jpjhouse.html
    General Information: Capt. Gregory Purcell built the house in 1758. After his death his widow operated the house as a genteel guesthouse. Most notable of her guests was John Paul Jones, who lived here in 1777 while supervising the outfitting

of the *Ranger* and again in 1781 while the *America* was being built. China, silver, books, portraits, costume and a model of the *Ranger* are displayed.
   Admission: Entry fee. Open June through mid-October, 10 A.M. – 4 P.M. Closed Tues& Wed.

PORTSMOUTH, NEW HAMPSHIRE
Piscataqua Gundalow Project
60 Marcy Street, P. O. Box 425
Portsmouth, NH 03802-0425
(603) 433-9505 Fax: (603) 433-6403
E-mail: info@gundalow.org
Location: Travel sixty-five-miles north of Boston on I-95. Gundalow in Prescott Park.
Highlights: Gundalow *Captain Edward H. Adams* (open-decked barge)
Website: www.gundalow.org/
   General Information: The Piscataqua Gundalow Project, founded in 1978, has assembled audio-visual exhibits on gundalow construction, regional history, and environment.the replica gundalow *Captain Edward H. Adams*, a simple, undecked barge, is berthed at a wharf in the Strawberry Banke Historical District. Powered only by tides and occasionally sweeps (long oars), the first gundalows carried agricultural, wood, and other regional products between port towns.
   Admission: Entry fee. Open May-September, and rest of year by appointment.

PORTSMOUTH, NEW HAMPSHIRE
Port of Portsmouth Maritime Museum
USS *Albacore* (Submarine)
Portsmouth Maritime Museum
600 Market Street, P. O. Box 4367
Portsmouth, NH 03801
(603) 436-3680 E-mail: info@ussalbacore.org
Location: Travel sixty-five miles north of Boston on I-95. The museum is at Albacore Park in Portsmouth, one-quarter mile from exit 7 on Market Street.
Highlights: USS *Albacore* (AGSS-569) (submarine), **Website:** www.ussalbacore.org
   General Information: The Portsmouth Maritime Museum, established October, 1985, features USS *Albacore* (AGSS-569: research submarine). Built at the Portsmouth Naval Shipyard and launched in 1953, Albacore served with the US Navy from 1953 to 1972 though it never fired a weapon, and it never went to war.
   Primarily, the submarine was used for testing dive brakes, sonar systems, and escape mechanisms, all manner of innovative theories. the *Albacore* was a laboratory afloat. Its teardrop hull design is a triumph and a model for contemporary submarines the world over.
   Activities: Tours of the *Albacore* and documentary

Admission: Entry fee. Open daily, 9:30 a.m.-5 p.m. daily in summer; Columbus Day until Memorial Day, 9:30 a.m.-3:30 p.m. Closed Tuesday and Wednesday.

PORTSMOUTH, NEW HAMPSHIRE
Portsmouth Athenaeum
9 Market Square
P.O. Box 848
Portsmouth, NH 03801
(603) 431-2538
Location: Downtown Portsmouth
Highlights: Library, ship models, **Website:** www. portsmouthathenaeum.org/about.html
   General Information: The Portsmouth Athenaeum maintains maritime history collections (manuscripts, log books, book collections, photograph collections). Visits to the Athenaeum's reading room may be made on Thursdays, 1 P.M.-4 P.M., to view half-lift builder's models, fully rigged ship models, and marine paintings. The Athenaeum research library, located at 6-8 Market Square on the third floor, provides access to the archives, books, maps, and historic photographs relating primarily to the history of the Portsmouth area and to the maritime history of New England.
   Admission: No entry fee. Open Tuesdays, Thursdays, Saturdays, 1 – 4 P.M.

PORTSMOUTH, NEW HAMPSHIRE
Strawbery Banke Museum
14 Hancock Street, P.O. Box 300
Portsmouth, NH 03802-0300
(603) 433-1100 Fax: 603-433-1115
E-mail: ingo@strawberybanke.org
Location: From I-95, take Exit 7 and follow the green "Strawbery Banke" signs down Market Street, left on Bow Street, right on Chapel Street, then left on State Street to Marcy Street where Strawberry Bank (area) is located on the Portsmouth waterfront.
Highlights: John Paul Jones House (corner of Middle & State Streets), historic houses. Free off-street parking. **Website**:www.strawberybanke.org/
   General Information: The Strawbery Banke Museum and site contains a number of restored and furnished houses containing the area's 300-year history in the Puddle Dock neighborhood. Numerous gardens comprise this restored village along the Portsmouth waterfront. Of maritime interest are the ship models and carvings of Captain Edward H. Adams and a boat builder's shop. Historic houses and the 1766 Pitt Tavern, the Governor Goodwin Mansion, and Abbott's Little Corner Store as it appeared in 1943 — all tell the story of the evolution of the neighborhood.
   Nearby are other maritime historically interesting sites including the submarine Albacore at the Port of Portsmouth Maritime Museum on the

extension of Market Street, The Portsmouth Athenaeum in Market Square which houses shipping records, ship models, and paintings from the nineteenth century maritime heyday of the city. Exhibits include archaeological digs, early tools, seventeenth and eighteenth century construction techniques. And across the river at Kittery, Maine, is the Portsmouth Naval Shipyard Command Museum.

Admission: Entry fee for museum. Open November 1 - April 30, Thursday through Saturday 10 A.M. – 2 P.M., Sunday 12 – 2 P.M. Closed holidays.

WOLFEBORO FALLS, NEW HAMPSHIRE
New Hampshire Boat Museum
397 Center Street, Rte. 28, P.O. Box 1195
Wolfeboro Falls, NH 03894
(603) 569-4554 E-mail: museum@nhbm.org
Location: The Museum is located on Route 28, 2 miles from the junction of Route 109 & 28 in Wolfeboro, NH.
Highlights: Region's boating heritage,
Website: www.nhbm.org/
General Information: The New Hampshire Antique & Classic Boat Museum, incorporated in 1994, honors the New Hampshire Lakes Region boating heritage and its role in the cultural and social fabric of the Lakes Region. This Museum collects, preserves, studies and interprets, and displays to the public, objects relating to the boating history of the United States in general and the Lakes Region in particular. Changing exhibits feature fifteen to twenty boats and related memorabilia from a bygone era. Exhibits also include outboards and inboards, runabouts, canoes, kayaks, and launches. The Museum is located in the theatre of the former Alla A Resort. Check calendar on the web to coordinate visits and scheduled events.
Admission: Entry fee. Open daily Memorial Day to Columbus Day, Monday-Saturday, 10 A.M. – 4 P.M., Sunday, Noon – 4 P.M.

NEW JERSEY

ATLANTIC CITY, NEW JERSEY
Absecon Lighthouse
31 South Rhode Island Avenue
Atlantic City, NJ 08401
(609) 449-1360 Fax: (609) 449-1919
E-mail: jean@abseconlighthouse.org
Location: Absecon Lighthouse is located in the Inlet Section of Atlantic City.
Highlights: Lighthouse,
Website: www.abseconlighthouse.org/
General Information: She's had 146 birthdays. She's seen a Civil War and two World Wars.

She's weathered hundreds of storms. And she's never looked better. On January 15, 1857, the First-Order Fresnel lens in Absecon Lighthouse shone over the infamous "Graveyard Inlet" in Atlantic City for the first time. By 1912, word of the stately beacon had spread, and she became the most visited lighthouse in the United States. At 171 feet high, with 228 steps, she remains the third tallest lighthouse in the country, and the tallest in New Jersey. Absecon Lighthouse has now been painstakingly restored to her original glory, complete with the First-Order Fresnel lens that first shone over 140 years ago. Come and visit Atlantic City's historic Absecon Lighthouse.

After you visit, the phrase "respect your elders" will take on a whole new meaning. (Note: The newly reconstructed Keeper's House is expected to open late summer 2001.)

Admission: Lighthouse: entry fee.
Operating Hours: Monday 11:00am – 4 P.M. Tues, & Wed, – closed Thur, - Sun, 11 A.M. – 4 P.M., July - August 10 A.M. - 5: P.M. Daily

ATLANTIC CITY, NEW JERSEY
Historic Gardner's Basin
800 N. New Hampshire Avenue and the Bay
Atlantic City, NJ 08401-2998
(609) 348-2880
E-mail: seamore@oceanlifecenter.com
Location: The basin is situated at the northeast end of Atlantic City on North New Hampshire Avenue.
Highlights: Aquarium/Marine Education Center, Daily sightseeing cruises, Deep Sea Fishing, restaurants and an antique shop,
General Information: Historic Gardner's Basin, founded in 1976, is a maritime village within the Atlantic City waterfront homes that pre-date 1900. The site where Atlantic City was founded were both the center of South Jersey's fishing industry and the hub of rum running.

The visitor will find maritime artifacts, seafaring memorabilia; working and livingexhibits on lobstermen; sculpture, paintings, and working and living exhibits of the clammer (clam digger).
Activities: Eco-tours, salt marsh and beach excursions, ecology cruises and festivals.
Admission: Entry fee but memberships are available. Group rates available. Open daily, year round, 9 A.M.-5 P.M.. Closed Christmas and New Year's Day and Thanksgiving.

BARNEGAT LIGHT, NEW JERSEY
Barnegat Lighthouse
Division of Parks and Forestry
State Park Service CN 404
5th Street and Central Avenue, PO. Box 167
Barnegat Light, NJ 08006
(609) 494-2016 E-mail: hhsms@worldnet.att.net

Location: Barnegat Light lies twenty-five miles north of Atlantic City on the northern tip of Long Beach Island in Ocean County. It can be reached from Garden State Parkway by exiting onto Rte. 72 (exit 63) to North Long Beach Island Boulevard. Then travel north some 10 miles to north end of Long Island to lighthouse.

Highlights: Barnegat Lighthouse, **Website:** www.nealcomm.com/nonprof/blhist.htm

General Information: This "Grand Old Champion of the Tides" is a great piece of American sculpture, with the power to move minds and seize hearts. The lighthouse was built in Barnegat Inlet, Barnegat City, in 1834. It cost $6,000, which was appropriated by Congress on June 30, 1834, for that purpose. The tower, fifty feet high, was built of brick and whitewashed from top to bottom. The light, which was the fourth placed on the coast of New Jersey, was white and "fixed" and did not flash. All of the exposed metal parts were painted a dead black, and whale oil was used for the illuminate.

The original structure fell into the water in the early part of 1856. At that time a temporary wooden tower was hastily constructed farther inland and lighted with lamps salvaged from the wreck of the old one. General George G. Meade had Barnegat reconstructed in 1857-58.

The red and white marvel rises 165 feet above the tides — with 217 steps — that mark Barnegat Shoals, the scene of more than 200 shipwrecks. An excellent view is available from the base. The great Fresnel lens was dismantled and stored in the Tomkinsville Lighthouse Depot on Staten Island for possible reuse and future service.

Although it was decommissioned in 1927, the Coast Guard used the lighthouse as a lookout tower during WW II. With the conclusion of the war, the lighthouse and its property were turned over to the state of New Jersey and opened as a park in 1958. When the town of Barnegat Light established a museum of local history in 1954, the lens was returned and is now on display.

The lighthouse contains informational exhibits that can be read along the climb to the top.

Activities: Visitors are invited to enjoy the lighthouse and the coastal panorama view from the light keeper's catwalk.

Admission: Entry fee. Open daily, June and Sept.: 2 P.M. – 4 P.M. on weekends. Jul/Aug 2 P.M. – 4 P.M. every afternoon.

BEACH HAVEN, NEW JERSEY
New Jersey Maritime Museum
Dock Road & West Avenue
Beach Haven, NJ 08008
609-492-0202 Fax: 609-492-7575
E-mail: curator@museumofnjmh.com

Location: The Museum of NJMH is located on the corner of Dock Road and West Avenue in Beach Haven, on Long Beach Island.

Highlights: Research facility, internet cafe, shipwreck artifacts

Web site: www.njmaritimemuseum.org

General Information: The Museum of New Jersey Maritime History includes, among other things, a facility for the public display of a significant number of marine artifacts. Such displays will encourage maritime research, historical instruction by guest lecturers and promote the education of the public about New Jersey's maritime history.

Also included is a lending library of New Jersey-Related Books, TV/DVD/VHS Units in 5 of the Museum's Exhibit Halls, Home of Alliance for a Living Ocean, of Maritime Photographs and Documents, and a computerized database of over 5,400 New Jersey Shipwrecks and Maritime Disasters.

Activities: Guest Presentations on NJ Shipwrecks & Coastal History, Wireless Internet Access

Admission: Open year round. Open daily June, July & August 10 a.m. – 8 p.m. September through May, open Thursday –Sunday, 10 a.m. – 4 p.m.

CAMDEN, NEW JERSEY
Battleship *New Jersey* Historical Museum Society
62 Battleship Place Box BB-62
Camden, NJ 08103
(866) 877-6262
E-mail: d.buchanan@battleshipnewjersey.org

Location: The Battleship New Jersey is berthed on the Delaware River in Camden, NJ. She is docked at a newly built pier adjacent to the Tweeter Entertainment Center, just south of the Aquarium. **Highlights:** Battleship *New Jersey*, **Website:** www.bb62museum.org/

General Information: USS Battleship *New Jersey* (BB-62) is one of the four battleships of the 45,000-ton Iowa class, the latest, largest, fastest, and most powerful ever built in the U.S. The "Big J" has an unmatched record of service to her country and was, at the conclusion of the Vietnam conflict, the only battleship ever to have served in three wars. The Battleship *Texas* served in both WW II and I.

Patriotic New Jersey citizens, ex-Navy people everywhere, battleship fans, naval history followers, and many others want to see this ship preserved. Progress is being made. The USS *New Jersey* Battleship Commission has been formed to carry out the state's functions in the acquisition of the ship and have chosen Camden, New Jersey as the permanent site. Here the ship would be

displayed in the populous Philadelphia, Pennsylvania and Camden, New Jersey metropolitan area.
Admission: Entry fee. Open April – Sept., 9 a.m. – 5 p.m. Oct. – April, 9 a.m. – 3 p..m.

CAPE MAY, NEW JERSEY
Cape May County Historical and Genealogical Society Museum in the John Holmes House and Barn
Cape May Court House,
504 Route 9 North
Cape May, NJ 08210-1953
(609) 465-3535
E-mail: museum@co.cape-may.nj.us
Location: Cape May County Court House is the southern terminus of the Garden State Parkway and forty-two miles south of Atlantic City. The Museum, on U.S. Rte. 9 (Shore Road) between Rte. 675 on south and Rte. 609 on the north.
Highlights: Lighthouse lens, John Holmes House, gift shop, library,
Website: www.cmcmuseum.org
General Information: The Cape May County Historical & Genealogical Society, housed in the vintage 1800's barn, displays a hand-carved duck decoy collection and the original Fresnel lens from the 1859 Cape May Point Lighthouse. The barn also has a maritime and whaling exhibit and a natural history display. In addition, tools and gadgets for the home, farm and business are exhibited including examples of carriages include a stagecoach, a peddler's wagon and a handsomely restored doctor's sulky.
Admission: Entry fee. Open: November through May: Saturdays, 9 A.M. – 4 P.M. (last admission at 3 P.M.); Memorial Day Weekend through October: Tuesday through Saturday, 9 A.M. – 4 P.M. (last admission at 3 P.M.) Members free. Please call ahead and make arrangements with the Librarian. For research, library staff are willing to perform their own search work. Non-Society members are charged $1.00 per hour while members may use the library free-of-charge.

EDGEWATER, NEW JERSEY
Binghamton **(ferry)**
725 River Road
Edgewater, NJ 07020-1195
(201) 941-2300 E-mail: access@hrfanj.org
Location: Located on the Hudson River three miles south of the George Washington Bridge.
Highlights: Modified but authentic Hoboken-Manhattan ferry,
Website:www.users.nac.net/chasstamm/hrfanjorg/binghamt.htm

General Information: The 231-foot-long *Binghamton* carried 125 million passengers over a 62-year career and traveled over 200,000 miles on this short route. Beginning service in March 1905, she accommodated twenty-four automobiles and 946 passengers. Now, she serves as a restaurant with tables set even in the space occupied by the intact double-compound marine steam engines.

GREENWICH, NEW JERSEY
John Dubois Maritime Museum
949 Ye Greate Street
P. O. Box 16
Greenwich, NJ 08323
(609) 455-1774 E-mail: lummis2@juno.com
Location: Greenwich is five miles off Rte. 49 from Bridgeton in southern New Jersey.
Highlights: Local maritime history,
Website: www.njht.org/profiles/john-dubois-maritime-museum.html
General Information: The John Dubois Maritime Museum is housed in the 1852 Lecture Room, 949 Ye Great Street of the Cumberland County Historical Society. It features displays of tools and equipment related to the days when Cumberland County was noted for the construction of the schooners which transported cargo to ports along the coast of America or were used to harvest oysters from the Delaware Bay.

Owner of the Mauricetown Shipyard for 30 years, John Dubois presented may shipyard items to the Society, including the scaled-down model of the *Samuel H. Sharp* schooner — complete with blueprints for the first ship buiding in Mauricetown in 1862. There are shipbuilding tools , the rigging mast equipment, fish net bouys, and the sisther hooks that also fill the room.

Displays feature many of the tools used by local baymen to gather clams and oysters in the nearby bays as well as tools used by the shipwrights who built their ships. There are hands-on exhibits where visitors can practice rope knots, caulk a boat or use tools at the workbench. The highlight of this museum is the outstanding collection of Tom Adams ship models including a whaling ship, four and five masted barkentines, a liberty ship, the *Cape May-Lewes*.

The Museum is dedicated to preserving the artifacts of the shipwrights, watermen, and seamen who were among Linwood's early inhabitants. Exhibits include maritime artifacts such as the last of the wooden garveys: durable boats, which served as platforms for baymen to harvest clams and oysters. The Museum provides a very complete descriptive guide to its exhibits and displays with pen-line drawings of the items for future reference.
Admission: No entry fee. Open April – November, Sunday 1 P.M.- 4 P.M.

HACKENSACK, NEW JERSEY
New Jersey Naval Museum/Submarine
USS *Ling*
78 River Street
Hackensack, NJ 07601-7110
(201) 342-3268
E-mail: njnavalmuseum@yahoo.com
Location: The USS *Ling* is docked at the corner of River and Court Streets in Hackensack, five miles west of the George Washington Bridge (I-80) at Borg Park.
Highlights: USS *Ling* (SS-297) (submarine), WWII Japanese *Kaiten* Submarine, WWII Nazi Seahund Submarine, Bietnam Era PBR, gift shop, overnight encampments, **Website:** www.njnm.com
General Information: The New Jersey Naval Museum/Submarine USS *Ling* Memorial Association was founded in 1973 as a memorial to those who served aboard submarines during World War II. The Memorial also includes displays of Polaris, Terrier, and Talos missiles; and three small craft: a Japanese Kaiten, a German Seehund, and a PBR Mark II.
The *Ling* was built at Cramp Shipbuilding Company in Philadelphia and outfitted in the Boston Navy Yard. She was commissioned June 8, 1945. When the *Ling* was struck from the Navy Register in December 1971, she was donated to the Submarine Memorial Association. On January 13, 1973, the Submarine Memorial Association brought the *Ling* to Borg Park in Hackensack.
Activities: Overnight encampments Friday and Saturday nights, Guided tours of the submarine seven days a week
Admission: Entry fee. Open Saturday-Sunday, 10 A.M. - 4 P.M.

HIGHLANDS, NEW JERSEY
Fort Hancock Museum
Gateway National Recreation Area Sandy Hook P. O. Box 530
Fort Hancock, NJ 07732-0530
(732) 872-0115 Museum direct: (732) 872-5970
(732) 354-4606
Location: To reach the Highlands take the Garden State Parkway to Keyport. Exit onto SR-36, heading east thirteen miles to Highlands. The Museum is located in Gateway National Recreation Area, one block west of the Sandy Hook Lighthouse on a long spit of sand extending north from the New Jersey shore. The Museum is 100-yards west of the Sandy Hook Lighthouse at Fort Hancock.
Highlights: Museum contains exhibits about Fort Hancock, Sandy Hood Proving Ground, and Sandy Hook Lighthouse, a gift shop, restroom, and park information, **Website:** www.nps.gov/gate/

General Information: The Museum was founded in 1968 when Fort Hancock was still an active military installation. The Museum building was original the Fort Hancock Guardhouse, which was built in 1899. In the future, the Museum will be relocated to the Fort's former barracks. Since 1975 the National Park Service has operated it.
The Sandy Hook Lighthouse is the oldest operating lighthouse in America (1764). Even though the Museum contains a limited number of maritime exhibits, the Gateway National Recreation Area is worth visiting because of the additional museums, including the Museum at Navesink Lighthouses.
Admission: No entry fee. Open weekends throughout the year 1 P.M.-5 P.M., and everyday during July and August 1 P.M.-5 P.M. From Memorial Day Weekend through Labor Day Sandy Hook charges a parking fee to park in the park's oceanside parking lots. Parking free in Fort Hancock. Tell fee collectors at park entrance that you are headed for Fort Hancock.

HIGHLANDS, NEW JERSEY
Twin Lights State Historic Site
Lighthouse Road
Highlands, NJ 07732
(732) 872-1814 E-mail: info@twin-lights.org
Location: To reach Highlands take the Garden State Parkway to Exit 117, Keyport. Exit onto SR-36, heading east twelve miles to Highlands.
Highlights: The Twin Lights, gift shop,
Website: http://twin-lights.org/home.htm
General Information: Twin Lights has served as a beacon for ships since 1828, having been rebuilt in 1862 during Lincoln's term as president. Today, a state-maintained occulting white light is seen from the north tower. The original lighthouse, which houses the nautical and lifesaving museum, is a brownstone structure with towers at both ends.
From Sandy Hook to Cape May, five major lighthouses marked New Jersey's 144-mile Atlantic coastline. Sandy Hook, Navesink (Twin Lights), Barnegat, Absecon, and Cape May lighthouses all had powerful lenses, the beacons of which could be seen eighteen to twenty miles from the shore. The most powerful beacon was installed at the Navesink Light Station (Twin Lights) in 1898. Marking the westerly side of the entrance to New York Harbor, the twenty-five-million-candlepower beam was the brightest in the country and could be seen twenty-two miles away. This lens is now exhibited in the Electric Power House on the grounds.
Activities: Audio stations assist in recounting the site's history. The public may climb sixty-four steps to an observation deck at the top of the north tower.

Admission: No entry fee, but donations accepted. Open daily, 10 A.M.-5 P.M. Memorial Day-Labor Day. Open Wednesday through Sunday the rest of the year.

KEYPORT, NEW JERSEY
Steamboat Dock Museum
American Legion Dr.& Broad Street
Keyport, NJ 07735
(732) 739-6390
Location: Keyport sits on the Raritan Bay about ten miles southeast of Sayreville. The Museum is located on American Legion Drive in the center of town, just at the foot of Broad Street.
Highlights: Model of the *Keyport* (steamboat), oystering displays and photos, aeromarine displays and photos.
Website:
keyportonline.com/History/History.html
General Information: The Steamboat Dock Museum, founded in 1976 and a part of the Keyport Historical Society, contains much of the history of the Kearney family, who settled in the area in 1714. A major shipping industry began in 1830, and the town grew and prospered. The Chingarora oyster, harvested from the Raritan Bay, became world famous. In the mid-1800s, not long after Fulton's first steamboat, Benjamin Terry, a builder and entrepreneur, began his steamboat industry, launching more steamboats from the Keyport shores than competitors in Jersey City and Camden.
Admission: No entry fee. Open Sundays, 1 P.M.-4 P.M., Mondays, 10 A.M.- 2 P.M., June through September.

LINWOOD, NEW JERSEY
James Kirk Maritime Museum
Linwood Library
301 Davis Avenue
Linwood, NJ 08221
(609) 927-2023 E-mail: admin@linwoodnj.org
Location: From I-295 (north or south), off on to Atlantic City Expressway forty-five miles to Rte. 50, then four miles south to Linwood where the Museum is located in the lower level of the Library.
Highlights: Boat models (Thomas E. Adams Collection), *Sinda* (bark) history, bay clam/oyster harvesting, **Website:**
www.linwoodnj.org/Museums/maritime1.html
General Information: The Kirk Maritime Museum is one of Linwood's little known treasures. Its creation was a labor of love by Jim Kirk, the first city historian, and Tom Adams, a nationally known ship modeler.
Cumberland County was noted for the construction of the schooners, which transported

cargo to ports along the coast of America or were used to harvest oysters from the Delaware Bay.
Owner of the Mauricetown Shipyard for 30 years, John Dubois presented many shipyard items to the Society, including the scaled-down model of the *Samuel H. Sharp* schooner — complete with blueprints for the first ship built in Mauricetown in 1862. There are shipbuilding tools, the rigging mast equipment, fish net buoys, and the sister hooks that also fill the room.
The Warren Lummis Genealogical and Historical Research Library offer researchers books, maps, deeds, cemetery, church and Bible records, genealogy records, and information on South Jersey history.
Admission: No entry fee but donations accepted. Open by appointment only.

MORRISTOWN, NEW JERSEY
Canal Society of New Jersey Museum at Waterloo Village
P. O. Box 737
Morristown, NJ 07963-0737
(908)-722-9556
E-mail: nj-cnal@googlegroups.com
Location: The Village is located near the junction of Rtes.I-80 and 206. Take Interstate 80 (I-80) to exit 25 follow the signs to Waterloo Vil.
Highlights: Morris Canal, Delaware and Raritan Canal, Waterloo Village,
Website: www.canalsocietynj.org
General Information: Waterloo Village was a nineteenth-century port on the Morris Canal. The Canal Museum was founded in 1975. It exhibits artifacts, documents, photographs, and memorabilia on New Jersey's two towpaths, canals. Canal works include: a watered section of the canal, the remains of a combined lock and aqueduct; the site of an inclined plane — a unique inclined plane where canal boats were carried up hills in cradles running on tracks; a canal store; a blacksmith shop; and two mule bridges. There is a thirteen-minute video presentation and two half-hour videos: Morris Canal and Delaware & Raritan Canal.
Admission: Entry fee for Waterloo Village. Call Waterloo Village at (973) 347-0900 for schedule.

NORTH WILDWOOD, NEW JERSEY
Hereford Inlet Lighthouse
111 North Central Avenue
North Wildwood, NJ 08260
Mail: P.O. Box #784, Rio Grande, NJ 08141
(609) 522-4520
E-mail: herefordlh@yahoo.com
Location: North Wildwood is four-miles east of Exit 6 of the Garden State Parkway.
Highlights: Fourth-order Fresnel lens on display,
Website: www.herefordlighthouse.org/

General Information: The Hereford Inlet Lighthouse, designed by Paul J. Pelz, architect of the Library of Congress and constructed in 1874 by the U.S. Army Corps of Engineers, is now a restored historic Victorian designed lighthouse which overlooks the wide Hereford Inlet. It leads from the Atlantic Ocean to the famed Intracoastal Waterway linking Maine to Florida.

57.5 feet high, the lighthouse was automated and re-activated in the 1980s by the Coast Guard.

Admission: Entry fee. Open daily, mid May to October 9 A.M.-5 P.M., mid October to mid May, Wednesday to Sunday 10 A.M.- 4 P.M. Please call for times, closed for some vacations and meetings.

OCEAN CITY, NEW JERSEY

Ocean City Historical Museum
Cultural Arts Center
1735 Simpson Avenue
Ocean City, NJ 08226
(609) 399-1801 Fax: (609) 399-0544
E-mail: info@ocnjmuseum.org
Highlights: Sindia shipwreck, gift shop, archives,
Website: www.ocnjmuseum.org/
General Information: An exhibit is located in the city museum on the wreck of the four-masted bark *Sindia,* which ran aground in 1901 just off Ocean City's beaches.

Admission: No entry fee. Open Summer May/Nov, Mon/Fri 10 A.M. – 4 P.M. , Sat 11 A.M. – 2 P.M. Winter: Nov/May, Mon/Fri 1 P.M. – 4 P.M.; Sat. 11 A.M. – 2 P.M.

PATERSON, NEW JERSEY

Paterson Museum
2 Market Street
Paterson, NJ   07501-1414
(973) 321-1260
E-mail: patersonmuseum@hotmail.com
Location: Paterson is sixteen miles west of New York City off I-80. I-80 West to exit for Main St. in Paterson. Turn left onto Main St., then left onto Grand St. Go approx. 4 blocks and turn right onto Spruce St. 2 blocks to Market St., and Museum on corner in the Rogers Locomotive Building.
Highlights: Submarines *Holland,* Boat I, and *Fenian Ram* (submersible),
Website: www.patersonmuseum.com
General Information: The Paterson Museum presents, in real and graphic form, a record of the City's accomplishments. The Museum was founded in 1925 as a branch of the Paterson Public Library, an adjunct to the Charles Danforth Memorial Library. Displayed are unusual items and artifacts that had been collected by Pattersonians.

Soon the many exhibits and specimens were relocated to the carriage house of former Mayor, Nathan Barnert. That building, located adjacent to the Library, remained home to the Museum for 55 years.

In 1982, Mayor Frank X. Graves, Jr., directed that the Museum be removed to the newly restored, Rogers Locomotive-Erecting Shop at number 2 Market street. Paterson owns this structure, built in 1872 and enlarged in 1878 and is located only 1,000-feet away from the focal point of early development, the Great Falls of the Passaic River in Totowa.

John Philip Holland, and Irish mathematician who came to this country in 1873, developed basic designs for submarine boats in the 1870s. The *Holland I,* a test vessel, was operated in the Passaic River above Great Falls. The *Holland II,* a true submersible boat, was built in New York City and operated in New York harbor. That ship, thirty-one-feet long and weighing 19 tons, contained all elements that form a modern submersible boat.

The *Holland II,* launched in 1881, has a torpedo tube that could discharge a six-foot long, Whitehead torpedo. The submarine was powered by a Brayton gasoline engine on the surface and operated by a crew of three men. Underwater, the engine was shut down.

John Holland designed and built six, small, submersible boats between 1866 and 1898. The last unit was purchased by the Navy in 1900 and was renamed the USS *Holland.* The *Fenian Ram* (1881), displayed at Museum, is the first "true" submarine built anywhere. Seldom does the "first:" model of any invention survive for any appreciable time. The *Fenian Ram* is an exception to that rule. It has been "moored" in Paterson since 1927. It's little sister, *Holland I* has been in The Paterson Museum since 1926.

Admission: Entry fee. Open Tuesday-Friday 10 A.M.-4 P.M.; Saturday-Sunday 12:30 P.M.- 4:30 P.M.

SOMERS POINT, NEW JERSEY

Atlantic Heritage Center
907 Shore Road
P. O. Box 301
Somers Point, NJ 08244
(609) 927-5218 E-Mail: ahcinfo@comcast.net
Location: Via the Garden State Parkway, take exit 30 South at Somers Point; travel approximately twelve miles south of Atlantic City.
Highlights: Ship models, half models, shipwright tools, ship building history, library,
Website: www.atlanticheritagecenternj.org/
General Information: In the 1700s and 1800s, sailing craft were used to transport cargo all over

107

the world. They also functioned as workboats in bay and coastal waters. Many large and small shipyards existed on the Great Egg Harbor and Tuckahoe River and its tributaries from Mays Landing down to Somers Point, which was then an official   port of entry. The Center displays a wide variety of ship models and shipbuilding tools. Especially important are the twenty-five boat and ship models carved by Charles Woolbert of Mays Landing, including a bugeye, cutter, barquentine, and many others. A research library contains ships' logs and documents. Next-door is the Somers mansion, also open to the public.

Admission: No entry fee. Open Wednesday - Saturday, 10 A.M.-3:30 P.M. First Thursday of Month -- 6:00 p.m. to 9:00 p.m. Fee for non-member research. Closed holidays.

TOMS RIVER, NEW JERSEY
Toms River Seaport Society & Maritime Museum
78 E. Water Street P.O. Box 1111
Toms River, NJ 08754-7554
(732) 349-9209 Fax: (732) 349-2498
E-mail: tomsriverssmm@yahoo.com
Location: Take the Garden State Parkway to exit 82 onto Rte. 38 E.
Then go to the second traffic light and turn right onto Hooper Avenue. Proceed one mile to the museum, which is at east corner of Hooper and Water Streets.
Highlights: Boat models, maritime artifacts, boat restorations of local watercraft, library,
Website: www.tomsriverseaport.org/
General Information: The Seaport Society's maritime museum displays many artifacts, maintains a maritime library, historic boats, and boat models. Exhibits include the twelve-foot Barnegat Bay sneakbox *Sheldrake* that the late F. Slade Dale sailed from New Jersey to Florida in the 1920's, an eleven-foot moth (c.1915), a 1902 Parrine sneakbox, a Beardslee row boat, two Diamond sneakboxes, and a Barnegat Bay garvey.
Admission: No entry fee. Donations accepted, Open Tuesday, Thursday, and Saturday, 10 A.M.-2 P.M., year-round.

TUCKERTON, NEW JERSEY
Tuckerton Seaport
120 West Main Street, #1
Tuckerton, New Jersey 08087
Phone: 609-296-8868
E-mail: info@tuckertonseaport.org
Location: Tuckerton Seaport is located on Route 9, 1/2 mile south of the intersection of Rte. 9 and Rte. 539 and go 1/4 mile past Lake Pohatcong to the Seaport. 27 Boat Slips are also available for seafaring visitors.

Highlights: Tuckerton's historic district, Gift Shop, lighthouse. Call for details or visit the Seaport's Official Website.
Website: www.tuckertonseaport.org/
General Information: The Barnegat Bay Decoy & Baymen's Museum (SEE: separate entry) has evolved into the Tuckerton Seaport, a 40-acre recreation of a 19th- and early 20th-Century Baymen's village.

Step back in time and see the Jersey Shore as it was in the days of yore. Inside Tucker's Island Lighthouse you'll find out about pirates, mooncussers, New Jersey lighthouses, the life of a lighthouse keeper, the origins of the U.S Life Saving Service, Life Cars, breeches buoys, shipwrecks, the Shore's actual "first resort"- Sea Haven — and whaling off our shores. Learn to speak Lenape. Wander the winding boardwalks on our 40-acre site and meet decoy carvers, boat builders, clammers, oystermen, and baymen and women doing what they did way back when.

And whalers, lighthouse keepers, ship captains and others are on hand to demonstrate the day-to-day life of the coastal New Jersey village of yesterday.

Activities: Visitors will enjoy living history at its best, as they explore thirteen (eventually to be thirty) recreated buildings and watch costumed trade- and craftsmen and women bring the area's rich maritime history to life.

Admission: Open daily, May/Sep, 10 A.M. to 5 P.M.

NEW YORK

ALBANY, NEW YORK
Half Moon **Visitor Center/New Netherland Museum**
P.O. Box 10609
Albany, NY 12201-5609
(518) 443-1609 (914) 413-9747
E-mail: info@newnetherland.org
Highlights: *Halve Maen* (*Half Moon*) (replica ship), **Website:** www.newnetherland.org
General Information: The Museum interprets the history of New Netherland and the Dutch contribution to the development of the United States of America. The *Half Moon* is a full-scale replica of the Dutch East India Company ship that Henry Hudson sailed in 1609. The ship is open for tours seasonally, and winters at King Marine in Verplanck, New York. It sails to ports in the Mid-Atlantic region.
Admission: Call for information. The *Half Moon* winters at King Marine in Verplanck, NY.

ALBANY, NEW YORK

New York State Canal System
New York State Canal Corporation
Director of Canals
P.O. Box 189
Albany, NY 12201-0189
(518) 436-2700 Toll Free: 1-800- 422-6254
E-mail: PublicInfo@canals.state.ny.us
Highlights: Historic vessels,
Website: www.canals.state.ny.us/
General Information: The New York State
Canal System is a linear park and living museum
unto
itself. Celebrating 175 years of continuous
navigation during the year 2000, this historical
water way is filled with representative examples of
times past.
The New York State Canal Corporation possesses
numerous historical vessels, including a 1920s fleet
of dredges and tugs, the majority are operational
and working. The flagship and educational
ambassador of the Canal Corporation, tug *Urger* is
one of two remaining bell boats in the United
States and
remains operational after almost 100 years!
Canal System is comprised of four canals, fifty-
seven locks—technological marvels, spanning the
525-mile Canal System. the Erie, Oswego,
Champlain, and Cayuga-Seneca Canals. Unique
structures across the Canals include the imposing
Water Flight of Five, a series of locks, which
circumvent the Cohoes Falls, providing
navigation from the Hudson River to the Mohawk
River and forming the entrance way into the
The New York legendary the Erie Canal. The
Flight of Five possesses the highest vertical lift
anywhere in the world, lifting and lowering boats
169 feet in the shortest distance. In the west at
Lockport, there is another historical flight of five
locks where one can see the original set next to
the "more modern" 1918 version of two locks.
When passing through, be sure to stop at one of the
historical locks and examine the original brass used
to operate and maintain these immense historical
structures.
Several locks still maintain hydroelectric
powerhouses. Originally there were nearly forty of
these pagoda-like structures, but today, only six
remain. Lock 17 is the highest lock on the system
at Little Falls and is breathtaking to behold. The
lock is dramatically situated between high rocky
cliffs.
In addition, the New York State Canal System
possesses lighthouses. Three lighthouses were
constructed in the 1900s on Oneida Lake as part
of the Erie Canal improvements.

ALBANY, NEW YORK

USS *Slater* Museum Ship
141 Broadway at Quay, P.O. Box 1926
Albany, NY 12202
(518) 431-1943 Fax: (518) 432-1123
E-mail: info@ussslater.org
P.O. Box 1926 Albany, NY 12201-1926
Location: The *Slater* is exhibited on the Hudson
River in downtown Albany at the Slater Wharf,
formerly Snow Dock.
Highlights: USS *Slater* (DE-766), gift shop,
overnight camping for youths, *Slater Signals*
Newsletter, **Website:** www.ussslater.org
General Information: The USS *Slater*
Museum Ship represents the 565 Destroyer
Escorts built during World War II. Only five
survive. In 1951, the *Slater* was transferred to the
Hellenic Navy where she served with distinction
for more than 40 years. Ultimately, the Destroyer
Escort Historical Foundation received the *Slater*
as a donation and she joined the *Intrepid* Sea: Air:
Space Museum in New York City in 1994 on a
temporary basis. The *Slater* has now been moved
up the Hudson River to Albany, where she has
been restored to her WW II configuration by
volunteers.
Admission: Entry fee. Open Wed - Sun, 10 A.M. –
4 P.M. April through November.

BEACON, NEW YORK

Hudson River Sloop *Clearwater*
724 Walcott Ave.
Beacon, NY 12508
(845) 265-8080 E-mail: office@clearwater.Org
Location: Poughkeepsie is seventy-five miles
north of New York City. From I-87 exit at New
Paltz, travel twelve miles east across the Hudson
River.
Highlights: Hudson River Sloop *Clearwater*,
Website: www.clearwater.org
General Information: The 106-foot Hudson
River Sloop *Clearwater* is part of a growing fleet
of historic replica wooden vessels on the Hudson
River. The *Clearwater*, with a mission to educate
the public about the river's heritage and the natural
environment, promotes efforts to clean up pollution
on the river. The *Clearwater* travels to some 45
docking locations on tidewater Hudson, New York
harbors, and Long Island Sound.
Admission: Free when in your port on the
Hudson River. Fee for program sails.

BELLPORT, NEW YORK

Barn Museum
Bellport-Brookhaven Historical Society
31 Bellport Lane
Bellport, NY 11713
(631) 286-0888

Location: Bellport, on south side of Long Island, via I-495 sixty-two miles east from New York City to Medford, then south seven miles to Bellport. The Museum is reached through the right-of-way at 12 Bell Street.
Highlights: Whaling history, ship models, scrimshaw, Museum Shop, waterfowl decoys, Sperry navigation instruments
Web Site: www.bbhsmuseum.org
General Information: Founded in 1972, the Barn Museum contains early American artifacts and a gallery devoted to whaling and fishing in the seventeenth and eighteenth centuries. Exhibits include Tangier Smith's whaling,scrimshaw, nautical implements, Gil Smith Boatyard artifacts, duck hunter instruments of Dr. Elmer A. Sperry.
Admission: No entry fee. Open Memorial Day-Labor Day, Friday-Saturday, 11 A.M.- 4:30 P.M.

BLUE MOUNTAIN LAKE, NEW YORK
Adirondack Museum
Attn.: Maritime Section
P. O. Box 99, Rte. 28N & 30
Blue Mountain Lake, NY 12812-0099
(518) 352-7311 Fax: (518) 352-7653
E-mail: info@adirondackmuseum.org
Location: Blue Mountain Lake is 103 miles north of Albany (forty-four-miles west of I-87) near junction of Rtes. 28 and 30.
Highlights: Collection of over 200 non-powered freshwater craft, gift shop,
Website: www.adirondackmuseum.org
General Information: Adirondack Museum, founded in 1957, is a regional Museum of history and art whose specialties are its maritime collections. A 12,000 square-foot exhibit on boats and boating in the region includes over sixty craft on display from the Museum's collection of 205. Some of these are the ten- and one-half pound Rushton canoes, *Sairy Gamp*. Rushton sailing canoes, sixty Adirondack guideboats, and an 32-foot Idem-class sailboat built in 1900 are also displayed. Power craft include the gold cup boats *El Lagarto* (1922) and *Skeeter* (1905). Still other exhibits include small boats, canoes, rowboats, and the Adirondack Guide Boat (circa 1800).
Activities: Craft workshops, No-Octane Regatta, Toy Boat Workshop, and special events.
Admission: Entry fee. Open May 26 – Oct. 15, daily 10 A.M.- 5 P.M. daily, closed September 21 for Antiques Show.

BRONX, NEW YORK
Maritime Industry Museum at Fort Schuyler
State University of New York College Campus
Fort Schuyler,
6 Pennyfield Ave.
Throggs Neck, NY 10465-4198

(718) 408-7218 Fax: (718) 409-6130
E-mail: ejohansson@sunymaritime.edu
Location: The Museum is on the campus of the State University of New York's Maritime College in the Throggs Neck section of the Bronx under the Throggs Neck Bridge. Take the Ft. Schuyler exit off I-295.
Highlights: Maritime Library, ship models, and training vessel *Empire State*, marine artifacts, historic Fort Schuyler (1844)
Website: http://maritimeindustrymuseum.org/
General Information: Founded in 1985, the Maritime Industry Museum at Fort Schuyler has various exhibits, including displays depicting the development and history of the international merchant marine, related shoreside industries, and ports. The history of the Maritime College is also a part of the Museum. Exhibits include marine paintings, watercolors, photographs, and artifacts. There is also a unique collection of 175 ship models from early sailing vessels to modern freighters and tankers and ocean liners. The Promenade Wing contains a collection of ocean liner models. Also displayed is a diorama of the Brooklyn Navy Yard during WWII and the new Victory Hall dedicated to WWII sailors.

The 565-foot training ship *Empire State* (formerly USNS *Barrett,* then the *Oregon,* then the *Moremoctide*) is the seventh training ship used by the Maritime College since its founding in 1874. Visitors may tour the ship when in port (nine months of the year) where high up on the aft loading stanchion are inscribed the words: "Student Driver."
Activities: Visitors may tour the fort and campus grounds
Admission: No entry fee but donations accepted. Open Monday-Saturday, 9 A.M. – 4 P.M.; Closed Thanksgiving, Christmas, and New Year's Day.

BROOKLYN, NEW YORK
Waterfront Museum and Showboat Barge
290 Conover Street, Pier 44
Brooklyn, NY 11231
(718) 624-4719
E-mail: dsharps@waterfrontmuseum.org
Location: The Museum barge is located at the Red Hook Garden Pier #45 at the foot of Conover Street in the Red Hook section of Brooklyn.
Highlights: Lehigh Valley Railroad Barge 79 (home of Museum), Garden Pier, views of working New York Harbor, cultural arts programming, near-by Trolley Museum,
Website: www.waterfrontmuseum.org
General Information: Established in 1989, the 1914 Lehigh Valley Railroad Barge #79, listed in the National Register of Historic Places as the only surviving wooden example of the Lighterage Age (1860-1960) afloat today and ready to receive

visitors. Aboard the 79 is the Museum's permanent collection of "Railroad Navy" photos, a riptide dinghy, a Peterboro sailing canoe, hawsers, tools, tugboat fenders, and much more.

Handcrafted wooden vessels of American origin were once nestled along the shores of the Port of New York. Prior to tunnel and bridge construction, cargo had to be transported by water across the Hudson River. To perform this function, various railroad companies maintained large fleets of barges (lighters) and tugs. This "Lighterage System" uses many types of craft including scows, hold barges, sticklighters, car floats, and covered barges — all called lighters.

There were also excursion barges, immigrant barges, produce barges, ice barges, livestock barges, and steel-covered barges. The Museum provides information on this historical past. *Activities:* Try your hand with a heaving line, throwing the eye of the line, and making up a Flemish coil. See a continuous video display "Tales of the Waterfront," and attend informational lectures and showboat entertainment. Call for current events schedule, rental, or appointments. Free and low-cost cultural programs, including "Circus Sundays" in June, Sunset Music Service evenings, July-August and more. *Admission:* Entry fee. Memberships are encouraged. Call for rental availability for corporate and special events. The Red Hook Pier #45 is open during daylight hours.

BUFFALO, NEW YORK
Buffalo and Erie County Naval and Military Park
1 Naval Park Cove
Buffalo, NY 14202-4114
(716) 847-1773   Fax: (716) 847-6405
E-mail: info@buffalonavalpark.org
Location: Buffalo lies at the west end of upper New York State on Lake Erie. The Park is immediately east of junction of I-190 and Rte. 5, south of the city's center. Take I-190 to downtown Buffalo — from the south take the Church Street exit, go right onto Lower Terrace (first intersection) and right again onto Pearl Street — from the north and Niagara Falls take the Niagara Street exit, go right on Niagara, and turn right onto S. Elmwood, which turns into Lower Terrace after the Church Street intersection. Or take the Kensington Expressway to downtown and the Goodell Street exit, bear left onto Pearl Street and continue to the Park. *Highlights:* The *USS The Sullivans* (DD 537) (destroyer), The USS Little *Rock* (CLG 4) (guided-missile light cruiser), The USS Croaker (submarine), ship models, **Website:** www.buffalonavalpark.org/

General Information: The Buffalo and Erie County Naval and Military Park, opened in 1979, is on a six-acre waterfront site, the largest inland park of its kind in the nation and one of the few inland naval parks in the country. Visitors may board two front-line fighting ships — the guided-missile cruiser USS *Little Rock* and the destroyer USS *The Sullivans*— and see on-shore, a PT boat.

The Sullivans is a lasting memorial to the five Sullivan brothers that gave their lives with the sinking of USS *Juneau* during WW II. Just forward of the 610-foot *Little Rock* is the 311-foot USS *Croaker*, which made six war patrols during WW II. The Museum displays include a model of the *Wolverine*, a side-wheeler converted into an aircraft carrier for flight training during World War II.

Snooks 2nd, one of the 9,500 P-39 airacobras built in Buffalo and Niagara Falls, NY, is on display. After WW II, the plane was abandoned in the jungles of New Guinea and was later salvaged and donated to the Park.

Activities: Guided tours, audiovisual programs, overnight encampment program, and social engagements aboard USS *Little Rock*
Admission: Entry fee. Open daily April - October 10 A.M.- 5 P.M.; November Saturdays and Sundays only, 10 A.M.- 5 P.M.

BUFFALO, NEW YORK
Lower Lakes Marine Historical Society
66 Erie Street
Buffalo, NY 14202-4007
(716) 849-0914   E-mail: museum@llmhs.org
Location: The museum is located in downtown Buffalo within walking distance of Erie Basin.
Highlights: Library, photo collection,
Website: www.llmhs.org
General Information: The Lower Lakes Marine Historical Society, founded in 1987, maintains and displays authentic objects, documents, and art relating to a vital period in Buffalo's maritime history.

"Queen City of the Lakes," Buffalo was for generations the gateway to westward expansion, and the region was the focus of French and British Colonial expansion and the flashpoint for major conflicts involving the great colonial powers of the world.

The museum now maintains a library and photo archive with over 300,000 photo images of Buffalo history. At Lower Lakes Marine Historical Society we have made a an effort to collect the history of the individuals that came to the Great Lakes as well as information on those of the vessels which they owned, or sailed. Other artifacts and historical items are finding their way into the exhibits, and displays making this museum a major repository of maritime history.

Smith's Guide to Maritime Museums of North America

Admission: Entry fee. Open: Tuesday,
Thursday, and Saturday, 10 A.M. – 3 P.M.

CAMILLUS, NEW YORK
Sims' Store Museum
c/o Town of Camillus
5420 West Genesee Street
Camillus, NY 13031-1422
(315) 488-7800 E-Mail: dwbeebe@verizon.net
Mail: 4600 W. Genesee St., Syracuse, 13219
Location: Camillus-Erie Canal Seven Mile Park
(300 acres).
Highlights: Canal, Gere Lock #50, original lock
gates, historical canal boat tours, "Clinton's Ditch,"
Nine Mile Creek Aqueduct, Lock Shanty, Sims'
Store Museum, replica of an 1856 canal store **Web
Site**: www.eriecanalcamillus.com/
General Information: The Sims' Store
Museum contains exhibits, early photos and
models reflecting canal life and history, rooms
depict boat building, digging the canal, structures
on the canal, and an 1800's Room. The park
includes seven miles of navigable canal and
thirteen miles of hiking and biking trails. Within
the park, consisting of 300 acres, you can visit the
1844 Nine Mile Creek Aqueduct.
Admission: No entry fee for Museum. Open
Saturdays, 9 A.M.-1 P.M., Sundays, 1 P.M.-5
P.M., year-round. Admission fee for boat rides
Sundays, May- October.

CANASTOTA, NEW YORK
Canastota Canal Town Museum
122 Canal Street
Canastota, NY 13032-1360
(315) 697-5002
E-mail: canalmus@dreamscape.com
Location: Canastota is forty-eight miles east of
Syracuse off I-90.
Highlights: Erie Canal history,
Website: www.canastota.com/
General Information: Canastota Canal Town
Museum, founded in 1970, was established to
preserve the Erie Canal's heritage. Construction of
the Erie Canal was hailed as the greatest
engineering accomplishment up to that time.
Under the leadership of De Witt Clinton, then
governor of the state, construction began in 1817
and was completed in 1825. The canal connected
Albany, on the east, to Buffalo, on the west, and
became the main route between the Atlantic Ocean
and the Great Lakes.
The 1860 canal-era museum building is filled
with authentic memorabilia as well as exhibits of
local businesses.
Admission: No entry fee. Open April-October,
Summer: Monday-Friday, 10 A.M.-4 P.M.,
Saturday, 11 A.M.-4 P.M. Fall, Monday-Friday,
11 A.M.-3 P.M. Closed Saturday/Sunday.

CAPTREE ISLAND, NEW YORK
Fire Island Lighthouse Preservation Society
4640 Captree Island
Captree Island, NY 11702-4601
(631) 661-4876 Fax: (631) 321-7033
E-mail: programs@fireislandlighthouse.com
Location: The Lighthouse is located along the
south shore of Long Island on Fire Island and is
accessible via Robert Moses Causeway. Pay
parking at Field 5, follow nature walkway to
lighthouse.
Highlights: Fire Island Lighthouse
Website: www.fireislandlighthouse.com
General Information: The Fire Island
Lighthouse will give you the opportunity to
experience maritime history, wildlife, and a
magnificent beach. A nautical Gift Shop and
Exhibit Area are located in the Keepers
Quarters/Visitors Center.
Activities: Guided tower tours (192-step climb
with panoramic view), fall-spring-weekends, July
and August, 7 days. Children must be at least 42"
tall, closed-toed shoes and reservations are
suggested. must be worn for tower tours. Guided
and self-guiding nature trail. School groups in
spring and fall by reservation only: (516) 661-4876
Admission: Tower tour-entry fee.
Spring - April Thru June. Open daily 9:30AM -
4:00PM Summer - July 1 through Labor Day
Open Daily 9:30AM - 5:00PM. Winter - January
through March open daily from noon until 4PM.

CENTERPORT, NEW YORK
Vanderbilt Mansion, Marine Museum,
Planetarium
180 Little Neck Road
P.O. Box 0605
Centerport, NY 11721-0605
(631) 854-5555
E-mail: info@vanderbiltmuseum.org
Location: Centerport, on the north side of Long
Island, is 38 miles east of New York City via I-
495 to Rte. 110 north six miles to Rte. 25A, then
east six miles to Centerport overlooking Northport
Harbor.
Website: www.vanderbiltmuseum.org/
Highlights: Ship models, gift shop, forty-three-
acre grounds with gardens and museum, 24-room
mansion and a state-of-the-art planetarium.
General Information: Marine museum with
2,000 marine specimens located in the Hall of
Fishes. The mansion contains a collection of fine
and decorative arts as well as a natural history and
ethnographic collection.
Admission: Entry fee. Open every Tuesday-
Sunday, 12 Noon – 5 P.M

112

CHITTENANGO, NEW YORK

Chittenango Landing Canal Boat Museum
7010 Lakeport Road
Chittenango, NY 13037-9594
(315) 687-3801 Fax: same number
E-mail: clcbm@centralny.twebe.com
Location: On the enlarged Erie Canal
Highlights: Library and on-site research center,
unique three-bay canal barge dry-dock, **Website:**
www.chittenangolandingcanalboatmuseum.com/
General Information: The Chittenango Landing
Canal Boat Museum is a historic preservation site.
The site features the original three-bay dry dock
with reconstructed miter anddrop gates. Along the
famous Erie canal, it was here where canal boats
were built and repaired in the nineteenth and early
twentieth centuries. Also on site are a blacksmith
shop, wood-working shopand saw mill, remains of
a sunken canal boat, and an interpretive center.

Activities: The Museum offers self-guided
tours, daylong school group programs, archaeology
instruction and digs, presentations to organizations,
towpath walks, and a picnic area.

Admission: No entry fee. Open ., May through
June, Saturdays and Sundays 1 P.M.- 4 P.M daily:
July-August, Saturday-Sunday, 10 A.M. - 4 P.M.

CITY ISLAND, NEW YORK

City Island Nautical Museum
190 Fordham Street P. O. Box 82
City Island, NY 10464-1496
(718) 885-0008
E-mail: CIHS@cityislandmuseum.org
Location: The Museum is on City Island, near
Pellham Bay Park.
Highlights: Yachting and boatbuilding exhibits,
City Island History from 1800, library (500
volumes) **Website:** cityislandmuseum.org/
General Information: City Island Historical
Society, founded in 1976, operates the nautical
historical Museum housed in the former public
school (P.S. 17), one of the first schools built in
Greater New York City (1887). The Museum
building is listed on the National Historic Trust.

Collections include paintings, photographs,
artifacts, documents, boats and models, and
memorabilia from pre-Plymouth landing times to
the present. The part played by City Island in
building defenders in the America's Cup Races
and in supplying Hell Gate Pilots is emphasized.
The library contains information on local history,
available for use on the premises.

Activities: Guided tours, lectures, videotapes,
and educational programs
Admission: No entry fee. Memberships are
available. Open Sunday 1 P.M.- 5 P.M or by
appointment only.

CLAYTON, NEW YORK

The Antique Boat Museum
750 Mary Street
Clayton, NY 13624-1119
(315) 686-4104 Fax: (315) 686-2775
E-mail: john@abm.org
Location: The Museum is located at 750 Mary
Street. Take I-81 north from Syracuse, New York,
to Exit 47. Follow Rte. 12 to Clayton,
approximately 20 miles. At Mary Street turn left
for two blocks to the Museum.
Highlights: Wooden Boat Collection — over 20
antique boats including the *Dixie II* and *Miss
Canada* III (Gold Cup racers), a library (500
volumes), and The River Memories Gift Shop,
Website: www.abm.org
General Information: The Antique Boat
Museum, initially founded in 1964 and more
formally organized in 1980, "is America's largest
freshwater boating museum with an impressive
collection of inland recreational boats. The
Museum is housed in a former lumberyard on the
Clayton waterfront and is a mixed bag of sheds and
buildings full of surprises, and for visitors who
grew up on a lake or river — full of nostalgia."
The Museum is a treasure of freshwater boating
history, housing a collection of wooden boats that
includes native American dugout and birchbark
canoes, St. Lawrence skiffs, early twentieth-
century speed-boats, launches, dispros (a small
fishing boat with a disappearing propeller, hence
the nickname dispro), skiffputts, sailing craft,
rowing craft, and pleasure boats. Collections also
include duck boats; outboards; outboard and
inboard engines; launches; runabouts; ice boats;
photography collection; and tools.

Featured are the *Dixie II*, winner of the 1908-
10 Gold Cup power-boat races, The *Miss Canada
III* and other Gold Cup boats; personal boat used
by Presidents Grant and Garfield; and other historic
craft. Also featured is the *Pardon Me*, one of the
largest and most elegant runabouts ever built, and
George Boldt's runabout, the *PDQ*.

The Cleveland E. Dodge Memorial Launch
Building is the largest single exhibit hall of the
Museum. Here you will walk among some of the
Museum's more than 200 antique boats plus 300
outboard motors, engines, and an extensive
collection of nautical memorabilia. Eight boats
from the Museum are on loan to the nearby Boldt
Castle Yacht House, a short boat tour ride from
Alexandria Bay, NY.

Activities: Guided tours, hobby workshops,
speedboat rides and skiff rentals are available.
Small craft boatbuilding. The Museum hosts a
festival of oar, paddle, and sail in mid-July, and the
Antique Boat Show & Auction the first weekend in
August with more than 125 boats on display. Also,

the Antique Raceboat Regatta is a biennial event held on even years.
Admission: Entry fee. Open daily, 9 A.M.-5 P.M., mid-May through mid-October.

COLD SPRING HARBOR, L.I., NY
Whaling Museum
279 Main Street   P. O. Box 25
Cold Spring Harbor, L.I., NY 11724-1438
(631) 367-3418   Fax: (631) 692-7037
E-mail: info@cshwhalingmuseum.org
Location: Take I-495 east from New York City forty-five miles to SR-110. Travel north six miles to Huntington (just two miles east of Cold Spring Harbor on Rte. 25A).
Highlights: Wonder of Whales gallery, nineteenth-century whaleboat *Daisy*, 700 pieces of scrimshaw, and changing-exhibit gallery, *A Whaling Account* (newsletter), museum store, **Website:** www.cshwhalingmuseum.org
General Information: Between the years 1836 and 1862, the town of Cold Spring Harbor supported a fleet of nine whaling vessels. Their voyages lasted between one and five years, sometimes taking them as far away as the Pacific Arctic. The oil secured by these stout vessels helped to keep American homes illuminated and her industrial machinery running smoothly.

The Cold Spring Harbor Whaling Museum, founded in 1936 displays a fully equipped whaleboat from the brig *Daisy*. Also displayed are whaling implements, marine paintings, ship models, a diorama of Cold Spring Harbor as a whaling port in 1850, and a permanent exhibition on Long Island's whaling industry, called "Mark Well the Whale!" The single largest group of objects consists of 700 scrimshawe items produced by whalers of the nineteenth century. The Museum also supports marine mammal conservation through its education programs and exhibits.

In 1989, a new changing-exhibit gallery opened that features displays on whaling history and traces Cold Spring Harbor's illustrious maritime past.
Activities: In-service workshops, adult tours, outreach lectures, and films
Admission: Entry Fee. Open June – Sept., Tuesday-Sunday, 11 A.M.-5 P.M., Closed Thanksgiving, Christmas, and New Year's Day.

CROWN POINT, NEW YORK
Crown Point State Historic Site/
Crown Point Reservation Campsite
739 Bridge Road (Mail: 27 Grandview Dr.)
Crown Point, NY 12928
(518) 597-4666 Fax: (518) 597-3668
E-mail: Thomas.Hughes@oprhp.state.ny.us

Location: To reach the Crown Point State Take I-87 to exit 28 (Ticonderoga/Crown Point Bridge) and follow NYS Route 74 East to Ticonderoga. At its intersection with NYS Routes 22 & 9N, turn left (north). Continue north through the village of Crown Point to the intersection of NYS Routes 22 & 9N with Bridge Road (NYS Route 910). Turn right (east) and the Crown Point State Historic Site and Crown Point Reservation are four miles up the road (before the bridge to Vermont)
Highlights: Champlain Memorial Light House with the Rodin sculpture "la France" on the Crown Point Reservation; across the road are preserved ruins of le fort St. Frédéric (1734-1759) and His Majesty's Fort at Crown Point (1759-1773); ruins of the Smith & Bullis Lime Kiln; and Prehistoric fossils throughout the Crown Point State Historic Site. **Website:** www.lakechamplainregion.com/cphistoricsite/
General Information: Crown Point State Historic Site Visitor Center, where your visit was preceded in 1609 by that of Samuel De Champlain, contains exhibits of artifacts found on site of the French and British occupation (1734-1783) and the American occupation (1775-1777). At the Crown Point Reservation stands the Champlain Memorial Light House, originally erected in 1858 and reconstructed in 1909 by the states of Vermont and New York to commemorate the 300th anniversary of the exploration of the lake in 1609 by Samuel de Champlain.

The lighthouse was erected on the site of the Grenadier Redoubt* built by the British in 1759 on the ruins of the French fortified Wind Mill. This site was used by the French as a "staging" area for raids into New England and New York and later by the Americans for their attack on Montreal in 1775.

Lake Champlain was an integral part of the eighteenth century highway linking Dutch and later British New York and French Canada. Crown Point is the narrowest part of Lake Champlain and is located approximately mid-way between Albany, New York and Montreal.

The ruins of le fort St. Frédéric and His Majesty's Fort at Crown Point are preserved by the NYS Office of Parks, Restoration and Historic Preservation, which also operates the Visitor Center/Museum. The Champlain Memorial Light House is maintained by the NYS Department of Environmental Conservation and is open by appointment.
Admission: Entry fee to Visitor Center. The Visitor Center is open May-October, Wednesday - Monday, 9:00 A.M. to 5:00 PM. The Crown Point State Historic Site is open until dusk at no charge.
* - A small defensive fortification.

CUDDEBACKVILLE, NEW YORK
Neversink Valley Area Museum/D and H
Canal Park
26 Hoag Road, P. O. Box 263
Cuddebackville, NY 12729
(845) 754-8870 E-mail: nvam@frontiernet.net
Location: The Delaware and Hudson (D and H)
Canal is on Rte. 209 about ten miles north of Port
Jervis, which is on I-84 at the juncture of New
York, Pennsylvania, and New Jersey.
Highlights: One mile of D & H Canal, six canal-
era structures, John A. Roebling's Neversink
Aqueduct, guided towpath tours, gift shop,
exhibits on local history,
Website: www.neversinkmuseum.org/
General Information: Neversink Valley Area
Museum, D and H Canal Park, founded in 1963,
were established to acquire and restore historical
sites within the area and to preserve in them
artifacts and memorabilia on a 300-acre site.
Within the D and H Canal Park is a one-mile
section of the canal, a national historic landmark.

Along this one-mile section are the stone
abutments for a canal aqueduct built by John
Roebling, builder of the Brooklyn Bridge; remains
of a lock; and many canal-era structures including
a lock keeper's house, canal store, blacksmith's
house, carpenter's house, and a full-size canal
barge replica. The early days are being re-created
by the Museum, in whose collections are examples
of the tools and household needs used by the
families that lived on and along the waterway. In
the early 1800s the United States was facing an
energy shortage. To transport anthracite coal (an
important fuel), the D and H canal was opened in
1828. It spanned the 108 miles on the Hudson
River from Honesdale, Pennsylvania, to an area
near Kingston, New York. The trip took ten days
by barge and included 108 locks.
Activities: Educational programs for children,
guided hikes, picnicking, cross-country skiing,
and a self-guided nature trail.
Admission: Entry fee. Open Friday-Sunday,
Noon- 4 P.M., March -December or by special
appointment.

EAST HAMPTON, NEW YORK
East Hampton Town Marine Museum
301 Bluff Road
Amagansett, NY 11930
(631) 267-6544 or Boat Shop at (631) 324-6850
Fax: (631) 324-9885
E-mail: info@easthamptonhistory.org
Location: From New York City take I-495 east on
Long Island to SR-46. Follow that Rte. south three
miles to SR-27. Head east on it to Atlantic Avenue
in Amagansett (East Hampton's neighbor to the
north.)

Highlights: Shore whaling, farmers, fishermen and
commercial fishing of the area, Edwards whaleboat
and Dominy whaleboat, Boat Shop on Three Mile
Harbor, boat models, **Website:**
www.easthamptonhistory.org/pages/marine.html
General Information: East Hampton Town
Marine Museum, founded in 1966, is located high
on Bluff Road in Amagansett, in a former World
War II navy barracks that overlook the Atlantic.
From its vantage point you can see the off-shore
dragger fleet from Montauk, seiners working their
dories through the surf, yachts sailing up the coast,
wildlife roaming the dunes, and, of course, people
walking the beach, swimming, or just looking out
to the sea.

The Town Marine Museum tells the story of a
town and its 300-year relationship to the sea. Its
unique perspective is not that of the historian or
scholar, although its exhibits are characterized by
thoughtful interpretation of historical research.
Rather, it looks at the people who work on the
water every day of their lives, to feed their families
and their nation. A visit the Museum's diorama
depicts early whaling and modern fishing, you will
see the east end of Long Island through the eyes of
the commercial fisherman.
Activities: Main floor galleries, top-floor
galleries, plus stairwell photography.
Admission: Entry fee. Memberships are
available. Open weekends, Memorial Day through
Columbus Day, other times by appointment
Open daily in July and August Hours 10 A.M. to
5 P.M. by appointment year-round.

DUNKIRK, NEW YORK
Dunkirk Historical Lighthouse & Veteran's
Park Museum
1 Lighthouse Point, P.O. Box 69
Dunkirk, NY 14048
(716) 366-5050
E-mail: dklighthouse@gmail.com
Location: Dunkirk is both forty-miles southwest of
Buffalo and forty- miles northeast of Erie,
Pennsylvania off Route 5 to Point Drive North.
The Lighthouse is privately owned and is near a
public park on the west side of the harbor.
Highlights: Historical lighthouse, Veterans
Museum,
Website: www.dunkirklighthouse.com/
General Information: Dunkirk Light Station,
sometimes called Dunkirk Lighthouse and Point
Gratoit Lighthouse, was established in 1875. The
light acted in tandem with a pier head beacon to
guide ships to the safety of Dunkirk Harbor. This
active lighthouse operated with a Third Order
Fresnel Lens bought from France in 1875 for
$10,000. The Lighthouse consists of the
downstairs with displays on how the Keeper lived
and pictures and history of the Lighthouse, the

115

upstairs is the Veterans Museum with displays for the Marines, Navy, Vietnam, Army and Air force. A tour of the tower is available.

A separate building has Coast Guard and Submarine Service displays with a third building, maritime history. Many artifacts are also displayed on the grounds along with a 45-foot Buoy Tender, lifeboat, 21-foot Coast Guard Rescue Boat and more.

Admission: Entry fee. Open third Monday in April to June, Monday, Tuesday, Thursday, Friday, Saturday, Closed Sunday and Wednesday. 10 A.M.-2 P.M., Last tour 1 P.M. Open July-August daily except Sunday and Wednesday 10 A.M.-4 P.M., (last tour 2:30 P.M.); Open September-October, 10 A.M. - 2 P.M. (last tour 1 P.M.), daily except Sunday and Wednesday. Closed November-March. Prices and hours are subject to change without notice.

FORT HUNTER, NEW YORK
Fort Hunter - Schoharie Crossing State Historic Site
129 Schoharie Street, P. O. Box 140
Fort Hunter, NY 12069
(518) 829-7516 Fax: (518) 829-7491
Location: Amsterdam is 34-miles northwest of Albany, Exit 27 off New York State Thruway onto 5S and then to Fort Hunter.
Highlights: Erie Canal Locks, Schoharie aqueduct, restored 1850's canal store building.
Website:http://nysparks.state.ny.us/sites/info.asp?siteID=26
General Information: At Schoharie Crossing State Historic Site, visitors can view the remains from all three phases of the Erie Canal, the most dramatic engineering achievement of its time. In addition to the original canal (1825), the Enlarged Canal (1840s), and the Barge Canal (1917), one can see many of the engineering structures which contributed to the canal's success. These include the Schoharie Aqueduct; several canal locks, culverts, and a canal basin.

The site also encompasses a Visitor Center, Putman's Store (a restored canal store dating from the 1850s) and a two- and one-half-mile nature and bike trail along the towpath.
Admission: No entry fee for tours and rides. Grounds are open dawn to dusk year-round. Visitor Center: May 1 thru Oct. 31, Wed.-Mon. 10 a.m.-5 p.m., Sun. 1-5 p.m. Site is CLOSED on Tuesdays. Grounds open dawn to dusk, year-round, weather permitting.

GREENPORT, NEW YORK
East End Seaport Maritime Museum
Third Street at Ferry Dock
P.O. Box 624
Greenport, NY 11944

(631) 477-2100 or 477-0004 Fax: (631) 477-3422
E-mail: eseaport@verizon.net
Location: Greenport is on the east end of Long Island (north side) via I-495 from New York City to Rte. 25 through Riverhead. Then twenty-two miles to Greenport turnoff. It is an easy stroll from downtown Greenport to the Museum.
Highlights: Wooden boatbuilding, oyster harvesting, WW II war-patrol-by- sailboats exhibit, USS *Holland* submarine replica,
Website: www.eastendseaport.org/
General Information: The East End Seaport Maritime Museum, overlooks the village and Shelter Island Ferry. The nearby Bug Island Lighthouse burned in 1963, and in 1990 volunteers completely rebuilt it in 60 days. The lighthouse, near Greenport, is the only all-season navigational aid between Plum Gut and Greenport, where the Coast Guard maintains the light. Greenport was an important part of transportation linkage from New York City via railroad to Greenport, then by ferry to Stonington, Connecticut, where passengers transferred to the railroad, which took them on to the New England area.

Among the exhibits displayed are: the Plum Island Lighthouse Fresnel lens; a model of "Bug Light" (the lighthouse looks like a bug because of its screw-pile legs); navigational artifacts; and aquarium displays of local fish. Also displayed are photographs showing the "Whisper Patrol," yachts donated to the Navy during World War II for U-Boat patrols off Long Island. In addition, the Museum has a full-size reproduction of a cross-section of the USS *Holland*, the U.S.Navy's first submarine. Also on display is a 22-foot handcrafted submarine.

Tools, drawings, and models from local shipyards that document the shipbuilding industry are displayed. More than 500 vessels — whaling ships to minesweepers and patrol boats — were built in Greenport yards between 1830 and 1950.
Activities: Community maritime events and ship visits; summer program for children
Admission: No entry fee but donations requested. Open: Spring, Open weekends starting May 17,
11 A.M. to 5 P.M.; summer, June 1, and through September, open daily (except Tuesdays) from 11 A.M . to 5 P.M.

HIGH FALLS, NEW YORK
Delaware and Hudson Canal Museum
23 Mohonk Road, P.O. Box 23
High Falls, NY 12440-0023
(914) 687-9311 E-mail: info@canalmuseum.org
Location: High Falls is twenty-five miles west of Poughkeepsie. Coming from the north on the New York Thruway, take exit 19, then south 9 miles on Rte. 209. Turn east onto Rte. 213 to High Falls.

Coming from the south on the New York Thruway, take exit 18 onto Rte. 299. At New Paltz turn north onto Rte. 32 6 miles to Rosendale. At Rosendale, turn west onto Rte. 213 into High Falls, then turn left on Mohonk Road.

Highlights: Exhibits of canal artifacts and detailed dioramas, canal history, working-scale-model of canal lock, Five Locks Walk — self-guided outdoor walking tour of canal and Roebling Aqueduct remains, library and archives. **Website:** www.canalmuseum.org/

General Information: In the hamlet of High Falls, where a flight of five locks compensated for a drop of 70 feet in elevation, the Delaware and Hudson (D and H) Canal Museum is located. Founded in 1966, the Museum seeks to inform the public of the great significance of the canal and its related communities; to provide a library and archival facility on the canal and its affiliated industries; and to promote the maintenance and restoration of the extant parts of the canal.

The D and H Canal Historical Society is actively engaged in restoration projects. Through the efforts of the Society, locks 16, 17, 18, 19, and 20 and the abutments of the two aqueducts in High Falls, plus the water filled section of the canal between Alligerville and Accord, have been designated National Historic Landmarks. The locks and the Five Locks Walk are being restored with a major grant.

The canal operated from 1828 to 1898, transporting newly found anthracite coal on a 108-mile journey from Hanesdale, Pennsylvania, to the Hudson River at Kingston, New York. It was then shipped down river to New York City. The Museum offers a revealing glimpse of what life was like during the canal era, when horses and mules pulled canal boats along the D and H canal route and through its 108 locks.

When other canal companies ceased to exist because of the advent of railroads, the directors the D and H Canal converted their company into a railroad, becoming America's oldest continuously operating transportation company.

Admission: Entry fee. Memberships available. Open: May through October, Friday, Saturday & Sunday, 11 A.M.- 5 P.M

HYDE PARK, NEW YORK
Franklin D. Roosevelt Library and Museum
4079 Albany Post Road
Hyde Park, NY 12538
(845) 486-7770
1-800-FDR-VISIT (1-800-337-8474)
E-mail: roosevelt.library@nara.gov

Location: Hyde Park is just four miles north of Poughkeepsie on Rte. 9 (approximately 100 miles north of New York City).

Highlights: Library (45,000 volumes) and archives (16 million pages of manuscripts), ship models, museum store,

Website: www.fdrlibrary.marist.edu/

General Information: Franklin D. Roosevelt Library and Museum, founded in 1939 by a joint resolution of Congress, was the first of several presidential libraries. The Museum, open to the public, contains displays on the lives, careers, and interests of both President and Mrs. Franklin D. Roosevelt. The President's naval/marine collections include ship models, books, artifacts, memorabilia, prints, paintings, photos, letters, logs, and state documents. (The library section is open only to researchers.)

Admission: Entry fee (includes admission to the Roosevelt Home). Open daily, 9 A.M.-5 P.M. daily November through April; and then from 9 A.M. to 6 P.M. May through October. Closed Thanksgiving, Christmas, and New Year's Day.

KINGS POINT, NEW YORK
American Merchant Marine Museum
US Merchant Marine Academy
300 Steamboat Road
Kings Point, NY 11024-1634
(516) 773-5515 Fax: (516) 482-5340
E-mail: fanucchid@usmma.edu

Location: Kings Point is in northwest Long Island, three miles north of the Long Island Expressway, Exit 33 Bronx, facing Long Island Sound.

Highlights: Thirty-five ship models, steam engine working model, National Maritime Hall of Fame, *The Manifest* (newsletter), **Website:** www.usmma.edu/about/Museum/default.htm

General Information: The United States is blessed with a rich maritime heritage. From coastal trade vessels of the American colonists to the swift nineteenth-century clipper ships to today's impressive supertankers and containerships, one message is clear — ships made America! This is the theme of the American Merchant Marine Museum (established in 1979), a national repository and exhibition center for the artifacts, artwork, ship models, and nautical memorabilia depicting America's maritime past.

Many unique and noteworthy items are included in the Museum's inventory. Among the some thirty-five-ship models regularly on display is a highly valued, eighteen-foot-long model of the famous passenger ship, SS *Washington.* A new exhibit is the re-creation of a 1945 Victory Ship radio room. The highlight of the Museum's collection, however, is the Hales Blue Riband Trophy, a magnificent gilt award last won in 1952 by the SS *United States* for the fastest transatlantic crossing ever by a passenger liner.

The Museum's National Maritime Hall of Fame is the only such exhibition in the nation dedicated to the great people and great ships of our maritime history. Each year, an individual and a vessel, which have made outstanding contributions to the maritime industry, are inducted in the Hall.

The Academy trains and educates officers for the merchant marine and naval reserve. The seventy-six-acre grounds include the estate of the late Walter Chrysler and the U.S. Merchant Marine Memorial Chapel.

The academy's primary responsibility, as stated in Federal law, is to train midshipmen (the term applies to the 58 women there as well as the 817 men) to navigate and operate ships. The training leads to licensing as deck officers or engineers. The Museum's archives and photograph collection are open by appointment to the public.

Admission: No entry fee. Open Tuesday-Friday, 10 A.M.-3 P.M., Saturday-Sunday 1 P.M.-4:30 P.M., year-round. Closed during July and federal holidays.

KINGSTON, NEW YORK
Hudson River Maritime Museum
50 Rondout Landing
Kingston, NY 12401
(845) 338-0071 Fax: (9845 338-0583
E-mail: hrmm@hvc.rr.com
Location: Kingston is situated on the west side of the Hudson River twenty-five miles north of Poughkeepsie. NYS Thruway to Exit 19: Kingston. Exit Thruway tollgate turning east to roundabout to third spoke off circle to Broadway (I-587). Follow Broadway east through seven stoplights; at eighth stoplight, turn left— Broadway continues. At the foot of Broadway follow road to left. The Museum is on your right at Rondout Landing.
Highlights: The *Mathilda* (an 1898 steam tug), *Focs'le News* (newsletter), Rondout Lighthouse, library (150 volumes), Gift Shop,
Website: www.hrmm.org
General Information: Rondout Waterfront was a thriving port on the Hudson River for over 300 years. The D & H Canal (see separate entry) brought coal from the mountains of Pennsylvania to Rondout. Today, this bulkhead looks quite different. At the Hudson River Maritime Museum, founded in 1980, the waterfront is home to historic vessels, which dock for a few days or a few years, for restoration, repairs, or rest. Museum members can also find dockage available for an overnight stay.

The Museum preserves the crafts, ships, and exhibits illustrating the maritime history of the Hudson River Region. Over the years, a number of specialized vessels were developed here to fill the transport needs of New York industry, including the steamboats, which raced each other up and down the Hudson in a battle for passengers and cargo.

Exhibits include collections containing over 4,000 items, from various boats used in Hudson River traffic as well as paintings depicting the early era of river use. The library collection pertains to steam and sail on the Hudson River and is available to the public.

As caretakers of Rondout Lighthouse, the Museum offers scheduled and charter boat rides to the lighthouse, located where the Rondout Creek joins the Hudson River. Built in 1913, it is the last and largest lighthouse built along the River.

Activities: Shad Festival in May, other festivals, visiting vessels, Guided tours, lectures, school trips, concerts, Rondout Light visits, and library.
Admission: Entry fee. Memberships are available. Open daily May-October: Sat/Sun/Mon/Tues Noon - 6 P.M.; Tues/Wed 11 A.M. – 4 P.M.

LOCKPORT, NEW YORK
Lockport Canal Museum
80 Richmond Avenue
Lockport, NY 14126
(716) 434-3140
Location: Lockport is some 20 miles northeast of Buffalo on Hwy 78 North/South or 31 East/West in upstate New York.
Highlights: Original flight of five locks and newer barge canal locks 34 & 35, **Website:** www.lockport-ny.com/Tourism/canal.htm
General Information: Nestled at the base of a historic flight of five locks, the Lockport Canal Museum offers an historical view of the original Erie Canal. Completed in eight years (1817-1825), the canal is considered to be one of the greatest engineering feats in the world. The canal expanded travel from towpaths to tugboats, opening the corridor of travel to the West by connecting the Hudson River with Lake Erie.

Since 1825, the world-famous locks of the old Erie Canal in Lockport, hewn mostly out of solid rock, have attracted poets, engineers, historians, and artists. Upon seeing the locks, General Marquis de Lafayette proclaimed them to be one of the greatest engineering feats of the world. The stonework of these famous five-twin locks is a monument to the skill and ingenuity of the canal builders. And they were not fully finished until 1847. By then, the south-side twin locks had been substantially enlarged and enlarged again to present large canal size in 1916/18.

Today, only the north-side five-flight locks exist. The New York State Barge System is 524 miles in length, including the Erie Canal, the Lake Champlain Canal, and the Oswego Canal.

The small Museum at the lower end of the locks, between the five-flight locks and the newer Locks 34 and 35, contains a wealth of photographic history of the building of the canal in its three stages: 1825, the first full opening of the canal; 1835, the construction and widening of the canal; and 1918, the opening of two much larger locks at Lockport with a rise of over 50 feet to the Lake Erie level. The stonework of the original flight of five locks still exists but the lock gates have been removed creating a five-step waterfall as a spillway for the canal.

Admission: No entry fee. Open daily May-October, 9 A.M.- 5 P.M.

MASSENA, NEW YORK
Dwight D. Eisenhower Lock
c/o Massena Chamber of Commerce
P. O. Box 387
Massena, NY 13662
(315) 769-2049
Location: Between Lake Ontario and the St. Lawrence Seaway two miles off Rte. 37, 160-miles northeast of Syracuse on the St. Lawrence River.
Highlights: Viewing deck for lock operation
General Information: Although not a canal lock museum, the Dwight D. Eisenhower Lock, built on the St. Lawrence Seaway near Massena, New York, is included to allow comparison to the locks of the 1800s. The Eisenhower Lock is the first lock east of Lake Ontario whose bottom lies below sea level but whose water surface is 246-feet above sea level.
Admission: Open May-October, daily 7 A.M.-11 P.M., November-April (viewing only).

MAYVILLE, NEW YORK
Chautauqua Lake Historic Vessels Co.
15 Water Street
Mayville, NY 14757-1326
(716) 753-2403/7535
Location: Mayville is in the southwest corner of upstate New York and on the north end of the Chautauqua Lake waterfront seven miles south I-86 and on Rte. 394.
Highlights: *Chautauqua Belle* (sternwheeler) and the Bemus Point-Stow Ferry (cable-drawn)
General Information: Chautauqua Lake Historic Vessels Co. owns and operates historic vessels, carrying passengers exactly as was done in the past. Once a secret, strategic water link between French Canada, the Mississippi River, and French Louisiana, Chautauqua Lake has been witness to a wide variety of vessels in her recorded history.

The Chautauqua Lake Historic Vessels *Chautauqua Belle*, an old-fashioned, steam-powered sternwheeler, which pays homage to that magnificent fleet of great steamboats that carried cargo and passengers to summer resorts a century ago. With a soft puff of steam and gentle splash of her paddlewheel, it quietly glides across an historic and scenic inland lake.
Activities: The *Chautauqua Belle* — one and one-half hour cruises in the summer.
Admission: Nominal fees.

MONTAUK, NEW YORK
Montauk Point Lighthouse Museum
2000 Montauk Highway
Montauk, NY 11954-5600
Toll Free: 1-888-685-7646
(631) 668-2544 Ext. 23   Fax: (631) 668-2546
E-mail: keeper@montauklighthouse.com
Location: The lighthouse and Museum are on Montauk Road six miles east of the town of Montauk on the south shore of the eastern tip of Long Island. *Highlights:* Lighthouse,
Website: www.montauklighthouse.com/
General Information: The Montauk Point Lighthouse is one of the oldest active lighthouses in the U.S. The 1796 lighthouse was commissioned, as were many others, by George Washington. There are 137 steps visitors may climb to the top of the tower. The Museum exhibits include displays about maritime history.
Admission: Entry fee. Open Memorial Day – Labor Day generally 10:30 A.M. – 5 P.M. For other times in during the year, contact the Museum for days and times.

NEW YORK CITY, NEW YORK
Intrepid **Sea-Air-Space Museum**
1 Intrepid Plaza
Pier 86, West 46th Street & 12th Avenue
New York, NY 10036-4103
(212) 245-0072 Toll Free: 1-877-957-7447
Fax: (212) 245-7289
E-mail: pr@intrepidmuseum.org
Location: The USS *Intrepid* is docked at New York City's Pier 86, located at 46th Street and 12th Avenue.
Highlights: The USS *Intrepid* (aircraft carrier), The USS *Growler* (guided missile submarine), The USS *Edson* (destroyer), forty-one aircraft ranging from pre-World War I through modern-day aviation on display on flight/hangar decks, library (5,000 volumes),
Website: www.intrepidmuseum.org/
General Information: Perhaps no ship in the annals of the US Navy has done more to live up to her name than the USS *Intrepid*. After a gallant thirty-one-years of service, the historic ship is now

the *Intrepid* Sea-Air-Space Museum, founded in 1982. The USS *Growler* may also be toured. She is a guided-missile submarine that served the country for six years armed with Regulus missiles, patrolling the western Pacific Ocean as a strategic nuclear defense deterrent during the Bay of Pigs and the Cuban Missile Crisis of the Cold War period.

The USS *Edson*, a Vietnam-era destroyer with the motto "Three Guns, No Waiting," served the country for thirty years. Named for USMC Major General and Congressional Medal of Honor recipient Merritt Austin ("Red Mike") Edson, this ship provided gunfire support during wartime and a training platform for officers and enlisted personnel during times of peace.

Collections include open flight deck with displays; World War II aircraft; Grumman Avenger; Grumman Hellcat; tools; suspended aircraft; vertical flight vehicles; space flight vehicles; ballistic missiles; and forty-one planes and helicopters, ranging from pre-World War I through modern-day aviation. A Congressional Medal of Honor Museum is housed here also.

The 710-foot-long hangar deck contains well-crafted exhibits, displays, and photographs, along with the Carrier Operations presentations: U.S. Navy Hall, which features the modern, peace-keeping Navy; *Intrepid* Hall, focusing on the *Intrepid* during World War II; Pioneer Hall, a tribute to early aviation; Technologies Hall, where exhibits and displays presenting some of the greatest advances in sea, air, and space technology can be found. Other notable exhibit areas include Combat Information Center, Air Traffic Control, and Undersea Frontier. The library has information pertaining to sea, air, and space, history, and technology.

Activities: Films, educational programs, and special event halls.

Admission: Entry fee. Memberships are available. Open Wednesday-Sunday, 10 A.M.-5 P.M., year-round (last admission at 4 P.M.). Call for times.

NEW YORK, NEW YORK
Museum of the City of New York
1220 Fifth Avenue, at 103rd Street
New York, NY 10029
(212) 534-1672 Fax: (212) 423-0758
E-mail: info@mcny.org
Highlights: Statue of Robert Fulton, ship models, Edward Moran's famous painting of "The Unveiling of the Statue of Liberty,"
Website: www.mcny.org/
General Information: The Museum is a repository of Port of New York maritime artifacts and paintings related to the Port, which are on

permanent display in the Marine Gallery on the second floor. Exhibits include the larger-than-life statue of Robert Fulton taken from the old East River ferry terminal, and a figure head of Andrew Jackson from the frigate U.S. *Constitution* ("Old Ironsides").

Admission: No entry fee, but donations accepted. Open Tuesday-Sunday, 10 A.M.-5 P.M.; Sunday, 12 P.M.-5 P.M.

NEW YORK, NEW YORK
The New-York Historical Society
170 Central Park West
New York, NY 10024
(212) 873-3400
E-mail: webmaster@nyhistory.org
Location: 77th Street and Central Park West.
Highlights: Library, Henry Luce III Center for the Study of American Culture,
Website: www.nyhistory.org/
General Information: The New-York Historical Society, founded in 1804, maintains a variety of records on maritime history including archives, ship logs, and other library and research information and paintings, drawings, prints, and ephemera related to maritime history.

Admission: Entry fee. Open all year: Tuesday-Sunday, 10 A.M. – 5 P.M.; library hours, Tuesday-Saturday, 10 A.M.- 5 P.M.

NEW YORK, NEW YORK
South Street Seaport & Ocean Liner Museum
12 Fulton Street
New York, NY 10038
(212) 748-8786
E-mail: On Website
Location: The Museum is situated in Lower Manhattan (south of the Brooklyn Bridge) on the East River in an area bounded by South, Water, Beekman and John Streets.
Highlights: Boardable historic vessels, The Titanic Memorial, special tours of historic district, maritime library, permanent exhibit of ocean liner memorabilia.
Website: www.southstreetseaport.org
General Information: South Street Seaport Museum, founded in 1967, is a twelve-block historic area created as a landfill starting in the late eighteenth century and was the city's bustling seaport in the nineteenth century. The brick and granite buildings that line the Belgian block streets were built as shops, warehouses, and counting houses in the early 1800s with hastiness attested to today by the crooked angles of the windowsills as the landfill settled.

Although many of the buildings are still being restored, the renovation of those along Fulton Street (its name is taken from Robert Fulton, who once docked his famous steamboat here) is complete. The first building of the Fulton Market was constructed by the city in 1869; today's building at the water's edge has been in use since 1907. The adjacent Fulton Market is the third market building to stand on its site since 1822. The Seaport Historic District contains the largest concentration of early 19th architecture remaining in NYC.

These and many other buildings included those between Beekman, Water, Front and Peck's slip all under restoration. Across Fulton Street from market is Schermerhorn Row, a row of early-nineteenth-century buildings housing more shops and restaurants. The upper floors were recently opened by the Museum as galleries, comprising some 30,000 square feet among 24 separate galleries.

Currently used to exhibit temporary exhibitions, the Museum's permanent World Port New York exhibition is in planning stages. The Museum also maintains three galleries of changing exhibits at 209 and 213 Water Street. Information on the seaport area is available at Museum's Schermerhorn Row entrance at 12 Fulton and the Pier 16 Visitors Center. Abundant parking is available in the Historic District. Museum ships are docked at the foot of Fulton Street at Piers 15 and 16. Vessels that may be boarded include the *Peking*, a 347-foot four-masted bark built in 1911; the *Wavertree*, 293-foot full-rigged ship built in 1885; schooner *Pioneer* built in 1885; original *Ambrose* Lightship; and others.

Activities: Maritime skill activities for on ships and piers during summer months, ship restorations and gallery exhibitions, craft demonstrations, guided tours, lectures, films, summer concerts and sailing on the schooner *Pioneer* and 1930 tug *W.O. Decker*, and excursions on Circle Line vessels.

Admission: Entry fee. Open Summer hours: 10 A.M. to 6 P.M.; Winter hours: Friday – Monday, 10 A.M. – 5 P.M.

NORTHPORT, L.I., NEW YORK
Northport Historical Museum
215 Main Street
P.O. Box 545
Northport (Long Island), NY 11768-1730
(631) 757-9859   Fax: (631) 757-9398
E-mail: info@northporthistorical.org
Location: On Long Island, Northport is thirty-eight miles east of New York City via I-495 to Rte. 110, north six miles to Rte. 25A. Then east six miles to Woodbine Avenue. Left on Woodbine to Main Street and turn right.
Highlights: Permanent exhibit of Northport history from pre 1656 to the present and five

rotating exhibits annually, maritime history and tools, museum shop,
Website: www.northporthistorical.org
General Information: Housed in the 1914 Carnegie Library, the Northport Historical Museum presents permanent and changing exhibits on history of 300-year-old village, shipbuilding tools, photographs, cultural, historical, and geographical features of Northport, Northport Harbor, Eaton's Neck, East Northport, and Fort Salonga, Long Island.
Admission: No entry fee, but donations accepted. Open Tuesday-Sunday, 1 P.M.-4:30 P.M., year-round.

OSWEGO, NEW YORK
H. Lee White Marine Museum
1 West First Street on Pier, P.O. Box 101
Oswego, NY 13126
(315) 343-0480 Fax: (315) 343-5778
E-mail: info@hleewhitemarinemuseum.com
Location: From Rte. 3 in mid-town Oswego, turn north on 1st Street several blocks to the end of the west pier at the mouth of the Oswego River; the pier extends into the middle of the harbor.
Highlights: Oswego Canal exhibits, shipbuilding exhibits, canoes, epic paintings, World War II tugboat (LT-5) National Historic Landmark, Derrick Barge No. 8, ship models, library
Website: www.hleewhitemarinemuseum.com
General Information: The H. Lee White Marine Museum is located at one of the most historic sites of the United States. Ever since Père Simon LeMoyne first entered the river in 1654 to the present day, events which have shaped our destiny as a nation have taken place here.

Exhibits touch on the 17th century down through 300 years to the present. And explore Lake Ontario with the Iroquois — the American Indian-master boat builder and navigator. March with Rogers Rangers and the leaders of colonial America, and hunt for treasure in the "Lost Treasures of Lake Ontario" exhibit. A fine group of paintings include the Van Cleve Collection, and others depict the Oswego Canal, which connects to the Erie Canal near Syracuse, New York. The canal is still an important commercial enterprise.

James Fenimore Cooper, noted American writer, hailed from this port city, and several exhibits present history on his participation in the community.

The Museum holdings include the National Historic Landmark U.S. Army Tug (LT-5) used in the D-Day landings on Normandy, France. And on the pier is the last steam powered derrick barge, the *Lance Knapp*. Other exhibits include documents, artifacts, models, shipwreck information, photographs, maps, reconstructed rooms, and an extensive collection of artifacts acquired through underwater archaeology, and audiovisual experiences.

Admission: Entry fee. Open daily: Mid May-December, Daily 1-5 P.M.; Jan-Mid May, Monday-Saturday 1-5 P.M., Sundays by Appointment; July & August, Daily 10 A.M. – 5 P.M.

OSWEGO, NEW YORK
Oswego Maritime Foundation
McCrobie Building
11 Lake Street
Oswego, NY 13126-1320
(315) 342-5753 (Main office) (315) 342-0882 (Education Center)
E-mail: omf@oswegomaritime.org
Location: The Museum is located at the harbor end of West First Street in Oswego (waterfront buildings).
Highlights: Schooner *OMF Ontario, Maritimes* (newsletter), boating education, Goble Dry Dock, library, **Website: www.oswegomaritime.org**

General Information: While the cargo of the original lake schooner may have been grain, coal, lumber, or travelers to a new land, the new schooner's cargo will be people of all ages eager to understand something of their maritime heritage, lake history, lake resources, and aquatic ecology. The "Education Through Involvement Program," made possible by the Oswego Maritime Foundation (OMF), is provided aboard the classic gaff-rigged 85-foot schooner OMF *Ontario* of the type that in the not-too-distant past sailed and served as a means of transportation, shipping, and communications on the Great Lakes. The program is operated as a public service project by OMF.

The OMF sponsors and/or helps facilitate research projects by accredited colleges or universities. Volunteer SCUBA divers locate and identify shipwrecks and other submerged cultural resources at such dive sites as "Mary Kay" and "David W. Mills," in order to document them before they are destroyed or obscured by Zebra mussels, using the information secured for and educational materials, presentations to community school groups, and providing it to historical and tourism agencies.

George Goble, who, on May 6, 1856, in his just-completed Ontario Dry Dock, later to be known as the Goble Dry Dock, blasted from solid rock, launched his first ship, the schooner *Titan*. The dry-dock is now a part of the OMF facilities at the end of 1st Street next to the pier. OMF used the watered area for its sailing, boating, sport

Admission: The OMF office, library, classroom facilities are open year-round. The educational is open May - September and located at harbor end of W First Street immediately east of the U.S. Coast Guard Station. Call for times/ locations.

PEEKSKILL, NEW YORK
National Maritime Historical Society
5 John Walsh Boulevard
P.O. Box 68
Peekskill, New York 10566-5307
(914) 737-7878 (800) 221-6647
E-mail: bgreen@seahistory. org
Location: NMHS is located in Peekskill, New York.
Highlights: Sea History magazine, Sea History Gazette, **Website:**
www.seahistory.org/public_html/frame.htm
General Information: The National Maritime Historical Society is dedicated to America's seafaring heritage. NMHS began in 1963 as a group of maritime enthusiasts working to save the bark Kaiulani and return her to the US from the Philippines. reorganized and established itself on the banks of the scenic Hudson River, a waterway rich in American history. NMHS began by publishing Sea History, at that time an annual journal, which served as a vehicle for disseminating information about maritime history and as a forum for marine museums and preservation projects.

PLATTSBURG, NEW YORK
Clinton County Historical Museum
98 Ohio Avenue
Plattsburg, NY 12903-4401
(518) 561-0340
E-mail: director@clintoncountyhistorical.org
Location: Plattsburg is located on the west shore of Lake Champlain. Exit I-87 at Rte 37. Go east on Rte 3, continuing straight ahead on Cornelia Street. When the road forks, bear left and follow Cornelia Street to Catherine Street, then on Oak for two blocks to Court Street. Oak Street is one-way north — go to next street east, then south two blocks to Court Street returning to Oak Street. The Museum is at the corner of Oak and Court Streets with parking off Oak Street behind the building.
Highlights: Lake Champlain battles in the War of 1812, Valcour Island Lighthouse, gift shop.
Website:
www.clintoncountyhistorical.org/museum.html
General Information: The Clinton County Historical Museum exhibits and interprets the area's history from the earliest recorded times (1600) to the present through its collections of paintings, maps, furniture, and decorative arts. The decisive Battle of Plattsburg in 1814 was the culminating event in a century of naval warfare on Lake Champlain among the French, British, and the fledgling American. Underwater archaeological discoveries highlight this period."

The Museum's collections include artifacts from the Battle in 1776 near Valcour Island and the Battle of Plattsburg through dioramas. Other maritime exhibits include artifacts relating to the exploration of the lake by Samuel de Champlain and its later use as an important trade and transportation route. The Museum is also the steward of the Bluff Point Lighthouse on Valcour Island.

The Museum's collections include artifacts from the Battle in 1776 near Valcour Island and the Battle of Plattsburg through dioramas. Other maritime exhibits include artifacts relating to the exploration of the lake by Samuel de Champlain and its later use as an important trade and transportation route.

Admission: Entry fee. Open: Tuesday-Friday, 9 A.M. - 2 P.M.; year round. Closed Weekends and public holidays. For lighthouse, call for dates/time open.

PORT JEFFERSON, NEW YORK
Mather House Museum
115 Prospect Street, P. O. Box 586
Port Jefferson, NY 11777
(631) 473-2665
Location: From New York City take I-495 east sixty-four miles to exit for SR-112. Follow north six miles to SR-25A, heading west to Port Jefferson on north shore of Long Island (just eighteen miles south of Bridgeport, Connecticut, across Long Island Sound).
Highlights: Maritime history of the region,
Website:
www.portjeffhistorical.org/pages/Museum.html
General Information: Historical Society of Greater Port Jefferson maintains a small maritime museum with general artifacts and displays, and clock museum.
Admission: Open July 3 to September 13, 1 - 4 P.M. on Tues, Wed, Sat & Sun.

RIVERHEAD, NEW YORK
Suffolk Historical Museum
300 W. Main Street
Riverhead, NY 11901-2894
(631) 727-2881 Fax: (631) 727-3467
E-mail: schsociety@optionline.net
Location: East end of Long Island off Sunrise Highway: Exit 61 via Riverhead-Moriches Road. (Rte. 51) or: Exit 72 onto Rte. 25. Then 3-miles east on Long Island Expressway. The Museum is on West Main Street.
Highlights: Ship models, The Weathervane Gift Shop, library (history and genealogical).
Website: www.riverheadli.com/rmuseum.html
General Information: The Suffolk Historical Museum, founded in 1886 to collect, preserves, and interpret the ongoing history of Suffolk County. The County story is told in terms of the people themselves through craft and trade tools,

ceramics, agriculture, and whaling. Here are the things they made and used and collected from the time of the first settlements of 1640 including exhibits on Eastern Long Island Native Americans. Tools, textiles, flags, firearms, and pictures are part of the exhibits.
Activities: Educational services and activities.
Admission: No entry Fee but donations accepted. Open Tuesday-Saturday, 12:30 P.M.- 4:30 P.M.; Library, Wednesday, Thursday and Saturday, 12:30 P.M.- 4:30 P.M. Closed Sundays and holidays. Library use requires a small donation.

ROME, NEW YORK
Erie Canal Village
5789 New London Road (Rts. 46 & 49)
Rome, NY 13440-8338
(315) 337-3999
E-mail: mandm2000@twcny.rr.com
Location: The Village is located about eighty miles northwest of Albany, on Rtes. 46 and 49 with three access exits from thruway I-90.
Highlights: Chief Engineer of Rome (horse-drawn canal packet-boat), restored canal village, gift shop,
Website: www.eriecanalvillage.net/
General Information: The Erie Canal Village was begun in 1973 in Rome. The 1840s reconstructed village is in a rustic setting near the spot where the first shovel full of dirt was turned for the old Erie Canal on July 4, 1817; a number of nineteenth-century buildings have been restored to recreate a canal-side village. A historical slide presentation gives background of the site from the days of the Durham boats on Wood Creek to the barge canal. The full-size packet boat *Chief Engineer of Rome,* named for Benjamin Wright who became the original Erie Canal chief engineer from Rome, offers horse-drawn rides along a three-mile section of the canal. Also on the site is a stone marker showing where the canal's construction called spitefully by some, "Clinton's Ditch."
Admission: Entry Fee. Open Memorial Day-Labor Day, every day 10 A.M.-5 P.M.

SACKETS HARBOR, NEW YORK
Sackets Harbor Battlefield State Historic Site
504 W. Main Street
P.O. Box 27
Sackets Harbor, NY 13685
(315) 646-3634 Fax: (315) 646-1203
E-mail: mail@sacketsharborbattlefield.org
Location: From Syracuse take I-81 north to exit 45 to SR-3. Follow it west eight miles to Sackets Harbor on Lake Ontario. The site is located at 505 West Washington Street at the west end of the village on Lake Ontario.

Highlights: U.S. Navy shipyard; "A Sailor's Life Aboard the Jefferson"; War of 1812 historical information; Battlefield of May 29, 1813, in which 1200 British, Canadian, and Indian troops from Canada failed in a four-hour battle to destroy this American shipyard on Lake Ontario; 1814 Fort Kentucky; Library (1000 volumes); an original War of 1812 32-pounder carronade cannon mounted on a rock adjacent to Washington Street near the Sacket Mansion; and an original carronade cannon flintlock.

Website: www. sacketsharborbattlefield.org/

General Information: Sackets Harbor Battlefield State Historic Site, founded in 1933 as a historical navy yard and battlefield complex, is housed in five buildings: The restored 1849 Commandant's and Master's houses; the 1848 Stable; and the 1850 Ice House; and the 1840 Farmhouse. All of these are located on site of a nineteenth-century naval base, which played an important part in the War of 1812. Nearby Seaway Trails Foundation operates a visitor center in the 1818 Union Hotel. Sackets Harbor Battlefield maintains an exhibit room in this facility featuring part of our archaeological collection, War of 1812 personal weapons, an artillery caisson and uniform accouterments.

Sackets Harbor was settled in 1801 and quickly became a flourishing Lake Ontario community. During the War of 1812 it was the center of U.S. Naval and military activity along the upper St. Lawrence River and into distant Lake Erie. The unfinished first-rate-ship-of-the-line, USS *New Orleans,* designed to carry a crew of 1,000, was enclosed in a huge wooden ship house to protect it for future use. In 1883, the Navy decided to scrap the vessel. By doing so, together with the improved Canadian-American relations, the need for a naval base at Sackets Harbor ended. The Navy maintained the facility until the 1960s, and was seldom used except by the State's naval militia.

Collections include restored 13-room 1850-61 Navy commandant's house complete with nineteenth century household furniture and accessories. In the 1948 Stable building, naval exhibits focus on the War of 1812 and its weapons, armament and accessories, including an original flintlock used to fire a carronade cannon, and military clothing. and outbuildings.

Activities: Guided and self-guided tours during the summer season, military encampments, picnic area, lectures, special summer programs, parking, and handicapped parking.

Admission: No charge for grounds admittance. Entry fee for Commandant's house. Open Memorial Day to Labor Day, Tuesday-Saturday, 10 A.M.-5 P.M.; Sundays, 11 A.M.- 5 P.M.; Grounds open year-round.

SAG HARBOR, NEW YORK
Sag Harbor Whaling Museum
200 Main Street, P. O. Box 1327
Sag Harbor, NY 11963
(631) 725-0770 Fax: 631-725-5638
E-mail: info@sagharborwhalingmuseum.org
Location: On Long Island, take the Long Island Expressway East to Exit 70, Manorville. Follow Manorville Road to the end, picking up Rte. 27 East. Follow Rte. 27 fifteen miles to Bridgehampton. At the end of the business district, turn left at the traffic light onto the Bridgehampton/Sag Harbor Turnpike. The Museum is located on this road just before the business district, on the left, across the street from the John Jermain Library.

Highlights: Whaleboat, whale tryworks, tools, and artifacts, ship models, scrimshaw, nautical gift shop,

General Information: Sag Harbor Whaling Museum, founded in 1936, is housed in the 1845 Benjamin Huntting home, an owner of whale ships. As you approach the building, you will know it by its beautiful Corinthian columns. A whaleboat is outside at the left of the Museum. At the right in front of the Museum are tryworks — three large kettles used on board whaleboats for boiling the blubber to render whale oil.

As you enter the Museum you will pass through the genuine jawbones of a right whale. These were brought back to Sag Harbor by a whaler and have been on display for almost one hundred years. Exhibits feature whaling equipment, scrimshaw, oil paintings, ship models, fishing equipment, logbooks, and other Colonial pieces connected with eastern Long Island.

Admission: Entry fee. Open Monday-Saturday, 10 A.M.-5 P.M., Sundays 1 P.M.-5 P.M., May 17th -October. Open October weekends only. Tours by appointment.

SAUGERTIES, NEW YORK
Saugerties Lighthouse Museum
168 Lighthouse Drive
Saugerties, NY 12477
(845) 247-0656
E-mail: info@saugertieslighthouse.com
Location: The lighthouse is only 100 miles north of the George Washington bridge and 42 miles south of Albany NY. Leave the Thruway (I-87) at exit 20 turn right at the traffic light onto route 212 and follow it into the center of the village of Saugerties where you will intersect with Route 9W. Proceed straight on route 9W North for four blocks. You will arrive at a T where 9W turns left. Turn right onto Mynderse Street. A sign for the lighthouse is there too. Follow this road and bear left at the stop sign. Proceed down the hill and

out to the lighthouse parking lot, which is just beyond the Coast Guard Station.

Highlights: Lighthouse, Bed & Breakfast all year, store,

Website: www.saugertieslighthouse.com/

General Information: The present Saugerties Lighthouse was built in 1869 and sits on a massive circular stone base sixty feet in diameter with a sixth-order Fresnel lens that used kerosene lamps for illumination.

Nearby, the first lighthouse at the mouth of the Esopus Creek at Saugerties was built in 1838 with funds appropriated from Congress. It was constructed to guide ships away from nearby shallows and into the Esopus Creek when Saugerties was a major port with daily commercial and passenger transportation. The first light was lit with 5 whale oil lamps with parabolic reflectors.

Automation of the light in 1954 made light keepers obsolete. The building was closed up and fell into disrepair and decay. Efforts of a local historian and architect succeeded in placing the lighthouse on the National Register in 1978 stimulating local citizens to restore the building. In 1986 the newly formed Saugerties Lighthouse Conservancy acquired the lighthouse and the adjacent wetlands and after extensive fundraising and restoration work the building was completely reconstructed. After 36 years the light was restored to operation in the light tower on August 4, 1990.

Admission: Entry fee: Open weekends and holidays, Memorial Day through Labor Day, 2 P.M. to 5 P.M. and by appointment or chance. It contains a small museum, keeper's quarters, two bedrooms, kitchen and living room. The lighthouse operates as a Bed & Breakfast all year — weekdays most available.

SODUS POINT, NEW YORK
Sodus Bay Lighthouse & Museum
Sodus Bay Historical Society
7066 N. Ontario Street
Sodus Point, NY 14555
(315) 483-4936 Gift shop: (315) 483-0775
E-mail: bmccreary@soduspointlighthouse.org
Location: East from Rochester, New York, thirty miles to Rte. 88. North two miles to Rte. 14, then east four miles to Sodus Point.
Highlights: Lighthouse, Great Lakes history,
Website: www.soduspointlighthouse.org/

General Information: Sodus Bay Lighthouse Museum, relates to cultural history and the seafaring activity carried on in the Sodus Bay region. Over the years the Bay has been known for its lumber trade, commercial fishing, grain exports, ice industry, shipbuilding, and summertime recreation

From the time of the first settlers in the late 1700s, Sodus Bay was considered an ideal harbor

for exporting farm products and other commodities. Commercial captains from Sodus Bay were engaged in transporting cargoes aboard schooners and steamers to ports on Lake Ontario.

In 1824 Congress appropriated $4,500 to construct a lighthouse tower and keeper's residence at Sodus Bay. By 1869 both structures had deteriorated to the extent that Congress appropriated $14,000 to build a second lighthouse to replace the original buildings. The new station was completed in 1871 and was in use until its closing in 1901.

Today, the lighthouse situated on the west side of Sodus Bay is a sought-out recreation area next to Lake Ontario providing summer time boating and sailing pleasure. The Museum's docents are well versed in local maritime and lighthouse history and will make your visit worthwhile.

Admission: No entry fee but donations appreciated. Open Tuesday-Sunday, 10 A.M. to 5 P.M., May 1 through October 31. Closed Mondays except holidays. Other times by chance or appointment.

SOUTHAMPTON, NEW YORK
Southampton Historical Museum
Captain Rogers' Homestead
17 Meeting House Lane, P.O. Box 303
Southampton, NY 11968-4911
(631) 283-2494 Fax:(631) 283-4540
E-mail: info@southamptonhistoricalmuseum.org
Location: The Museum is located at 17 Meeting House Lane, just off Main Street.
Highlights: Southampton Town whaling, library, information in a historic 1843 whaling captain" Greek revival home. **Web Site:**
www.southamptonhistoricalmuseum.org/

General Information: The Historical Museum was set up in 1951 in 1843 the house built by Captain Albert Rogers, a whaling captain, The home was owned by Rogers' ancestors from 1648. The home has period rooms, changing exhibition galleries, and a research library with logbooks and material relating to local whaling culture.

On the grounds are a number of historic structures that have been moved here to preserve them. There is an 1880s carriage barn that displays a large collection of whaling tools, a whaling boat and other memorabilia, a one-room school house, a blacksmith shop, and several other late 19th century buildings that help create the look of a coastal town.

Admission: Entry fee. Open Tuesday-Saturday, 10 A.M.- 5 P.M., Sunday, 10 A.M.-3 P.M.; Open Monday by appointment for group tours.

SOUTHOLD, NEW YORK
Nautical Museum at Horton Point Lighthouse
Lighthouse Road P.O. Box 1
Southold, NY 11971-0001
(631) 765-5500 E-mail: eastlite@optonline.net
Location: On Long Island follow I-495
approximately seventy-five miles to Riverhead. At
the traffic circle, bear east on S.R. 25 twenty-
three miles to Southold. The Museum is at Horton
Point north off SR-25 on Lighthouse road.
Highlights: A National Historic Register.
Working lighthouse, oil house, lower accessibility,
Website:
www.longislandlighthouses.com/hortonpt.htm
General Information: Southold Historical
Society's Nautical Museum was established to
preserve artifacts including paintings, logs,
scrimshaw, tools, letters of maritime interest and
the 1857 lighthouse. Horton's Point rises 110 feet
above the sea level. Thus, it provides navigational
aid in an area characterized by many shipwrecks.
Admission: No entry fee but donations
suggested. Open Saturdays and Sundays only,
11:30 A.M.-4 P.M., Memorial Day-Columbus
Day.

STATEN ISLAND, NEW YORK
The Noble Maritime Collection
1000 Richmond Terrace, Building D
Staten Island, NY 10301-1181
(718) 447-6490 Fax: (718) 447-6056
E-mail: ErinUrban@noblemaritime.org
Location: Staten Island is accessed from the
Battery in Manhattan via Staten Island Ferry
Terminal and is easily reached by S-40 Bus. By
car from Brooklyn, Queens, Long Island via
Verrazano Bridge and to Staten Island
Expressway (I-278) to Clove Rd. /Richmond Rd.
Exit. At the traffic light, turn left onto Clove Rd.,
follow to Richmond Terrace, turn right and follow
Richmond Terrace to Snug Harbor.
Highlights: Noble's Maritime Art and writings and
his fully restored houseboat studio inside the
museum; maritime library and archives, Sailors'
Snug Harbor exhibitions, including recreations of
original 1801 Writing Room and Dormitory
Room; the Noble Crew Exhibition, showing $1
million the volunteer effort to restore the
Museum's home.
Website: www.noblemaritime.org/
General Information: Founded in 1986, the
Noble Collection first occupied *Opossum Acres*,
Noble's former home overlooking the Kill van Kull
on Staten Island's North Shore. In April of 1992,
the Collection moved to Building D, one of the
landmark front buildings of Snug Harbor
Cultural Center, which had from 1833 to 1976
been Sailors' Snug Harbor, a home for retired
seamen.

The Collection's relocation enabled it to realize
its goal to interpret the work of John A. Noble; to
celebrate the people and traditions of Sailors' Snug
Harbor and the working waterfront of New York;
and to operate a maritime museum and study
center.
The 1844 National Historic Landmark building
which houses the Museum was transformed in a
$3.4 million adaptive reuse project into galleries,
a library and archives, classrooms, studios, and a
Museum shop, and its centerpiece is Noble's
houseboat studio, where his works were "breech-
birthed" for 40 years at the abandoned pier of the
old Port Johnston.
Activities: Education programs for children and
adults, changing exhibitions, and special events are
on tap all year.
Admission: Entry fee. Open Thursday-
Saturday, 1 P.M. - 5 P.M. and by appointment.

SYRACUSE, NEW YORK
Canal Society of New York State
22527 Cherry Valley Turnpike
Marcellus NY 13108
(315) 730-4495 Fax: (315) 673-1864
E-mail: mbellman@twcny.rr.com
Location: Take I-690 into Syracuse. Exit onto Erie
Boulevard, which intersects with Montgomery.
Highlights: Library (300 volumes),
Website: www.canalsnys.org/
General Information: Canal Society of New
York State, founded in 1956, is a historical
museum with a collection of graphics on the
history of the New York State canals. A library is
available for research on the premises. *Activities:*
Guided tours lectures, research on New York State
canals
Admission: No entry fee. Memberships are
available. Open by appointment only.

SYRACUSE, NEW YORK
Erie Canal Museum
Weighlock Building
318 Erie Blvd. East at Montgomery Street
Syracuse, NY 13202-1106
(315) 471-0593 Fax: (315) 471-7220
E-mail: contactus@eriecanalmuseum.org
Location: Take either east west I-90 or north south
I-81 into Syracuse. The Museum is located near
the downtown area in the Weighlock Building on
the corner of Erie Boulevard East and Montgomery
Street.
Highlights: Full-size canal boat, nation's leading
Erie Canal collection, Children's hands-on
activity area, *Canal Currents* (newsletter), gift
shop,
Website: www.eriecanalmuseum.org/index.asp
General Information: "Fifteen Miles on the

Erie Canal..." The Erie Canal is a symbol of American ingenuity; it captures the spirit of a young nation striving to achieve its dreams. The construction of this inland waterway is a story of determination and innovation, unheard of engineering feats and, ultimately, the triumph of man over nature. Erie Canal Museum, founded in 1962, is housed in the Weighlock Building, the last administrative structure in use on the Canal. Visitors may explore the beginnings, construction, use, life, and effects of this great symbol.

A thirty-five-mile stretch of the canal is preserved in Old Erie Canal State Park. Starting near Syracuse in DeWitt and extending to New London near Rome, the park provides an excellent hiking and biking trail on the original towpath trod by mules and horses in the 1800s.

Activities: Group tours, weekend workshops, and special events, slide shows, and exhibitions. Visitors may board the canal boat to experience canal life and work.

Admission: No entry fee but donations appreciated. Open: Tuesday-Saturday, 10 A.M.- 5 P.M., Sunday, 10 A.M. – 3 P.M. year-round. Open Monday by appointment for group tours.

WATERFORD, NEW YORK
Tugboat *Urger*
New York State Canal Corporation
Waterford, NY 12188
(518) 436-2799 Fax: (518) 237-4452
1-800-4CANAL4 (422-6254)
Highlights: Tugboat *Urger*, **Website:** www.nyscanals.gov/cculture/tugboat.html
General Information: The *Urger*, flagship of New York's Canal System. . She was launched in Michigan in 1901 working in the Great Lakes before she began working for the State of New York in 1922.

The tug leaves wistful smiles on the faces of people wherever she goes and the year 2001 marks the *Urger's* centennial. Share the *Urger* experience and let your imagination wander back to the far away rollers of Lake Michigan and to the glorious heyday of tugboats and barges on the New York State Canal System. She makes appearances at various festivities. Contact the New York State Canal Corporation for further information.

WEST SAYVILLE, NEW YORK
Long Island Maritime Museum
86 West Avenue
P. O. Box 184
West Sayville, NY 11796-0184
(631) 494-9888
E-mail: limm@limaritime.org

Location: West Sayville is on the south-central shore of Long Island. From New York City, take I-495 east to exit 59 south (Lakeland Avenue). Follow Lakeland Ave. south for 6 miles into the village of Sayville. Make a right on Main Street, follow for 1 mile to West Avenue South.
Highlights: Priscilla (1888 oyster vessel), *Modesty* (1920 oyster dredger), *Charlotte* (1880 tugboat), ship models, *The Dolphin* (newspaper), U.S. Lifesaving Service Exhibit, Penny Boatshop library, **Website:** www.limaritime.org
General Information: Long Island Maritime Museum, formerly Suffolk Marine Museum, was founded in 1966 to preserve Long Island's unique maritime heritage for educational purposes. The Museum features a significant small craft collection, with boats ranging from a six-foot sharpie to the sixty-five foot *Priscilla*, an 1888 oyster sloop. Permanent exhibits include the history of the south shore oyster industry, a restored Bayman's Cottage residence, over sixty small craft and a working 19th century boatshop.

The Elward Smith III Library and Archive are available to researchers by appointment.
Activities: Ongoing Boatbuilding programs, lectures, and workshops. Major events include antique boat show, Seafood Festival and Maritime Folklife Festival.
Admission: Entry fee. Open Monday-Saturday 10 A.M.-4 P.M., Sunday, noon-4 P.M.; closed major holidays.

WHITEHALL, NEW YORK
Skenesborough Museum
Skenesborough Drive off Rt. 4, Box 238
Whitehall, NY 12887
(518) 499-1155/0716
E-mail: cbgbird@yahoo.com
Location: Take I-87 north from Albany fifty-four miles to Glen Falls. Exit east to SR-149 13-miles to Fort Ann and then 11-miles on Rte. 4, northeast to Whitehall. In Whitehall follow Rte. 4 just over the railroad bridge turning at the first left street to the Museum on right just past park buildings along the Champlain Canal.
Highlights: Dioramas of 1776 shipyard, nineteenth-century canal lock system (Champlain Canal), ship models, gift shop, **Website:** www.adirondack.net/orgs/arccleader/skenes.html
General Information: Nestled in a wooded valley at the head of Lake Champlain, Whitehall's Skenesborough Museum, founded in 1959, is located in a building constructed by the New York State Canal System in 1917. In 1759, British Captain Philip Skene settled here, building saw and gristmills and an iron foundry and raised horses for the West Indies trade. In the first months of the American Revolution in 1775,

Britisher Skene's trading schooner *Katherine* was captured from the Skene estate on a Green Mountain Boys' foray. Benedict Arnold, using this vessel, led a small band of volunteers down the lake to raid the British Fort in St. Johns, Quebec. Two days later Benedict Arnold's men sailed it to Crown Point, where he armed it for a definite act of war capturing a British naval ship and renamed it *Enterprise*. In the summer of 1776, the Americans learned that the British were building ships to take back the lake.

George Washington sent Benedict Arnold and Philip Schuyler to Sekenesborough to direct shipwrights who raced to build the American fleet, the first naval boats for the newly developing country, that fought in the decisive Battle of Valcour Island in Lake Champlain just south of present-day Plattsburgh. Of Arnold's gunboats built over two hundred years ago, the *Philadelphia*, now in the Smithsonian, and the *Providence* found in 1997, still under water there, are the only remaining evidence of the ships built at Whitehall.

Skenesborough Museum sits beside the Champlain Canal, completed in 1819, which is still in use today. In the Museum, are displays that explain the Whitehall's place in history in relation to navy, lake, canal, and railroad. The visitor finds photographs, artifacts, and models of the ships of the American Revolution and War of 1812 and the Lake-boat period of 1811-1873. Outside, under cover, is found the hulk of the *Ticonderoga* that fought in the Battle of Plattsburg. Boaters may tie up along the newly rebuilt canal wall while visiting the Museum. Nearby is Lock 12 of the Champlain Canal System.

Admission: No entry fee, but donations accepted. Open mid-June to Labor Day, Monday-Saturday, 10 a.m.-4 p.m.; Labor Day to mid-October, Saturday, 10 a.m. -3 p.m.; Sunday, noon-4 p.m. Other times by appointment.

NORTH CAROLINA

BEAUFORT, NORTH CAROLINA
North Carolina Maritime Museum
315 Front Street
Beaufort, NC 28156
(252) 728-7317 Fax (252) 728-2108
E-mail: maritime@ncdcr.gov
Location: The Museum is approachable from land or water (Intracoastal Waterway). From Raleigh take Rte. 70 southeast approximately 140 miles to Beaufort, passing through Goldsboro, Kinston, and New Bern. The Museum is on the inland waterway just east of Morehead City.
Highlights: Historic Beaufort (1709), a restored North Carolina seaport, ship models, wooden boat building, library, gift shop, bookstore, National

Oceanographic and Atmospheric Administration (NOAA) Chart Shop, **Website:** www.ah.dcr.state.nc.us/sections/maritime/
General Information: North Carolina Maritime Museum, founded in 1975 and operated by the State of North Carolina, but first established in 1951 as the Hampton Marine attempts to break the Union blockade of the Charleston Harbor. In August 2000, the original *Hunley* was raised from the waters off South Carolina.
Admission: Entry fee. Open daily, Monday-Saturday 9 A.M.-5 P.M., Saturday, 10 A.M. – 5 P.M., Sundays 1 P.M.-5 P.M.

BUXTON, NORTH CAROLINA
Museum of the Sea - Hatteras Island Visitor's Center
Cape Hatteras Lighthouse
Buxton, NC 27920
(252) 995-4474 Fax: (252) 995-6268
Location: Cape Hatteras National Seashore is approachable by land and water. Coming from the south, entry is via a Cedar Island ferry or the Swan Quarter toll ferry; from the north, via Rtes. 158 and 12 south; from the west, via Rtes. 64 and 12 south. A free ferry travels between Ocracoke Island and Hatteras. The visitor's center is in Buxton, on the southern tip of the island.
Highlights: History of life on Hatteras Island, Cape Hatteras Lighthouse (Cape Hatteras Seashore, NC),
Website: www. hatteras-nc.com/light/
General Information: The Museum of the Sea, founded in 1953, exhibits history, Cape Hatteras Lighthouse (1870), the lighthouse keeper's dwellings, natural history, historic houses circa 1870. Collections include maps, charts, and maritime artifacts. The Visitor's Center is the restored keeper's quarters. The thin strand of Cape Hatteras National Seashore, seventy miles long, winds between the windy, pounding Atlantic and the shallow Pamlico Sound.

The 208-foot Cape Hatteras Lighthouse (1870) is the tallest such structure in the United States and warns ships off the treacherous Diamond Shoals, the so-called "Graveyard of the Atlantic." It is a grim, but fitting epithet, for here more than 600 ships have wrecked, victims of shallow shoals, storms, and war. The former keeper's quarters contain a visitor center and exhibits on the history of the area. Visitor programs are held throughout the summer.

As early as the 1870's villagers served as members of the US Life-Saving Service. Others manned lighthouses built to guide mariners. The first tower erected at Cape Hatteras was in 1794. A 90-ft tower was erected in 1854, and the final tower was completed in 1870.
Activities: One may visit the remains of two

shipwrecks along the shore: *Laura A. Barnes*, four-masted schooner; *Oriental*, a Civil War (Federal) transport. Guided tours and lectures. *Admission:* No entry fee. Open daily, 9 A.M.-6 P.M., year-round. Lighthouse closed but keeper's quarters open.

ELIZABETH CITY, NORTH CAROLINA
Museum of the Albemarle
501 South Water Street
Elizabeth City, NC 27909-4863
(252) 335-1453 E-mail: moa@ncdcr.gov
Location: Museum is located on the banks of the Pasquotank River. It is an approximate 1 hour drive from Norfolk via I-464 south to US 17 to Elizabeth
City where Hwy. becomes US 17/158. Follow US 158 E/Elizabeth St. and on to Water St. turning right 4 blocks to Museum. From Outer Banks of NC, US 158 W to Elizabeth City. Upon crossing Pasquotank River, turn left onto Water St.. Museum 4 blocks on corner. From Raleigh, US 64 E. to Williamston, then N. to Elizabeth City. At junction of US 17 & US 17 Business, take right fork to US 17 Bus/Ehringhaus St. Continue about 2 miles until Ehringhaus St. intersects Water St. Museum on right.
Highlights: Local and maritime history, 1904 shad boat, museum tours, archives, Museum Shop
Website: www.museumofthealbemarle.com
    General Information: The Museum of the Albemarle interprets the history and material culture of the thirteen counties of northeastern North Carolina. The region includes a vast area of water with the Atlantic Ocean: Albemarle, Currituck, Roanoke, Croatan, and Pamlico Sounds; Roanoke, Chowan, Perquimans, Pasquotank, Alligator, and other rivers; Lake Mattamuskeet; the Great Dismal Swamp and the Dismal Swamp Canal.
    The museum is located in a new 50,000 square foot facility on the Elizabeth waterfront. The water and waterways of the region will be a central theme in the new core gallery being planned. Such aspects of our history such as early exploration, the naval history of our maritime conflicts, and the waterways as transportation venues are all heavily interpreted. In addition, the centerpiece of our lobby will be a restored 1904 shad boat.
    Activities: Civil War Naval Living History in February, A Student's Day on the River in the Spring, A day on the River in September, and Christmas program.
    Admission: No fee. Open Tuesday-Saturday, 9 a.m. – 5 p.m., Sunday, 2 p.m. – 5 p.m. Closed Mondays and all state holidays.

FAYETTEVILLE, NORTH CAROLINA
Cape Fear Museum
801 Arsenal Avenue
P.O. Box 53693-5300
Fayetteville, NC 28305
(910) 486-1330 Fax: (910) 486-1585
E-mail: david.reid@ncdcr.gov
Location: Fayetteville is fifty-five miles south of Raleigh.
Highlights: Cape Fear River history, museum shop, **Website**:
www.fayettevillenc.net/sites/st_capefear2.htm
    General Information: The Museum of the Cape Fear (River) is a branch of the North Carolina Museum of History. Here the history and culture of southeastern North Carolina are interpreted through exhibits on subjects indigenous to the region. Whether a whistle from a nineteenth-century steamboat or a prehistoric projectile point dated 8,000-10,000 B.C., the artifacts collected, preserved, and exhibited provide a better understanding of the events that have shaped the region
    Admission: No entry fee. Memberships available. Open Tuesday-Saturday, 10 A.M.-5 P.M., Sunday, 1 P.M.-5 P.M.

HATTERAS, NORTH CAROLINA
The Graveyard of the Atlantic Museum
59200 Coast Guard Road
PO Box 284
Hatteras, NC 27943-0191
(252) 986-2995 Fax: (252) 986-1212
E-mail: museum@graveyardoftheatlantic.com
Location: The Museum site is adjacent to the Hatteras village ferry terminal on Ocracoke Island, The Outer Banks.
Highlights: USS *Monitor* history,
Website: www.graveyardoftheatlantic.com/
    General Information: The Graveyard of the Atlantic Museum, founded in 1986, was established to interpret the maritime history of the Outer Banks. Since 1524 as many as 1,000 ships have wrecked along this coastline—one of the highest densities of shipwrecks in U.S. waters.
    The Museum presents exhibits detailing seafaring during colonization, the Civil and global wars, and the role of the unpredictable power of the Atlantic Ocean. Displays explain the OuterBanks' geographic and natural forces and trace the toll of wrecked vessels from the first explorations and settlements, through commercial expansion and passenger transportation by sea. The Museum expands the current-day interpretation and education efforts of the National Park Service and the Chicamacomico Historical Association.
    The Museum is also the anchor and southern end of the *Monitor* Trail. The USS *Monitor*, the

Civil War ironclad vessel that ushered in the modern age of naval warfare, is one of the most historic subjects treated by display. The sinking of the *Monitor* off Cape Hatteras in 1862 and its discovery and exploration in 1973, is the subject of one of many quality exhibits. Museum, exhibits ship models; marine artifacts; small-craft collection mounted marine specimens; seashells, and aquaria.

The Museum's varied programming, reflecting maritime history and coastal natural history, has achieved a level of excellence in both education and entertainment that is recognized nationwide. The "Wooden Boat Show" and the Junior Sailing Program are annual programs. "Summer Science School for Children," coastal habitat field trips, and special programs are but a few examples of the unique *Activities* provided. In addition, there is a substantial ship's library of plans and charts and volumes on traditional boatbuilding. For those cruising the Intracoastal Waterway, a book loaner vehicle available also.

Activities: Lectures, year-round field trips, and special programs.

Admission: No entry fee. Memberships available. Open Monday-Friday, 9 A.M.-5 P.M.; Saturday, 10 A.M.-5 P.M.; Sunday, 1 P.M.-5 P.M. Closed Christmas and New Year's Day.

KINSTON, NORTH CAROLINA
CSS *Neuse* State Historic Site
(and Governor Caswell Memorial)
2612 W. Vernon Ave. (U.S. 70 Bus.)
P. O. Box 3043
Kinston, NC 28502
(252) 522-2091 Fax: (252) 527-7036
E-mail: cssneuse@ncdcr.gov
Location: Southeast of Raleigh approximately eighty miles, Kinston is equidistant between Virginia and South Carolina.
Highlights: The CSS *Neuse* (ironclad hull), nautical blacksmithing, **Website:** www.nchistoricsites.org/neuse/neuse.htm
General Information: CSS *Neuse* State Historic Site and Governor Richard Caswell Memorial, founded in 1965, includes a museum; a memorial to Richard Caswell, the first Governor of North Carolina; and the sunken ram CSS *Neuss*, one of five remaining Confederate naval vessels. They are: CSS *Chattahoochee*, CSS *Jackson*, *H.L. Hunley*, and Mystery sub (Pioneer?) in New Orleans.

Union forces had already taken several small forts and port towns in North Carolina when the Confederate States Navy commissioned construction of the gunboat *Neuse* (c. 1862-65). She was one of twenty-two Confederate ironclad-ramming vessels built. The existing hull measures 141 feet long and 37 feet wide.

The museum presents exhibits and a slide show unfolds the story of the ironclad ram *Neuse*.
Activities: Guided tours; lectures, audiovisual programs, and self-guided tour/ exhibits depict the governor's life and times. Nineteenth-century rope-making demonstrations
Admission: No entry fee. Open Monday – Friday, 10 A.M. – 5 P.M. Closed Sat/Sun.

KURE BEACH, NORTH CAROLINA
Fort Fisher Historic Site
1610 Fort Fisher Blvd., South, P. O. Box 169
Kure Beach, NC 28449
(910) 458-5538   Fax: (910) 458-0477
E-mail: fisher@ncdcr.gov
Location: From Wilmington, travel south on US 421 eighteen miles to Kure Beach and Fort Fisher.
Highlights: Largest naval bombardment and amphibious operation of the Civil War, gift shop.
Website: www.nchistoricsites.org/fisher/
General Information: Before its fall in January 1865, Fort Fisher protected blockade-runners in route to Wilmington with supplies vital to the Confederate armies. It was the largest of the earthen; seacoast fortifications defending the last major port open to the Confederacy. Site boasts scenic easements of both the Cape Fear River and the Atlantic Ocean.

A quarter mile tour trail surrounds the archaeological remains of the fort. Wayside exhibits, a reconstructed palisade fence, and a partially restored gun emplacement enhance historic interpretation. Visitor's Center features an A/V room; gift shop, temporary exhibits and ADA approved restroom facilities. Permanent exhibit hall scheduled opened in the summer of 2001 display expansive collections of artifacts recovered from blockade-runners, blockaders, and the grounds.

Admission: No entry fee (donation only). Open: Summer hours begin April 1-September 30: Monday-Saturday 9 A.M.-5 P.M. Sunday 1 P.M. - 5 P.M.; Oct. 1 – March 31, Tues/Sat 10 A.M. – 4 P.M. Closed Veteran's Day, Thanksgiving Holidays, Christmas Holidays,

MANTEO, NORTH CAROLINA
North Carolina Maritime Museum on Roanoke Island
George Washington Creek Boathouse
106 Fernando Street
Manteo, NC 27954
(252) 475-1750 Fax: (252) 475-1507
E-mail: michelle.mcconnell@ncdcr.gov
Location: The Museum is located in downtown Manteo easily reached from Roanoke Island Festival Park by a stroll along the waterfront.
Highlights: Small craft, Creef Shadboats,

130

Website:www.
ncmaritime.org/branches/roanoke_default.htm
General Information: The North Carolina
Maritime Museum on Roanoke Island in located in
a building named after George Washington Creef,
a local boat builder who developed a
unique style of workboat suited to the surrounding
waters of the Albemarle and Pamlico Sounds.
Commonly known as "Shad Boats," these crafts
were later honored when they were named the
State Boat of North Carolina.

On display in the boathouse is a number of
small craft that represent a portion of the region's
rich maritime history. Included in the displays is
an original Creek Shadboat built in 1883, a variety
of sailing skiffs, and a Davis Runabout. A
multimedia presentation on the construction of the
Elizabeth II and its first sail reflect on the use of
the site for the building of the ship.

As a working shop, there is always plenty of
opportunity to see boatbuilding and repair work
first hand. Currently underway is the construction
of a 25-foot Shadboat funded by a grant from the
Percy and Elizabeth Meekins Trust. This sailing
shadboat will join other traditional boats for use
and display in the water adjacent to the Museum.
During a visit, you will see staff and volunteers
working on a variety of projects.
Admission: No entry fee. Open: Tuesday -
Saturday: 9 P. M. to 5 P.M.

MANTEO, NORTH CAROLINA
Roanoke Island Festival Park
Home port of *Elizabeth II*
1 Festival Park
Manteo, NC 27954-9396
(252) 475-1500   Fax: (252) 475-1507
E-mail: kim.sawyer@ncdcr.gov
Location: From Rocky Mount take Rte. 64 east
approximately 154 miles to Roanoke Island. Take
Rte. 400 four blocks to the Manteo Waterfront.
Cross small bridge to Festival Park.
Highlights: The *Elizabeth II* (replica ship), 16th-
Century military encampment, 8500 square foot
interactive Roanoke Adventure Museum, The
Legend of Two-Path film, outdoor Pavilion
amphitheater, Fossil Search, Museum Store, Art
Gallery, Boardwalks, picnic areas,
Website: www.roanokeisland.com
General Information: Roanoke Island Festival
Park the history of Roanoke Island as the
birthplace of Virginia Dare, the first English child
born in the New World. Between 1584-1587, Sir
Walter Raleigh sponsored three voyages to
Roanoke Island in the New World. The first was
exploratory, the second a military settlement, and
the third a first attempt at colonization, which
resulted in the "lost colony."

The Park focuses on the second 1585 voyage
with *Elizabeth II*, a 50-tunne bark named after one
of the vessels on that voyage. Interpreters portray
men of the voyage, in speech and dress aboard the
ship and in the *Settlement Site*. The Native
American point of view is explored in The
Legend of Two-Path, a 50-minute film that plays
daily at the Park. Four hundred years of Outer
Banks history is explored in the interactive
Roanoke Adventure Museum, and area
boating and fishing exhibits are highlighted.

Artistic presentations are produced in the
Pavilion amphitheater by the North Carolina
School of the Arts from late June through mid
August. the festival Park Art Gallery features a
new visual artist each month.
Activities: Self-guided tour of Elizabeth II,
Settlement Site, Roanoke Adventure Museum, the
Legend of Two-Path film, fossil search, Art
Gallery, and Museum Store. Call the events line
for a list of *Activities* and Gallery information.
Admission: No entry fee. Open: Monday-
Friday: 10 P. M. to 5 P.M. Saturday: 10 A.M. to
5 P.M. Sunday: 1 P.M. to 5 P.M.

PLYMOUTH, NORTH CAROLINA
Roanoke River Lighthouse Replica & Museum
206 West Water Street
Plymouth, NC 27962
(252) 217-2204
E-mail: info@roanokeriverlighthouse.org
Location: Follow signs from Hwy. 64. From
Washington Street NW to Water Street at Roanoke
River, turn left to end of Water Street.
Highlights: Roanoke River (replica) Lighthouse
and Museum **Website:**
www.roanokeriver.com/news_features/lighthouse.h
tm
General Information: This true replica of the
original Roanoke River Light is to tell the story of
inland waters of eastern North Carolina and
provide a repository for all the history of the inland
light stations. The Roanoke River Light had three
lives: first in 1835 when Congress funded the
construction of a lightship for the mouth of the
Roanoke River. But the Civil War ended its
existence; the second was a screwpile lighthouse
set in the river itself. Thawing of winter ice
fractured two of the piles and the lighthouse sank;
the third was constructed in 1866 and remained in
operation until it was decommissioned in the
1950s.

The current replica, constructed from the
original 1866 plans, was completed in 2002. In
conjunction with the replica lighthouse, a maritime
museum was established across the street where
maritime transportation history of Plymouth and
Washington County will be exhibited with
information about the Roanoke Light Service.

Activities: Traditional boat-building, guided tours and annual wooden boat show.
Admission: Entry fee. Tuesday – Saturday 11 a.m. to 3 p.m.; Sunday, 1 p.m. to 4 p.m.

ROANOKE RAPIDS, NORTH CAROLINA
Roanoke Canal Museum and Trail
15 Jackson Street
Roanoke Rapids, NC 27870
(800) 522-4282 (252) 537-2769
E-mail: canalmuseumr@roanokerapidsnc.com
Location: Museum is located just off Roanoke Avenue where it crosses the Trail at 15 Jackson Street Extension
Highlights: Canal locks, canal trail, Chockoyotte Creek Aqueduct
Website: www.roanokecanal.com/
General Information: The Roanoke Canal Museum, opened in 2005, interprets the History of the Roanoke Navigation Canal, which was built in the early 1800's to transport goods around the "fall line" rapids in this area.

The museum tells the fascinating story of transportation and navigation on the Roanoke River. Exhibits and information weaves together the navigational history of the Roanoke River and the beginning of the railroad transportation during the Civil War.

The canal was later used for hydro-mechanical power and hydro electricity and had much to do with the development of Roanoke Rapids and Weldon. The Canal carried goods from 1824 until the 1850's when railroads put it out of business.

Activities: An 8 mile trail along the canal and the museum where visitors can explore Roanoke Navigation Canal.
Admission: Entry fee. Open 10 A.M. – 4 P.M. daily

RODANTHE, NORTH CAROLINA
Chicamacomico Life Saving Station
Chicamacomico Historical Association, Inc.
23645 NC Highway 12, P.O. Box 5
Rodanthe, NC 27968
(252) 987-1552 (during open hours) or 987-1302
Location: Rodanthe is on the Outer Banks. From Manteo, travel south on Ste. Rte.-12 twenty-four miles to Rodanthe — Cape Hatteras is just beyond.
Highlights: Rescue drills, life saving, Coast Guard, and shipwreck memorabilia, research facilities, gift shop.
Website: www.hatteras-nc.com/chicamacomico/
General Information: The Chicamacomico Life Saving Station was established in 1874, one of the first seven stations on the Outer Banks of North Carolina. The buildings on site survive as one of the most complete U.S. Life-Saving Service/ Coast Guard Station complexes on the Atlantic Coast.

The station was in service from 1874 to 1954, and its seven buildings are all now under restoration. During World War II, 367 ships were sunk by eight German U-Boats off the Cape Hatteras shore with loss of life estimated at over 5,000. This information was never widely published — even today.
Activities are available including the "Beach Apparatus Drill." This is the same drill done by the Lifesavers from the 1800s and is done at 2 P.M. on Thursday.
Admission: No entry fee. Open Tuesday-Saturday, 11 A.M.-5 P.M., May 1- October 20.

SOUTHPORT, NORTH CAROLINA
North Carolina Maritime Museum at Southport
116 North Howe Street
Southport, NC 28461
(910) 457-0003 (Fax: same #)
E-mail: mary.strickland@ncdcr.gov
Location: Southport is 25 miles south of Wilmington on St. Rte. 133 on the mainland side across the Cape Fear River from Smith Island.
Highlights: Nautical history of "The Lower Cape Fear" area, ship models, Civil War blockade exhibits, research library, gift shop **Web Site:** www.ncmaritime.org/branches/southport_default.htm
General Information: The Southport Maritime Museum houses a collection of memorabilia pertaining to the vast nautical history of "The Lower Cape Fear" area of southeastern North Carolina. You can easily follow the self-guided tour through the 12 designated stations, or ask a knowledgeable guide to lead the way.

A local expert has made a nine-foot model of a shrimp-net for the Museum, complete with "doors." Other exhibits include a 200-pound pile torpedo retrieved from the historic waters of the Cape Fear River, a 2,000-year-old Indian canoe fragment, the shipwreck *City of Houston* treasures, the *Frying-Pan* lightship, and so many other pieces of Cape Fear and Frying Pan Shoals history await your discovery.
Admission: Entry fee. No charge for children and tour groups. Open Tuesday-Saturday, 9 A.M.-5 P.M. year-round.

WILMINGTON, NORTH CAROLINA
Cape Fear Museum
814 Market Street
Wilmington, NC 28401-4731
(910) 798-4350   Fax: (910) 798-4382
E-mail: ssullivan@ncdcr.gov
Location: Take Interstate-40 to Wilmington, in southeastern North Carolina. The Museum is eight blocks east of the Cape Fear River on Market Street.

Highlights: Ship models, newsletter, Maritime Pavilion exhibiting maritime objects/vessels, gift shop, **Website:** capefearmuseum.com/
General Information: The Cape Fear Museum, previously known as the New Hanover County Museum of Lower Cape Fear, was founded in 1898 and is an agency of New Hanover County. The Museum exhibits a collection of Civil War artifacts, nineteenth- and twentieth-century photographs, book, textiles, and toys.

It's has evolved into a museum with a collection numbering over 45,000 artifacts, including ship models, small arms, paintings, ship guns, and relics salvaged from sunken vessels. "The Wilmington Waterfront," a diorama of the Wilmington Riverfront in 1863, shows the blockade-runners, shipyards, sail lofts, and warehouses. Exhibits examine imported goods, the naval stores, and cotton industries.

Activities: Programs and special classes are frequently offered
Admission: Entry fee. Open Tuesday-Saturday, 9 A.M.-5 P.M.; Sunday, 1 P.M.-5 P.M., year-round. Closed national holidays.

WILMINGTON, NORTH CAROLINA
USS *North Carolina* Battleship Memorial
Eagles Island #1 Battleship Road
P. O. Box 480
Wilmington, NC 28401-2577
(910) 251-5797 Fax: (910) 251-5807
E-mail: leads@battleshipnc.com
Location: Take Hwy I-95, or I-40 to Wilmington, in southeastern North Carolina. The battleship is moored at Eagle Island on the Cape Fear River, just across from downtown Wilmington at the junction of Highways 17/74/76/421.
Highlights: USS *North Carolina* (battleship), paintings, and photographs, Kingfisher float plane, changing exhibits; Ships Store and Coca-Cola Canteen, "Measure 32" camouflage paint scheme, *The Annunciator* Newsletter, **Website:** www.battleshipnc.com
General Information: The Battleship *North Carolina* is the State's Memorial dedicated to the men and women who served in the U.S. military during WW II, particularly those North Carolinians who died in that war. At the time of her commissioning on 9 April 1941, the USS *North Carolina* was considered the most powerful sea weapon in the world.

Visitors may view the gun turrets, galley, engine room, bridge, radio rooms, analog computer rooms, machine shop, engine room, crew's quarters and mess hall, sickbay, and a restored Vought Kingfisher floatplane. The museum displays photographs and artifacts of the ship's participation in every major naval offensive in the Pacific during

World War II and includes the Roll of Honor of 10,000 North Carolinians who lost their lives in that war.
Activities: Self-guided tours, orientation film, picnic grounds.
Admission: Entry fee. Open: Summer Hours (16 May through 15 September) 8 A.M. – 8 P.M. Winter Hours (16 September through 15 May) 8 A.M. – 5 P.M.

NORTH DAKOTA

BISMARCK, NORTH DAKOTA
State Historical Society of North Dakota
612 East Boulevard Avenue
Bismarck, ND 58505-0830
(701) 328-2666 Fax: (701) 328-3710
E-mail: histsoc@nd.gov
Location: The collection is located in the North Dakota Heritage Center on the State Capitol grounds. From I-94, take exit 159 south to the Capitol grounds.
Highlights: Paddlewheel steamboat models, artifacts from the USS *North Dakota* (BB-29), **Website:** www.state.nd.us/hist/
General Information: The Society operates the North Dakota Heritage Center and exhibits models of three paddlewheel steamboats (Missouri River traffic) and artifacts from the USS *North Dakota* (BB-29); also displayed are the bow plate and silver service of the USS *North Dakota* — a permanent exhibit.
Admission: No entry fee. Open Monday-Friday, 8 A.M.-5 P.M.; Saturday, 9 A.M.-5 P.M.; Sunday, 11 A.M.-5 P.M., year-round. Closed Easter Sunday, Thanksgiving, Christmas, and New Year's Day.

OHIO

ASHTABULA, OHIO
Ashtabula Maritime Museum
1071 Walnut Boulevard, P.O. Box 2855
Ashtabula, OH 44004-3249
(440) 964-6847
Location: Ashtabula is fifty-five miles east of Cleveland off I-90 on the lakefront. The Museum is on Walnut Boulevard two miles east of Rte. 11 on Rte. 531 high on the hill overlooking the harbor.
Highlights: "Hulett" Ship Unloader (model), pilothouse for *Thomas Walters*, ship models, gift shop
Website: www.ashtabulamarinemuseum.org/
General Information: The Great Lakes Marine and U.S. Coast Guard Memorial Museum, founded in 1984, is housed in the former residence of the

local lighthouse keepers and Coast Guard commanders.

The Museum displays ship models, marine artifacts, paintings, hundreds of photos of early Ashtabula harbor, photos of ore boats and tugs, miniature hand-made tools, and the pilothouse from the ore-carrier *Thomas Walters*.

The Museum acquired from the Smithsonian Institution an incredible working-scale-model of the Hulett ore-unloading machine. The last of these behemoth machines is located on Whisky Island near Cleveland, Ohio, and is destined to be dismantled soon — there will be no more.

Admission: Entry fee, but donations accepted. Open Memorial Day-Oct. 31, Thursday-Monday, 11 A.M.-6 P.M.

BOWLING GREEN, OHIO
Historical Collections of the Great Lakes
Bowling Green State University
Jerome Library, 6th Floor
Bowling Green, OH 43403-0001
(419) 372-2531 Fax: 372-0155
E-mail: rgraham@bgnet.bgsu.edu
Location: The Historical Collections of the Great Lakes (HCGL), formerly The Institute for Great Lakes Research is located on the campus of Bowling Green State University on the 5th & 6th floor of the Jerome Library. From north or south from I-75, take Exit 181 west one-quarter mile to stoplight; turn right (north) to university Information Center. Register, pick up parking pass and map, and proceed to center of campus and Jerome Library.
Highlights: Special collections-library,
Website: www.
bgsu.edu/colleges/library/cac/page39984.html
General Information: HCGL collects and preserves material related to the Great Lakes and its connecting waterways. The HCGL's facilities are available to the maritime history researcher, persons just curious about the Great Lakes and its lore, and open to the general public where they can review significant historical materials documenting the history of the American and Canadian Great Lakes region.

HCGL is one of the nation's largest repositories emphasizing Great Lakes topics, including books, pamphlets, manuscripts, and 140,000 photographic images depicting the vessels, people, and ports of the Great Lakes from the late nineteenth century to the present. Also included are periodicals, marine architectural drawings of documents and technical history of vessels built on the Lakes by American Ship Building Co., Great Lakes Engineering Works, and the Defoe Shipping Company from the 1860s to the 1980s.

A large collection of maps and navigational charts provides information documenting the evolution of Great Lakes harbors, channels, and shorelines as well as information on shipping routes, shipwrecks, and the development of navigation aids such as lighthouses.
Admission: No entry fee. Open Summer, May 8 – August 3, Monday-Friday, 8 A.M. – 5 P.M. Closed Saturdays, Sundays, and holidays.

CANAL FULTON, OHIO
Canal Fulton Heritage Society
116 South Canal Street
P. O. Box 584
Canal Fulton, OH 44614-1044
(330) 854-3808 1-800-435-3623
E-mail: cfhs@discovercanalfulton.com
Location: Canal Fulton is twelve miles south of Akron on the Tuscarawa River on State Rte. 93.
Highlights: The *St. Helena III* (canal freighter), Historic Oberlin House, Old Canal Days Museum, Ohio and Erie Canal history and local history, gift shop, **Website**: www.discovercanalfulton.com/
General Information: Since it's founding in May 1968, the Canal Fulton Heritage Society has advanced, encouraged, and promoted the design, development, and preservation of a historically attractive environment for the village of Canal Fulton. The Society operates the *St. Helena III*, an authentically reproduced horse-drawn canal freighter; the Heritage House/Old Canal Days Museum and gift shop; and the salt-box style Oberlin House, where life as it was lived during the canal days is depicted. Collections include furnishings, canal artifacts, photographs, and maps.
Activities: Canal boat and Museum tours, including award wining video on the Ohio and Erie Canal, and tours of the Oberlin House. Walking tour of historic downtown is also available.
Admission: Memberships are available. Museum: Open daily, 1 P.M.-4 P.M., June-August. Saturday and Sunday free with boat ride: May, September, and October. Boat rides: fee. Open daily except for Monday, 1 P.M., 2 P.M., 3 P.M., June-August; open Saturday and Sunday, May, September, and October. Oberlin House: Entry fee. Open by appointment and Saturday and Sunday, 1 P.M.-4 P.M. Group Charters May-October, and call about Dinner Cruises.

CINCINNATI, OHIO
Inland Rivers Library
Public Library of Cincinnati and Hamilton County
800 Vine Street
Cincinnati, OH 45202-2009
(513) 369-6900
Location: The library is in the center of downtown Cincinnati.
Highlights: Inland Rivers library,

Website: www.cincinnatilibrary.org/main/rb.asp
General Information: The Inland Rivers
The Sons and Daughters of Pioneer Rivermen
established library in 1956 in cooperation with the
Library of Cincinnati and Hamilton County.
Moved from Marietta, Ohio the Library is housed
in the Library's Rare Books and Special
Collections Department, the Inland Rivers Library
is a major resource for books, manuscripts,
photographs, maps, and ephemera dealing with the
history of the Western Rivers. The Library
Continues to enhance this collection through
purchases as well as donations by S & D members
and others.
    Much has been added to tell the River Story
visually and with boat models, paintings, pictures,
relics, and steamboat haberdashery. All these
exhibits are now in Cincinnati. The library has
published a full catalog of the Inland Rivers
Library and in 1989 published a supplement.
Admission: No entry fee. Mon - Wed 9 A.M. –
9 P.M., Thu - Sat 9 A.M. - 6 P.M., Sun P.M. –
5 P.M.

CLEVELAND, OHIO
Steamer *William G. Mather* Museum
601 Erieside Avenue
Cleveland, OH 44114-1003
(216) 694-2000 Fax: (216) 574-2536
E-mail: wgmather@aol.com
Location: The *Mather* is permanently moored at
downtown Cleveland's East 9th Street Pier,
adjacent to the new Rock and Roll Hall of Fame
and the Great Lakes Science Center.
Highlights: The Steamship *William G. Mather*
(Great Lakes ore carrier museum-ship), gift shop,
eighteen-minute video on the *Mather* and Great
Lakes shipping,
Website: http://wgmather.nhlink.net/
General Information: The Steamship *William
G. Mather* was built in 1925. The Museum tells the
story of the vanishing fleet of ore boats that played
a vital role in the industrial development of the
Great Lakes. The 618-foot ship incorporated many
innovations for efficient on- and off-loading of iron
ore. Her capacity of 14,000 long tons
(equivalent to 250 railroad cars) made her the
queen of the Great Lakes at that time.
    When her 618-foot riveted-steel hull was
launched in 1925, she was among the largest
vessels afloat. For the next 55 years, this grand
lady of the Great Lakes carried millions of tons of
iron ore, coal, and other bulk cargoes to Cleveland
through some of the worst storms the Great Lakes
could brew. Now a floating maritime Museum in
Cleveland's North Coast Harbor Park, the
Steamship *Mather* chronicles the history of Great
Lakes shipping and how she helped transform
Cleveland into a great industrial center.

Come see the oak-paneled, brass-appointed Pilot
House, dining rooms, crews' and guest quarters,
huge engine room, galley, and a cargo hold filled
with exhibits. The 1,000-foot-plus ore freighters
brought the golden age of the smaller classic
steamers to a close.
Admission: Entry fee. Open June, - August,
Monday-Saturday, 10 A.M.- 5:15 P.M., Sundays,
Noon-5 P.M.; May, September, October, open
10 A.M.-5:15 P.M., Sunday, 12 Noon – 5:15 P.M.

CLEVELAND, OHIO
USS *Cod* Submarine Museum
1089 N. Marginal Road
Cleveland, OH 44114
(216) 566-8770 E-mail: usscod@usscod.org
Location: In downtown Cleveland, USS *Cod* is
docked on North Marginal Road, between East 9th
Street and Burke Lakefront Airport, just east of the
Rock and Roll Hall of Fame & Museum.
Highlights: The USS *Cod* (SS 224) a restored
U.S. Fleet submarine, *Cod Chronical* Newsletter,
Website: www.usscod.org
General Information: The USS *Cod* (SS 224)
is the last completely authentic fleet submarine
afloat and serves as a memorial on Cleveland's
North Coast Harbor. USS *Cod* made seven war
patrols and rescued the crew of the Dutch
Submarine 0-19 during WW II and helped train
NATO anti-submarine forces during the Cold
War. USS *Cod* has not been modified for visitor
access, preserving her original condition. Visitors
must use the original vertical ladders and hatches
to enter and exit the sub.
Activities: Self-guided tours.
Admission: Entry fee. Open daily, 10 A.M.-
5 P.M. May 1-September 30.

CLEVELAND, OHIO
Western Reserve Historical Society Library
10825 East Boulevard
Cleveland, OH 44106-1777
(216) 721-5722 E-mail: reference@wrhs.org
Location: From I-90 take the Martin Luther King,
Jr. Drive exit, then south about two miles to traffic
circle. Drive counterclockwise around the traffic
circle and turn right on East Boulevard.
Then left at East 108th Street, then turn right on
Magnolia Drive into the parking lot. From the
east: Take Ohio Turnpike, exit at Streetsboro exit,
and proceed north on I-480 to I-271. From I-271
proceed to I-90 west and exit at Martin Luther
King, Jr. Drive and proceed to East Boulevard.
Turn left at East 108th Street, then turn right on
Magnolia Drive.
Highlights: Extensive library, photo, and
manuscript collections on Great Lakes maritime
history, Ohio canal history,
Website: www.wrhs.org/

135

General Information: The Library is the principal repository for histories, records, and papers relating to the growth and development of Cleveland and that portion of northeastern Ohio once known as the Western Reserve of Connecticut. Maritime history of Cleveland and the Great Lakes is explored in the Museum's transportation gallery.

Western Reserve of Connecticut. Maritime history of Cleveland and the Great Lakes is explored in the Museum's transportation gallery.

Admission: Entry fee. Open Tuesday-Saturday, 9 A.M.-5 P.M. Closed Sunday and Monday.

COSHOCTON, OHIO

Historic Roscoe Village
381 Hill Street
Coshocton, OH 43812-1027
Toll Free: 1-800-877-1830 (740) 622-4693
E-mail: rvmarketing@coshocton.com
Location: Coshocton is located on State Rtes 16 & 83 near the junction of US-36 twenty miles west of I-77, seventy miles east of Columbus, and ninety-five miles south of Cleveland.
Highlights: Canal history, horse-drawn replica canal boat, *Monticello III*, 51-room Inn, seven-building living-history tour, offering hands-on learning exhibits, nationally accredited Johnson-Humrickhouse Museum, horse-drawn wagon ride, retail shops, restaurants, perennial gardens,
Website: www.roscoevillage.com/
General Information: Roscoe Village is a nineteenth-century living History community in Coshocton, Ohio, near the heart of Amish Country. This section of east-central Ohio was total wilderness with no outlet for its produce except by primitive wagon roads or infrequent river rafts/boats. The idea of an inland waterway connecting Lake Erie to the Ohio River was thus revolutionary, and the advent of cheap inland transportation changed Ohio almost overnight.

Roscoe Village was a booming canal port along the Ohio & Erie Canal until the demise of the canal after the flood of 1913. Today, the Village has been restored into a living-history community offering fun for the entire family including hands-on children's activities.

On display are canal artifacts, models of a lock and gristmill, a blacksmith shop, a one-room schoolhouse, a tin shop, a broomsquire, hands-on learning exhibits, village artisans, a printing office, and nineteenth-century homes. In 1992 a Visitor Center was built that features a wide-screen theatre show, dioramas, and a Founders Gallery. In addition, a hillside project offers displays outside for guests to view a waterwheel, a brickmaking demonstration, a still, and a fully interactive canal boat replica.

A seasonal seventy-eight foot, twenty-five ton replica of a 1830s packet (a passenger boat carrying mail and cargo regularly), drawn by a team of horses, carries passengers along a restored tree-shaded section of the Ohio & Eric Canal.

Roscoe Village features eleven restored, ten preserved, two reconstructed, and five new buildings and includes thirteen shops, five restaurants, multiple exhibits, and a charming fifty-one room Shaker-style country inn.

Activities: Canal boat rides (seasonal), horse-drawn trolley rides (seasonal), seven-building exhibit tour, Johnson-Humrickhouse Museum, shopping, dining; strolling through the many perennial gardens; and walking, jogging, and bicycling the towpath.

Admission: Entry fee. Open April through December, 11:00 A.M. to 5:00 P.M., call for current tour schedule

EAST LIVERPOOL, OHIO

Sandy and Beaver Canal
c/o Beaver Creek State Park
12021 Echo Dell Road
East Liverpool, OH 43920-8786
Toll Free: 866-644-6727 (330) 385-2927
E-mail: jkingphoto@gmail.rr.com
Location: Beaver Creek State Park is on the east side of Ohio approximately 8 miles north of East Liverpool off Rte. 7.
Highlights: Canal history, **Web Site:** dnr.state. oh.us/parks/beaverck/tabid/714/Default.aspx
General Information: The history of the Sandy and Beaver Canal era in Ohio began with the construction of the Ohio-Erie Canal in 1825. It connected the Ohio River at Portsmouth with Lake Erie at Cleveland. Several feeder canals were later built connecting with this important waterway to access the larger markets and promote economic development. The Sandy & Beaver Canal was one of these feeder canals.

The Canal company was formed in 1828 and construction began in November 1834. Some 90 locks were constructed along the creek as well as the "Big Tunnel" which was the longest canal tunnel in America measuring 106 football fields in length—blasted out of solid rock. When it took four horses to pull a wagon with a load of one ton 12 miles per day over a dusty road, it became apparent that the same four horses could transport 100 tons 24 miles per day.

The canal was operated with moderate success for approximately four years. The end came when the Cold Run Reservoir Dam broke in 1852 just outside of New Lisbon causing extensive property damage, as well as ruining a large section of the canal. Today, some of the finest masonry in the canal lock construction can be seen in Beaver Creek State Park at Lusk's Lock, and the other

locks between Gaston's Mill and Sprucevale.
Activities: Canal walks and many other early-village activities.
Admission: Call for info: (330) 385-3091

FAIRPORT HARBOR, OHIO
Fairport Harbor Marine Museum & Lighthouse
129 Second Street
Fairport Harbor, OH 44077-5816
(440) 354-4825 E-mail: fhhs@ncweb.com
Location: Fairport Harbor is thirty miles east of Cleveland on Lake Erie. Take I-90, east to Rte. 44, north to Rte. 2, east to Rte 535 to High Street in Fairport Harbor.
Highlights: Pilot House from SS *Frontenac*, Fairport lighthouse tower, 3rd-Order Fresnel lens,
Website: www.ncweb.com/org/fhlh/
General Information: The Fairport Marine Museum, founded in 1945, is housed in the 1871 Fairport Lighthouse and keeper's residence. Exhibits include collections of navigation instruments; marine charts; manuscripts; pictures and paintings of ships; lanterns; lighthouse lens; ship carpenters tools; models and half-hulls of ships; iron ore; Indian relics; pilot house from Laker *Frontenac*.
A library of marine books is available for use by appointment, and there is an observation tower.
Activities: Guided tours.
Admission: Entry fee. Open Wednesday, Saturday, Sunday, and holidays, 1 P.M.-6 P.M., Memorial Day through second weekend in September; group tours by appointment. Memberships available.

FREMONT, OHIO
Rutherford B. Hayes Presidential Center
Spiegel Grove
Fremont, OH 43420-2796
(419) 332-2081 E-mail: admin@rbhayes.org
Location: Fremont is twenty-five miles southeast of Toledo on I-80/90. The Center is on the south side of town on Hayes Avenue.
Highlights: Hamilton Collection on Great Lakes shipping history, Hayes's 1873 home, Presidential Library and Archives,
Website: www.rbhayes.org
General Information: The Rutherford B. Hayes Presidential Center commemorates the 19th President of the U.S. in the library Museum on his beautiful 25-acre homesite where he lived from 1873 to 1893. The Center maintains collections of documents and artifacts from the prison ship *Success* which are currently on long-term loan to the Sandusky Maritime Museum. (See Sandusky Maritime Museum entry.)
Also available is Great Lakes research material and displays of artifacts and photos from the Capt. Frank E. Hamilton collection.

Activities: Visitors may tour the President's fully furnished home, where his descendants resided until the mid-1960s.
Admission: Separate entry fees for Museum and home tour. Open Monday-Saturday, 9 A.M.- 5 P.M., Sundays, holidays Noon - 5 P.M., year-round.

MARIETTA, OHIO
Ohio River Museum
Campus Martius/Ohio River Museum Complex
601 Front Street
Marietta, OH 45750
(740) 373-3750 or 1-800-860-0145
E-mail: cmmoriv@ohiohistory.org
Location: Marietta lies in southeast Ohio on the Ohio River near the West Virginia state line. Take I-77 south from Cambridge. Follow signs from Exit 1.
Highlights: The W. P. Snyder, Jr. (1918 steam, sternwheel towboat), nineteenth-century steamboat artifacts and models, paintings and photographs, *Tell City* pilothouse (the nation's oldest riverboat pilothouse), gift shop,
Website: www.ohiohistory.org/places/ohriver
General Information: The Ohio River Museum was founded in 1941. Its exhibits include: the 1918 sternwheeler, *W. P. Snyder Jr.*, the sole 175-foot surviving steam-powered towboat of her type; and the pilothouse from steam packet *Tell City*; a one-half-hour video presentation on steamboat history; scale models of nineteenth-century riverboats; pictures; whistles; a full-size steam calliope; several rowboats; and a replica of a nineteenth-century flatboat.
Activities: Guided tours of the *W. P. Snyder, Jr.* and a thirty-minute video program, with special school group programs on steamboat history
Admission: Entry fee. Group discounts. Open May 27 - Oct 31, Wednesday-Saturday, 9:30 A.M.-5 P.M., Sunday, Noon-5 P.M.,

NEWSCOMERSTOWN, OHIO
USS *Radford* National Naval Museum
228 W. Canal Street
Newscomerstown, OH 43832
Main: 132 W. Canal Street
Newscomerstown, OH 43832
(740) 498-4446
E-mail: vanescott@sbcglobal.net
Location: The Museum is in Newscomerstown in east-central Ohio. From I-77 north/south, off at Exit 65, then west on US-36 1-1/2 miles to Newscomerstown.
Highlights: History of USS *Radford* (DD/DDE 446) *Website:* www.ussradford446.org/
General Information: The USS *Radford* Naval Museum highlights the 17 commanders of *Radford* during her twenty-five years at sea. Exhibits show the four configurations of the ship

137

during *the 1940s, 50s, and 60s.*

Radford was active in WW II as part of the famous DesRon 21 Cactus Force. In a second gallery, the "Cactus Squadron," made up of ten destroyers, displays dress uniforms of ten admirals who and served aboard the *Radford.* In addition, there is a display of Japanese war booty, a Soviet Naval Officer's uniform, and a complete display of the evolution of the U.S. Navy uniform.

The personal effects of the ship's first captain, William K. Romoser, are included such as a sword, Japanese weapons, and flags. In another gallery, an observation deck to view a large, three-dimensional diorama of the "Battle & Rescue at Kula Gulf," when the cruiser Helena (CL-50) was sunk in 1943. *Radford* and Nicholas rescued over 700 men — at night — under fire. Sank two destroyers and a cruiser while firing over the heads of the survivors.

Admission: Entry fee. Open weekends, Memorial Day to Labor day, 1 P.M. – 3 P.M. and by request, anytime for family or group.

PIQUA, OHIO
Piqua Historical Area
Ohio Historical Society
9845 North Hardin Road
Piqua, OH 45356
Toll Free: 1-800-752-2619 (937) 773-2522
E-mil: ahite@ohiohistory.org
Location: Location: Piqua is twenty-five miles north of Dayton on Interstate 75 and State Rte. 36 and on North Hardin Road just off of State Route 66, 3 1/2 miles northwest of Piqua in Miami County.
Highlights: The *General Harrison* (replica canal boat), gift shop,
Website: www.ohiohistory.org/places/piqua/
General Information: The sixty-eight-foot *General Harrison*, replica Passenger-freight boat of Ohio's canal heyday, offers mule-drawn rides on a mile-long restored section of the Miami & Erie canal. Display panels illustrate Ohio's canal history. Also on site are the restored 1812 home and farm of Ohio canal John Johnston, commissioner A museum and gift shop is located at the 250-acre historical park.
Admission: Entry fee. Open Wednesday -Sunday, 9:30 A.M.-5 P.M., Memorial Day to Labor Day weekend; Sundays, noon-5 P.M. only in September and October. Call for information.

PUT-IN-BAY, OHIO
Lake Erie Islands Historical Society Museum
443 County Road 215   P.O. Box 25
Put-in-Bay, OH 43456
(419) 285-2804

E-mail: director@leihs.org
Location: The Museum is in downtown Put-in-Bay, South Bass Island, on Catawba Avenue.
Highlights: Library/vertical file archive, gift shop, **Website**: www.leihs.org
General Information: The Museum, on South Bass Island (formerly known as Edwards Island), shares the site with the Perry's Victory and International Peace Memorial that commemorates Perry's victory over the English fleet in the Battle of Lake Erie in the War of 1812 fought on September 10, 1813 just off Put-in-Bay harbor.

The Museum displays a variety of artifacts relating to the history of the region. These displays include history of the Ford Tri-Motor, Victory Hotel, Ferry Boats of Lake Erie, Inter-Lakes Yachting Association, an intact 4th-degree Fresnel lens from South Bass Lighthouse, ship models of ferries, steamers, and freighters.

The Horton Ship Model Collection consists of 44 ship models all in 1/16-inch-per-foot scale. The collection shows the development of transportation on the Great Lakes from 1600 until the present. Each model shows growth in technology and size right up to the present day of 1000-foot freighters. In the Museum's new building, 14 small-craft are displayed, including a Francis Joseph Life-Saving Surf Boat made with 24-inch-square steel plates riveted and re-pressed flat — each boat having six oarsmen and a helmsman. Also, there is an extensive Vertical File System relating to the islands of Lake Erie. And a 58-foot-long mural that will surround you with an historical picture of the area.

Battle of Lake Erie maritime paintings by American artist Julian Davidson and Canadian artist Peter Rindlisbacher are shown with prints available from the Museum. The Museum invites us to "Get lost in time amid artifacts and photos of our area's rich history, one of Ohio's oldest resort islands."

Admission: No entry fee. Open: May, June & September: Daily 11 A.M. to 5 P.M.; July & August: 10 am to 6 pm October: Weekends 11 A.M. to 5 P.M.

SANDUSKY, OHIO
Maritime Museum of Sandusky
125 Meigs Street
Sandusky, OH 44870-2834
(419) 624-0274
E-mail: sanduskymaritime@bex.net
Location: Sandusky is 60 miles west of Cleveland. The museum is in the eastern part of the downtown area on Meigs Street across from Battery Park.
Highlights: Ship models, boat building, fishing and ice harvesting, gift shop,
Website: www.sanduskymaritime.org/

138

General Information: The Sandusky Area Maritime Center reflects maritime history from the earliest days of Great Lakes navigation where fishing was regarded as the city's principal industry, exporting over 10 million pounds annually.

In the days before refrigeration, Sandusky was a leader in production of natural ice from the frozen Sandusky Bay. Sandusky's west end was the site for the shipping of coal since 1893.

Displays in the Museum exhibit collections of early ice-cutting tools, boat building, fishing, and local maritime history. Also displayed is the history of Lyman Boat Works, the builder of the famous "Lyman sports boat," and *G. A. Boeckling* memorabilia. The Museum is a resource reflecting all aspects of maritime influence on this area, and *G. A. Boeckling* (former Cedar Point ferry) information.

Admission: No entry fee. Open: June through August, Tuesday-Saturday 10 A.M. to 4 P.M. Sunday noon to 4 P.M. Sept. thru May: Fri & Sat, 10 A.M. – 4 P.M., Sun Noon - 4 P.M.

SUGARCREEK, OHIO
Warther Carving Museum
Warther's of Ohio
331 Karl Avenue, P.O. Box 6
Dover, Ohio 44622-0006
330-343-7513 Daytime Number (EST)
Email: info@warthers.com
Location: Take I-77 eighty-five miles south of Cleveland to the Dover/Sugarcreek exit (Exit 83). Turn west on Rte. 39; drive seven miles to Dutch Valley at Sugarcreek. The David Warther Carving Display is located at Dutch Valley near Sugarcreek, Ohio. Dutch Valley features a superb Amish restaurant and interesting gift shops situated in the scenic hills of Ohio's Amish country.
Highlights: Ship models, all of carved ivory,
Website: www.ivorybuyer.com
General Information: David Warther II, a fifth-generation carver of Swiss heritage, is continuing his family's carving legacy in the heart of Ohio's beautiful Amish country.

He has devoted his life to carving solid ivory model ships, which depict "The History of the Ship" from the First Dynasty Egypt (3000 B.C.) to the present day. The ivory Warther carves is legal antique ivory purchased from museums and private collections here in America and meets the strict legal requirements set forth by the U.S. Government.

Refusing to sell his carvings, Warther instead is working to develop an artistic and educational display for visitors to enjoy, appreciate, and learn from for many generations to come.
Admission: Entry fee. Open daily except Sunday. Closed July 4th, Thanksgiving Day, Christmas, and New Year's Day.

TOLEDO, OHIO
SS *Willis B. Boyer* Museum Ship
International Park
1 Maritime Plaza, P.O. Box 50406
Toledo, OH 43604-1866
(419) 936-3070 Fax: (419) 936-3068
E-mail: willisboyer.org@hotmail.com
Location: The SS *Willis B. Boyer* is docked at International Park, directly across from downtown Toledo, on the east side of the Maumee River near Woodville Road.
Highlights: The SS *Willis B. Boyer* (bulk carrier), gift shop, **Website:** www.internationalpark.org/boyermain.html
General Information: The ship offers visitors the unique opportunity to experience the shipping lifestyle in a hands-on setting. As one of the few of its kind remaining, the *Boyer* will intrigue you with its vastness, its fascinating engineering *William G. Mather* in Cleveland, SS *William A. Irvin* in Duluth, SS *Meteor* in Superior, and the SS *Valley Camp* in Saulte Ste. Marie, MI.)
Activities: ship tours.
Admission: Entry fee. Open daily May through October, Monday-Saturday, 10 A.M.-5 P.M., Sunday Noon – 5 P.M. Pre-scheduled guided tours available.

VERMILION, OHIO
Inland Seas Maritime Museum
480 Main Street P.O. Box 435
Vermilion, OH 44089-0435
(440) 967-3467 Fax: (440) 967-1519
Toll Free: 1-800-893-1485
E-mail: glhs1@inlandseas.org
Location: Vermilion is thirty miles west of Cleveland on Lake Erie and two miles north of junction of SR-2 and SR-60, at 480 Main Street, Downtown Vermilion, at the Lake.
Highlights: Ship models, the Clearance S. Metcalf Memorial Library (2,000 volumes), Fresnel lenses, 1905 Pilothouse, the Lake Erie Shipwreck Research Center, *The Chadburn* (newsletter), *The Inland Seas* (quarterly publication), replica of Vermilion lighthouse, museum store,
Website: www.inlandseas.org/
General Information: The Inland Seas Maritime Museum, founded in 1944, returns visitors to August 1679, when Rene Robert Cavelier and Sieur de La Salle sailed his *Griffon*, (the first white man's vessel on the Lakes) west and north, in search of furs, only to disappear and become the first legend of the Lakes. Exhibits span a 300-year period, all the way to the loss of the *Edmund Fitzgerald* (November 1975) and beyond.

The pictures, paintings, models, and marine artifacts displayed in this fine Museum help viewers rediscover to the period of our country's greatest development. Taking the wheel on the simulated ship's bridge overlooking Lake Erie, a visitor can become master for a moment on a giant bulk carrier. The Museum store contains a fine selection of history-related stories, old magazines, and other purchasable items.

The Clearance S. Metcalf Library in the Museum contains one of the largest collections of books, periodicals, records, and photographs of Great Lakes vessels, facilities, and maritime activities to be found anywhere.

Activities: Boat shows, fairs, model ship building.

Admission: Entry fee. Memberships available. Open Mon/Fri, 10 A.M.-4 P.M., Sat/Sun 10 A.M. – 5 P.M. Closed on major holidays.

OKLAHOMA

CATOOSA, OKLAHOMA
Arkansas River Historical Society Museum
5350 Cimarron Road
Catoosa, OK 74015
(918) 266-2291 Fax: (918) 266-7678
E-mail: museum@tulsaport.com
Location: The Museum is located in the Port Authority Building at the Tulsa Port of Catoosa, the terminus of the McClellan-Kerr Arkansas River Navigation System just off Maine Parkway on Cimarron Road. Take 193rd Street (Rte 167) off I-44 near Catoosa, or 46th Street North off U.S. 169 near Owasso.
Highlights: Arkansas River Hall of Fame, motorized model of lock and dam, Native American artifacts, slide and photo archives, library/collections, gift shop.
Website: www.tulsaweb.com/port/
General Information: The Arkansas River Historical Society Museum is located in the City of Tulsa-Rogers County Port Authority Building at the Tulsa Port of Catoosa. The Museum's two galleries are devoted to the history of the Arkansas River and the development of its basin and the McClellan-Kerr Arkansas River Navigation System. The system, running some 445 miles west from the Mississippi River, provides transportation through its 17 locks and dams for over 10 million tons of freight each year.
Admission: No entry fee, but donations accepted. Open Monday-Friday, 8 A.M.-4 P.M. year-round.

MUSKOGEE, OKLAHOMA
USS *Batfish* (SS-310) Submarine
Muskogee War Memorial Park and
   Military Museum
3500 Batfish Road,   P. O. Box 253
Muskogee, OK 74402-0253
(918) 682-6294 E-mail: ussbatfish@yahoo.com

Location: Muskogee is forty miles southeast of Tulsa on the Arkansas River via SR-51 (Muskogee Turnpike - Port of Muskogee).
Highlights: The USS *Batfish* (SS-310) (submarine), 52 lost-boat memorials,
Website: www.ussbatfish.com/
General Information: Muskogee War Memorial Park and Military Museum, founded in 1972, exhibits artifacts from all branches of the service — Army, Navy, Marine, and Air Force — particularly the USS *Batfish*. (submarine)

She was commissioned on August 21, 1943, at Portsmouth, New Hampshire, and entered World War II in 1944. Almost thirty years later, the *Batfish* was berthed in Muskogee, where she is fully opened to the public. Visitors may tour the maneuvering room, the diving station, the control room, and the after-torpedo tubes.

Activities: Self guided tours
Admission: Entry fee. Closed Tuesdays, Open Weekdays and Saturdays. 9 A.M.- 4 P.M., Sundays, 12 Noon-4 P.M., March 15 - October 15.

OREGON

ASTORIA, OREGON
Clatsop County Heritage Museum
Clatsop County Historical Society
1618 Exchange at 16th Street, P.O. Box 88
Astoria, OR 97103-0088
(503) 325-2203 E-mail: cchs@cumtux.org
Location: In downtown Astoria.
Highlights: Columbia River history,
Website: www.clatsophistoricalsociety.org
General Information: In Astoria, named and made famous by John Jacob Astor, who made this area an important part of his fur-trading empire, the Clatsop County Historical Society's Heritage Museum was established to exhibit the history of fur trading, logging, lumbering, and fishing along the Columbia River. Displays include natural history, geology, and Native American and early immigrant and settler history. The Museum is housed in Astoria's old city hall, a neo-classic building (c. 1904).
Admission: Entry fee. Open daily, May thru September, Tuesday thru Friday 11 A.M. to 3 P.M.

ASTORIA, OREGON
Columbia River Maritime Museum
1792 Marine Drive
Astoria, OR 97103
(503) 325-2323   Fax: (503) 325-2331
E-mail: E-mail on website
Location: Astoria is at the mouth of the Columbia River on Rte 30.

Highlights: The *Columbia* (lightship moored alongside the Museum on the Columbia River next to the Museum), ship models, library, museum store, full-sized boats,
Website: www.crmm.org
General Information: Columbia River Maritime Museum, founded in 1962, is housed in a 37,000-square-foot building, with its soaring, wave-form roofline, which accommodates several salmon-fishing boats, a Coast Guard lifesaving craft, marine engines, operating lighthouse lenses, nautical artifacts, and marine art of all sorts as well as a research library and museum store.

One can study coastal exploration of the Northwest, the maritime fur trade, navigation, marine safety, ship wrecks of the Northwest Coast, fishing, whaling, inland steam boating in the Northwest, shipbuilding on the Columbia River, sailing vessels, steamships, and U. S.Naval history. The Museum's largest exhibit isthe former U.S. Coast Guard lightship *Columbia* (WLV-604), which served for twenty-eight years. She is the last lightship to see active duty on the Pacific Coast off the mouth of the Pacific Coast off the mouth of the Columbia River and is docked in the Columbia River next to the Museum.

Activities: The library is accessible by appointment only. One can stand at wheel of a Columbia River steamboat pilothouse or "take the con" on the actual bridge of the World War II destroyer *Knapp.*
Admission: Entry fee. Open daily, 9:30 A.M.-5 P.M. Closed Thanksgiving and Christmas.

BANDON, OREGON
Coquille River Lighthouse
At Bullards Beach State Park
P. O. Box 569
Bandon, OR 97411
(541) 347-2209
E-mail: kraig@lighthousefriends.com
Location: On the southern Oregon shoreline, Bandon is 25 miles south of Coos Bay. The Lighthouse is at Bullards Beach State Park off US-101. It is reached via the State Park road through the Park.
Highlights: Coquille River Lighthouse, gift shop,
Website:
www.lighthousefriends.com/light.asp?ID=127
General Information: Coquille River Lighthouse, once known as the guardian of "navigator's nightmare" (where river and ocean meet), is at the northern end of the spit. The interpretive center exhibits include numerous historical plaques.

In 1963, the Oregon State Parks became the guardians of the Coquille River Lighthouse. It

was built in 1896 and restoration began in 1978 by the Army Corps of Engineers and the Oregon State Parks, and continues today. The Lighthouse is no longer in operation but is open for viewing. For children there is a height requirement of 4-feet, 10-inches.
Admission: No entry fee. Open April, Wednesday-Sunday, 10 A.M.-4 P.M.; May, 7 days a week, 10 A.M.-4 P.M.; June-September, Monday-Tuesday, 10 A.M.-4 P.M., Wednesday-Sunday, 9 A.M.-6 P.M.; October, 7 days a week, 10 A.M.- 4 P.M.; closed November-March.

CASCADE LOCKS, OREGON
Cascade Locks Marine Park
355 WaNaPa Street, P.O. Box 307
Cascade Locks, OR 97014
(541) 374-8619 Fax: (514) 374-8428
E-mail: cdaughtry@portofcascadelocks.org
Location: Cascade Locks is on the Columbia River forty-four miles east of Portland off I-84/Rte. 44.
Highlights: River locks, 2 hour daily sternwheeler cruises.
Website: www. portofcascadelocks.org/
General Information: Cascade Locks and Marine Park is a scenic 200-acre riverfront park that contains historic locks, a marina, a museum, and a visitor center. The 3,000-foot canal, taking 10 years to complete, was opened in 1896. The locks, cut through solid rock, were "drowned" in 1938 by the rising pool behind the Bonneville Dam. The museum has tools, photographs, and other regional artifacts.
Admission: Entry fee. Open daily, noon-5 P.M., June 1-October 1. By appointment rest of year.

NEWPORT, OREGON
Log Cabin Museum
579 S/W Ninth Street
Newport, OR 97365
(541) 265-7509
E-mail: coasthistory@newportnet.com
Location: Newport is on the Oregon coast some 128 miles south of Astoria on US-101. The Museum is located one block east of Hwy 101 in Newport, behind the armory building. Next to it is the historic Burrows House, also a part of the Museum complex.
Highlights: Log Cabin Maritime Exhibit Room, Burrows House Museum, *LCHS* (newsletter), research library, bookshop **Web Site:** www.u-s-history.com/or/l/linccohs.htm
General Information: The Log Cabin Museum has a room of exhibits relating to local maritime history. Also exhibited is a large collection of historic photographs relating to local

lighthouses, the U.S. Life-Saving Service, shipwrecks, shipping, and fishing in general. There is a research library and local history publications.

Admission: No entry fee. Memberships are available. Open June-September Tuesday-Sunday, 10 A.M.-5 P.M.; October-May 11 A.M.-4: P.M.

NEWPORT, OREGON
Yaquina Bay Lighthouse
846 SW Government Street
Newport, OR 97365
(541) 265-5679 Fax: (541) 574-3140
E-mail: krag@lighthousefriends.com
Mail: Yaquina Bay Lights, Inc.
        P.O. Box 410
        Newport, OR 97365-0410
Location: The Lighthouse is located in the Yaquina State Park on the oceanfront at the south end of Newport on Hwy 101.
Highlights: Lighthouse, life-saving history, gift shop, **Website:**
www.lighthousegetaway.com/lights/yaqbay.html
General Information: U.S. Life-Saving Service (later called the U.S. Coast Guard) established a Yaquina Bay crew quarters where lifeboats were launched directly through surf at South Beach in 1896. The crew moved to the north side of the bay entry in 1906, and used the Yaquina Bay Lighthouse as living quarters and lookout station until 1915.

The newly named U.S. Coast Guard continued to use the Lighthouse until 1933. The Lighthouse has been furnished with authentic pieces representative of the 1870s; most of these antiques are on loan from the Oregon Historical Society. The Lighthouse is now a popular tourist attraction and source of community pride. Shipwrecks of note at this location include: the Sailing Schooner *Juliet*, 1852; SS *Yaquina City*, 1887; SS *Yaquina Bay*, 1888; Steam Schooner *Mini Kelton* — 11 lost, 1908; Steam Schooner *J. Marhoffer* — 1 lost, 1910; Sloop *Pilgrim* — 5 lost, 1912.

A Visitor Center, under-development, will be located in a replica of the original Life-Saving Station.

Admission: No entry fee but donations accepted. The Lighthouse is open to the public every day except for holidays such as Christmas, New Years, and Thanksgiving. The hours during the summer, Memorial Day - September, are 11 A.M. to 5 P.M. and October to Memorial Day, 12 Noon until 4 P.M.

NORTH BEND, OREGON
Coos Historical and Maritime Museum
1220 Sherman Avenue
North Bend, OR 97459
541-756-6320 E-mail: info@cooshistory.org

Location: The Museum is just off Hwy 101 in North Bend at the north end of town near Simpson Park and Visitor Information Center
Highlights: Ship construction and shipwreck exhibits, gift shop
Website: www.cooshistory.org/
General Information: The Coos County Historical Society was founded in 1891 and is one of the oldest continuously operating local historical societies in the state of Oregon. The Society operated a museum for ten years in Coquille prior to moving to our current North Bend location in 1958. In 2004, the current name was adopted.

Ship construction and shipwrecks are a big part of Coos County maritime history. Exhibits include: shipbuilding tools; "From Stones, Bones, and Baskets," and a 300year-old fish weir and much more.

Admission: Entry fee: Open 10 a.m. – 4 p.m. Tues-Sat except major holidays.

PORT ORFORD, OREGON
Port Orford Lifeboat Station
92331 Coast Guard Hill Road
P.O. Box 1132
Port Orford, OR 97465
(541) 332-0521 State Blanco-Humbug State Parks
(541) 332-6774
E-mail: info@portorfordlifeboatstation.org OR station@francona.com
Location: To reach the Port Orford Lifeboat Station, proceed west on 9th street (at mile marker 301) off Hwy 101, and up Coast Guard Hill to the park. The Lighthouse is located 5miles north at Cape Blanco State Park.
Highlights: Lighthouse,
Website: www.portorfordlifeboatstation.org/
General Information: Established in 1934 as the southernmost Coast Guard Station on the Oregon coast, Port Orford was one of the three earliest stations constructed in Oregon. Neither of the other two retains the degree of integrity as found here. Port Orford's Coast Guard complex gracefully combines Cape Cod and classical building forms with Craftsman features, presenting a style typical of the Pacific coast.

The lifeboat station served the area for over 30 years and is the only Chatham-type remaining on the coast.

Admission: No entry fee. Open April through October, Thurs.–Monday, 10 A.M. –3:30 P.M.

PORTLAND, OREGON
Oregon History Center
1200 Southwest Park Avenue
Portland, OR 97205-2483
(503) 306-5189   E-mail: orhist@ohs.org

Location: The Museum is at the Oregon History Center in downtown Portland at southwest Jefferson and Park Avenues (just north of Hwy. 26 and east of I-405).
Highlights: Ship models, watercraft models, *OHS Spectator,* quarterly, research library, gift shop,
Website: www.ohs.org
General Information: Founded in 1873, the Oregon History Society succeeded the Oregon Pioneer Association and has promoted the preservation and study of Oregon's heritage. The Center notes: "...steamboats plied wide calm rivers, transporting goods and settlers into the heart of the Northwest. Images of ships, sailing across the sea... or sternwheelers steaming up the Columbia (River) comes readily to mind. Jolly boats, cutters, and launches carried the first Europeans from their ships into the Oregon bays and inland waters."

Besides a variety of permanent and changing exhibits, the Center includes a comprehensive Regional Research Library.
Activities: Group tours, special programs, and demonstrations of pioneer crafts at the annual "Wintering-In" harvest festival on Sauvie Island.
Admission: Entry fee. Open Tuesday-Saturday, 10 A.M.- 5 P.M., Sunday 12 - 5 P.M., Thursdays, until 8 P.M. Closed Monday.

PORTLAND, OREGON

Oregon Maritime Center and Museum
115 SW Ash Street, Suite 400C
Portland, OR 97204-3568
(503) 224-7724
E-mail: info@oregonmaritimemuseum.org
Location: The Museum is at the riverfront park just near the downtown area of Portland.
Highlights: The *Portland* (restored sternwheeler), ship models,
Website: www.oregonmaritimemuseum.org/
General Information: Portland's historic waterfront has a maritime heritage that matches any seaports on the West Coast. The Museum contains a collection of ship models — merchant ships and riverboats— permanent and changing exhibits, navigational instruments, and a variety of ship hardware, paintings, and photographs. Featured are artifacts from the USS *Oregon,* area shipyards, and Columbia River steamboats.

Maritime educational programs are presented periodically. Of special interest is the sternwheeler steam tug *Portland,* on the National Historical Registry, which operated as an "assist boat" in the Portland Harbor 1947-1981. The vessel has been fully restored and is open to visitors as part of the Museum.
Admission: Entry fee. Open Mon-Sat, 10 A.M. – 5 P.M.

PORTLAND, OREGON

Oregon Museum of Science and Industry
1945 Southeast Water Avenue
Portland, OR 97214-3354
(503) 797-4000 Fax: (503) 797-4500
(800) 955-OMSI (6674) E-mail: info@omsi.edu
Highlights: USS *Blueback* (submarine), gift shop,
Website: www.omsi.edu/ AND:
www.omsi.org/visit/submarine/
General Information: The Oregon Museum of Science and Industry (OMSI) is the home of the U.S. Navy's last non-nuclear submarine, the USS *Blueback* (SS 581). After 31 years of service in the U.S. Navy throughout the Pacific Ocean, and appearing in the movie "The Hunt for Red October," the *Blueback* is now on permanent display at OMSI.

The *Blueback's* latest mission is to educate the public at OMSI by displaying how a submarine works, showing how a crew of 85 can live within the 581-foot hull for months at a time, and serving as a memorial to submarine veterans on "eternal patrol."
Activities: Overnight encampment program.
Admission: Entry fee. Open daily from 9:30 A.M. to 5:30 P.M. Submarine: Daily 10 A.M. – 4:30 P.M. Closed Christmas day.

REEDSPORT, OREGON

Umpqua Discovery Center Museum
409 Riverfront Way
Reedsport, OR 97467
(541) 271-4816 Fax: 271-2809
E-mail: info@ umpquadiscoverycentr.com
Location: The museum is at a dock on the east end of town on the Umpqua River.
Highlights: New "Tidewaters & Time" exhibits and boat models, gift shop,
Website: www.harborside.com/~discover/
General Information: The Umpqua Discovery Center Museum features natural and cultural history exhibits that show how the land, water, and people have shaped and changed each other. The new cultural history wing features the "Tidewaters & Time" Exhibit Series that tells the unique history of a tidewater town whose daily life revolved around the ebb and flow of the tides. The exhibits series includes: "Paradise of the Past" which explores the lost culture of our coastal Indian tribes, "Early Explorers," "Coastal Lifestyles," "The Maritime Connection," "Tidewater Towns" and "Highways of Water and Sand."

"The Maritime Connection" lets you linger on the boardwalk and see the larger schooners bringing in needed supplies and delivering lumber, salmon, and agricultural products to the rest of the world.

In the natural history wing of the Center, exhibits help you learn about the unique geology and landscape of the Lower Umpqua Area. Exhibits featuring the estuary, Oregon Shelf and Slope, and the Dunes help us learn about he land and the changes taking place. The Center features other exhibits on Coastal Weather, GrayWhales, Birds and Sand and Surf, the majestic Roosevelt Elk and other plant and animal life.

Activities: The Center includes a theater with numerous video tapes is available for viewing.

Admission: Entry fee. Open seven days a week year round except for Thanksgiving and New Year's Days. Summer hours (June 1 through September 30) are from (9 A.M. to 5 P.M. Winter hours (October 1 through May 31) are from 10 A.M. to 4 P.M. Group tours available by appointment — call (503) 271-4816.

PENNSYLVANIA

EASTON, PENNSYLVANIA
National Canal Museum and Hugh Moore Park
30 Centre Square
Easton, PA 18042-7743   (610) 559-6613
Fax: (610) 559-6690 E-mail: toms@canals.org
Location: Easton is located where the Lehigh River meets the Delaware River, fifteen miles east of Allentown via I-78 or US 22. Once in town, follow the brown "Canal Boat" signs to the park or the red and gray "Easton Attractions" signs to the Museum.
Highlights: Hugh Moore Park, Lehigh Canal, mule-drawn canal boat, Lock tender's House Museum, picnic tables, playground, gift store, National Canal Museum, archives/library,
Website: www.canals.org/
General Information: The National Canal Museum is located in the Two Rivers Landing building in Centre Square, Easton. The Museum's exhibits tell the stories of America's towpath canal era and modern inland waterways.The archives/library maintains manuscript collections, photo archives, library, and artifacts of the canal era and its related industries. Hugh Moore Park consists of six miles of the restored Lehigh Canal and structures, including a Locktender's House, three locks, waste weirs, and feeder gate. Hugh Moore Park also has a mule-drawn canal boat ride, Chain Dam, the Glendon and Abbott Street industrial ruins, bike and hiking trails, picnic areas, pavilions, playground, and boat rental.
Activities: Annual Canal Festival, Annual Canal History and Technology Symposium, Railroad Film Night, lectures, boat rides, and rentals.
Admission: Entry fee. Memberships are available. National Canal Museum: Open Tuesday-Saturday, 9:30 A.M.-5 P.M., Sunday,

12 P.M.- 5 P.M., extended hours during summer. Closed Mondays except Martin Luther King, Jr., President's, Memorial, Labor, and Columbus days. Closed New Year's Day, Easter, Thanksgiving, and Christmas Eve and Day. Canal Boat ride: Open May - September including Memorial Day, Labor Day, and July 4. Please call for exact departure times.

ERIE, PENNSYLVANIA
Erie Maritime Museum,
  Homeport U.S. Brig *Niagara*
Pennsylvania Historical and Museum Commission - Flagship *Niagara* League
150 East Front Street
Erie, PA 16507-1594
(814) 452-2744 Fax: (814) 455-6760
E-mail: wrybka@state.pa.us
Location: Erie is a port city on Lake Erie, north of the Junction of I-90 on I-79 where it ends on Bayfront Parkway, Turn north on Holland Street to west on East Front Street.
Highlights: The U.S. Brig *Niagara* (reconstructed ship), interactive exhibits, USS *Wolverine* Exhibit, Shipwright Museum store, Lecture Concert Series, gift shop,
Website: www.brigniagara.org
General Information: Commodore Oliver Hazard Perry commanded the U.S. Brig *Niagara* as his relief flagship in the Battle of Lake Erie, a major U.S. naval victory during the War of 1812. Reconstructed by the Pennsylvania Historical and Museum Commission between 1988 and 1990, *Niagara* incorporates a few timbers of the original 1813 brig in her hull, and the fully restored vessel now carries six cast 1812-type carronades identical to the 18 she carried originally to defeat the British in the famous Battle of Lake Eriein 1813 near Put-in-Bay on South Bass Island.
The Museum, which is the home port of the U.S. Brig *Niagara*, is a part of the waterfront redevelopment, which includes exhibits on the Live Fire Exhibit, USS *Wolverine* exhibit, the first Iron Hull vessel built by the United States Navy and more recent local Maritime Heritage.
Activities: The *Niagara* sails to commemorate and interpret a significant part of national maritime history; provide the community with an educational tool and cultural amenity; preserve the knowledge and skills of traditional seamanship; and serve as the Commonwealth's flagship and a focal point of Erie's Bayfront development. Guided tours.
Admission: Entry fee. Open Monday-Saturday, 9 A.M.-5 P.M.; Sunday, noon-5 P.M.;
NOTE: *Niagara* maintains a sailing schedule; however, the site is open with activities when the ship is sailing. Call (814) 452-2744 to check if ship is in port.

144

ERIE, PENNSYLVANIA
Watson Curtze Mansion and Planetarium
356 Sixth Street
Erie, PA 16507
(814) 871-5790 Fax: (814) 879-9088
E-mail: aamendola@eriecountyhistory.org
Location: Erie is on the lakefront along I-90,
which runs east/west from New York to Ohio. At
the junction with I-79 head north to Erie. The
Museum is just west of Gannon University Campus
on Lake Erie.
Highlights: Planetarium, ship models, library (500
volumes),
Website: www.goerie.com/erieyesterday/watson-
curtze_mansion.html
General Information: The Erie Historical
Museum and Planetarium was founded in 1899.
The Museum offers exhibits on regional and
maritime history. An archive of letters,
documents, and books on local history is available
for research.
Activities: Guided tours, lectures, films, and a
Victorian Christmas show. In addition, a research
planetarium has shows Saturday and Sunday
2 P.M. and 3 P.M. From August, Planetarium show
hours are 11 A.M., 1, 2, and 3 P.M.
Admission: Entry fee. Memberships available.
Open: May-Sept, Tuesday-Sunday, 11 A.M.-
5 P.M., Sundays, 1 P.M.- 5 P.M., October-April,
Wednesday-Saturday, 11 A.M.- 5 P.M.

GREENVILLE, PENNSYLVANIA
Greenville Canal Museum
60 Allan Avenue, P.O. Box 224
Greenville, PA 16125-2117
(724) 588-7540/4810 E/M:
Location: Greenville is located off I-79, I-80, and
Ohio Route 11. Follow signs to center of town
and look for Canal Museum signs.
Highlights: The *Rufus A. Reed* (forty-foot replica
canal barge)
Website:www.greenvillecanalmuseum.org
General Information: The Canal Museum in
Greenville provides the history of the Erie
Extension Canal during its heyday in the 1840s,
complete with a full-size replica of an original
canal boat. Canal-day artifacts fill the Museum,
where hours can be spent reliving this period of
western Pennsylvania lore. Exhibits include
dioramas of a canal section, working model of a
canal lock, and a learning experience for all —
children and adults.
Admission: Entry fee. Open Thursday-Friday,
1 P.M.-5 P.M., Saturday-Sunday 10 A.M.-6 P.M.,
June-August, Saturday-Sunday 1 P.M.-5 P.M.,
other times by appointment

NEW HOPE, PENNSYLVANIA
New Hope Canal Boat Company
149 South Main Street, P. O. Box 164
New Hope, PA 18938
(215) 862-0758 Fax: 215-862-0965
E-mail: sales@canalboats.com
Location: Take I-95 and exit on Rte. 32 northwest
ten miles to New Hope on the south side of the
Delaware River.
Highlights: Mule barge/canal,
Website: www.canalboats.com/
General Information: In Delaware Canal State
Park, the company operates an historic
eighty-seven-foot barge on the constantly repaired
Delaware Canal. The Delaware River, stretching
from the Delaware Bay to Catsberg, New York, is
approximately 300 miles long. The Delaware
Canal, which runs parallel to the river, starts at
Easton and ends at Bristol. Construction started on
the canal in 1827 but it was not fully operational
until 1840 for commercial use. The old barges may
be seen today and in the warm months; sightseers
leaving from the little village of New Hope, Bucks
County, Pennsylvania, take regular barge trips.
Admission: Entry fee. Open: Wednesday,
Saturday, and Sunday, Daily: 12:30 P.M. and
3 P.M.; May 1st through October31st, Daily:
12 P.M., 1:30, 3:00, 4:30 P.M.

PHILADELPHIA, PENNSYLVANIA
American Philosophical Society Library
105 Fifth Street
Philadelphia, PA 19106-3386
(215) 440-3400 Fax: (215) 440-3423
Location: Near downtown Philadelphia
Highlights: Ship models, library,
Website: www.amphilsoc.org
General Information: The American
Philosophical Society Library, founded in 1743,
offers one of America's richest collections of
materials on the development of modern science
since 1700, early American history to 1840, and
native North American languages and culture. A
number of unique ship models and instruments are
on display with the Society's 247-year-old
collection.
Admission: No entry fee. Open Monday
through Friday, 9 A.M. to 5 P.M.

PHILADELPHIA, PENNSYLVANIA
Cigna Museum and Art Collection
1601 Chestnut Street TL07E
Philadelphia, PA 19192
(215) 761-4907 Fax: (215) 761-5596
E-mail: Melissa.hough@cigna.com
Location: The Museum is located at 1601 Chestnut
Street in downtown Philadelphia.
Highlights: Ship models, marine paintings
(American and British)

145

General Information: Founded in 1925, Cigna Museum exhibits a collection of eighteenth- and nineteenth-century marine and fire-fighting objects and eighteenth- and nineteenth-century American fine art. Included are paintings, models, prints, equipment, and manuscripts.

Activities: Permanent and changing exhibits, loan exhibits, and guided tours by appointment.

Admission: No fee. Open Monday-Friday 9 A.M.-5 P.M., by appointment only, year-round. Closed national holidays.

PHILADELPHIA, PENNSYLVANIA
Independence Seaport Museum
211 S. Christopher Columbus Blvd. & Walnut St.
Philadelphia, PA 19106-3199
(215) 413-8655 Fax: (215) 925-6713
E-mail: mblazer@phillyseaport.org
0Location: The Museum is located on Philadelphia's historic Penn's Landing at Walnut Street and Columbus Boulevard on the Delaware River. It is easily accessed from I-95 north/south.
Highlights: Home Port Philadelphia, Divers of the Deep, small craft gallery, rotating exhibit space, ship models, Workshop on the Water, research library, National Historic Landmarks, USS *Olympia* and USS *Becuna*, the Lenthall collection — 342 volumes on naval architecture, nautical gift shop, Newsletters: *The Masthead* and *Olympia Update*,
Website: www.phillyseaport.org
General Information: Independence Seaport Museum captures the Delaware Valley regions maritime heritage with family-oriented interactive exhibits, historic ship tours, working boat shop, and special exhibitions that lead visitors on exciting journeys of discovery through the history and traditions of our maritime past.

The Museum's more than 14,000 artifacts combine with hands-on exhibits, large-scale models and audiovisuals to present a dynamic environment that is both entertaining and educational. It examines the events, people and technologies that shaped the history of the Delaware River and Bay. Through its permanent exhibits Home Port Philadelphia, Divers of the Deep, and On the Rivers, On the Shores: Small Craft of the Delaware River Valley, the Museum explores aspects of maritime history from the commercial shipping and shipbuilding to navigation, immigration, defense, outdoor recreation, the environment, and underwater exploration.

Experience a general-quarters drill on the actual bridge of the destroyer, USS *Lawrence*, which last saw action in the Persian Gulf Conflict. Tour the WWII submarine *Becuna* and climb aboard Admiral Dewey's Spanish-American War

flagship, *Olympia*. Watch first-hand as artisans build wooden crafts traditional to our local waterways in Workshop on the Water.

A premier regional research library comprised of more than 14,000 volumes, 35,000 historical photographs and 12,000 boat/ship plans is also housed in the Museum offering research materials to the public by appointment or via mail requests for a nominal fee.

An extensive gift shop is also available offering nautical pieces, ship models, jewelry, books, videos, clothing, and children's items.

Admission: Entry fee. Open daily, 10 A.M.- 5 P.M. year-round. Closed Thanksgiving, Christmas, and New Year's. Discounted River Pass tickets include the Museum and its two ships, and round-trip to the New Jersey State Aquarium in Camden.

PHILADELPHIA, PENNSYLVANIA
The Philadelphia Ship Preservation Guild
301 South Columbus Boulevard
Philadelphia, PA 19106
(215) 238-0280 Fax: (215) 238-0281
E-mail: office@gazela.org
Location: Penns Landing vicinity. Please contact the Ship Guild for access information and directions.
Highlights: The tall ship *Gazela* and the tug boat *Jupiter,* and the barge *Poplar*
Website: www.gazela.org
General Information: The Ship Guild has been in existence since 1972. We own and operate the historic 1902 tug *Jupiter* in conjunction with Penn's Landing Corporation.

The tall ship *Gazela* was built in Cacilhas, Portugal as "*Gazela*" in 1883. Records of current configuration date from a major rebuild in 1900-1901 in Setubal, Portugal. She emerged from that refit as the barkentine we know today and joined the Portuguese Grand Banks/Davis Straits cod fishing fleet.

She sailed with that fleet well into the 20th century (her last season: 1969). *Gazela* carried 35 cod fishing dories. After filling their dories with cod (then called the "beef of the sea") weighing 40-60 pounds each, the dorymen would return to *Gazela* to process and preserve the fish with salt. The better the catch, the longer the workday but the bigger the catch, the better their income as they worked on a system much akin to piecework. The fishing season lasted 4-6 months.

Gazela was laid up after the 1969 season having become obsolete for fishing. She was purchased in 1971 for the Philadelphia Maritime Museum (now known as the Independence Seaport Museum) by a wealthy Philadelphian. She is now owned by the volunteer organization that maintains her, the Ship Guild.

Gazela serves as a maritime ambassador for Philadelphia, and a living museum for the preservation of traditional sailing skills. Her crew is volunteer and inter-generational. After participating in Opsail 2000, *Gazela* has become the focus for our new student cadet and apprentice programs, both of which are cooperative ventures with local schools. Major *Gazela* project in 2001 — replace her deck.

The historic tug, *Jupiter* was built in Philadelphia at the Neafie & Levy Shipyard in 1902 and built of charcoal iron and was originally steam powered. During World War II she assisted vessels through the Chesapeake & Delaware Canal. She also towed barges and assisted in laying submarine cable across the Delaware River to prevent German U-Boats from coming upriver.

She was the first tug to catch a line from the battleship USS *New Jersey* during her launching. In 1949 *Jupiter* was refitted with a diesel engine from an LST. She worked as a commercial tug until 1989 and continues to function as a tug when needed for such vessels as the *Gazela* and the *Olympia*. *Jupiter* also serves as a Philadelphia maritime ambassador and is tended by her own dedicated volunteer crew.

Activities: Both vessels are boardable when in port.

Admission: Contact the Guild for information.

PITTSBURGH, PENNSYLVANIA
USS *Requin* SS-481 (submarine)
The Carnegie Science Center
1 Allegheny Avenue
Pittsburgh, PA 15212-5850
(412) 237-3400
E-mail: On website
Location: USS *Requin* is moored on the banks of the Ohio River in front of The Carnegie Science Center.
Highlights: USS *Requin* (SSR 481) (submarine), Website: www.carnegiesciencecenter.org/Default.aspx?pageId=38
General Information: The USS *Requin* is a World War II submarine, which was converted to the first U.S. Navy Radar Picket Submarine (1946), later converted to a Fleet Snorkel Submarine (1959). The *Requin* is presently restored to her 1968 Fleet Snorkel condition. Visitors are provided with very detailed guided tours emphasizing the science and technology contained in a submarine of this type. The guided tours last approximately 60 minutes.
Activities: Overnight camping program.
Admission: Entry fee. Open Sunday-Friday, 10 A.M.-5 P.M., Saturday, 10 A.M.-5 P.M. Summer

Hours: Open daily June 19-September 4, 10 A.M.-6 P.M.; Winter hours, December 8-February 28, weekends, 10 A.M.-5 P.M., closed weekdays. May close during inclement weather. Holiday hours: Open December 26-31, 10 A.M. - 5 P.M., Martin Luther King Day: 10 A.M. - 5 P.M., President's Day: 10 A.M. - 5 P.M. Closed Thanksgiving Day, Christmas Day, New Year's Day.

WYOMISSING, PENNSYLVANIA
C. Howard Hiester Canal Center
Berks County Heritage Center
2201 Tulpehocken Road
Wyomissing, PA 19610
(610) 374-8839   Fax: (610) 373-7066
Location: Off Red Bridge Road one mile south of Rte. 183 near Reading, PA.
Highlights: Nineteenth-century Union Canal history and memorabilia, Web Site: www.countyofberks.com/parks/cwp/view.asp?a=1229&q=447562
General Information: The Berks County Parks and Recreation Department operates the C. Howard Hiester Canal Center, which is located at Stop No. 8 Berks County Heritage and Wertz's Covered Bridge. The Center chronicles the life of the canal people and how the Union (canal operated 1827-1884) and Schuylkill Canals fit into the larger network of canals that served the Berks County area and Philadelphia. Displays include the pilothouse from the tugboat *Dolphin* and a hands-on program in the houseboat *Mildred*.
Admission: Entry fee. Open May-October, Tuesday-Saturday 10 A.M.-4 P.M., Sunday, 12 Noon-5 P.M.

RHODE ISLAND

BLOCK ISLAND, RHODE ISLAND
Block Island Southeast Lighthouse
Old Town Road and Ocean Avenue
P.O. Box 949
Block Island, RI 02807
(401) 466-5009 E-mail: selight@verizon.net
Location: Block Island is approximately 15-miles south of Narragansett Bay on Mohegan Bluffs
Highlights: Lighthouse,
Website: www.lighthouse.cc/blockisoutheast/
General Information: Southeast Light is a restored lighthouse built in 1875. In a tower were its lantern is 240 feet above sea level, sends its light 35 miles out to sea. The Block Island Historical Society provides archival information about the island and lighthouse.
Admission: Entry fee. Open daily, May through Labor Day, 10 A.M.-4 P.M.

BRISTOL, RHODE ISLAND
Herreshoff Marine Museum and Monument
One Burnside Street
P. O. Box 450
Bristol, RI 02809-0450
(401) 253-5000 Fax: 401-253-6222
E-mail: info@herreshoff.org
Location: The Museum and Monument are located on the site of the old family shipyard one-half-mile south of downtown Bristol (twelve miles southeast of Providence) and one- and one-fourth miles north of Mt. Hope Bridge on Rte. 114. From I-95, take exit 7 (Seekonk/Barrington), follow Rte. 114S through Barrington, Warren, and Bristol; turn left on Burnside Street. From Newport, take the Mount Hope Bridge to Rte. 114 N, turn right at Burnside Street.
Highlights: Exhibits of Herreshoff-built yachts and steam engines, photographs and other memorabilia, ship models, America's Cup Museum, gift shop,
Website: www.herreshoff.org/
General Information: The Herreshoff Marine Museum, founded in 1971, displays yachts, steam engines, fittings, photographs, and memorabilia commemorating the unique accomplishments of the Herreshoff Manufacturing Company, which existed from 1863 to 1946 during the "Golden Age of Yachting." John Brown Herreshoff founded the Company and in 1878 he took his younger brother, Nathaniel Greene Herreshoff, into partnership.
    After attending Massachusetts Institute of Technology, Nat was employed by the famed Corliss Engine Works in Providence for nine years. Upon joining his brother's firm of boat builders, he concentrated initially on designing steam vessels.
    In the early 1890s Nat turned to designing sailing yachts; the creation of these vessels — of all sizes and descriptions — occupied most of the rest of his professional career. Yachts of his design, built at the family's yard, defended the America's Cup six times from 1893 to 1920, and the Herreshoff Manufacturing Company also built the Cup Defenders of 1930 and 1934.
    Activities: Rendezvous of Herreshoff-designed boats every 3 years (next, 2002), annual summer waterfront clambakes, lectures, and workshops.
    Admission: Entry fee. Open Monday-Friday, daily 10 A.M.- 5 P.M.

EAST GREENWICH, RHODE ISLAND
Varnum Memorial Armory
6 Main Street
East Greenwich, RI 02818-3827
(401) 884-4110 or 6158
E-mail: karmory@varnumcontinentals.org
Location: East Greenwich is twenty miles south of Providence.

148

Highlights: Limited maritime exhibits,
General Information: The Varnum Memorial Armory, in the medieval castle style armory, was built by the Varnum Continentals in 1913. A variety of collections focus on naval and marine items and artifacts, military weapons and artifacts from the 16th-century to present.
    Various military artifacts are displayed from WW I including uniforms, 1883 Gatling Gun and Limber, and several artillery pieces form the Civil War and WW I. Other collections housed here contain Home of Revolutionary officer and lawyer. The General Varnum House Museum displays a few marine exhibits in a fine mansion furnished with period furniture, magnificent paneling, Colonial and Victorian Children's Playrooms, and Colonial garden.
    Admission: Entry fee. Open June - August, Sat - Sun, 10 A.M. - 4 P.M. and by appointment.

JAMESTOWN, RHODE ISLAND
Beavertail Lighthouse Museum
Beavertail State Park, P.O. Box 83
Jamestown, RI 02835
(401) 423-3270 E-mail: info@beavertaillight.org
Location: Located on Conanicut Island in the middle of Southern Narragansett Bay.
Highlights: Beavertail Lighthouse,
Website: www.beavertaillight.org
General Information: Since 1749, the Beavertail Lighthouse has guided mariners from its site at the tip of Narragansett Bay on Conanicut Island. The lighthouse is located in a beautiful state park, where the surf crashes on the shore rocks and is just a short drive from Newport.
    A small museum was established in the 1898 Assistant Keeper's House. A fourth-order Fresnel lens is on display along with exhibits on Rhode Island lighthouse history. Current efforts have been successful in maintaining this granite tower built in 1856 that rises 64 feet above the bay. It was here that local inventor David Melville demonstrated the first gas-fired lamp for lighthouse use in 1817. He devised a system that burned coal to generate hydrogen that was funneled through copper tubes to the lamp mechanism.
    Another "first" for Beavertail was established when it was chosen a as the test facility for new fog signals in the second half of the nineteenth century.
    Admission: No entry fee. Open Memorial Day-Mid June, weekends only; open daily Noon - 3 P.M., Mid-June-Labor Day, 10 A.M. to 4 P.M.; Labor Day - Columbus Day weekends only Noon – 3 P.M.

JAMESTOWN, RHODE ISLAND
The Jamestown Museum
92 Narraganset Avenue, P.O. Box 156
Jamestown, RI 02835
(401) 423-0784

E-mail: info@jamestownhistoricalsocitety.org
Location: Located on Conanicut Island at the
mouth of Narragansett Bay, Jamestown can be
easily reached by following Rte. 138 between
Newport and Saunderstown. The Jamestown
Museum is located on Narragansett Avenue in the
village of Jamestown.
Highlights: Narragansett Bay ferryboat exhibit,
Web Site: www.jamestown-ri.info/
   General Information: The Museum (1886) is a
repository for Jamestown's past history. Exhibits
include ship models, pictures, maps, and operating
gear from the ferries that connected the island to
neighboring communities (Newport) for over three
hundred years until the Newport Bridge was
completed in 1969.
   Admission: No entry fee, but donations
accepted. Open Tuesday -Saturday, 1 P.M.- 4 P.M.,
mid-June-Labor Day

KINGSTON, RHODE ISLAND
University of Rhode Island Library
Special Collections Department
15 Lippitt Road
Kingston, RI 02881-2011
(401) 874-2666   Fax: (401) 876-4608
E-mail: libadmin@etal.uri.edu
Location: Kingston is thirty-two miles southwest
from Providence on Rte. 138.
Highlights: Ferryboat records, mill, oyster bed,
and fishery records,
Website: www.uri.edu/library/
   General Information: The University of
Rhode Island Special Collections Department
includes 6,075 linear feet of eighteenth- and
nineteenth-century material, including ferryboat,
mill, oyster bed and fishery records, personal and
political papers, store ledgers, journals, and
weather statistics. The collection also contains over
137,500 photographs from 1889 to present.
   Admission: No entry fee. Open Monday-
Friday, 9 A.M.-4 P.M.

NARRAGANSETT, RHODE ISLAND
South County Museum
100 Anne Hoxsie Lane,   P.O. Box 709
Narragansett RI 02882-3169
(401) 783-5400 Fax: (401) 783-0506
E-mail info@southcountymuseum.org
Location: The Museum is on Canonchet Farm,
Boston Neck Road (Scenic 1A),
Highlights: Local maritime history
Website: www.southcountymuseum.org/
   General Information: The South County
Museum in Narragansett Rhode Island opened in
1933 to preserve the rural and village heritage of
Rhode Island. The newly opened Schmid
Maritime Gallery focuses on life in the coastal

southern part of the state where fishing was
combined with farming and millwork. Sunrise to
Sunset — at Work on the Water tells the story of
the various fisheries from fish traps to shell
fishing.
   Church Steeples and Barking Dogs introduces
the visitor to the art of navigation before
electronics. Also included are exhibits on Rhode
Island Whaling and Boatbuilding.
   Admission: Entry Fee. Open May to
November, Wed - Sunday 11 A.M. –4 P.M.

NEWPORT, RHODE ISLAND
The International Yacht Restoration School
459 Thames Street
Newport, RI   02840-6748
401/848-5777   E-mail: info@iyrs.org
Location: The unique and valuable facility is
located on a 2-acre waterfront wharf on Thames
at 449 Thames Street with administrative offices
across the street at 458 Thames. Parking available
in front of the School.
Highlights: Yacht restoration,
Website: www.iyrs.org/
   General Information: The International Yacht
Restoration School is a not-for-profit educational
institution in Newport, Rhode Island. A full-time,
state licensed vocational program in the restoration
and construction of classic watercraft is enhanced
by an historic waterfront campus and marina,
which is open to the public year-round. IYRS
acquired the site in 1995, and immediately began
the rehabilitation of the 1905 Newport Electric
Company generating plant. This building is now
our main restoration facility. An active marina
hosts classic restored yachts from around the
world.
   The second building on the campus, originally
built in 1831 as a steam-powered cotton mill, is
on the National Register of Historic Places. This
building has been stabilized and will later be
renovated for use as classrooms, workrooms,
offices and student housing.
   Our purpose is clear: To teach the skills, history,
science and art of restoring, maintaining and
building classic yachts; to preserve the knowledge,
heritage, craftsmanship and aesthetic genius
inherent in these yachts; to maintain a fleet of
restored watercraft for the purpose of teaching
seamanship, navigation and maintenance skills; to
safeguard our site and historic buildings as an
important piece of America's working waterfront,
and to show that honest work, integrity, and
mastery of a craft are among life's greatest
achievements.
   IYRS is committed to remaining open to the
public, and providing access to our waterfront. We
are dedicated to preserving and continuing an

important local tradition of fine nautical craftsmanship. We believe that preserving the past informs and improves the future. *Admission:* No entry fee. Donations suggested. Open Monday - Saturday, 10 A.M. – 5 P.M., Sunday - Seasonal. Open for tours.

NEWPORT, RHODE ISLAND
The Museum of Newport History
Newport Historical Society
82 Touro Street
Newport, RI 02840
(401) 846-0813 Fax: (401) 846-1853
E-mail: info@newporthistorical.org
Location: The Museum is located at Thames Street at the foot of Washington Square adjacent to the Brick Market just one block from the famous dock area of downtown Newport.
Highlights: Ship models, research library (9,000 volumes), historical photographs (100,000), **Website:** www.newporthistorical.org
    General Information: The rehabilitation of the Historic Brick Market (1772) now houses the Museum of Newport History first opened in 1993. The Museum is a collaborative effort of the Newport Historical Society and the Brick Market (1762) Foundation formed by the city in 1988. The space-intensive Brick Market building span 350 years.
    The Museum offers a spectacular multi-dimensional, interactive exhibit highlighting Newport's long and colorful history brings Newport's history to life. Displays include interactive computers, artifacts of everyday life, graphics, thousands of historic photographs, and audiovisual programs on laser discs to tell Newport's story.
    The Museum contains fine ship models, brilliant paintings, exquisite Colonial silver, the printing press used by James Franklin, brother of Benjamin, the figurehead from the yacht *Aloha*, and much more.
    The Newport Historical Society maintains a research library including ship logs that are especially helpful in genealogical research in Rhode Island. The Society also operates the Wanton-Lyman-Hazard House (1670), the Friends Meeting House (1699), and the Seventh Day Baptist Meeting House (1729).
    Activities: Guided walking tours Thursday-Saturday mornings, June-September. Board a reproduction 1890s omnibus to watch a video tour of historic Bellevue Avenue.
    Admission: Entry fee. Open Tuesday through Saturday, 10 A.M. - 4 P.M.; Sunday, 1 P.M.-4 P.M.; summer weekend hours. Fall – Winter, Sept. 7 – Dec. 23, Thurs/Sat. 10 A.M. – 4 P.M., Sunday 1 P.M. – 4 P.M.

NEWPORT, RHODE ISLAND
Museum of Yachting
Fort Adams State Park,
45 Washington Square, P. O. Box 129
Newport, RI 02840-2913
(401) 847-1018 Fax: (401) 847-8320
E-mail: info@museumofyachting.org
Location: Newport lies nineteen miles south of Fall River, Massachusetts, on SR-24. The Museum of Yachting is at Fort Adams State Park, the landing for the Newport to Block Island Ferry. Newport may also be reached from south and west by using State Rte. 138, east off I-95 North.
Highlights: 12-Meter yacht *Courageous*, ship models, small-craft collection, Singlehanded Sailors Hall of Fame, America's Cup Gallery, *Spinnaker* (quarterly newsletter), library, gift shop, **Website:** www.moy.org/
    General Information: The flagship of the Museum is the 12-Meter yacht *Courageous*, winner of the America's Cup challenges in 1974 and 1977, is berthed at the Museum. She is available for charter and participates in racing on Narragansett Bay in the summer season.
    The Museum's developers envisioned a facility where visitors could learn something about yachting history, technology, and the people who have been instrumental in that evolution. Its exhibits include the America's Cup Gallery, the Hall of Fame for Singlehanded Sailors, Phil Weld Library, the Golden Age of Yachting, and The Great Designers. Other craft, such as a Bris "amphibie" sailing craft fifteen feet in length are also included. And a special Exhibits Gallery has an in water classic boat collection. The Museum's library contains over 2000 volumes of nautical-oriented books and other material available to members or qualified researchers by appointment.
    A voluminous America's Cup scrapbook collection, covering the period from 1885 to the present, is available as a research tool.
    Activities: An annual classic regatta on Labor Day weekend, an unlimited regatta in August, winter educational program, and a School of Wooden Boat Building are conducted at the Museum. The Museum also sponsors the Sparkman-Stephens Regatta in June. There are thirteen 12-meters in Newport which race in this event under the auspices of the Museum of Yachting.
    Admission: Entry fee. Open daily, 10 A.M. – 5 P.M., May 13 - October 31. Call for hours.

NEWPORT, RHODE ISLAND
Naval War College Museum
686 Cushing Road
Newport, RI 02840-1207
(401) 841-4052/1317
E-mail: museumj@nwc.navy.mil

Location If approaching from New York, Connecticut, and the South on I-95, take RI Exit 4 heading West on SR 136, cross the two Narragansett Bay bridges to Newport and follow signs for Gate One, U.S. Naval Station; If approaching from Boston and the North, follow SR-24/114 heading South. After thirteen miles exit west onto Admiral Kalbfus Road to the Naval War College on Coasters Harbor Island, U.S. Naval Station, Newport. Access at Pass Office, Gate One, Naval Station Newport, Rhode Island.

Highlights: History of naval warfare, history of naval activities in Narragansett Bay area, including torpedo development, training station history; Naval War College history, ship models.

Website: www.visitri.com/navy.html

General Information: Founded in 1952, the Naval War College Museum has been at its present location since 1978. The museum is one of the U.S. Navy's twelve official museums and occupies a RegisteredNational Historic Building, the Federal style, ca. 1820 Newport Poor Asylum that was acquired by the Navy in 1884 to serve as the first home of Naval War College.

It was here in this building that Captain Alfred Thayer Mahan first delivered the lectures that became his world-famous book, The Influence of Sea Power upon History, 1660-1783. The museum exhibits a fine collection of art, artifacts, ship models, imprints, and prints on the history of naval warfare and the navy in the Narragansett Bay region. The history of the "art and science" of naval warfare, as chiefly studied at the Naval War College through the years, is the principal exhibit theme of the Museum.

Exhibits explain the importance of the sea as a factor in the formulation of national policy objectives and as the arena wherein decisions are wrought through diplomacy and trial by arms. A second exhibit theme is the naval heritage of Narragansett Bay and exhibits tell the story of the long and eventful relationship of the Navy with Narragansett Bay and people of Rhode Island, including the development of the torpedo on Newport's Goat Island, the Perry family's contribution to the Navy.

Activities: Guided tours

Admission: No entry fee. Due to current security considerations at Naval Station, Newport, 24-hour advance reservations are required for admission, unless one has an active, reserve, or retired U.S. Military ID card and a Department of Defense car decal. Telephone or e-mail requests for reservations. Open Monday-Friday, 10 A.M.-4 P.M, year around., Saturdays and Sundays, 12 Noon-4 P.M., June through September. Closed on holidays.

NEWPORT, RHODE ISLAND
Rose Island Lighthouse and Museum
P. O. Box 1419
Newport, RI 02840
(401) 847-4242 Fax: (401) 847-7262
E-mail: keeper@roseisland.org

Location: Rose Island is a 17-acre island located just one mile off Newport in Narragansett Bay between Newport and Conanicut Island and may be reached by ferry from Newport or Jamestown.

Highlights: Lighthouse and keepers' quarters, *Rose Island Lighthouse News* (newsletter), overnight accommodations, clambake and pig roast events,

Website: www.roseislandlighthouse.org/

General Information: The Rose Island Lighthouse was established in 1870 and kept by civilian families in the U.S. Lighthouse Service until 1941; it remained a part of the U.S. Coast Guard until 1971. Abandoned, it deteriorated, as did the rest of the island which had its initial use as a military base first established during the American Revolution. Much later, during World War I and II, Rose Island was an explosives depot that was part of the Navy's Torpedo Station. The Navy's torpedoes and mines (manufactured at nearby Goat Island) were filled at Rose Island where nearly one and one quarter million pounds of dynamite were stored, making life on the island about as comfortable as living on a powder keg.

In 1984, local residents, who were concerned about developers' plans for the island, formed the non-profit Rose Island Lighthouse Foundation to restore the lighthouse. The island is divided into two parcels: The smaller -- 1.5 acres -- contains the lighthouse and was deeded to the City of Newport in 1985 for the Foundation to manage.

The other 17 acres was recently purchased by the Foundation and is a protected wildlife refuge. It contains the remains of the nation's first Fort Hamilton, which is 200 years old and includes two circular bastions and a 9-room barracks building with brick-and-stone walls that are 3-4 feet thick and still in good shape.

During the earlier wars, other buildings used by the military, including the concrete igloos where ammunition was stored for the defense of Narragansett Bay, are still in place but completely overgrown with the island's natural vegetation. Nary a shot was fired in anger from this fort. This part of the island is privately owned.

The lighthouse restoration efforts were successful and in 1993 the light was relit by the Foundation as a private aid to navigation for the Bay. Today, the lighthouse is host to four types of visitors: day visitors, school groups, overnight guests, and guests who may become, for a week's stay for a week's stay, "Rose Island Lighthouse Keepers." Such residence requires full agreement to maintain the station, which includes collecting any rainwater that falls on the island for the lighthouse-basement cistern — there is no running water. Also, mowing the lawn and repairing any minor items such as door hinges.

The weekly guests are an important part of the ongoing maintenance of the lighthouse, and reservations are booked years in advance, but you should check the website for cancellations.

Today's visitors can get a glimpse of what keepers' lives were like through photographs and memorabilia provided by the grandchildren of two of the longest-termed keepers, Charles S. Curtis (1887-1918) and Jesse Orton (1921-1936). *Activities:* Guided tours. Learn about self-sufficient utilities and island conservation practices.

Tour the operating Lighthouse and Fort Hamilton (which is in the process of being restored), picnic tables, shell beaches, and public toilets available. Events include an Opening Day Pig Roast over 4th of July, the world's most "trashless" clambake in August, and a rowing/paddling race in September. We encourage visitors to come via the Jamestown-Newport Ferry and get a dollar off their admission when they land at the lighthouse. We have only a small drop-off float where the ferry also comes in and no dockage for people to tie up boats.

Depending on the weather, people can anchor their boats and beach their dinghies near the lighthouse, but nowhere else on the island, since it's private property and a sensitive wildlife refuge -- no trespassing while birds are nesting from 1 April to 15 August. *Admission:* Entry fee. Memberships are available. Open daily, 10 A.M.-4 P.M., when keepers are on site with guided tours during the summer. Call (401) 847-4242 for reservations and schedule. Lighthouse tours daily during July and August, other times by appointment.

NEWPORT, RHODE ISLAND
Single Handed Sailors Hall of Fame
c/o Museum of Yachting
Fort Adams State Park
P. O. Box 129
Newport, RI 02840
(401) 847-1018 Fax: 401-847-8320
E-mail: museum@moy.org
Location: Newport lies nineteen miles south of Fall River, Massachusetts, on SR-24. The Museum of Yachting is at Fort Adams State Park.
Highlights: Singlehanded Sailors Hall of Fame,
Website: www.moy.org
General Information: The Singlehanded Sailors Hall of Fame opened in 1986 in the old mule barn at Historic Fort Adams in Newport. The

Hall of Fame is filled with charts; a world map showing the records of the twenty-four men and three women now inducted in the Hall of Fame. On exhibit is the eight-foot sloop *Bris* built by Sven Lundin of Sweden. Lundin sailed this very small boat here from Sweden and then donated it to the Museum of Yachting. *Admission:* Entry fee. Open seven days a week, 10 A.M.-5 P.M., May 15-October 31.

PROVIDENCE, RHODE ISLAND
Alfred S. Brownell Collection of
  Atlantic Coast Fishing Craft Models
Providence Public Library
150 Empire Street
Providence, RI 02903
401-455-8000 E-mail: pplref@provlib.org
Location: This particular collection is housed in the Providence Public Library on Level A. The Library is in downtown near I-95.
Highlights: Small craft collection, log book collection, scrimshaw, Nicholson Whaling Collection, library,
Website: www.
provlib.org/resources/books/special/special.html
General Information: The Alfred S. Brownell Collection of Atlantic Coast Fishing Craft Models comprises eleven ship models of Atlantic Coast Fishing Craft. Mr. Brownell presented them to the Library about 1950, himself a marine historian and one of the most highly regarded model-boat builders. The eleven distinct types of fishing craft were evolved as early as the Colonial times to meet the needs of men fishing in such diverse areas as the sheltered waters of Long Island Sound, the stormy ocean off the coast of Maine, and the shallow oyster beds of the Chesapeake Bay.

Thousands of hours were required to prepare scale drawings and produce each model. The fishing fleet contained in the Collection includes a Block Island Double Ender, Chesapeake Bay Bugeye and Skipjack, a Colonial Fishing Schooner, an Eastport Pinky, a Friendship Sloop, a Gloucester Sloop, a Maine Pinky, a New Haven Sharpie, a Quoddy, and a Tancook Whaler. The collection may be viewed during regular Library hours.

Most of the collections are displayed on level A of the library. In addition, the Nicholson Whaling Collection of over 1,000 whaling logs, books, and seventy-seven pieces of scrimshaw is in the Special Collections Department.
Activities: Library available for research
Admission: No entry fee. Regular Library hours are: Monday-Thursday 9 A.M. - 8 P.M., Friday-Saturday 9 A.M.-5:30 P.M. and Sunday 1 P.M.-5 P.M. October - May only. Nicholson Whaling Collection logbooks on microfilm are available during regular library hours; also available through interlibrary loan. Nicholson

Collections materials in the Special Collections Department librarian only works part-time on Monday-Thursday and is available by appointment only - the Call 401-455-8021 to make an appointment.

PROVIDENCE, RHODE ISLAND
Providence **(Reproduction-18th Century Sloop)**
c/o Providence Maritime Heritage Foundation
408 Broadway P. O. Box 1261
Providence, RI 02901
(401) 331-8575 Fax: (401) 828-8788
E-mail: kathleen_sloopprovidenceri@cox.net
Location: The replica is moored on the Providence River off I-95 in the city.
Highlights: The *Providence* (replica sloop),
Website: www.providenceri.com/sloop-providence.html
General Information: Providence merchant John Brown built sailing ships until 1775, which engaged in highly prosperous trade with ports in the WestIndies. Rhode Island, the first colony to organize a navy, commissioned Katy (later renamed the *Providence*) to confront British customs ships in Narragansett Bay.

She was the first ship commissioned into the Continental Navy; the first command of John Paul Jones, the first ship to land U.S. Marines on foreign soil, the first ship to fly the U.S. flag on foreign soil, and the most successful ship of the Colonial Navy in the Revolutionary War (over forty captures or sinkings)!

Five months after the first at-sea fight of the Revolution, in May 1775, the *Katy,* renamed *Providence*, was Rhode Island's initial contribution to the Continental Navy. John Paul Jones described her four years of fighting: "Hers is a record unmatched by any other Continental vessel, and her quarter deck served as a proving ground for some of the greatest Revolutionary captains." Her own crew in Penobscot Bay, Maine, burned her in August 1779 to avoid capture by the British.

Today from Narragansett Bay comes a fully operational 110-foot reproduction of the *Providence*, the ship that sailed in those waters two hundred years ago.

Activities: Available for charter, visits to patriotic or historical events in U.S. seaports. American Sail Training programs, Apprenticeships, school programs, and dockside tours.

Admission: Call or write the Museum for information about sailing on *Providence*.

PROVIDENCE, RHODE ISLAND
The Rhode Island Historical Society
121 Hope Street
Providence, RI 02906
(401) 273-8175 Fax: (401) 351-70127

E-mail: research@rihs.org
Location: The Society is in the east side area of Providence.
Highlights: Whaling records, photographs, Customs House records, ship's logs,
Website: www.rihs.org
General Information: The Rhode Island Historical Society houses the third largest genealogical collection in New England. Manuscript collections date from 1636 to the present. They include maritime records, which document Rhode Island's coastal and global trade, as well as Customs House records for Providence and Bristol-Warren, hundreds of ship's logs, and records of many mercantile firms.

The graphics collection houses a quarter-million architectural drawings, maps, and broadsides. It is equally rich in watercolors, drawings, engravings, etchings, and ephemera.

Audiovisual holdings contain 4 million feet of amateur, feature, and news film, and sound recordings. It provides researchers with the best available visual documentation of Rhode Island's landscape and culture.

Admission: Entry fee but members free. Membership info on website. Open Wednesday & Friday 10 A.M.-5 P.M., Thursday 12 noon – 8 p.m. Call to verify times open.

PROVIDENCE, RHODE ISLAND
Steamship Historical Society of America
1029 Waterman Avenue
East Providence, RI 02914
(401) 274-0805 Fax: (401) 274-0836
E-mail: info@sshsa.org
Location: The collection is now housed at the Providence offices.
Highlights: Library (4,700 volumes),
Website: www.sshsa.org
General Information: Steamship Historical Society of America Collection was founded in 1940. We are dedicated to recording, preserving, and distributing information of and about the history of engine powered vessels. Simply put, we strive to be the most comprehensive power ship history resource for education, information, and research purposes.

Although "Steamship" is our first name, we welcome any, and all, maritime enthusiasts, professional or amateur historians, and nautical buffs.

The library contains books and over 200,000 photographs in the field of powered shipping and navigation; 25,000 postcards; microfilm and microfiche readers; slide-viewing equipment.

Activities: Marine research in person and by mail
Admission: No entry fee. Open for research Monday-Friday, 8:30 A.M.-4:30 P.M.

WOONSOCKET, RHODE ISLAND
Chafee Blackstone National Corridor
1 Depot Square
Woonsocket, RI 02895
(401) 762-0250 Fax: (401) 762-0530
E-mail: On web site.
Location: Visitor Center and museums: Off State
Rte. 146 at Woonsocket, follow signs to visitor
center. Slater Mill Visitor Center is off State Rte.
146 on County Rte. 15.
Highlights: Blackstone Canal historical
information, **Website:** www.nps.gov/blac
General Information: The John H. Chafee
Blackstone River Valley National Heritage
Corridor was founded in 1986 through legislative
act. It was established to create an interworking
network of parks and three visitor centers. One, in
Woonsocket, one in Uxbridge, MA, and the other
in Pawtucket, RI. The centers, and river access,
provide historical views through the parks and
museums along the Blackstone Canal and Towpath
cutting through town limits and south across the
state line into Rhode Island in its rush to
Narragansett Bay, forty-three miles to the south.
Originally, there were 45 locks providing
transportation between Providence, RI and
Wooster, MA, the 2nd and 3rd largest towns in
New England.
Admission: Check at Visitor Centers for
information and tours.

SOUTH CAROLINA

CATAWBA, SOUTH CAROLINA
Landsford Canal
2051 Park Drive
Catawba, SC 29704
(803) 789-5800
E-mail: landsfordcanal@scprt.com
Location: The Canal is located between Lancaster
and Rock Hill off U.S. 21 in Chester County.
Highlights: Landsford Canal, **Website:** www.
southcarolinaparks.com/park-finder/state-
park/916.aspx
General Information: Landsford Canal, the best
preserved of numerous nineteenth-century South
Carolina river canals, has all its major structural
features intact. It is the uppermost of four canals
constructed on the Catawba-Wateree river system
during the period of 1820-1835. Boats used the
canals to bypass the rapids while carrying goods
from Charleston, SC.
The 448-acre park has a lockkeeper's house
which contains interpretive exhibits about the canal
system in South Carolina. A nature trail is a
favorite with visitors as is the one- and one-half-
mile towpath along the 1820 Canal with
lockkeeper's house where various remnants of the

canal works including stone locks, culverts, and
mill site are viewable.
Activities: Picnic area with shelter; nature trail;
river fishing
Admission: Entry fee. Sunday, Monday,
Thursday, Friday, and Saturday, 9 A.M. – 6 P.M.

CHARLESTON, SOUTH CAROLINA
The Charleston Museum
360 Meeting Street
Charleston, SC 29403
(843) 722-2996 Fax: (843) 722-1784
E-mail: info@charlestonmuseum.org
Location: From I-26 take the Meeting Street Exit
south to John Street. The Museum is on the corner
of Meeting and John Streets. Turn left for
parking. *Highlights: Hunley* (Confederate
submarine replica), gift shop,
Website: www.Charlestonmuseum.com
General Information: Founded in 1670
through land grants to settlers from England and
Barbados, the city of Charles Towne in Carolina
rapidly became one of the leading cultural centers
in British Colonial America. As a keen interest in
"natural curiosities" of the region developed, the
Charles Towne Library Society "fitted up a
Museum for the Reception and Preservation of
Specimens of these...natural Productions."
Thus, the Charleston Museum, founded in
1773, is the first and oldest museum in America.
The Museum collections preserve and interpret the
social and natural history of Charleston and the
South Carolina coastal region. Objectsfrom natural
science, cultural history, historical archaeology,
ornithology, and ethnology departments are
presented to illustrate the important contribution
each had to the history of the area.
A replica of the Confederate submarine *Hunley*
is on display in this 1773 museum. The original
Hunley was used in one of the many daring
attempts to break the Union blockade of the
Charleston Harbor. In 1995, the original *Hunley*
was located in the waters off South Carolina.
Admission: No entry fee. Open daily, Monday-
Saturday 9 A.M. – 5 P.M., Sundays 1 P.M. –
5 P.M.

MONCKS CORNER, SOUTH CAROLINA
Old Santee Canal Park
900 Stony Landing Road
Moncks Corner, SC 29461
(843) 899-5200 Fax: (843) 761-7032
E-mail: parkinfo@santeecooper.com
Location: Old Santee Canal Park is located at the
end of Stony Landing Road in Moncks Corner,
S.C. Stony Landing Road meets U.S. Highway 52
Bypass (Rembert C. Dennis Boulevard) at the
traffic light.

Highlights: Santee Canal — first canal in United States, CSS *Little David* (scale model), gift shop, freshwater swamp and marsh,
Website: www.oldsanteecanalpark.org/
 General Information: The Santee Canal, which began operations in 1800, is considered one of the earliest engineering achievements in American history and a pioneer economic development project of South Carolina. The Canal connected the Santee River and its watershed — covering two-thirds of the state of South Carolina — to the Cooper River and its harbor, which was a major port of South Carolina during the nineteenth century.
 The Santee Canal was designed to handle a 34-foot rise through a series of three locks and a sixty-nine-foot fall through seven more, for a net difference of thirty-five feet between the Santeeand Cooper Rivers. The Canal was twenty-two-miles long and took seven years to construct. The Canal was in operation until the railroads and steam vessels put it out of business in the mid-1850s. Local residents used the southern end of the Canal until the start of the Civil War.
 The Park features a three-eighths scale model of the CSS *Little David* — the first successful semi-submersible torpedo boat. The Confederate torpedo-ram David made history on the night of October 5th, 1863 when it made the first ever torpedo attack on the Union sub the New Ironsides. A replica of the CSS *David* is located at the Berkeley Museum — a nineteenth-century plantation house, over three miles of boardwalks and nature trails, and picnic shelter. The Park's Interpretive Center houses displays including history of the Santee Canal, lock operation, as well as the natural history found in the park.
 Admission: Entry fee. Open daily, 9 A.M.-5 P.M., year-round.

MT. PLEASANT, SOUTH CAROLINA
Patriots Point Naval and Maritime Museum
40 Patriots Point Road
Mt. Pleasant, SC 29464-4377
Toll Free: 1-866-831-1720
(843) 884-2727 Fax: (843) 884-2727
E-mail: ppgroups@patriotspoint.org
Location: From Charleston, cross the Cooper River Bridge on Hwy 17 North, stay to the right at the foot of the bridge, and turn right at the traffic light.
Highlights: The USS *Clamagore* (submarine), The USS *Laffey* (destroyer), The USS *Yorktown* (aircraft carrier), The USCGC *Ingham* (Coast Guard cutter), 25 aircraft, Newsletter: *To the Point*,
Website: www.state.sc.us/patpt
 General Information: The USS *Yorktown* dominates Patriots Point Naval and Maritime Museum, founded in 1973, the second of the

World War II Essex class aircraft carriers. She received eleven battle stars for service in the Pacific during WWII, and five thereafter. Visitors may tour many of the ship's compartments including the flightdeck, hangar bays, ship's brig, sickbay, and other areas.
 Twenty-four carrier aircraft are on display. Special exhibits include a mine collection, a shipbuilding and repair display, and artifacts from several other noted carriers. The ship's theatre regularly shows the film *The Fighting Lady*.
 Also at Patriots Point are the World War II submarine *Clamagore*, which operated in the Atlantic and Mediterranean and patrolled Cuban waters during 1962, the destroyer *Laffey*, which participated in the D-Day landings of the Allied troops at Normandy before being transferred to the Pacific. Also, the Coast Guard Cutter *Ingham*.
 Activities: Films, concerts, Boy/Girl Scout/youth overnight camping aboard the *Yorktown*, and a golf course
 Admission: Entry fee. All vessels may be toured daily April 1-October 31, 9 A.M. – 7:30 P.M.; rest of the year 9 A.M. - 5 P.M.

NORTH CHARLESTON, SC
The *H. L. Hunley* Museum
1250 11th Street,   Building 255
Charleston, SC
Toll Free: 877 /448-6539 (843) 744-2186
North Charleston, SC 29015
(843) 723-9797
Info: Kellen Correia at 843/722-2333 or
E-mail: kellen@rqasc.com
Location: The *Hunley* and its artifacts are located at the Warren Lasch Conservation Center located on Charleston's Old Naval Base. From I-26, take Exit 216-B, North Cosgrove Ave. At the 3rd traffic signal proceed straight into the Charleston Naval Complex. At the first stop sign, take a left. At the second stop sigh, take a right. Proceed to the gate. You may be stopped and asked you destination, (*Hunley* Conversation Laboratory). Turn right at the first traffic signal onto Hobson Ave. Go approximately 1000 years and take a left onto Supply Street. Pass the Charleston Public Works building with the blue roof. The lab will be on your left.
Highlights: *H. L. Hunley* submarine research, gift shop, models site.
Website: www.csshlhunley.com
 General Information: On February 17, 1864, the Confederate submarine, *H.L. Hunley*, attacked and sank the USS *Housatonic* four miles off Sullivan's Island in the Atlantic Ocean, becoming the first modern submarine to sink a ship
 The *Hunley* signaled to shore that she had completed the attack and was on the way home,

but instead, she disappeared in the dark with her brave crew. History recorded this mission as a valiant exercise of duty and the *Hunley* as a pioneer in technological innovation.

Surrounded over time in mystery, the *Hunley* was raised on August 8, 2000, 136 years after her triumph and tragedy. She was brought to the Warren Lasch Conservation Center, a technological workplace designated to seek out and record the facts of the *H.L. Hunley's* journey into history.

Models from the TNE Movie The *Hunley* are exhibited along with artifacts found inside the submarine, including Lt. Dixon's coin.

Admission: Entry fee. Open Sat. 10 a.m. to 5 p.m. Sunday, 12 noon to 5 p.m.

ST. HELENA ISLAND, SOUTH CAROLINA
Hunting Island State Park
2555 Sea Island Parkway
St. Helena Island, SC 29920-5604
(843) 838-2011   Fax: (843) 838-4263
E-mail: Thru Website
Location: The Park is located sixteen miles east of Beaufort on US #21.
Highlights: The Hunting Island Lighthouse, Beach Shop, Campground Store,
Website: www.huntingisland.com/
General Information: The original Hunting Island Lighthouse was built in 1859 at the northern end of the island but was destroyed by Confederate forces during the Civil War.

A second light station was established between 1873-1875. The 132-foot-tall cast-iron tower displayed a second-order Fresnel lens. The lighthouse had to be relocated a distance of one-and one-fourth miles in 1889 due to the effects of erosion. The lighthouse was decommissioned in 1933.

Today, the tower is open to the public daily, spring through fall. The surrounding grounds include two original outbuildings, the original oil house, and the ruins of the keeper's residence.
Activities: Education programs on the lighthouse's history are given weekly in the summer, and by appointment the rest of the year for organized groups and see/purchase Lighthouse history video.
Admission: Parking fee for Park, which includes four miles of beach, a visitor center with exhibits on lighthouse and natural history, and several nature trails. Lighthouse entry fee in peak season. Park open daylight-dusk every day of the year. Lighthouse hours may vary, but are generally 10 A.M.- 4 P.M. May be closed in winter. Call to be sure it is open.

SOUTH DAKOTA

SIOUX FALLS, SOUTH DAKOTA
Battleship *South Dakota* Museum
12th & Kiwanis
Mailing:
600 E. 7th Street
Sioux Falls, SD 57103
(605) 367-7060 E-mail:USSDAKOTA@aol.com
Location: Sioux Falls is at the junction of I-29 north/south and I-90 east/west. The Museum is on 12th Street (just east of I-29) at the corner of South Kiwanis.
Highlights: The USS *South Dakota* (battleship model),
General Information: The Battleship *South Dakota* Museum, founded in 1968, is a military and nautical museum that exhibits collections of memorabilia of the Battleship USS *South Dakota*, including silver service, gun barrels, a scale model of the ship, the ship's log, bell, books, photographs, mast, anchors, and flags.
Activities: Films and crewmember reunions.
Admission: No entry fee. Open daily, 9 A.M.- 5 P.M., Memorial Day-Labor Day.

TENNESSEE

GERMANTOWN, TENNESSEE
PT Boats, Inc. Headquarters
P.O. Box 38070
Germantown, TN 38183
(901) 755-8440 Fax: (901) 521-0522
E-mail: ptboats@ptboats.org
Location: Germantown is 10 miles east of Memphis on Rte U.S.72. The headquarters is at 1384 Cordova Road, Suite 2. **Web Site:** www.ptboats.org/
General Information: The PT Boats, Inc. Headquarters has films and videos available. Lectures can be arranged. Reprints of photographs in the collection of thousands of images may be purchased. A small gift shop contains PT boat items. Items may also be mail-ordered.
Admission: No entry fee. Call for hours.

MEMPHIS, TENNESSEE
Mississippi River Museum at Mud Island
125 North Front Street
Memphis, TN 38103
1-800-507-6507 (901) 576-7241
Fax: (901) 576-6666 E-mail: On web site.
Location: The Museum is adjacent to downtown Memphis, just south of I-40 across the Wolf River.
Highlights: Civil War gunboat and riverboat, scale model of the river,
Website: www.mudisland.com/museum.asp

General Information: The Mississippi River Museum at Mud Island, founded in 1978, exhibits reconstruction's of a riverboat and Civil War gunboat with period furnishings; artifacts and archives relating to prehistoric and historic Indian settlements, and boat development; Civil War music; boat models and engines; river engineering; natural history and sciences; related art collection; outdoor exhibition: a five-block-long scale model of river focusing on cultural and natural history of the lower Mississippi River.

Activities: Guided tours, lectures, films, gallery talks, and concerts.

Admission: Entry fee. Open: April 8-May 26 10 A.M.- 5 P.M,; daily May 24-Sept. 4, 10 A.M.- 6 P.M.; Tuesday – Sunday, Sept. 5-Oct. 31 10 A.M.- 5 P.M.

TEXAS

CORPUS CHRISTI, TEXAS
Corpus Christi Museum of Science & Industry
1900 North Chaparral Street
Corpus Christi, TX 78401
(361) 826-4667 Fax: (361) 884-7392
E-mail: On web site.
Location: In Corpus Christi, the Museum is on North Chaparral Street (near the Harbor Bridge at the end of I-37), on Ocean Drive.
Highlights: "Seeds of Change" exhibit, Discovery gift shop, *Science and History Quarterly,* *Calendar* (monthly), library **Website:** www.ccmuseumedres.com/history.htm
General Information: The Corpus Christi Museum of Science & Industry includes the Xeriscape Learning Center and Design Garden. Exhibits and displays include demonstrations, multi-media presentations, on-going ship repair and maintenance, and guides in period costume.

The Smithsonian Institution's Quincentenary exhibition "Seeds of Change" is now on permanent display. Also, the museum's children's exhibit area includes hands-on displays: "Reptiles of South Texas" featuring live alligators; Hurricane Center and Weather Station; "Shipwreck," an award-winning story of a 1554 Spanish shipwreck; touch tables; changing exhibits; and much more.

Xeriscape Learning Center and Design Garden and an outdoor educational area is located at the entrance to the World of Discovery.

Activities: Family activities include lectures, workshops, demonstrations, and gallery theatre presentations on each Saturday. Multi-media presentations, on-going ship repair and maintenance at the shipyard. Library (used only by permission).

Admission: Entry fee. Open Monday TO Saturday, 10 A.M.-5 P.M., Sunday, 1 P.M.-5 P.M. Closed Christmas Day and New Year's Day.

CORPUS CHRISTI, TEXAS
USS *Lexington* Museum on the Bay
2914 North Shoreline Boulevard
PO Box 23076
Corpus Christi, TX 78402-1116
1-800-LADY LEX (361) 888-4873
E-mail: rocco@usslexington.com
Location: The *Lexington* resides just offshore of Corpus Christi Beach and adjacent to the Texas State Aquarium on North Shoreline Boulevard.
Highlights: The USS *Lexington* (aircraft carrier), *Lex Letter* Newsletter,
Website: www.usslexington.com/
General Information: The fifth U.S. Navy ship to bear the name Lexington; the name dates back to the original *Lexington* that served in the American Revolution. During World War II, the *Lexington* was reported sunk no less than four times! Nevertheless, she returned to fight again. Commissioned in 1943, the 910-foot *Lexington* served its last tour of duty in training Navy pilots based out of Pensacola, Florida. In 1992, Corpus Christi was selected as the permanent home of this national treasure.
Activities: Overnight camping program and daily tours
Admission: Entry fee. Open: Mem/Day – Labor Day, 9 A.M. – 6 P.M.; Labor Day – Mem/Day, daily 9 A.M. until 6 P.M.

FREDERICKSBURG, TEXAS
National Museum of the Pacific War
340 East Main Street, P. O. Box 777
Fredericksburg, TX 78624
(830) 997-8600 Fax: (830) 997-8902
E-mail: info@nimitzfoundation.org
Location: From San Antonio travel northwest on I-10 fifty miles to Comfort, Texas. Head north on US-87 twenty-two miles to Fredericksburg.
Highlights: The new George Bush Gallery, The Pacific War Combat Zone featuring tanks, guns, aircraft and other large relics, PT 309, The Admiral Nimitz Museum (located in the Old Steamboat Hotel), Japanese Garden of Peace, Japanese mini-sub HA-19, The Memorial and Victory Walls, The Plaza of Presidents, theSurface Fleet, archives on Admiral Nimitz an Pacific war topics, and gift shop,
Website: www.nimitz-museum.org/
General Information: The National Museum of the Pacific War administered by Texas Parks and Wildlife, and formally The Admiral Nimitz State Historical Park, was originally founded in 1967 in the old Nimitz Hotel, which was the Nimitz family business from 1850 to 1926. The hotel now features one floor of exhibits detailing Admiral Nimitz's career.

157

The George Bush Gallery houses over 23,000 square-feet of exhibits on World War II in the Pacific including a Japanese Mini-sub (HA-19), and over 760 other artifacts. It is the only museum in the country dedicated primarily to detailing that conflict from all points of view. Many hands-on and audiovisual exhibits are featured in the George Bush Gallery.

Collections include over 14,000 artifacts used in the Pacific campaigns, from uniforms and small arms, to tanks, artillery, and aircraft. Some of the aircraft on exhibit include a B-25 bomber depicting Doolittle's Raid on Tokyo, a Wildcat fighter, a TBM torpedo plane, the most complete Japanese "Val" dive-bomber in the United States, and a Japanese "Rex" float plane.

A research library including a photo collection which houses more than 8,000 pacific War photos, over 3,000 books and 200 linear feet of archival material, is open by appointment.

Activities: Temporary and traveling exhibits, special events including re-enactments throughout the year, and annual symposium on various Pacific War topics.

Admission: Entry fee. Open daily 9 A.M.-5 P.M. except Thanksgiving and Christmas.

GALVESTON, TEXAS

Seawolf Park
Pelican Island
2104 Avenue F, P.O. Box 3306
Galveston, TX 77552
(409) 744-5738 E-mail: subsim@subsim.com
Location: Seawolf Park is on Pelican Island. The island is fifty miles south of Houston and immediately across the channel from Galveston Island's east end via Seawolf Parkway (51st St).
Highlights: The USS *Cavalla* (SSK-244), The USS *Stewart* (DE-238),
Website: www.cavalla.org/
General Information: Once an immigrant quarantines station, Seawolf Park is now a relaxing tropical oasis at the entrance to Galveston Harbor. On display are the World War II submarine USS *Cavalla*, one of the most famous submarines from WWII, and the destroyer escortUSS *Stewart*, the only remaining destroyer escort of its class. Also exhibited is military hardware. Displays open year-round.
Activities: Ships open for self-guided tours year-round.
Admission: Open seven days a week, 8 A.M.- 6 P.M.

GALVESTON, TEXAS

Texas Seaport Museum/*ELISSA*
Galveston Historical Foundation
Pier 21, Number 8
Galveston, TX 77550
(409) 763-1877

E-mail: elissa@galvestonhistory.org
Location: From Houston take I-45 south to Galveston Island. The Texas Seaport Museum and tall ship *Elissa* are located at Pier 21 (at the foot of 22nd Street) and Harborside Drive.
Highlights: The *Elissa* (1877 iron barque),
Website: www.tsm-elissa.org/
General Information: The Texas Seaport Museum houses exhibits on the ships, immigrants, seaports, and seaborne commerce in Texas history.

The *Elissa* is the centerpiece of the Texas Seaport Museum. A square-rigged iron barque built in Scotland in 1877; *Elissa* is one of the oldest merchant ships afloat. In the last 1960s, she was condemned to a Greek shipyard and destined for scrap when she was rescued by Galveston Historical Foundation and restored to her former grandeur. Having visited Galveston in 1883 and 1886, *Elissa* is now a "seaworthy" exhibit for the whole family, interpreting Galveston's ties to the sea.

Admission to the Texas Seaport Museum includes a film describing the history and restoration of the ship. *Elissa* leaves her moorings at once each year for sail, sometimes more often, as funds allow.

Admission: Entry fee. Open daily, 10 A.M.-5 P.M., year-round. Closed Thanksgiving & Christmas

HOUSTON, TEXAS

Houston Maritime Museum
2204 Dorrington Street   **155**
Houston, TX 77030-3210
(713) 666-1910 Fax: (713) 838-8557
E-mail: houstonmaritimemus@sbcglobal.net
Location: In the Medical Center area of Southwest Houston. L From the intersection of Main Street (north/south) and Holcomb Boulevard (east/west), go west on Holcomb Blvd. Two blocks to Montclair Street. Turn south one block to Dorrington Street. Turn west and the Museum is just past corner on north side.
Highlights: Local maritime history, ship models, nautical library, exclusive gift shop.
Website: www.houstonmaritimemuseum.org
General Information: The Houston Maritime Museum, founded in 2000, provides a setting for ship modelers and exhibits featuring collected artifacts including an 1812 diving helmet, coal form the Titanic, and small reference library where visitors are welcome to browse though and explore the oceanic literature, maritime history, and maritime reference materials.

Besides historic objects on display, visitors can tour the "shipyard" where they can get a peek at how model boats and ships are made and restored. Over 60 elaborate historic ship models are on display throughout the Museum. Favorites include the SS *United States*, the fastest passenger ship ever built, and the USS *Missouri*, on which the Japanese signed their surrender ending World War II.

Admission: No entry fee, although donations are encouraged. Open Tuesday-Saturday, 10 A.M. – 4 P.M. By appointment on Saturdays. Museum closed Thanksgiving, Christmas and New Year's days.

LA PORTE, TEXAS

Battleship *TEXAS*
3523 Highway 134
La Porte, TX 77571
(281) 479-2431
E-mail: park.information@tpwd.state.tx.us
Location: Battleship *TEXAS* State Historical Site is twenty-two miles east of downtown Houston off Rte. 225 East and two miles north on Texas Highway134 on Farm-to-Market Road 134.
Highlights: The USS *TEXAS* (battleship), gift shop, **Website:** www.battleshiptexas.org
General Information: The *TEXAS* is the last of the dreadnoughts and the only surviving naval vessel to have seen service in both World Wars. When the USS *TEXAS* was commissioned in 1914, she was the most powerful weapon in the world and the most complex product of an industrial nation just beginning to become a force in global events. The *TEXAS* projected American pride and power over the world's oceans for 32 years. Her big guns brought dread to her enemies and hope to her friends in the Pacific in 1945 as she had in the North Sea in 1918.

Always a proud ship, imbued with the spirit of her namesake, the *TEXAS* serves today as a monument to those who built and served in her, a powerful reminder of the skill and sacrifice, hardship, and courage demanded and freely given by Americans in their country's defense.

The *TEXAS* has undergone much modification in guns, armor, and propulsion. She helped pioneer naval aviation between the wars, and was kept up-to-date with advances in fire control, radio, and radar as the focus of her defense shifted to the sky. Her basic reasons for being, however, remained the same: to float the big guns of her main battery into action, and to keep them firing against any enemy response.

Activities: Self-guided tours, gift shop, picnicking, snack shop, San Jacinto Battleground State Historic Site and San Jacinto Monument. Battleship *TEXAS* Foundation Youth Group Overnight Program: (713) 827-9620.
Admission: No entry fee. Open daily 10 A.M.-5 P.M. except December 24-25.
The Battleground is open daily from 8 A.M.-9 P.M., March 1- October 31, and from 8 A.M.-7 P.M., November 1-February.
The San Jacinto Museum of History (281-479-2421), located in the San Jacinito Monument, is

open daily 9 A.M.-6 P.M., except Thanksgiving Day, and December 24-25.

PORT ISABEL, TEXAS

Port Isabel Historical Museum
Museums of Port Isabel
317 E. Railroad Avenue
Port Isabel, TX 78578
(956) 943-7602 Fax: (956) 943-4346
E-mail: director@portisabelmuseums.com
Location: From Harlingen and points north: heading southbound on Hwy 77, turn east onto Hwy 100. Exit is marked "South Padre Island." Proceed approximately 23 miles.
Highlights: Shrimp and Fish industry history, 1848 U.S./Mexican War Gallery with collection of rare military artifacts from the Mexican Army.
Website: www.portisabelmuseums.com/
General Information: The Port Isabel Historical Museum houses exhibits on the history and culture of Port Isabel and the Laguna Madre area in the historic 1899 Charles Champion building, second oldest structure in the area.

This two-story museum interprets the history from the Native Americans to the shrimp and fish industry with hands-on exhibits, videos, and artifacts. There is a twelve minute film on the history of the area. The building has the "fish mural" painted in 1906 and restored in 1996 which depicts approximately 200 images of marine life found in the Laguna Madre.
Admission: Entry fee. Tuesdays - Saturdays 10:00 A.M. - 4:00 P.M.

PORT ISABEL, TEXAS

Point Isabel Lighthouse Complex
Museums of Port Isabel
408 Queen Isabella Blvd..
Port Isabel, Texas 78578
(956) 943-2262
E-mail: director@portisabelmuseums.com
Location: From Harlingen & Points North: heading southbound on Hwy 77, turn east onto Hwy 100. Exit is marked 'South Padre Island'. Proceed approximately 23 miles. The Lighthouse is located north of The Treasures of the Gulf Museum and the Port Isabel Historical Museum across Hwy. 100 at the mouth of the Queen Isabella Causeway.
Highlights: Restored 1852 Lighthouse with a replica of the Lighthouse Keepers Cottage.
Website: www.portisabelmuseums.com/
General Information: Constructed in 1852, the Point Isabel Lighthouse was built to protect and guide ships through Brazos Santiago and the barrier islands. In 1952, the Lighthouse was opened as a State Park and remains the only lighthouse on the Texas coast open to the public. The Lighthouse Keeper's Cottage, on the grounds,

houses the Chamber of Commerce and an exhibit on the history of the lighthouse.

Admission: Entry fee. Open: Summer, Mon/Fri 9 A.M. – 5 P.M.; Fri/Sat 11 A.M.–8 P.M.

PORT ISABEL, TEXAS

Treasures of the Gulf Museum
Museums of Port Isabel
308 Queen Isabella Blvd..
Port Isabel, TX 78578
(956) 943-7602
E-mail: director@portisabelmuseums.com
Location: Port Isabel is 15-miles northeast of Brownsville, TX, near the border of Mexico. From Harlingen & Points North: heading southbound on Hwy 77, turn east onto Hwy 100. Exit is marked "South Padre Island." Proceed approximately 23 miles. The Treasures of the Gulf Museum is connected with the Port Isabel Historical Museum with a wooden dock walkway. Entrance is through Railroad Ave.
Highlights: Artifacts from the 1554 Spanish Shipwrecks found off Padre Island, 30 miles from Port Isabel, Nautical Gift Shop,
Website: www.portisabelmuseums.com/
General Information: Treasures of the Gulf Museum puts the focus on three Spanish shipwrecks. Meeting their fate in 1554, just 30 miles north of Port Isabel, and brought to life with murals, artifacts and hands-on Activities.
Activities: Also featured is a Children's Discovery Lab, Ship Theatre & Nautical Gift shop.
Admission: Entry fee. Tuesdays - Saturdays 10:00 A.M. - 4:00 P.M.
Combination tickets available.

ROCKPORT, TEXAS

Texas Maritime Museum
1202 Navigation Circle
Rockport, TX 78382
Toll Free: (866) 729-2469
(361) 729-1271 Fax: (361) 729-9938
E-mail: curator@texasmaritimemuseum.org
Location: The Museum is located on Rockport Harbor, 35 miles north of Corpus Christi. Just look for the lighthouse.
Highlights: Library, Museum Store, fully-rigged model of the *La Belle*, a seventeenth century schooner, the "Bullwinkle," oil-drilling platform scale model, *The Log Line* (newsletter), Museum Store, **Website:** www.texasmaritimemuseum.org
General Information: Within the Texas Maritime Museum, founded in 1975 and the official maritime museum of the state of Texas, alongside Rockport Harbor, you will find exhibits and artifacts that reflect the rich maritime history of Texas. Permanent exhibits look at the early days of French and Spanish exploration and

progress through a timeline to the modern search for offshore oil and gas.

The newest addition to the Museum's collection is an eight-foot scale model of French explorer La Salle's *La Belle*. Interactive exhibits and activities are available for families. There is also an extensive maritime library that includes books, photographs and videos. Exterior exhibits include a lifeboat from an offshore oil platform and a full-scale replica of a Scow Sloop. Watch the main gallery for changing exhibits.

Through changing exhibits, educational programs and special events, it explores the rich maritime history of the Texas coast. While you're here, check out the Museum Store for gifts and collectibles, all with a nautical theme.

Activities: Education programs; Rockport Festival of Wines; the free Winter Brown Bag Lunch Lecture Series; Music of the Sea Festival.

Admission: Entry fee. Open Tuesday through Saturday, 10 AM to 4 PM and Sunday, 1 P.M. to 4 PM, year-round.

VERMONT

BASIN HARBOR, VERMONT

Lake Champlain Maritime Museum
4472 Basin Harbor Road
Vergennes, VT 05491
(801) 475-2022 Fax: (801) 475-2953
E-mail: info@lcmm.org
Location: From Burlington: Rte. 7 south twenty miles to Vergennes, follow Rte. 22A through Vergennes, follow "Maritime Museum" signs. Seven miles west of Vergennes.
Highlights: *Philadelphia II* (54-foot Revolutionary War gunboat), new Nautical Archaeology Center, operational boatshop, Coast Guard Buoy Tender (CG 52302), research library by appointment.
Website: www.lcmm.org/
General Information: Though nautical exploration, hands-on exhibits and learning adventures for all ages, Lake Champlain Maritime Museum brings to life the stories of Lake Champlain and its people. Discover why Lake Champlain History and characters of theChamplain Valley through its military, commercial, and recreational periods. View a large collection of original small watercraft built over the last 150 years. Learn about the largest collection of wooden shipwrecks in North America and talk to archeological conservators in our Nautical Archeology Center.

Step back in time as you climb aboard the 54-foot square-rigged Revolutionary War gunboat replica *Philadelphia II* and learn about the life of citizen soldiers in the Champlain Valley in 1776.

Watch craftsmen continue traditional maritime skills of boatbuilding and blacksmithing in our working shops. Museum store, children's playground, picnic area on site. Red Mill restaurant next door.

Special Exhibits: There are over a dozen exhibit buildings at the Lake Champlain Maritime Museum at Basin Harbor. These present the maritime history and nautical archeology of the Champlain Valley through hands-on interactive learning stations, video and audio displays, historical artifacts and images. Long term exhibitions are enhanced by new research, new acquisitions and special short-term installations each season.

Admission: Entry fee. Open daily, June 17 - October 15, Wed/Sun 11 A.M. – 5 6.M. Offices are open year round Monday to Friday 8:30-4:00.

SHELBURNE, VERMONT
Shelburne Museum, Inc.
6000 Shelburne Road, P.O. Box 10
Shelburne, VT 05482
(802) 985-3346 (tape recording); 985-3346
E-mail: info@shelburnemuseum.org
Location: Shelburne lies seven miles south of Burlington, on Rte. 7.
Highlights: Thirty-seven historic buildings on forty-five park-like acres, The SS *Ticonderoga* (lake paddle-wheeler), Colchester Reef Lighthouse, Covered bridge, Scrimshaw, Newsletter, Research library, Gift shop
Website: www.shelburnemuseum.org/
General Information: Shelburne Museum, Inc., founded in 1947, exhibits a collection of American fine, folk and decorative art; utilitarian art; regional architecture; SS *Ticonderoga*, built at Shelburne Harbor, Vermont in 1906, is the last vertical beam passenger and freight side-wheel steamer intact in the United States; steam train and private car; carriages; horse-drawn vehicles; toys; tools; dolls; weapons; hunting trophies; American Indian artifacts; American paintings; oil paintings of side-wheelers by James Bard, paintings of ships by Fitzhugh Lane and Albert Bierstadt, and French Impressionist paintings, drawings, and sculptures; horticultural and arboreal collection. The Museum is a "collection of collections" well worth seeing.

A scrimshaw exhibit is shown in the Variety Unit Building, and canoes — guide and dugout — are shown in the Beach Lodge. And in the Circus Building, along with a complete miniature circus parade, are two model canal barges. The original barges owned and operated in the late 1800s by Sig Sawtelle, transported a 150-animal-and-people circus along the Erie and Oswego Canals.

In the Dorset House miniature bird carvings, and firearms including , wildfowl decoys,

two large punt guns used to take ducks and geese for market. A punt gun, with a barrel over 8 feet long, is muzzle-loaded with one-half to two-pounds of bird shot rammed over an equal measure of black powder, and then wadded with pieces of old rope, cork, and paper. Over 100 ducks could be taken, but a good shot would be 30 ducks or ten geese.

Also exhibited is Colchester Reef Lighthouse (1871), from Lake Champlain, contains maritime prints, figureheads, scrimshaw, early maps, and charts. The Covered bridge (c.1845) is the only double lane covered bridge with footpath in Vermont.

The Museum is an assembly of everything that is distinctively characteristic of New England. Each structure is unique, including the 220-ft steam paddlewheeler, SS *Ticonderoga*, hauled from nearby Lake Champlain to its final "port," the Shelburne Museum. A research library is available on the premises.

Activities: Lectures, tours, and research library.
Admission: Entry fee. Open: May 1 – Oct. 31, 10 A.M. – 5 P.M

VIRGINIA

ALEXANDRIA, VIRGINIA
Alexandria Seaport Foundation and Seaport Center
1000 South Lee Street P.O. Box 25036
Jones Point Park
Alexandria, VA 22313
(703) 549-7078 Fax: (703) 549-6715
E-mail: ASFOffice@alexanderiaseaport.org
Location: Jones Point Park
Highlights: Maritime history, Potomac River Dory Boat, youth training programs, boatbuilding classes,
Website: www.alexandriaseaport.org/
General Information: The Alexandria Seaport Foundation and Seaport Center uses the power and beauty of the Potomac River waterfront and Alexandria's wealth of Maritime history to benefit our community. The Foundation runs the Craddock Boat Building program where historic watercrafts are restored and conducts a marine environmental sciences program. More than 500 volunteer members accomplish the bulk of our work. The Seaport Center (703) 684-0569, is the home of many of the boats that have been built by ASF volunteers.

Training youths and adults in sailing, rowing, boat building, and other maritime skills, thereby developing leadership, building confidence, and teaching teamwork and discipline is the goal of the Foundation. It takes the best of our maritime past to meet the needs of today and to prepare us for the challenges of the future by strengthening the public's awareness of Alexandria's rich heritage, training youths and adults in sailing, rowing, boat building, and other maritime skills, thereby developing leadership and building confidence, and teaching teamwork and discipline.

The Craddock Boat Building Program is located in on the first floor of the Seaport center. Here is based our traveling youth/adult boat building program which is based on the 12.5 foot Foundation designed Bevin' skiff for rowing and/or sailing.

Activities: The Foundation also offers a wide selection of boat building classes that are available to the public and offers courses that include four different types of boat construction, sail making, bronze casting, and lofting.

Admission: Open: Daily 10 A.M. – 5 P.M. On Tuesday evenings, from 6 P.M.-9 P.M.

ALEXANDRIA, VIRGINIA
Torpedo Factory Art Center
105 N. Union Street
Alexandria, VA 22314
(703) 838-4565 Fax: (703) 549-6877
E-mail: rjohnson@torpedofactory.org
Location: From Washington, D.C., take SR-400 south past National Airport to King Street head toward the intersection with North Union Street and turn east on Queen Street. The museum is on the Potomac River in Historic Old Town Alexandria.
Highlights: Torpedo Factory history, art center, **Website:** www.torpedofactory.org/
General Information: The Torpedo Factory Art Center, founded in 1974, is an art museum housed in a World Wars I and II torpedo factory. It consists of eighty-four artist studios, four cooperative galleries, an Art League School, and the Alexandria Archaeology Center. Collections and displays emphasize the history of the factory and include torpedoes and related objects.
Activities: Guided tours, lectures.
Admission: No entry fee. Open daily, 10 A.M.-5 P.M., year-round. Closed Easter Sunday, 4th of July, Thanksgiving , Christmas, and New Year's Day.

CHINCOTEAGUE, VIRGINIA
The Oyster & Maritime Museum
7125 Maddox Boulevard   P. O. Box 352
Chincoteague Island, VA 23336
(757) 336-6117
E-mail: oystermuseum@verizon.net
Location: Chincoteague sits across from the southern tip of Assateague Island. Take Rte. 13 north/south to the Delmarva Peninsula, just south of the Maryland state line on the Atlantic coast. The Museum is on Maddox Boulevard in the town center.

Highlights: Shellfish farming and seafood industry, **Website:** www.chincoteaguechamber.com/oyster/omm.html
General Information: The Oyster & Maritime Museum exhibits depict the history of oystering (including a narrated diorama) from the 1600s to the present. There are shell collections, displays on predators of the oyster, and the tools used by oystermen. Also displayed is the First Order Fresnel lens from the Assateague Lighthouse. Of special note is the history of Chincoteague Island.
Admission: Entry fee. Open daily, Memorial Day and after Labor Day until October 31, 10 A.M. to 4 P.M., Sundays, 12 Noon - 4 P.M.

GREAT FALLS, VIRGINIA
The Patowmack Canal
National Park Service - Box 66
Great Falls, VA 22066
(703) 285-2965 Fax: (703) 285-2223
Location: Fifteen miles northwest of Washington, D.C., at the end of Old Dominion Drive and 4 miles west of the Beltway on VA-193 in Great Falls Park, Virginia
Highlights: Interpretive Center, **Website:** www.nps.gov/gwmp/grfa/canal/pato.htm
General Information: An entire town grew up around the canal construction site at Great Falls to serve as headquarters for the Patowmack Company and home for the workers. Founded by the Revolutionary War hero "Light Horse" Harry Lee and named for his first wife, Matildaville, at its height, boasted the company superintendent's house, a market, gristmill, sawmill, foundry, inn, icehouse, workers' barracks, boarding houses, and a sprinkling of small homes. Although the Patowmack Company was a financial failure, the canal builders pioneered lock engineering and stimulated a wave of canal construction important to the country's development. Things to see: wing dam, upper guard gate, dry-laid walls, gristmill, iron forge, locks 1, 2, 3, 4, and 5, and Mather Gorge.
Admission: No entry fee. Open: Visitor Center, Summer 10 A.M. – 5 P.M., weekends 10 A.M. – 6 P.M. year-round.

NEWPORT NEWS, VIRGINIA
Dorothy **(The Iron Tugboat)**
Newport News Shipbuilding
4101 Washington Avenue
Newport News, VA 23607-2770
(757) 380-2000
Location: The *Dorothy* is displayed at the Newport News Shipbuilding yard.
Highlights: The *Dorothy* (iron tugboat)
General Information: The *Dorothy* survived through a career of multiple owners, multiple name changes, multiple modifications, multiple

damage-producing crashes, and finally an ignominious sinking — only to rise again to be refurbished and proudly displayed at her place of beginning as "Hull Number One." 1890 was the year of launch bearing the name of *Dorothy* for Dorothy Payne Whitney, infant daughter of Secretary of the Navy William C. Whitney serving in the Cabinet of President Grover Cleveland.

Now permanently displayed in the parkland site at the Newport News Shipping company, she is completely reconditioned into her original elegance. Among all the facts researched to accomplish the reconstruction, finding the original linen drawings at the Mariners' Museum were, perhaps, among the most important finds. The libraries of the maritime museums constantly serve us all.

Admission: Public viewing from 41st Street and Washington Avenue.

NEWPORT NEWS, VIRGINIA
The Mariners' Museum
100 Museum Drive
Newport News, VA 23606
(800) 581-7245 (757) 596-2222
Fax: (757) 591-7320
E-mail: frontdeskstaff@marinersmuseum.org
Location: Newport News lies at southern end of the Chesapeake Bay, just twenty minutes southeast of Williamsburg. Take exit 258A off I-64 onto J. Clyde Morris Blvd. and drive 2.5 miles to the intersection of J. Clyde Morris and Warwick Boulevards. The Museum is located at this intersection.
Highlights: Small-craft collection, ship models, restored engine room from an 1895 steam tug, figureheads, paintings, hands-on exhibits, actual artifacts from the Civil War ironclad USS *Monitor* including its 30-ton engine just recovered, library (67,000 volumes, 350,000 photographs), Newsletter: *The Mariners' Pipe*, gift shop, **Website:** www.marinersmuseum.org
General Information: The Mariners' Museum, founded in 1930, preserves and interprets the story of man's relationship with the sea through its international collection of figureheads, ship models, small craft, paintings, scrimshaw, and other maritime artifacts. The scope and depth of the Museum's collections have made it one of the best maritime museums in the world.

Ten galleries at the Museum interpret more than three thousand years of nautical experience on stream, bay, and ocean. The Great Hall of Steam showcases the Museum's extensive ship model collection. Man's many uses of the ship model are examined in a separate gallery.

Of special significance is the August F. Crabtree Collection of Miniature Ships. Sixteen

models illustrating the evolution of merchant vessel design are displayed. Other exhibits include the evolution of the U.S. Navy in an exhibition called Defending the Seas. This exhibition includes an aircraft carrier ready room, the hull from the submarine USS *Narwhal*, and artifacts from the USS *Monitor*.

In 1990, commemorating Christopher Columbus Smith (129th birthday), founder of the worldwide Chris-Craft boat-building empire, a collection of thirty volumes and more than 25,000 document pages was donated to the Museum. The collection, known as the Rodengen/Chris-Craft Reference Library and named after the marine historian and boating journalist Jeffrey L. Rodengen, was presented to the Museum by Write Stuff Syndicate, publishers of Rodengen's book, "The Legend of the Chris-Craft." This collection now joins the Museum's over 90,000 hull cards detailing individual boats, and over 15,000 photographs, Chris-Craft Industries donated most of which in 1987; also, the Crabtree Collection of 16 ship models built to 1:48 scale representing development from Egyptian vessels to the Cunard Line *Britannia* of 1840.

The records are available to historians and for reference in boat restoration. The library and research facility houses one of the most complete collections of maritime-related materials in the country.

Activities: Guided tours of the 10 unique galleries, lectures, gallery talks, slide, and film shows.

Admission: Entry fee. Open Mon/Sat, 10 A.M.- 5 P.M.; Sunday 12 Noon – 5 P.M. Closed Thanksgiving and Christmas.

NEWPORT NEWS, VIRGINIA
USS *Monitor* Ironclad
The Mariners' Museum
100 Museum Drive
Newport News, VA 23606
(757) 596-2222 1-800-581-7245
E-mail: community@mariner.org
Location: All information on the *Monitor* is located at the Mariners' Museum.
Highlights: *Monitor* artifacts and historical information, **Website:** www.monitorcenter.org.
General Information: The USS *Monitor* was the first ironclad ship to be commissioned into the U.S. Navy. Built during the Civil War in response to the Confederate Navy's ironclad CSS *Virginia*, *Monitor* played an integral role in the transformation of military vessels from wood to iron.

The *Monitor* was launched on January 30, 1862. Under the command of Lieutenant John L.

Worden, *Monitor* was ordered to Hampton Roads, Virginia, where she fought the Confederate ironclad CSS *Virginia* in the first battle between ironclad ships. The two ships engaged each other for nearly four hours with neither inflicting serious damage on the other. The battle ended in a draw, although both sides claimed victory.

On December 31, 1862, while in tow by USS *Rhode Island* to Beaufort, North Carolina, *Monitor* sank during a severe storm off the coast of Cape Hatteras. Four officers and twelve crewmen lost their lives. On March 8, 1974, the Duke University research team, with others, had located the wreck of the USS *Monitor*.

Currently, *Monitor's* 9-foot tall gun turret, the two 19,000 bound guns, and engine have been raised. Many other artifacts are on exhibit in the newly constructed outdoor tanks as part of The Mariners' Museum's permanent exhibition "Defend the Seas." For the past several years the National Oceanic and Atmospheric Administration (NOAA) has worked with the U.S. Navy to raise large pieces of the Monitor from her watery grave. Identified as the national repository for all *Monitor* artifacts recovered, The Mariners' Museum conserves, exhibits, and interprets these historic objects once received. The Mariners' Museum has plans to open the first ever USS *Monitor* Center in 2006.

NORFOLK, VIRGINIA
Hampton Roads Naval Museum
One Waterside Drive, Ste 248
Norfolk, VA 23510-1607
(757) 322-2987   Fax: (757) 445-1867
E-mail: gordon.b.calhoun@navy.mil
Location: The Hampton Roads Naval Museum and the entrance to the battleship Wisconsin, is located on the second floor of Nauticus, The National Maritime Center right on the Elizabeth River in the heart of downtown Norfolk.
Highlights: Battleship *Wisconsin* (BB-64) is berthed alongside the Museum, a superb collection of Naval ship models and artwork and the only repository for two Civil War shipwrecks, USS *Cumberland* and CSS *Florida*, Newsletter: *The Daybook*. **Website:** www.hrnm.navy.mil/
General Information: The Hampton Roads Naval Museum, located on Nauticus' second deck, is one of 10 official U.S. Navy museums in the country, and the only one dedicated to regional history. More than two hundred years of Naval history are covered, beginning with the Revolutionary War and continuing to the present day.

The USS *Wisconsin*, the largest battleship ever built by the U.S. Navy, is berthed adjacent to Nauticus and open for main deck tours. The

Wisconsin, one of the four Iowa-class battleships, began her career in the middle of WW II. She reported for duty with the Pacific Fleet in October 1944 joining Admiral William F. Halsey's 3rd Fleet when the liberation of the Philippines was underway.

In 1948, the *Wisconsin* entered the Atlantic Reserve Fleet at Norfolk only to be recommissioned in March 1951 for the Korean War. She returned to the inactive fleet in 1958, where she remained until 1988, when she was reactivated. After Desert Storm, she was placed in reserve status. *Wisconsin* was moved to a berth next to Nauticus, the National Maritime Center, in downtown Norfolk on December 7, 2000.

Admission: Free entry to the Hampton Roads Naval Museum and the battleship. Summer (Memorial Day to Labor Day): Open Daily, 9 A.M. to 5 P.M.; Between January and early March, the ship is open for limited periods during the day. Call for more information. All other times of the year it is closed on Mondays, open from 10 a.m. to 5 p.m. Tuesday through Saturday, and open on Sunday 12 Noon to 5 P.M.

NORFOLK, VIRGINIA
Nauticus, The National Maritime Center
One Waterside Drive, Suite 248
Norfolk, VA 23510-1607
1 (800) 664-1080 (757) 664-1000
Fax: (757) 623-1287 E-mail: info@nauticus.org
Location: Nauticus is located at One Waterside Drive on the Elizabeth River in the heart of downtown Norfolk.
Highlights: Battleship *Wisconsin* (BB-64) and three interactive battleship-related exhibits, Aegis Command Center, branch office of National Oceanic and Atmospheric Administration (NOAA), visiting ships to board, and The Galley Restaurant,
Website: www.nauticus.org
General Information: Nauticus, The National Maritime Center, is a fun and exciting interactive science and technology center exploring the power of the sea. It features more than 150 exhibits including computer and video interactive, films on a giant screen, exotic aquaria, touch pools, shark petting, national-caliber traveling exhibits, and the Hampton Roads Naval Museum, The USS *Wisconsin*, the last and largest battleship ever built by the U.S. Navy, is berthed adjacent to Nauticus (and Hampton Roads Naval Museum) and open for main deck tours.

The Hampton Roads Naval Museum is located on Nauticus' second deck. It is a U.S. Navy operated museum. The Museums maintains a collection of historic artifacts and conducts research.

Admission: Nauticus: Entry fee. Open daily, Memorial Day - Labor Day, 9 A.M.- 5 P.M.; rest of the year; Closed Mondays, Open Tuesday - Saturday, 10 A.M. - 5 P.M.; Sunday, 12 - 5 P.M. Closed Thanksgiving Day, Christmas Eve, and Christmas Day. Call for other holiday hours.

ONANCOCK, VIRGINIA
Hopkins & Bros. Store
#2 Market Street
Onancock, VA 23417
(757) 787-3100
Location: Onancock lies sixty-four miles northeast of Norfolk (across the Chesapeake Bay Bridge-Tunnel) on the Delmarva (**DEL**aware, **MAR**yland, **V**irgini**A**) Peninsula. Follow Rte. 13 out of Norfolk.
Highlights: Early Marine General Store, restaurant
    General Information: Hopkins & Bros. Store, founded in 1838, is an architectural museum with original furnishings. Marine general store dating back to 1842, when Captain Stephen Hopkins built it, thus beginning a family business, which spanned four generations and 125 years. As one of the oldest general stores on the East Coast, it is both a Virginia and American historic landmark.
    Activities: Cruise trips to Tangier Island
    Admission: No entry fee. Thursday-Saturday 10 A.M. -9:00 P.M. Sundays lunch only 12 – 4 P.M.

PORTSMOUTH, VIRGINIA
***Portsmouth* Lightship Museum**
London & Water Sts. – Portsmouth Waterfront
P. O. Box 248
Portsmouth, VA 23705
(757) 393-8591
E-mail: navalmuseums@portsmouthva.gov
Location: Portsmouth lies immediately west of Norfolk on the Elizabeth River. The Museum is on Water Street at the foot of London Boulevard (one block from Portsmouth Naval Shipyard Museum) just off I-264 at Exit 7.
Highlights: The *Portsmouth* (lightship), gift shop at Portsmouth Naval Museum, **Website**: www.portsnavalmuseums.com/about_lightship.ht ml
    General Information: The *Portsmouth* Lightship Museum, formerly in the Lightship Service and later the U.S. Coast Guard, exhibits the important functions of lightships in maritime history. Visitors will experience the history of the heralded Lightship Service that began off Portsmouth's Craney Island in 1820. The Lightship has been painstakingly restored to its original condition and was designated a national historic landmark in 1989.

Visitors will likewise see how lightship crew members lived and worked, where they dined, and the quarters where they slept. The galley is fully stocked and ready for sea duty. A large windlass room adjoins the crew members' Spartan living quarters. Magnificent lenses, some nearly a century old, designed to warn ships, miles away, of dangerous sea conditions are on display.
    The *Portsmouth* Lightship, measuring 101 feet 10 inches in length and 25 feet 8 inches across, with a 360-ton water displacement, originally served off Cape Charles after she was commissioned in 1915.
    Activities: Self-guided tours.
    Admission: Entry fee. Between Memorial Day and Labor Day; Open Monday through Saturday 10 A.M. to 5 P.M.; Sunday, 12 P.M. to 5 P.M. Winter: Open Tuesday through Saturday 10 A.M. to 5 P.M..; Noon..to 5 P.M.. Sunday.

PORTSMOUTH, VIRGINIA
Portsmouth Naval Shipyard Museum
2 High Street, P. O. Box 248
Portsmouth, VA 23705
(757) 393-8591 Fax: (757) 393-5244
E-mail: navalmuseums@portsmouthva.gov
Location: Portsmouth lies immediately west of Norfolk on the Elizabeth River. Its Naval Shipyard Museum lies at the foot of High Street off I-264 at Exit 7.
Highlights: The CSS *Virginia* model (formerly the *Merrimac*), US *Delaware* (ship-of-the-line), ship models, library (6,000 volumes), gift shop, **Website:**
www.portsnavalmuseums.com/about_naval.html
    General Information: The Portsmouth Naval Shipyard Museum, founded in 1949, is on the Elizabeth River waterfront. Paintings, models, and exhibits trace the history of the US Navy, with emphasis on local history and armed forces in the area. Particularly noteworthy are the models of the CSS Virginia, the US ship-of-the-line *Delaware*, the first ship dry-docked in the nation, and the narrated model of Portsmouth as it appeared in 1776.
    Collections include: history of the naval shipyard and the armed forces of the locality; the CSS *Virginia*, formerly the USS *Merrimac*; ship models; uniforms; flags; arms of all types; early regional maps, prints, memorabilia; and model planes. A library of general reference books is available for research by special appointment.
    Activities: Guided tours.
    Admission: Entry fee Between Memorial Day and Labor Day; Open Monday through Saturday10 A.M. to 5 P.M.; Sunday, 12 P.M. to 5 P.M. Winter: Open Tuesday through Saturday 10 A.M. to 5 P.M.; Noon - to 5 P.M.. Sunday.

REEDVILLE, VIRGINIA
Reedville Fishermen's Museum
504 Main Street, P.O. Box 306
Reedville, VA 22539-4401
(804) 453-6529   Fax: (804) 453-7159
E-mail: office@rfmuseum.org
Location: The Museum is located on the banks of
Cockrell's Creek in Reedville's historic district.
Highlights: Fishing vessel models, William
Walker House, watermen's history, buy-boat
Eluac, skipjack *Claude Somers,*
Website: www.rfmuseum.org/
   General Information: The Reedville
Fishermen's Museum presents the historic
Reedville's golden age of prosperity from the
menhaden fishing industry and is reflected in the
Victorian mansions, which line Main Street.
   The Covington Building houses a collection of
artifacts and historical material covering the history
of menhhaden fishing from its inception to the
present. Unique models of fishing vessels and
tools used for building and maintaining the fleet
are on display. And the Museum's exhibits include
a history of watermen's *Activities* from early
Native American practices to those used today by
oystermen, pound fishermen, and crabbers. The
Covington Building also provides space for
rotating exhibits and educational
programs.
   The Museum facilities include the William
Walker House, built in 1875, a modest waterman's
home furnished as it might have been early in the
twentieth century. The home is on land bought in
1875 from Captain Elijah Reed, who set up his
first small fishery in 1867.
   Activities: Year-round lecture programs.
   Admission: Entry fee. Hours: Open: May
1 – October 31, daily, 10:30 A.M. - 4:30 P.M.;
Winter, Nov 4th –Jan 15th , Fri/Sun 10:30 A.M. -
4:30 P.M.; Jan 16 – Mar 10, by appointment for
groups; Spring, Mar 10 – Apr10, Sat/Sun
10:30 A.M. - 4:30 P.M.

RICHMOND, VIRGINIA
Museum of the Confederacy
1201 East Clay Street
Richmond, VA 23219-1615
(804) 649-1861 Fax: (804) 644-7150
E-mail: info@moc.org
Location: The Museum is located in downtown
Richmond. From I-95 take exit 74C to Route 250
West (Broad Street). At 11th Street turn right and
go two blocks to Clay Street. Turn right on Clay.
The Museum and White House are on the corner of
12th and Clay Streets.
Highlights: Civil War history, White House of the
Confederacy, world's largest Confederate artifact
collection, Haversack Museum Shop, Eleanor S.
Brockenbrough Library, **Website:** www.moc.org/

General Information: The Museum of the
Confederacy, opened in 1896, was created to
collect military, political, and domestic artifacts
associated with the period of the Confederacy,
1861-1865. The Museum building, opened in
1976, is adjacent to the restored White House of
the Confederacy — Jefferson Davis' Civil War
residence. The Museum has the world's most
comprehensive collection of Confederate art,
artifacts, and documents. Several of these artifacts
relate to the Confederate Navy.
   They include a drive shaft (part) and anchor
from the CSS *Virginia* — originally the U.S. Navy
ship *Merrimac* — that fought in a no-decision
battle with the USS *Monitor.* Both the drive shaft
and anchor are outside on Museum property. Also
displayed are a model of the *Alabama,* naval china,
naval uniforms and accouterments, and naval flags.
Artifacts in the Museum's collections are
associated with several ships, including, but not
limited to, the CSS *Albemarle,* the CS Privateer
Jeff Davis, the CSS *Shenandoah,* and the CSS
Virginia.
   The Eleanor S. Brockenbrough Library has
several original documents relating to the
Confederate Navy. Among these are the logbooks
and private journals of the CSS *Shenandoah.*
   Admission: Entry fee. Open Mon/Sat,
10 A.M.-5 P.M., Sunday, Noon-5 P.M. Closed
Thanksgiving, Christmas, and New Year's Day.
Library is by appointment only: reserve at
extension 24.

RICHMOND, VIRGINIA
Science Museum of Virginia
2500 West Broad Street
Richmond, VA 23220-2054
1-800-659-1727 (804) 864-1400
E-mail: smvfeedback@smv.org
Location: From I-95 and I-64, take Exit 78 and
follow the Museum signs on the Boulevard to
Broad Street. Then left on Broad to 2500 West
Broad Street.
Highlights: The research submarine *Aluminaut,*
Website: www.smv.org/info/aluminautEX.htm
   General Information: The Science Museum of
Virginia, an agency of the Commonwealth of
Virginia, is headquartered in Richmond,
Virginia's historic Broad Street Railroad Station at
2500 West Broad St., Richmond, VA 23220.
We are dedicated to improving the science literacy
of all Virginians. The Museum contains a variety
of exhibits, shows, programs, films, classes,
outreach
   Activities and satellite museums. You'll also find
many other resources and resource links related to
science and science education.
   The new exhibit galleries contain our newest
exhibition, BioScapes, centered on the Unity and

Diversity of Life. The bioscape *Aluminaut* broke records in deep ocean dives. The sub designed by Reynolds Metals Company and made of—you know the answer—aluminum. She was operated by Reynolds Submarine Services Corp., based in Miami, Fla. until 1970. With 4 viewports, active and passive sonar, manipulators, side scan sonar, and 6000 lbs. of scientific payload, the submersible was outfitted for many types of oceanographic and salvage missions available to commercial activities and the U.S. Navy.

Admission: Entry fee. Open Monday-Saturday, 9:30 A.M.-5 P.M., Sun, 11:30 A.M. – 5 P.M. Please call 1-800-659-1727 for latest information

RICHMOND, VIRGINIA
Virginia Canals and Navigations Society, Inc.
35 Towana Road
Richmond, VA 23226
(804) 288-1334 E-mail: bill@vacanals.org
Location: The Society is based in Richmond, VA.
Highlights: *The Tiller* (newsletter), history of the waterways of old Virginia,
Website: http://vacanals.org/
General Information: Virginia Canals and Navigations Society, Inc., formed in 1977 to preserve and enhance Virginia's rich inland waterways heritage in all its fascinating aspects. History, exploration, archaeology, modeling, local lore and legend, restoration, preservation, park and trail development — these are some of the many areas of interest the society pursues. An index to the canals is located in the Appendix under **Canal Parks** in this guide to Maritime Museums of North America.
Admission: Check each site for information.

TRIANGLE, VIRGINIA
U.S. Marine Corps Museum
Marine Corps History Division
18900 Jefferson Davis Highway
Triangle, Virginia 22172-1938
1 (877) 635-1775 (703) 221-1581
E-mail: lin.ezell@usmc.mil
Location: The Marine Corps Museum is located on the first floor of the Marine Corps Historical Center, Building 58, just inside the 6th and M Street SE gate to the Washington Navy Yard. Limited parking.
Highlights: The Museum treats the visitor to a presentation of the Marines' role in American history from 1775 to the present. Gift shop,
Website: http://hqinet001.hqmc.usmc.mil/HD/
General Information: The U.S. Marine Corps Museum's exhibits include weapons, maps, photographs, equipment, and art. Featured are the two American Flags raised on Mt. Suribachi, Iwo

Jima in February 1945. A temporary exhibit commemorates the 50th Anniversary of the Korean War. Research facilities include collections of personal papers, art, and a library of over 30,000 volumes.
Activities: Self-guided tour. Researchers may study the art collection by appointment.
Admission: No entry fee. Open year-round except Tuesdays, Thanksgiving, Christmas, and New Year's Day. Open Monday, Wednesday-Saturday, 10 A.M.- 4 P.M., Sundays and holidays, 12 noon- 5 P.M., and Friday evenings (summer), 4 P.M.-8 P.M.

VIRGINIA BEACH, VIRGINIA
Cape Henry Lighthouse
583 Atlantic Avenue, P. O. Box 5064
Virginia Beach, VA 23459
(757) 422-9421 E-mail: clong@apva.org
Location: In Virginia Beach, From I-64 in Norfolk take Exit 282 for Route 13 North - Northampton Blvd. Then take the exit for Route 60 - Shore Drive and turn right. Or, if coming from the north on the Chesapeake Bay Bridge-Tunnel, take the first exit for Route 60 - Shore Drive and turn left. After crossing into Seashore/ First Landing State Park turn left into the west gate of Fort Story. Follow this road; it will take you right between the two lighthouses.
Highlights: Cape Henry Lighthouse,
Website: www.apva.org/capehenry/
General Information: The Cape Henry Lighthouse, founded in 1791, is the first commissioned public works building in the United States, built near the monument that marks the first landing of the Jamestown colonists. The facilities include the Lighthouse and Lynnhaven House.
Admission: Entry fee. Combination tickets for the Lighthouse and Lynnhaven House. Open: Nov. 1-March 15, 10 A.M. to 4 P.M.; March 16-Oct. 31, 10 A.M. - 5 P.M.; Closed Thanksgiving Day and Dec. 5 – Jan 4.

VIRGINIA BEACH, VIRGINIA
Old and New Lighthouses
Fort Story
583 Atlantic Avenue
Virginia Beach, VA 23459
(757) 422-9421
Location: From Norfolk, take Rte. 60 east eighteen miles to Fort Story. From the Oceanfront in Virginia Beach, take Pacific Ave (Route 60) north, or Atlantic Ave. – The two will merge. Near 82nd street the road will make a turn to the left. There is a traffic signal there. Follow the road to the right (Atlantic Ave.) and into the main gate of Fort Story. Follow this road it will take you right to the lighthouse.

Highlights: Lighthouses **Website:** www.apva.org
General Information: Old Lighthouse is within
the Fort Story army post, adjacent to the Cape
Henry Memorial. Built in 1791-92, the
Lighthouse was the first erected by the United
States.

New Lighthouse, erected in 1881 is also within
Fort Story. It has one of the most powerful lights in
the world. It sits 163 feet above sea level and is
visible for twenty miles.

Admission: Visitors' passes to Fort Story are
issued at the East Gate (at the north end of
Atlantic Avenue) or at the West Gate (on Rte. 60).
The Lighthouse is open 10 A.M. till 5 P.M. in the
summer and only until 4 P.M. in the winter.

VIRGINIA BEACH, VIRGINIA

Old Coast Guard Station
24th 2401 Atlantic Ave, P.O. Box 1035
Virginia Beach, VA 23451-3276
(757) 422-1587 Fax: (757) 491-8609
E-mail: director@oldcoastguardstation.com
Location: The Museum is located at 24th Street
and Atlantic Avenue in Virginia Beach, twelve
miles east of Norfolk.
Highlights: Ship models, shipwreck exhibit,
"War Years" (World War II exhibit), *The Keeper*
(newsletter), Museum Store,
Website: www.oldcoastguardstation.com
General Information: The Old Coast Guard
Station, founded in 1980 and opened in 1981, is
housed in a restored former U. S. Life-Saving and
Coast Guard Station (c. 1903). It is the only
existing station in Virginia—among a mere handful
on the entire Atlantic coast—now open to
the public, preserving the history of these life-
saving services. Visitors to the galleries are
given a rare insight into the early days of
shipwrecks and life-saving efforts. Visual
exhibits of many of these wrecks along the city's
shoreline tell tales of bravery and sometimes of
disaster.

An extensive collection of maritime
memorabilia is featured, as are changing displays.
Collections include ship models, photographs,
maritime artifacts, maritime art, audiovisual
programs, and uniforms. The upper gallery (added
in 1989) contains an exhibit on America's
involvement in World War II.

Activities: Guided tours, lectures, films, Home
of Tower Cam— a view of Virginia Beach
oceanfront and the boardwalk;
Admission: Entry fee. Memberships are
available. Open Tuesday-Saturday, 10 A.M.-
5 P.M., Sunday Noon-5 P.M.; open Mondays,
Memorial Day-October 1st. Closed Thanksgiving,
Christmas, New Year's Eve, and New Year's Day.

WILLIAMSBURG, VIRGINIA

Jamestown Settlement
P.O. Box 1607
Williamsburg, VA 23187-1607
Toll Free: 1-888-593-4682 (757) 253-4838
Fax: (757) 253-5299
Highlights: Re-creations of 17th-century ships,
Discovery, Godspeed, and *Susan Constant,*
Website: www.historyisfun.org/jamestown/jame
stown.cfm
General Information: Jamestown Settlement
tells the story of the founding of America's first
permanent English settlement and the Powhatan
Indians through film, dramatic exhibition
galleries, and outdoors living history.

Jamestown Settlement is located about a mile
from the original site of Jamestown, established
in 1607 — thirteen years before the Pilgrims
landed at Plymouth.

Outdoors, a pathway leads from re-creations
of a Powhatan Indian village and colonial fort
to the ships' pier, where full-size reproductions
of the three square-rigged sailing ships that
transported 104 English colonists to Virginia,
are docked. Visitors can board and explore all
three ships, including the largest, the 110-foot
Susan Constant, and listen to a costumed
historical interpreter talk about the 144-day
voyage from England and the navigational
techniques used by 17th-century mariners to sail
across the ocean.

Admission: Entry fee. Open daily 9 A.M.-
5 P.M., year-round. Closed Christmas and New
Year's Day. Allow approximately 2 hours for a
visit.

YORKTOWN, VIRGINIA

The Watermen's Museum
309 Water Street - P.O. Box 519
Yorktown, VA 23690-0519
(757) 887-2641 Gift Shop: (757) 888-2089
E-mail: info@watermens.org
Location: Exit the Colonial Parkway at the
Yorktown Victory Center Exit. Then turn left at
the Victory Center entrance but do not enter the
Victory Center. Just follow the road until it turns
into Water Street. The Waterman's Museum is on
your left. (100-150 yards).
Highlights: History of Chesapeake watermen, gift
shop, paintings, Chesapeake boats,
Website: www.watermens.org/
General Information: The Watermen's
Museum, founded in 1981, is located on the banks
of the York River in historic Yorktown, VA. The
museum interprets the environment of the Bay, the
economic impact of the seafood industry, and the
unique heritage of the Chesapeake's watermen."
Indoor and outdoor exhibits focus on the history of
the watermen of the Chesapeake Bay from the
Native Americans and colonists to the present.

Displays feature their boats, their tools and equipment, and information on their catches. On display outside are three boats unique to the Chesapeake Bay: a 100-year-old three-log-Poquoson canoe with centerboard; a shad boat, designed specifically for pulling in nets; and a skipjack, which has been modified as a cruiser.

Also on display outside is a 16-foot model of *The Betsy*, a twin masted sloop used by the British navy as a transport vessel and scuttled just downriver from our museum during the Battle of Yorktown (See National Geographic June 6, 1988). Inside we have a soft crab skiff and sixteen models of various sizes of other boats used in our area, including a skipjack, a deadrise, a pound boat, a shallop and others. The Museum also exhibits numerous paintings of boats.

With the exception of *The Betsy*, all the boats we display are related to the people who harvest fish, crabs, clams, oysters, and other seafood of the Chesapeake Bay — the only region of America where they are called "watermen."

Admission: Entry fee. Open April 1 through Thanksgiving, Tuesday-Saturday: 10 A.M. – 5 P.M., Sunday, 1 P.M. - 5 P.M. Thanksgiving through March, Saturday 10 A.M. - 5 P.M., Sunday, 1 P.M. - 5 P.M.

YORKTOWN, VIRGINIA
Yorktown Battlefield Visitor Center
Colonial National Historical Park
P. O. Box 210
Yorktown, VA 23690
(757) 898-2410 Fax: (757) 898-6346
Location: The Center is on Rte. 238, near the Colonial Parkway and US 17.
General Information: The Center's museum interprets the Battle of Yorktown with displays and reconstruction of a section of a gun deck, British frigate captain's cabin, original artifacts from the land battle, and the preceding naval engagement — the Battle of the Capes. A fourteen-minute film relates the events of the siege. Also exhibited are recovered cannons.
Admission: Entry fee. Open daily 9 A.M.-5 P.M. Extended summer hours and Ranger-guided programs.

YORKTOWN, VIRGINIA
Yorktown Victory Center
Rte. 238 and Colonial Parkway
P.O. Box 1607
Yorktown, VA 23187-1607
Toll-free 1-888-593-4682 (757) 253-4838
Fax: (757) 253-5299
Location: The Center is on old Rte. 238 in Yorktown; twelve miles from Williamsburg, and six miles from I-64, Exit 247.

Highlights: Website:
www.historyisfun.org/yorktown/yorktown.cfm
General Information: Yorktown Victory Center, a museum of the American Revolution, chronicles America's struggle for independence from the beginnings of colonial unrest to the boatbuilding. For those cruising the Intracoastal Waterway, a book loaner vehicle available also.
Activities: Lectures, year-round field trips, and special programs.
Admission: No entry fee. Memberships available. Open Monday-Friday, 9 A.M.-5 P.M.; Saturday, 10 A.M.-5 P.M.; Sunday, 1 P.M.-5 P.M. Closed Christmas and New Year's Day.

WASHINGTON

ABERDEEN, WASHINGTON
Grays Harbor Historical Seaport
712 Hagara Street, P. O. Box 2019
Aberdeen, WA 98520-2019
Toll Free: 1-800-200-5239 (360) 532-8611
Fax: (360) 533-9384
E-mail: ghhsa_admin@historicalseaport.org
Location: Aberdeen is almost directly west of Olympia on Grays Harbor, off Rte. 101.
Highlights: The *Lady Washington* (170-ton brig), *Capt. Matt Peasley* and *Hewitt R. Jackson* (eighteenth-century longboat reproductions), ropes course (ship's lines),
Website: www.ladywashington.org/
General Information: The Grays Harbor Historical Seaport Authority was founded in 1987 to construct a seaport, build tall ships, and develop a nautical museum. The seaport finished building its tall ship, the 112-foot brig *Lady Washington*, in spring 1989 to commemorate the centennial of Washington's statehood. The original *Lady Washington* was named for Martha Washington even before she became first lady. Today she is equipped to carry passengers and is the first replica of a U.S. tall ship ever built. Summer sailing is done in Washington State, winter sailing in California, and is available to the general public and school groups.

Over 200 years ago the original *Lady Washington* and the *Columbia* were sailed by Captain Robert Gray in his West Coast explorations, during which both Grays Harbor and the Columbia River were discovered. Gray was also the first U.S. sea captain to sail around the world.)   Nautical exhibits, a museum, and other training programs are found at the Seaport, including, on the museum property, a sail-training set of masts, identical to those on the *Lady Washington*, which can, if necessary, is used to replace those on the *Lady Washington*.

169

Admission: Entry fee. Ship available year-round in various ports of call. Information line is: 800-200-5239

ANACORTES, WASHINGTON
W. T. PRESTON (Sternwheeler)
Anacortes History Museum
U.S. Army Corps of Engineers Snagboat
Dry-berthed at 7th and R Avenue
Anacortes, WA 98221
(360) 293-1915   Fax: (360) 293-1929
E-mail: coa.museum@cityofanacortes.org
Location: Anacortes is seventy-two miles north of Seattle, is reached via I-5. Exit at Mount Vernon on Rte. 20, and then travel sixteen miles to Anacortes adjacent to the Depot Arts Center.
Highlights: The *W. T. PRESTON* (sternwheeler),
Website:http://museum.cityofanacortes.org/Infor
mation/index.asp
General Information: The *W.T. PRESTON* is a museum of Puget Sound snagboat history. She was the last working sternwheeler on the Sound. Powered by steam, she was used to clear and maintain the navigable waterways from the Canadian border to Olympia, Washington.
The *PRESTON* began life in 1914, as the *Swinomish*. She was renamed the *W.T. PRESTON* in 1929. Ten years later she received a steel hull, new deckhouse, boilers and other gear, but retained the original sternwheel, main engines and steam hoisting gear from 1914. The boat is 163-feet long and 35-feet wide. She was retired in 1981.
Admission: Entry fee. Open June – September, 11 A.M. - 5 P.M. daily

BAINBRIDGE ISLAND, WASHINGTON
Bainbridge Island Historical Museum
215 Ericksen Avenue NE
Bainbridge Island, WA 98110-1855
(206) 842-2773   Fax: (206) 842-0914
E-mail: on website
Location: Bainbridge Island is directly west from downtown Seattle seven miles across Puget Sound—35 minutes by ferry. The Museum is located in Strawberry Hill Park, about one and one-half miles west of Rte. 305 on High School Road.
Highlights: Hubbard Collection (construction photos; marine railway), Weld Collection (minesweeper construction), Lincoln Collection (photos), films, library,
Website: www.bainbridgehistory.org/
General Information: The Bainbridge Island Historical Museum was founded in 1974 to preserve island history. The Museum maintains and displays passenger steamboat artifacts and photos, music and recordings of steamer captains, and ships whistles and horns from early Puget

Sound Passenger vessel fleets, small boats, and shipbuilding. Shipbuilding includes tall ships and schooners built in international export lumber mill towns at Port Madison (1854-1893) and Port Blakely (1863-1922).
The Hall Brothers, after migrating to Washington from Cohasset, MA, built over eighty-eight sailing ships at Port Blakely (1880-1903) and operated the region's largest marine railway (4000 ton) in Eagle Harbor, commencing in 1903. Winslow Marine Shipyard and Railway continued that enterprise, including construction of twenty-two minesweepers during World War II. The Museum offers periodic special programs on these and other maritime themes unique to the island. The library and collections are open regularly and by appointment.
Admission: By donation. Open: Winter hours, Tuesday, Thursday, and Sunday, 1 P.M. - 4 P.M.; Summer hours, (May-September), Tuesday, Thursday, Saturday and Sunday, 1 P.M. - 4 P.M.

BELLINGHAM, WASHINGTON
Whatcom Museum of History and Art
121 Prospect Street
Bellingham, WA 98225
(360) 770-8930 E-mail: museuminfo@cob.org
Location: Bellingham is eighty-seven miles north of Seattle off I-5. The Museum is located in the center of town at 121 Prospect Street.
Highlights: H. C. Hanson naval architectural collection, engine from steam tug *Charlotte*,
Website: www.whatcommuseum.org
General Information: The collection contains thousands of blueprints and line drawings, seventeen half-models and other artifacts, documents, and magazines relating to the shipbuilding industry and the architect's career. Temporary exhibits on regional maritime history are frequently scheduled.
Admission: No entry fee. Open Tuesday – Sunday, Noon – 5 p.m. Please call archivist for appointment to view collections.

BLAINE, WASHINGTON
Semiahmoo Park Museum
Whatcom County Park and Recreation Board
9261 Semiahmoo Drive
Blaine, WA 98230
County parks, (360) 733-2900
Blaine Visitor Center, (360) 332-4544.
Location: From Blaine, travel I-5 and exit at Rte. 270. Travel west on Lynden-Birch Road, then turn right on Harborview, left on Lincoln Road, which becomes Semiahmoo Parkway, and continue for three and one-half miles. The park entrance is on Semiahmoo Parkway, at the foot of Semiahmoo Spit on the west side of Drayton Harbor.

Highlights: Bristol Bay sailboat, canning memorabilia, museum gift shop **Web Site:** www.co.whatcom.wa.us/parks/semiahmoo/semia hmoo.jsp

General Information: The Semiahmoo Park Museum preserves and relates the history of salmon fishing and canning days, local history, and natural history. Within the park is a collection of three old cannery bunkhouses. One building is a small museum containing a Bristol Bay sailboat and other fishing and canning displays.

Content focuses on the Alaska Packers Association cannery once at Semiahmoo. During the summer, the historic passenger ferry Plover runs from Blaine to Semiahmoo.

Admission: No entry fee. Open March-Labor Day, Wednesday-Sunday, 1 P.M.-5 P.M. Winter hours: Wednesday-Sunday 1 P.M.-4 P.M. Closed November-February.

BREMERTON, WASHINGTON
Naval Memorial Museum of the Pacific
(Bremerton Naval Museum)
251 First Street
Bremerton, WA 98337-5612
(360) 479-7447 FAX: 360/627-2273
E-mail: Bremnavmuseum@aol.com
Location: Bremerton is directly west across Puget Sound from Seattle. The Museum is on Washington Street one block from the ferry terminal.
Highlights: "Story of Attack" (a display by the Pearl Harbor Survivors Association), artifacts of the USS *Washington* (display by CV6 *Enterprise* Association), mock-up of ship's bridge (a hands-on area), gift shop, **Web Site:** www.museumsusa.org/museums/info/1157719
General Information: The Bremerton Naval Museum was established in 1954 for the purpose of depicting and preserving the history of the United States Navy. The Museum includes photos and artifacts regarding the history of the Puget Sound Naval Shipyard, who's primary mission is to repair and overhaul ships and submarines of the United States Fleet. Maritime history displays include ship models, early steam engines, naval weapons, naval history, articles, and photos pertaining to history of Puget Sound Naval Shipyard.
Admission: No entry fee, but donations accepted. Open Monday-Saturday, 10 A.M.-4 P.M., Sunday, 1 P.M.-4 P.M., year-round. Closed Mondays Labor Day through Mem. Day.

BREMERTON, WASHINGTON
USS *Turner Joy*/Bremerton Historic Ships
300 Washington Beach Avenue #8
Bremerton, WA 98337-5668

(360) 792-2457 Fax: (360) 377-1020
E-mail: dd951@sinclair.net
Location: The museum is on the Bremerton waterfront.
Highlights: The USS *Turner Joy* (DD 951) (destroyer), gift shop,
Website: www.ussturnerjoy.org/
General Information: An impressive Bremerton downtown revitalization program on the waterfront is the site of a developing commemorative project including a city boardwalk and marina where the USS *Turner Joy*, a 418-foot-long 1957 Forrest Sherman Class destroyer, is located, serving as a permanent floating memorial.

She honors the many servicemen and women of our peacetime and wartime Navy, and the countless civilians who help build and maintain our naval ships. The destroyer is located near the improved ferry terminal, the new Port of Bremerton marina and recreational pier, and the Puget Sound Naval Shipyard. The historic combat ship has living history interpretive exhibits, including active video and media presentations about the ship and its heritage.

A host dock for other significant visiting ships is available along with a gift shop featuring ship and naval memorabilia.
Activities: The *Turner Joy* is open for tours.
Admission: Entry fee. Open daily, May 15-October 1. Call for hours open.

EDMONDS, WASHINGTON
Edmonds Historical Museum
118 Fifth Avenue North, P. O. Box 52
Edmonds, WA 98020
(425) 774-0900 E-mail: jonisein@yahoo.com
Location: Edmonds is just eighteen miles north of Seattle on I-5. Exit west on SR-104 into Edmonds to 5th Avenue North in the downtown area and one block north of the fountain and directly across the street from the Edmonds City Hall.
Highlights: Ship models, maritime library for in-house research only (200 volumes), gift shop
Website: www.historicedmonds.org/
General Information: Edmonds Historical Museum, formally opened in 1973, was established by the Edmonds-South Snohomish County Historical Society to perpetuate the memory and spirit of our pioneers; to identify and preserve historical documents, relics, and incidents; and to encourage historical research, today and tomorrow.

The ground floor of the Museum houses the marine room. An extensive display of photographs of early steam passenger vessels and later-day auto ferryboats depicts Edmonds link with the sea.

Displayed, too, are numerous ship models,

marine paintings, navigating instruments, and other marine artifacts. A large diorama of Edmond's waterfront, circa 1910, with a working model of a shingle mill, is an important attraction for visitors. There is also a permanent display of the history of the U.S. Coast and Geodetic Survey and its successor, the National Oceanic and Atmospheric Administration (NOAA), which have played an important role in charting this area, following the explorations of Captain George Vancouver in 1792 and Lieutenant Charles Wilkes in 1841.

Admission: No entry fee but donations suggested. Open Wednesday - Sunday, 1 P.M.-4 P.M., year-round.

GIG HARBOR, WASHINGTON

Gig Harbor Peninsula Historical Society & Museum
4218 Harborview Drive, P.O. Box 744
Gig Harbor, WA 98332
(253) 858-6722 Fax: (253) 853-4211
E-mail: vicki@gigharbormuseum.org
Location: The Museum is on Harborview Drive. From Route 16, Exit on Burnham Dr., or Pioneer/City Center, or Olympic Dr. Exits. From the Pioneer/City Center Exit, proceed NE along Harborview. The museum entrance will be on your left. From the Olympic Drive Exit, proceed NE along Soundview. Soundview becomes Harborview. The Museum entrance will be on your left.
Highlights: Maritime history, library
Website: www.gigharbormuseum.org/
General Information: The Gig harbor Peninsula Historical Society & Museum grew out of personal collections, which remain an important part of our community's effort to preserve our history. Here you can navigate through Gig Harbor's maritime heritage, our logging past, and trace the community family tree to the old country. Entertain yourself with stories of rooster races and round rock contests.

"Collectors and Their Collections," focuses on local collectors and the historical treasures they have gathered—five collectors and their passions are the focuses of the exhibit: Ken Jones and his collection of pharmaceutical bottles, Martin Stenbak and his collection of gas engines; Joe Hoots and his collection of woodworking tools; and Roberta Keyes and her collection of cameras.

Steamboat *Victor* on display at museum: Raft Island artist Bob Bryant's painting, The *Victor*, is on display at the Gig Harbor Peninsula Historical Society and Museum (GHPHS). Bryant's artwork was recently exhibited at the 21st International Maritime Exhibition at Mystic Seaport. The exhibit showcased the best contemporary maritime paintings from around the world.

The steamboat *Victor* was designed by Emmett Hunt and built by Gig Harbor's Hunt brothers in 1892. The Hunt brothers then operated her in the early 1900s. Bryant based his painting on a photograph in the GHPHS archives. He used computer scanning and software to enhance the photograph and bring out details blurred in the original image. The realistic details in Bob's work provides a glimpse into the daily lives of the people of the Peninsula.

The ship was 59 feet long and had a ladies' cabin, smoking room, pilot house and closets. The *Victor* traveled between Gig Harbor, Quartermaster Harbor on Vashon Island, and Tacoma. For more information, contact the museum at (253) 858-6722.

Admission: Entry fee but donations encouraged. Open Tuesday-Sat 10 A.M.-4 P.M.

ILWACO, WASHINGTON

Columbia Pacific Heritage Museum
115 SE Lake Street, P.O. Box 153
Ilwaco, WA 98624-0153
(360) 642-3446 Fax: (360) 642-4615
E-mail: ihm@ilwacoheritagemuseum.org
Location: Ilwaco is on the north side of the Columbia River near its entrance, adjacent to Cape Disappointment and opposite Astoria, Oregon across the Columbia River. The Museum is one block south of US 101 in the center of town, across from the U.S. Post Office.
Highlights: General history and natural history of the Columbia-Pacific region, including several marine and maritime exhibits, such as shipwrecks, lifesaving, and the estuary of the Columbia River.
Website: www.ilwaco-heritagemuseum.org/
General Information: The Columbia Pacific Heritage Museum exhibits include displays that highlight the fishing, logging, and cranberry industries and Native American and pioneer artifacts. Also featured are photos of shipwrecks that occurred off Cape Disappointment—the cape named for other men's failures. Robert Gray sailed the *Columbia Rediviva* into the river (now the Columbia River) in 1792.

Near the Heritage Museum are the Port of Ilwaco and Fort Canby State Park, where one may find the Lewis and Clark Interpretive Center, in addition to Cape Disappointment and North Head Lighthouses. Cape Disappointment is also the home of the National Motor Lifeboat School, where all U.S. Coast Guard coxswains come for surf and rescue training on the dangerous Columbia River bar. The library, the city park and tennis courts, shopping, and restaurants — all lie within easy walking distance of the Museum.
Admission: Entry fee. Open Monday-Saturday, 10 A.M.-4 P.M., Sunday, 1P.M.- 5 P.M.

172

KEYPORT, WASHINGTON
Naval Undersea Museum
1 Garnett Way
Keyport, WA 98345-7610
(360) 396-4148   Foundation: (360) 697-1129
Store: (360) 692-1537
Fax: (360) 396-7944
E-mail: underseainfo@kpt.nuwc.navy.mil
Mail address:
Naval Undersea Museum
Navy Region Northwest
1103 Hunley Road
Silverdale, WA 98315-1103
Location: Keyport is in Kitsap County. From
Seattle, visitors can take the Bainbridge Island,
Bremerton, or Kingston ferries to the Kitsap
Peninsula. In Kitsap County, take Hwy 3 to Rte.
308 and follow the signs to Keyport and the Naval
Undersea Museum. From Southworth Ferry of
Pierce County, take Rte. 16 to Rte. 3 toward Hood
Canal. Take Keyport exit; follow signs to the
Museum.
Highlights: Beautiful 68,000-square-foot museum
facility, The *Deep Quest* and *Trieste II* (deep
submergence vehicles), museum store, 6,000
volume research library, Newsletter: *Undersea
Quarterly*,
Website: www.
history.navy.mil/museums/keyport/index1.htm
General Information: The Naval Undersea
Museum is an official U.S. Navy Museum opened
in 1991. It combines naval history, undersea
technology, and marine science to create an
exciting and educational experience for visitors.
The modern building offers visitors over 20,000-
square feet of exhibits and is the largest collection
of naval undersea artifacts, technology, and
science in the United States.Major exhibits
interpret the Ocean Environment, Torpedo
Technology, Mine Warfare Technology, Navy
Diving and Salvage, and U.S. Submarines in
WWII.
   Significant artifacts include major U.S.
torpedoes dating from early Whitehead and
Howell torpedoes to the modern Mk 48 and 50
weapons. Submarine exhibits include the torpedo
tubes from USS *Tecumseh* (SSBN 628), a
Submarine Rescue chamber, and a simulation of
the control room of USS *Greenling* (SSN 614),
which incorporates major equipment from the
submarine. Mine warfare exhibits include a
Confederate mine from the Civil War and mines
used in each major American conflict. The
exhibits incorporate numerous video, audio, and
hands-on, interactive displays to encourage
visitors to learn about life and activities in the
undersea.
   The Museum has an extensive reference and

technical library directed toward undersea
history, science, and operations. It also has a
complete collection of WWII submarine war
patrol reports and over 115 histories from the U.S.
Naval Institute's oral history collection.
Exterior Exhibits: The deep submergence
vessels *Trieste II* and *Deep Quest* are on display
outside the Museum; as is the 55-ton sail from the
nuclear fast attack submarine USS *Sturgeon* (SSN
637).
Admission: Free admission and parking. The
Museum is fully accessible to the disabled.
Open daily, June-September, 10 A.M.-4 P.M.;
open daily except Tuesdays, October-May,
10 A.M.- 4 P.M. Closed on Thanksgiving,
Christmas, New Year's Day, and Easter We are
open on all other federal holidays

MUKILTEO, WASHINGTON
Light Station Mukilteo 1906
Mukilteo Historical Society
608 Front Street
Mukilteo, WA 98275
(425) 513-9602
E-mail: info@mukilteohistorical.org
Location: The lighthouse is on the Mukilteo
waterfront just south of the ferry landing.
Highlights: Lighthouse and museum, gift shop,
Website:www.mukilteohistorical.org/index.html
General Information: Light Station Mukilteo,
established in 1906, was given to the City of
Mukilteo and the Mukilteo Historical Society's
volunteers are the devoted caretakers. The
Mukilteo Historical Society proposes to turn them
into bed and breakfasts if and when the Coast
Guard relinquishes ownership. In the main (but
small) lighthouse building — the light tower
is only 30 feet tall — is the display area where
docents tell the lighthouse history. In the
meantime, an adjacent building acts as gift shop
and bookstore.
Admission: No entry fee Open: April through
September Noon until 5:00 P.M. Weddings
invited.

NEAH BAY, WASHINGTON
Makah Museum
P.O. Box 160
Neah Bay, WA 98357
(360) 645-2711 Fax: (360) 645-2656
E-mail: makahmuseum@centurytel.net
Location: Neah Bay is approximately seventy
miles west of Port Angeles at the furthermost
northwest tip of the State of Washington — a
slow road but worth the trip.
Highlights: Makah Indian whaling and sealing
canoes (replicas), Makah longhouse, sea life
dioramas, museum shop,

173

Website: www.makah.com/mcrchome.htm
General Information: The Makah Museum features full-scale replicas of whaling, sealing, and fishing canoes, complete with harpoons, paddles, bailers, and floats. A unique aspect of these replicas is that it is possible for the Museum visitor to have a "hands-on" experience with the canoes and gear — touching is definitely allowed. Also displayed are whaling, sealing, and fishing implements.

Along with the canoes — hand-hewn from single cedar trees — sea life dioramas (complete with natural sound) are exhibited and a full-size Indian longhouse, where a conversation is heard in the Makah language. Dried fish hang from the rafters, and sealskins, baskets of wool, woven mats, and basketry materials hang from the walls and cover the floors and sitting benches.

The Museum's definitive archaeological collection from Ozette provides historical information on a Makah Indian village that was partially buried by a mudslide some 500 years ago. The preserved artifacts include items from everyday life, such as baskets, combs, and beautifully carved bentwood storage boxes. Woodworking technology, weaving, and clothing are also featured, as are artifacts associated with games and leisure.

Activities. A Museum shop offers baskets, carvings, beaded necklaces and earrings, as well as a complete selection of books on Makah and other Northwest Indian cultures.

Admission: Entry fee. Open daily, Memorial Day through September 15th, and closed Monday and Tuesday from September 16th through Memorial Day. Call (360) 645-2711 for tour information.

PASCO, WASHINGTON
Ice Harbor-Lower Monumental Project
2339 Ice Harbor Drive
Burbank, WA 99323
(509) 547-7781 Fax: (509) 543-3201
Public Affairs Office, Corps of Engineers
Walla District Building 602, City-County Airport
Pasco, WA 99362
Location: From Burbank, go five miles east on Rte. 124, then three miles north on Ice Harbor Dam Road. The Project is on Lake Sacajawea and the Snake River.
Highlights: Navigation lock, visitor center
General Information: Primary focus: Fish viewing and navigation on the Snake River at the Ice Harbor Lock and Dam.
Admission: No entry fee. Visitor center is open daily, from 9 A.M.-5 P.M., April-October.

PORT TOWNSEND, WASHINGTON
Museum of the Jefferson County Historical Society
540 Water Street
Port Townsend, WA 98368
(360) 385-1003 E-mail: marsha@jchswa.org
Location: The Museum is located at the corners of Water and Madison Streets in the Historic City Hall on the waterfront of Port Townsend.
Highlights: Shipwreck information, Maritime Heritage Exhibit, archives, maritime photographs,
Website: www.jchsmuseum.org
General Information: The Museum of the Jefferson County Historical Society honors the people of Jefferson County through its collection of artifacts, archives, family history, and photographs. For explorers and mariners, there is information on ships, navigation, customs, immigration, and "shanghaiing," (to kidnap a man for compulsory service aboard a ship). And ask about how Victor Smith "stole" the Customs Office and whisked it off to Port Angeles.

Other collections exhibit baskets, tools, weaving, carving and includes information on land claims, logging, and fishing. And on display is the detritus (accumulated material; debris) of shipwrecks found in the waters around Port Townsend, including a huge barnacle-covered rudder.

Admission: Entry fee. Open Monday-Saturday, 11 A.M.-4 P.M.; Sundays, 1 P.M.-4 P.M., year-round.

RAYMOND, WASHINGTON
Willapa Seaport Museum
310 Alder Street
Raymond, WA 98577-2434
(360) 942-4149 (360) 942-2855
E-mail: angus35@willapaba.org
Location: The museum is located next to the city dock in downtown Raymond; two blocks off highway 101, at the west end of 3rd Street. There, signage is plentiful.
Highlights: Maritime artifacts of local, regional, and North American maritime history, ship models, library and archive, *Krestine* (ketch),
Website:www.visit.willapabay.org/pages/todo/museum_seaport.html
General Information: The Willapa Seaport Museum, founded in 1995, is in a 6000 square feet building on two levels with colorful and dramatic displays on all aspects of the sea and local history.

The museum contains the personal collection of Captain Pete Darrah with donations of artifacts from local residents. The collections feature all aspects of local and North American maritime history from Marine Corp, Revenue Cutter Service, Coast Artillery Corps, and U.S. Life

Saving Service items. Also included is information relating to shipbuilding, logging, First Peoples, shipwrecks, slavery, and pirates.

See maritime art, ship models, nautical paraphernalia and minutia to satisfy the most exacting historian. View uniforms, pirate treasure, sea service weapons and life saving equipment, tall ship wheels, binnacles, capstans, bells, whistles, and rigging.

Children are delighted with various hands on displays, and are quick to point out pirates, signal light, and various rats, (no, not real!), and other varmints strategically hidden just for them.

Activities: Willapa Seaport Museum is a family museum that facilitates tours, meetings, luncheons, and dinners for groups of fifty or less. A library and archive are maintained and available to the public. Special tours are always available for one to fifty. Raymond is also homeport for the *Krestine*, a 100-year-old 100-foot Baltic topsail gaff headed rigged ketch available for viewing through the Museum.

Admission: Entry by donation. Open Wednesday to Saturday, noon to 4 P.M. year round, or anytime by special arrangement. Call (360) 942-4149 or (360) 942-2855 for info

SAN JUAN ISLAND, WASHINGTON
Whale Museum
62 First Street North   P. O. Box 945
Friday Harbor, WA 98250-0945
(360) 378-4710 (800) 946-7227
Fax: (360) 378-5790
E-mail: storelstaff@whalemuseum.org
Location: Follow I-5 north sixty-six miles from Seattle to Burlington. Exit onto SR-20, heading west fifteen miles to Anacortes, where ferries leave for San Juan Island and Friday Harbor.
Highlights: Whale models, library,
Website: www.whalemuseum.com
General Information: The Whale Museum, founded in 1978, occupies one of the islands oldest buildings. Museum exhibits depict the biology, behavior, and sounds of marine mammals. Included are a comparative skeletal display of a human, an otter, and a dolphin; complete with skeletons of a baby gray whale and an adult orca (killer) whale. Also included are exhibits of baleen and related ethnological artifacts; killer, humpback, and sperm whale models. A new exhibit is based on our Sea Sound underwater acoustical study, including live video and audio of local whales.
Activities: Guided tours; lectures, films; gallery talks; workshops.
Admission: Entry fee. Memberships are available. Open daily, 10 A.M.- 5 P.M.; Call for Winter hours. Closed Thanksgiving , Christmas, and New Year's Day.

SEATTLE, WASHINGTON
Burke Museum
University of Washington
17th Avenue N.E. and N.E. 45th Street
P.O. Box 353010
Seattle, WA 98195-3010
 (206) 543-5590 Fax: (206) 685-3039
E-mail: theburke@uw.edu
Location: The Museum is on the campus of the University of Washington in the Thomas Burke Memorial Washington State Museum.
Highlights: Three rare nineteenth-century Salish canoes, racing canoe, model canoes (twenty), museum store, and cafe,
Website: www.washington.edu/burkemuseum/
General Information: The Burke Museum concentrates on regional natural history and artifacts of the Northwest Coast Indians. A long-term exhibit — Canoes of the Northwest Coast — opened in 1992. Eight full-size canoes from the Museum's collection are on view, ranging from a massive thirty-seven-foot Kwakwaka'wakw (Kwakiut) seagoing canoe to a slender twenty-six-foot racing canoe as well as model canoes, paddles, bailers, canoe-making tools, and historic photos and drawings of canoes on the Northwest coast.

The canoe represents Native life at its fullest: the economic necessities of transportation, hunting, fishing, and whaling; ceremonial uses, including burial; and recreation, which persists in the sport of canoe racing. Despite the advent of motor-driven boats during the late 1800s, canoes retain a deep-rooted place in the lives of many Native people.

Engaging exhibits, public programs, and publications educate and inspire the diverse and multicultural community, which the Museum serves. Use "touch-screen" computer to explore a superb collection of historic Native American materials, including canoes, kayaks, and fishing equipment.

Admission: No entry fee. Open daily, 10 A.M. - 5 P.M. On the FIRST Thursday of each month, the museum is open 10 A.M. – 8 P.M. Closed: January 1, July 4, Thanksgiving Day, December 25.

SEATTLE, WASHINGTON
The Center for Wooden Boats
1010 Valley Street
Seattle, WA 98109-4468
(206) 382-2628 Fax: 206-382-2699
E-mail: cwb@cwb.org
Location: The Center is on the north side of downtown Seattle at the south end of Lake Union on Valley Street (adjacent to the South Lake

Highlights: Traditional wooden boats for rent, traditional boat-building instruction, *Shavings* Union Park. (newsletter),
Website: www.cwb.org
   General Information: The Center for Wooden Boats, founded in 1978, is a small watercraft museum that features wooden-boatbuilding and maritime skills in its preservation center, and it is Seattle's most educational waterfront park. The Center offers a unique chance to experience the dimensions of an earlier time or the chance to put one's hands to the oars of an eye-sweet pulling boat or the tiller of a traditional wooden catboat (a sailboat having a single mast far forward and usually a centerboard).
   A living museum, its traditional wooden boats are all unique. A new waterfront park has been created with a turn-back-the-clock pavilion on Lake Union.
   Activities: Rowboats, sailboats, classes in traditional wooden- boat construction and other heritage skills workshops. FREE classic boat rides every Sunday 2:00 - 3:00 p.m.
   Admission: No entry fee. Memberships are available. Open Daily Boathouse 10 A.M. – 8 P.M. Boathouse 11 A.M. –8 P.M. Livery (Boat Rental) Noon – 6 P.M.. (Full livery - last boat out by 4:45, back by 5:45) Livery (Boat Rental) Noon – 8 P.M. (Full livery - last boat out by 6:45, back by 7:45)

SEATTLE, WASHINGTON
Coast Guard Museum/Northwest
1519 Alaskan Way South, Pier 36 ISC Seattle
Seattle, WA 98134   (206) 217-6993
Location: The Museum is located next to the U.S. Coast Guard Station on Pier 36 at Seattle's waterfront near the downtown area.
Highlights: Ship models, lighthouse and buoy lenses, photographs (15,000),
Website:www.rexmwess.com/cgpatchs/cogardmu seum.html
   General Information: The Coast Guard Museum/Northwest, founded in 1976, exhibits ship models, lighthouse and buoy lenses, uniforms (old and new), and a number of nautical artifacts.
Note: Located next to the Museum is the Puget Sound Vessel Traffic Center on the 4th floor of the main building, open to visitors daily: 8 to 4.
   Activities: Pier 36 is the homeport for the 400-foot Polar Class and 420-foot Healy Class Icebreakers and two of the 378-foot-high-endurance cutters.
   Admission: No entry fee. Memberships are available. Open Monday, Wednesday, and Friday, 9 A.M.- 3 P.M.

SEATTLE, WASHINGTON
Hiram M. Chittenden Locks
3015 N.W. 54th Street
Seattle, WA 98107
(206) 783-7059
E-mail: craig.m.lykins@usace.army.mil
Location: From south of Seattle: Take I-5 north to exit 169. Take 50th Street to the west. Follow signs carefully to the locks. From north of Seattle: Take I-5 to exit 172. Go west on 85th Street to 24th NW Street. Turn south to NW Market Street. Turn west to the locks. From downtown Seattle: Take Denny Way west to its end. Follow curve to right until it becomes Elliott. Follow Elliott north; it changes into 15th Street. Follow 15th Street north to NW Market Street. Turn west and follow signs to the locks.
Highlights: Hiram M. Chittenden Locks, fish ladder and viewing windows, fish viewing area, Carl S. English Botanical Garden, Corps of Engineers Regional Visitor Center,
Website: www.nws.usace.army.mil/
   General Information: The visitor center displays the history and operation of the Lake Washington Ship Canal and Hiram M. Chittenden Locks, the role of the U.S. Army Corps of Engineers in the Pacific Northwest, and the fish that pass through the fish ladder. The eight-mile-long canal winds through the Seattle communities of Ballard, Fremont, Wallingford, and Montlake and University districts. It provides an important link between the salt water of Shilshole Bay and Puget Sound with the fresh water of Salmon Bay, Lake Union, and Lake Washington.
   July through November is the best time to view adult salmon in the Fish Ladder and Viewing Windows. The seven-acre Carl S. English, Jr. Botanical Garden offers an extensive and colorful selection of trees, shrubs, and herbaceous plants that have come from many lands. Free tours are conducted daily during summer operation hours, and on weekends the rest of the year.
   Admission: No entry fee. Grounds open daily, 7 A.M.-9 P.M., year-round. Winter hours (October 1 through April 30) of operation are from 10 A.M. to 4 P.M., closed on Tuesdays and Wednesdays. Summer hours (daily, May 1 through September 30) are from 10 A.M. to 6 P.M. Free guided tours are provided from March 1 through November 30.

SEATTLE, WASHINGTON
Museum of History and Industry (MOHAI)
2700 24th Avenue East
Seattle, WA 98112-2099
(206) 324-1126 Fax: (206) 324-1346
E-mail: information@seattlehistory.org

Location: MOHAI is located across the canal from the Husky Stadium (University of Washington), just east of Montlake Boulevard. From Rte. 520 westbound, take the Lake Washington Boulevard exit. Eastbound, take the Montlake Boulevard exit.

Highlights: Maritime history of Pacific Northwest, McCurdy Maritime Collection, *SeaChest Journal* (quarterly), ship models, library,

Website: www.seattlehistory.org

General Information: The Museum of History and Industry (MOHAI) in Seattle houses the Puget Sound Maritime Historical Society's collection in addition to its own. Displays and changing exhibits are arranged jointly with the Society. A 2,500-volume research collection is available by appointment. Exhibits are presented in the context of history of the region and often consist of photographs, artifacts, and ship models.

SEATTLE, WASHINGTON
Nordic Heritage Museum
3014 Northwest 67th Street
Seattle, WA 98117-6215
(206) 789-5707 Fax: (206) 789-3271
E-mail: nordic@nordicmuseum.org*Location:*
The Museum is located in a three-story 1907 elementary school building in Seattle's Ballard neighborhood. Just a ten-minute drive north from downtown Seattle. The entrance to the Museum parking lot is located on NW 68th St.

Highlights: Authentic fishing gear, including two dories, fishing/logging history of the Northwest, reference library, gift shop, *Nordic News* (newsletter),

Website: www.nordicmuseum.org

General Information: The Nordic Heritage Museum, the Pacific Northwest's largest ethnic museum, opened in 1980, recognizes the Nordic countries of Denmark, Finland, Iceland, Norway, and Sweden and focuses on Scandinavian cultural contributions to life in the Pacific Northwest from the eighteenth century to the present.

On the Museum's main level are two large galleries focusing on the fishing and logging industries that attracted many of the Scandinavians. Displays trace immigrants' journeys from Europe to America, and exhibits include handicrafts, textiles, personal effects, and changing displays form Scandinavia.

Admission: Entry fee. Open Tuesday-Saturday, 10 A.M.-4 P.M.; Sunday, Noon-4 P.M. Closed on Mondays, Thanksgiving Day, Christmas Eve Day, Christmas Day and New Year's Day

SEATTLE, WASHINGTON
Northwest Seaport
Maritime Heritage Center
1002 Valley Street
Seattle, WA 98109-4468
(206) 447-9800 Fax: (206) 447-0598
E-mail: info@nwseaport.org

Location: The Seaport is on the south end of Lake Union on Valley Street (adjacent to Center for the Wooden Boat).

Highlights: Three historic boardable vessels,

Website: www.nwseaport.org/

General Information: Northwest Seaport was founded in 1964 and owns three Northwest vessels:

1) The *Wawona*, built in 1897, launched at the yard of Hans Ditlev Bendixsen at Fairhaven (Humboldt Bay), California, was the largest three-masted sailing schooner built in North America. Today she is the only survivor of the once immense commercial sailing fleet in the Pacific Northwest. Carrying lumber between West Coast ports for Dolbeer and Carson Company, the *Wawona*, like other coastal schooners, had a reputation for speedy runs down the coast with cargo and a quick return, sailing without ballast.

2) The tugboat *Arthur Foss*, built in 1889 in Portland, Oregon, as the *Wallowa* for the Oregon Railway and Navigation Company. Originally equipped with a steam engine, she towed sailing ships across the Columbia Bar. Also, star of 1933 MGM movie Tugboat Annie; last US flagged vessel to leave Wake Island before Japanese takeover during WWII.

3) The lightship *Swiftsure* was built in Camden, New Jersey, in 1904 for the Lighthouse Service. She sailed around the Horn to her first station at Blunts Reef in California, thus beginning fifty-six years of lightship duty. She joined Northwest Seaport's fleet in 1970.

Admission: Entry fee by donation. Open daily, 10 A.M.-4 P.M., year-round.

SEATTLE, WASHINGTON
Puget Sound Maritime Historical Society
901 Fairview Avenue North, C-160
P.O. Box 9731
Seattle, WA 98109-9731
(206) 324-1685
E-mail: admin@pugetmaritime.org

Location: South end of Lake Union at Chandlers' Cove

Highlights: History of Pacific Northwest maritime, ship models, library, *Sea Chest Journal* (quarterly),

Website: www.pugetmaritime.org/

General Information: The Society collects, preserves, and displays objects, relics, and data of maritime interest, with special emphasis on the history of Pacific Northwest maritime activities through Museum displays and historical publications.

Also included is information on commercial fishing, tugboats, shipwrecks, sailing ships, and even the construction of the battleship *Nebraska*. The Society maintains a research library at the Museum of History and Industry with over 7000 books and 60,000 photographs.

Activities: Monthly general membership meeting with programs of maritime historical interest. Library:
c/o Museum of History and Industry,
2700 24th Avenue East
Seattle, WA 98112
(206) 324-1126 E-mail: phyllis-kelly@msn.com
Admission: Entry fee. Open daily, Noon.-5 P.M.,

SEATTLE, WASHINGTON
Steamer *Virginia V* Foundation
901 Fairview Ave North, P.O. Box 9566
Seattle, WA 98109-0566
(206) 624-9119 Fax: 206-381-3715
E-mail: info@virginiav.org
Location: The steamer is under restoration at Lake Union.
Highlights: Steamer *Virginia V* (passenger steamer), **Website:** www.virginiav.org/
General Information: The Steamer *Virginia V* Foundation is a non-profit organization of steamboat enthusiasts. The Foundation's project is to restore the steamer — which has been named a Seattle landmark, National Historic Site, and National Historic Landmark — as a working museum.

Whether moored conveniently on Seattle's waterfront or steaming out around Puget Sound waters, the stately and historic *Virginia V* offers a unique setting that will linger in the minds of visitors. Carrying up to 150 passengers, the steamer affords visitors an opportunity to inspect firsthand the wondrous workings of the old triple-expansion steam engine built in 1903 continuing to propel the steamboat at a cruising speed of ten knots.

Admission: For charter, public cruise and membership information, please call the Foundation.

TACOMA, WASHINGTON
Working Waterfront Maritime Museum
705 Dock Street
Tacoma, WA 98402-4625
Business Office: 2602 N. Proctor St., #202
(253) 272-2750 Fax: 253-272-3023
E-mail: info@fosswaterwayseaport.org

Location: The Museum is located at 705 Dock Street in the Balfour Dock Building on the Foss Waterway in Tacoma, the Pacific Northwest's largest port city.
Highlights: Interpretive museum, small-craft displays, boatbuilding, library,
Website: www.wwfrontmuseum.org/
General Information: The Working Waterfront Maritime Museum, founded in 1997, offers activities and exhibits that showcase the history of Tacoma's working waterfront and demonstrates, teaches past, and current maritime crafts and skills. The Museum's facility is one of two remaining structures of what was once the famous "mile-long warehouse" located at the northwestern terminus of the Northern Pacific Railroad, Tacoma's maritime heritage is captured in photographic exhibits.

Gallery areas feature permanent and short-term interpretive exhibits about regional maritime history, small boat building in progress, with many locally built wooden craft on display, along with tools and antique motors.

Activities: In the Discovery Wharf, children can build their own toy boat, look through a selection of children's nautical literature, and go aboard Faith, a reconstructed Columbia River Gillnetter that is securely moored inside the Museum.

Admission: Entry fee. Open weekdays 9 am – 5 pm; Weekends (April – October) 12 noon – 5 P.M., (November - March) 12 noon - 4 P.M.; Closed Thanksgiving, Christmas, New Year's Day, Easter, Day, Easter, Mothers' Day, and 4th of July.

WESTPORT, WASHINGTON
Westport Maritime Museum
2210 Westhaven Drive, P.O. Box 1074
Westport, WA 98595-1074
(360) 268-0078 Fax: (360) 268-1288
E-mail: wmmvista@comcast.net
Location: The Museum is located in the fishing and tourist town of Westport on the south side of Grays Harbor entrance off State Scenic Rte. 105, twenty miles west of Aberdeen.
Highlights: local maritime, Coast Guard, 1st order Fresnal light from Destruction Island.
Website: www.westportwa.com/museum
Highlights: local maritime, Coast Guard, 1st order Fresnal light from Destruction Island.
Website: www.westportwa.com/museum
General Information: The Museum, organized in 1984, includes photographs and artifacts related to local maritime, Coast Guard, Coastal living, and industry history including reconstructed skeletons of marine mammals and a children's discovery room. A new building, on the

five building campus, houses the working Fresnel Lens, made in France in 1888, from the Destruction Island Lighthouse. The Museum is housed in the former Grays Harbor Coast Guard Station; a historically registered Nantucket style building that saw service from 1940 to 1974. The Grays Harbor Lighthouse is located approximately two miles from the Museum.
Admission: No entry fee, but donations accepted. Summer Hours: Open daily Memorial Day to Labor Day 10 A.M. to 4 P.M. Fall & Spring Hours, Thursday thru Monday 12 P.M. to 4 P.M. Jan-Feb Hours, Weekends and Holidays, 12 P.M. to 4 P.M.

WASHINGTON, D.C.

WASHINGTON, D.C.
Decatur House
1610 H Street, N.W.
Washington, D. C. 20006-4912
(202) 218-4338 Fax: (202) 842-0030
E-mail: decaturhouse@whha.org
Location: Decatur House faces Lafayette Square and is convenient to Farragut West and Farragut North Metro stations.
Highlights: Mementos of Commodore Stephen Decatur, **Website**: www.decaturhouse.org/
General Information: Commodore Stephen Decatur, who began his naval career in 1798 on board the new frigate *United States* a sister ship to the USS *Constitution*, moved into his Washington, D.C., and mansion in 1819. The three-story townhouse, with stable and garden, exists nearly the way it was when the Decatur's lived there. Decatur's mementos are displayed throughout the house. The *United States* was one of six vessels commissioned by the government in 1793 and included the *Constitution* ("Old Ironsides"), the only survivor of that 1798 commissioning.
  The formal Victorian rooms on the second floor reflect the taste of a wealthy household environment of the 1870s. Tiny etchings depicting Decatur's role in the Barbary Wars hang in a downstairs hall. Other paintings are seen throughout the house including portraits of many other residents of the house. Decatur was killed in a duel with Commodore Barron on March 22, 1820 — he was forty-one.
Activities: Tours on the hour and half-hour.
Admission: By donation only. Open Tuesday - Saturday: 10 A.M. – 5 P.M.; Sunday: Noon – 4 P.M., Museum shop open Monday-Friday, 10 A.M. - 5:30 P.M.; Saturday, Noon. - 4 P.M.

WASHINGTON, D.C.
National Maritime Heritage Initiative
National Park Service, Dept. of Interior
1849 C Street, NW 2261
Washington, D.C. 20240-0001
(202) 354-2260 Fax: (202) 371-5180
E-mail: kevin_foster@nps.gov
Location: The Maritime Initiative is a part of the National Park Service in Washington, D.C.
Highlights: National maritime history resource
Website: www.cr.nps.gov/maritime/
  General Information: The National Park Service Maritime Heritage Program works to advance awareness and understanding of the role of maritime affairs in the history of the United States. Through leadership, assistance, and expertise in maritime history, preservation, and archeology we help to interpret and preserve our maritime heritage by:
 • Maintaining inventories of historic U.S. maritime properties
 • Providing preservation assistance through publications and consultation
 • Educating the public about maritime heritage through our web site
 • Sponsoring maritime heritage conferences and workshops
 • Funding maritime heritage projects when grant assistance is available
 • Maintaining inventories of historic U.S. maritime properties
 • Large Preserved Historic Vessels
 • Historic Light Stations
 • Historic Lifesaving Stations (developed through a partnership with the U.S. Life-Saving Service Heritage Association)
 • Shipwrecks and Hulks
 • Small Craft (developed through a cooperative agreement with the Museum Small Craft Association)
U.S. Coast Guard, the Naval Historical Center, the National Oceanic and Atmospheric Administration, the Advisory Council on Historic Preservation, State Historic Preservation Offices, the National Trust for Historic Preservation, and the maritime preservation community in general.

WASHINGTON, D.C.
The Navy Museum
Naval Historical Center
805 Kidder-Breese S.E.
Washington Navy Yard-Bldg. 76
Washington, D.C. 20374-5060
(202) 433-4882   Fax: (202) 433-8200
Location: The Museum is on the grounds of the Washington Navy Yard, south of the downtown area on 9th and M Streets, Southeast.

Highlights: Research Vessel *Trieste*, LCVP, PBR Mark I, and Swift Boat, Fighting top from USS *Constitution*, F4U Corsair, submarine periscopes, World War II gun mounts, Naval Historical Center (research library and archives), *Navy Museum News*, gift shop,
Website: www.history.navy.mil/branches/nhcorg8.htm
  General Information: The Navy Museum opened in 1963 and was established to collect, preserve, and display naval artifacts, models, documents, and fine art. Through its exhibits, the Museum chronicles the history of the U. S. Navy from the Revolution to the present. The exhibits commemorate the Navy's wartime heroes and battles as well as its peacetime contributions in such fields as exploration, diplomacy, space flight, navigation, and humanitarian service. Tools, equipment, and personal artifacts offer the visitor a unique opportunity to gain an understanding of naval customs, ways of life, and contributions to society.
  Open to the general public, major exhibits include: *In Harm's Way*: The U.S. Navy in World War II, Korea 1950-1953: and *The Navy in the Forgotten War*.
  Admission: No entry fee. Open Monday through Friday: 0900-1600 (9 A.M. until 4 P.M.) Weekends and Holidays: 1000-1700 (10 A.M. until 5 P.M.) Closed: Thanksgiving Day, December 24, Christmas and New Years' Day

WASHINGTON, D.C.
Smithsonian Institution
Smithsonian Information
PO Box 37012
SI Building, Room 153, MRC 010
Washington, D.C. 20013-7012
(202) 633.1000   E-mail: info@si.edu
Location: The National Museum of American History is on the Mall in Washington, D.C., between George Washington Monument and the Capitol at 14th Street & Constitution Avenue, NW.
Highlights: Ship models, Hall of Armed Forces History, Continental Gunboat *Philadelphia* in National Museum of American History,
Website: www.si.edu/
  General Information: The Smithsonian Institution's National Museum of American History houses its maritime and naval exhibits in the Hall of American Maritime Enterprise and the Hall of Armed Forces History. Models and graphics show development of water commerce, inland waterways, development of steam and sail, and various other exhibits relate to United States maritime service. Ship models are on display in the Hall of American Enterprise, the Technology Building, and Air and Space Museum.

Research facilities include drawings by Howard I. Chapelle and H.V. Sucher; the Historic American Merchant Marine Survey, Cropley Collection (maritime clipping file), photo files.
Note: The Transportation Collection also offers three catalogs of ship plans from which watercraft designs can be ordered at nominal fees. Write for information.
  Activities: Research facilities (Admission by appointment only, weekdays between 10 A.M.-4:30 P.M.)
  Admission: No entry fee. Open daily 10 A.M.-5:30 P.M. Closed Christmas.

WASHINGTON, D.C.
Society of the Cincinnati
Anderson House
2118 Massachusetts Avenue, NW
Washington, DC 20008-2810
(202) 785-2040 Ex. 40   Fax: (202) 785-0729
E-mail: admin@societyofthecincinnati.org
Location: Anderson House is at the intersection of Q Street and Massachusetts Avenue on south side of street one block west of Dupont Circle.
Highlights: Maritime history,
Website: www.societyofthecincinnati.org
  General Information: The officers of the Continental line and their French compatriots who served together during the American Revolution founded The Society of the Cincinnati in 1783. Its original purpose, "to perpetuate the remembrance of the achievement of national independence," is being carried forth today through historical and educational programs.
  Collection Content: General areas - Naval history, shipbuilding. Revolutionary War period. Library: Houses a growing collection of more than 42,000 titles focusing on military and naval history of the American Revolution and the art of war in the eighteenth century. Among its holdings are treatises on military and naval art and science, shipbuilding, maritime law and naval medicine. Material of interest to maritime scholars can also be found among the collection's historical manuscripts, maps and works of art on paper. In addition, the modern reference collection includes general and local histories, biographies, bibliographies and periodicals supporting research on the Revolutionary War period.
  Admission: No entry fee. Open Monday-Friday, 10 A.M.-4 P.M. Closed federal holidays.

WEST VIRGINIA

BERKELEY SPRINGS, WV
Museum of The Berkeley Springs
Old Roman Bathhouse
P.O. Box 99
Berkeley Springs, WV 25411

1-800-447-8797 (304) 258-3743
E-mail: history@museumoftheberkeleysprings
Location: From I-70, thirty-eight miles east of
Cumberland, Maryland, or twenty-six miles west
of Hagerstown, Maryland, exit on US-522 south
six miles to Berkeley Springs. Exit 522 of I-70.
Highlights: Gift shop, Rumsey steamboat
invention history,
Website: www.museumoftheberkeleysprings.com/
General Information: The Museum
concentrates on the history and geology of the
springs and its role in the growth of the town of
Bath (now known as Berkeley Springs), which was
a spa. An important display examines the life
of James Rumsey, a pioneer of steam navigation
and the inventor of the first steamboat *Columbian
Maid.* During the time that Rumsey lived in the
area he was an innkeeper of the town's first
bathhouse (spa). He demonstrated the *Columbian
Maid* on the Potomac River in 1787. Nearby in
Shepherdstown is the Rumseian Society with a
small working model of Rumsey's boat.
Admission: No entry fee, donations welcome.
Open April through October, Monday and Tuesday
10 A.M. to 12 Noon, Thursday from 10 A.M. to 2
P.M., Friday 3 P.M. to 6 P.M., Saturday 10 A.M.
to 4 P.M. and Sunday 12 Noon to 4 P.M..

WISCONSIN

BAYFIELD, WISCONSIN
Apostle Islands National Lakeshore
415 Washington Street, Rt. 1, Box 4
Bayfield, WI 54814
(715) 779-3397
E-mail: on website
Location: Bayfield is eighty miles east of the
Duluth/Superior twin ports on State Highway 13.
Highlights: Island fish camp, six lighthouses,
library (500 volumes),
Website: www.nps.gov/apis/
General Information: Apostle Islands National
Lakeshore was founded in 1970. Collections
include lighthouse artifacts and objects;
building and docks from small family commercial
fishing operations; an island fish camp; a 1930s
fishing boat; and other local exhibits.
    The library collection on the natural and cultural
history of Northern Wisconsin is available for use
on the premises.
    Activities: Guided tours during summer, films,
exhibits, and slide programs
    Admission: No entry fee. Open daily, 8 A.M.-6
P.M., Memorial Day-Labor Day; day after Labor
Day-October 22, 8 A.M.-5 P.M.; Monday-Friday, 8
A.M.-4:30 P.M., October 23-April 29; open daily,
8 A.M.-4:30 P.M., April 30-Memorial Day.

BAYFIELD, WISCONSIN
Bayfield Heritage Association, Inc.
30 N. Broad Street. P.O. Box 137
Bayfield, WI 54814
(715) 779-5958
E-mail: bayfieldheritage@centurytel.net
Location: Bayfield is sixty miles east from
Duluth/Superior on Rte. 2 and twenty miles north
on Rte. 13. The museum is located at 30 N. Broad
Street near the Bayfield Carnegie Library, Old
Iron Bridge, historic jail, and the association's
Knight Apple Shed.
Highlights: *Courier* (newsletter), *Historical
Happenings* (newsletter), research archives,
photographs
General Information: The Bayfield Heritage
Association, Inc., was founded in 1973. Originally
the Association resided in an 1883 native
brownstone courthouse, which is now leased to the
Apostle Islands National Lakeshore for its local
headquarters. The Association promotes
awareness, appreciation, and preservation of
Bayfield's distinctive history.
    The museum maintains exhibits on Bayfield
and Apostle Islands areas history, and includes the
Roger Bodin Memorial Maritime Exhibit. The
Blue Water Boat Guild Museum's artifacts have
been moved over to the Association.
    A research collection with an extensive
photograph inventory is an important part of the
Association and includes a video-taped collection
of local history interviews. Artifacts and archival
materials relating to maritime history, including
commercial fishing, boat building, ferryboat
service, and pleasure boating, are parts of the
Association's collections.
    Admission: No entry fee. Open Memorial Day
through first weekend in October, or by appmt.

BAYFIELD, WISCONSIN
Hokenson Brothers Fishery
Apostle Islands National Lakeshore
Route 1, Box 4
Bayfield, WI 54814
(715) 779-3397
Location: Bayfield is ninety miles east of the
Duluth/Superior twin ports on State Highway 13.
Highlights: Local fishery history,**Website:**
www.howderfamily.com/travel/wisconsin/little_sa
nd_bay.html
    General Information: The Hokenson Brothers
Fishery, located at Little Sand Bay near Bayfield,
Wisconsin, includes of three major structures, the
fishing tug *Twilite,* and one-pound net boat, and a
pile driver raft. These have been preserved to
represent a small family-operated commercial
fishing business in the Apostle Islands region of
Lake Superior during 1928-1963. Exhibits cover

181

fish processing, ice harvesting, fishermen's techniques and skills.
Admission: National Lakeshore entry fee. Open second week in June to Labor Day, daily 9 A.M.-5 P.M. Admission at fishery is free.

FISH CREEK, WISCONSIN
Eagle Bluff Lighthouse
Peninsula State Park
Fish Creek, WI 54212
(920) 839-2377 E-mail: info@dcmm.org
Location: From Green Bay take SR-57 north to Sturgeon Bay. Follow SR-42 thirty miles further north to the village of Fish Creek in Peninsula State Park. *Highlights:* Lighthouse,
Website: www.eagleblufflighthouse.org/
General Information: The Eagle Lighthouse is located in Peninsula State Park. The Lighthouse contains and exhibits a collection of maritime and period furnishings in a historic house.
Admission: Entry fee to Park and Lighthouse. Open daily, 9:30 A.M.- 4 P.M., mid-June-mid-October.

GILLS ROCK, WISCONSIN
Door County Maritime Museum
12724 Wisconsin Bay Road
Gills Rock, WI 54210
(414) 854-1844 or (414) 743-5958
E-mail: rdesh@dcmm.org (**See also:** Door County Marine Museum - Sturgeon Bay, WI)
Location: Take SR-57 northeast of Green Bay to Sturgeon Bay, then follow SR-42 to Gills Rock at the extreme north end of the peninsula. Museum is at Gills Rock Memorial Park.
Highlights: Boardable fish tug,
Website: www.dcmm.org/gillsrock.html
General Information: Located in the former offices of Roen Steamship Company, Gills Rock Maritime Museum is one of two Door County Maritime Museums founded in 1974 on the water corridor between Green Bay and Lake Michigan. The interesting fragments and objects retrieved from these waters and displayed in the Museum, relate to the vast history of commercial fishing and shipbuilding in Door County.
  Collections includes a full-sized fish tug that may be boarded to see, first hand, how gill-net fishing was done; a gill-net drying reel; several very old marine engines used in various sized fishing boats; a large collection of marine historic pictures and writings; and a multitude of artifacts recovered by scuba divers from the many sunken shipwrecks around Door County's shores; many sunk in the nineteenth century.
Activities: This museum is the only one in Door County that provides free conducted-narrated tours (six daily), 40 - 45 minutes, explaining various items and related procedures.

Admission: Entry fee. Open daily, 10 A.M.-5 P.M.

GILLS ROCK, WISCONSIN
Door County Maritime Museum at Cana Island Lighthouse,
Baileys Harbor, WI 54202
(920) 743-5958
Contact: Door County Maritime Museum & Lighthouse Preservation Society, Inc.
120 N. Madison Ave.
Sturgeon Bay, WI 54235   (920) 839-2377
E-mail: info@eagleblufflighthouse.org
Location: Cana Island, Wis. The lighthouse is located north of Baileys Harbor off County Highway Q.
Highlights: Cana Island Lighthouse,
Website: www.dcmm.org/canaisland.html
General Information: Yes, it is possible to stroll to an island. Cana Island, with its historic lighthouse facilities where you can walk across the rock causeway from the Door County mainland to the island. Step inside the keeper's house where, beginning in 1869, the first of a number of lighthouse keepers tended to the light, which guided sailors and protected them from the dangerous shoals extending out from the island into Lake Michigan. Take a look in the oil house, where fuel for the light was stored prior to days when electricity came to the island.
  The buildings and grounds have been maintained by the Door County Maritime Museum for nearly 30 years while the United State Coast Guard continues to oversee the tower with its stunning third order Fresnel lens and light.
Admission: Cana Island Lighthouse and Grounds, Cana Island near Baileys Harbor, grounds only, open daily, 10 A.M.-5 P.M. Buildings open; tower not open. Limited parking available, and causeway access may be wet. Lighthouse open each weekend until last weekend in October.

KEWAUNEE, WISCONSIN
Ship's Wheel Gallery & Nautical Museum
224 Ellis Street
Kewaunee, WI 54216
(920) 388-0777   E-mail: trotter@infopages.net
Location: Right in the middle of Kewaunee, at the corner of Milwaukee (Hwy 42) and Ellis (Hwy 29)
Highlights: Local harbor history, Potawatomi Indian display, Great Lakes shipwrecks,
Website: http://trotter.infopages.net/shipwhel.htm
General Information: The Ship's Wheel Gallery & Nautical Museum gallery is devoted to paintings and exhibits on local maritime history and related matters. Underwater Archaeology Society of Chicago provided material on the luxury steamer *Lady Elgin* and other famous wrecks in

182

Great Lakes history. Materials include videotapes of exploratory dives, artifacts found in wrecks and brought back, and sidelights on Great Lakes underwater archaeology in general.

The store offers paintings, half-hulls, and gifts with a maritime theme. Some artists featured are William L. Trotter, Charles Vickery, and the half-hulls of Captain J. Peter Jones. In the inner rooms are displays on famous wrecks of the Great Lakes; The *Pueblo* built by Kewaunee Engineering; the history of Kewaunee area before its settlement by Europeans; World War II ships including the USS *Chicago* and maritime artifacts and lighthouses; as well an 8-foot-long model ship under full sail; the *Cary Elton* of Chicago.

The Native American exhibits include dioramas made by Potawatomis from Chicago. In the seventeenth century, Potawatomis, Ottawas, and Hurons lived here, the largest such settlement in Wisconsin, with a palisaded fort at the top of the slope where Svoboda Industries is now. In 1652, 800 Iroquois warriors came here by canoe and tried for two years to defeat this community, but failed. Eventually — peace.

Admission: Open June through mid-October.

MANITOWOC, WISCONSIN
Wisconsin Maritime Museum
75 Maritime Drive
Manitowoc, WI 54220-6843
Toll free 1-866-724-2356 (920) 684-0218
Fax: (920) 684-0219
E-mail: museum@wisconsinmaritime.org
Location: Manitowoc is eighty-three miles north of Milwaukee on I-43. The Museum is located on Maritime Drive, two blocks east of 8th Street.
Highlights: The WW II submarine USS *Cobia*, model ships, Gift Shop, Museum publishes *Anchor News* maritime journal.
Website: http://wisconsinmaritime.org/
General Information: Over 150 years of Great Lakes' maritime heritage is preserved at the Wisconsin Maritime Museum, founded in 1968 in Manitowoc, Wisconsin. The lakeshore community, north of Milwaukee, boasts a rich maritime history in ship and submarine construction. Currently, Manitowoc is the Wisconsin port for the Lake Michigan Carferry earning the city the title of Wisconsin's Maritime Capital.

Two floors of fascination await you in the main galleries. From the streets of an historical Great Lakes port, you will relive its story of shipbuilding including WW II submarines, commerce from sail to steam to today's diesel freighters, pleasure yachts, and work boats.

The Museum is justly proud of its Model Ship Gallery. Historical information from sailing ships

to modern Great Lakes ships and shipping is displayed along with other maritime treasures — a must see if traveling to the area. Moored adjacent to the museum is a National Historic Landmark USS *Cobia*, a gato class sub similar to the 28 built by Manitowoc Shipbuilding Company during World War II.

Visitors today can also visit Rogers Street Fishing Museum, seven miles north in Two Rivers, Wisconsin, but the first stop should be at the Wisconsin Maritime Museum on the bank of the Manitowoc River in downtown Manitowoc.

Activities: Take a guided tour on the USS *Cobia* daily, Overnight Program (advance reservations required for groups of 20-65 people. Special events throughout the year. Listings available on our website.

Admission: Entry fee. Discounted group and family rates available. Open: summer hours, daily, 9 A.M. – 6 P.M; Winter hours, Labor Day weekend through Memorial Day weekend, 9 A.M. – 5 P.M. Closed Thanksgiving, Christmas Day, New Year's Day, and Easter Sunday.

MILWAUKEE, WISCONSIN
Milwaukee Public Library
Local History and Marine Collection
814 West Wisconsin Avenue
Milwaukee, WI 53233-2385
(414) 286-3000   Fax: (414) 286-2137
Location: The Library is near I-94 and I-43 junction at the western edge of downtown Milwaukee, near the Marquette University campus and the Milwaukee Museum.
Highlights: Great Lakes Marine Collection, Wisconsin Marine Historical Society, ship models, research material, The Great Lakes Archival Catalogs of 50,000 photographs, historical quarterly *Soundings*,
Website: http://www.mpl.org/File/contact_us.htm
General Information: The Great Lakes Marine Collection is part of the Humanities Department, whose rooms are on the second floor. While primarily a library emphasizing historical records of individual ships, there are a number ßof permanent and rotating three-dimensional displays concentrating on nineteenth- and twentieth-century Great Lakes commercial shipping.

The Collection consists of books, periodicals, photographs, charts, prints, and 50,000 photographs. There is also an impressive array of original materials — log books, vessel plans, wreck reports, and government documents. The collection also includes ship models, house flags from shipping lines, ships' artifacts, ship files, and nautical art. The Library is also the location of the Wisconsin Marine Historical Society, founded in

1959 to collect, record, and preserve material relating to Great Lakes marine history and conducts fee-for-service research and publishes an historical quarterly — *Soundings*.
Admission: No entry fee. Open Monday-Thursday, 9 A.M.-8:30 P.M.; Friday and Saturday, 9 A.M.-5:30 P.m.; Sunday, 1 P.M.-5 P.M. The Library is closed on Sundays in the summer.

PORTAGE, WISCONSIN
Portage Canal Society, Inc.
311 Johnson Street, P.O. Box 847
Portage, WI 53901
(608) 742-2889 or 742-2739
E-mail: dollar1@charter.net
Location: Portage is 112 miles northwest of Milwaukee. Highways leading into Portage are I-90-94, east and west, Rtes. 33, 16, and 51.
Highlights: Portage history of the Canal, **Website:**www.portagecanalsociety.com/DesktopDefault.aspx/
General Information: The Canal, when finished, allowed large boats to transverse between the Fox and Wisconsin Rivers and the boat, the *Boscobel*, passed through the Canal in 1876. But because of the ultimate arrival of the railroads, water transportation declined.
Large boats used the Portage Canal until the early 1900s. After that, pleasure boats used the Canal until 1951, when the Wisconsin Locks were finally welded shut and the Fort Winnebago Lock was bulldozed to create an earthen dam. Since 1975, restoration has been in progress to create more access for the public use of the canal area.
Admission: Contact by phone or mail for information.

PORT WASHINGTON, WISCONSIN
Port Washington Light Station
311 Johnson Street, P.O. Box 491
Port Washington, WI 53074   262-284-7240
E-mail: 1860lightstation@sbcgolbal.net
Location: Directly north of downtown business
Highlights: 1860 Light Station,
Web Site: www.portlightstation.org
General Information: Port Washington's first lighthouse was built on purchased land, in 1849. The land was bought from Henry and Emma Allen, for $200 in 1848 and includes the current site. The Light Station beacon was discontinued October 31, 1903 and Lightkeeper Charles Lewis, Jr. retired in 1924. The pierhead light was automated and the city ran the fog siren from the water works.
Come to the Light Station where shipwreck artifacts and the blues share the same room. The watch shack/generator building now contains a

steamboat's wheelhouse with a full compliment of equipment, including the binnacle and pilothouse telegraph from the whaleback *CHRISTOPHER COLUMBUS*. Step up to the wheel and gaze out over Lake Michigan (between the trees!) and take time to sign the logbook recording the date and weather conditions during your time at the helm.
Activities: Tours.
Admission: Entry fee. Open Mother's Day to Columbus Day, May-Oct. 11 a.m.-4 p.m. Sat.

STURGEON BAY, WISCONSIN
Door County Maritime Museum
120 North Madison Avenue
Sturgeon Bay, WI 54235-2216
(920) 743-5958   Fax: (920) 743-9483
E-mail: E-mail: info@dcmm.org
Location: From Milwaukee take I-43 north 121 miles to Green Bay. Then follow SR-57 thirty-eight miles northeast to Sturgeon Bay. The Museum is adjacent to the downtown bridge.
Highlights: New 20,000 square-foot museum, Cana Island Lighthouse (North of Baileys Harbor), **Website:** www.dcmm.org
General Information: Door County Maritime exhibits include: a refurbished pilot house of a Great Lakes vessel; Kahlenburg Marine Engine; and antique out-boards to single-cylinder stationary engines used in small boats of all kinds; and WWII shipbuilding exhibit with periscope; and lighthouse exhibit.
Collections include a large number of marine pictures and historical papers and books covering a great deal of marine history of the Door County area. Available for research are miscellaneous papers, pictures, and books from the shipyards and steamship operation on the premises.
Activities: Door County Lighthouse Walk — third weekend in May. Includes several lighthouse locations and various boat tours. For information call (414) 743-5958. Annual Door County Maritime Museum Classic & Wooden Boat Show, Sturgeon Bay, first weekend in August, includes wooden-boat exhibits. Call (414) 743-5958 for information.
Admission: Entry fee. Open daily, 10 A.M.-5 P.M., Memorial Day-Labor Day.

SUPERIOR, WISCONSIN
SS *Meteor* Maritime Museum
Barker's Island
906 Harbor View Parkway   P. O. Box 775
Superior, WI 54880-3246
(715) 394-5712 or (715) 392-5742
Location: Superior is in the northwest corner of Wisconsin across the mouth of the St. Louis River at Lake Superior from Duluth, Minnesota. The ship

is moored on Barker's Island.
Highlights: Tour through the last whaleback ship in the world, working 1896 triple expansion steam engine, ship models, **Website:** www.superiorpublicmuseums.org/ssmeteor/
General Information: The SS *Meteor* Maritime Museum is under the administration of Superior Public Museums. The SS *Meteor*, a "whaleback" bulk freighter, is among the most interesting maritime architectural achievements for transporting ore and other cargoes. *Meteor* transported iron ore, gravel, cars, and oil in her career from 1896-1969. The whalebacks, named for their rounded hull design, were conceived and built by Captain Alexander McDougall of Duluth, Minnesota. McDougall purportedly dreamt of a cigar shaped boat that was able to plow through the water, shedding rough seas. Forty-one of the forty-three whalebacks built between 1888 and 1898 were built in the Superior harbor. All were lost — rammed, wrecked, sunk, or scrapped — all that is, but the SS *Meteor.*

Meteor returned to Superior in 1973 and was opened as a historic ship museum with tours through the ship and exhibits housed in the cargo holds. The museum's collections include whaleback artifacts, equipment used aboard Great Lakes ships, and photographic displays. Spacious parking provided easy access to the Museum, with picnic area, unique gift shops, cafe, and Seamen's Memorial nearby. The Seamen's memorial was dedicated in 1979 as a monument to all seamen, living or dead, who ever worked on the Great Lakes. It was inspired by the 1975 sinking of the Great Lakes ore vessel *Edmund Fitzgerald.*

One of the whalebacks even made it to the West Coast and transported cargo to and from Everett, Washington. It was the SS *Charles W. Wetmore,* and when it arrived in Everett in 1891, carried all the steel necessary to build another whaleback in that city — the SS *City of Everett,* which served until lost in 1925 in the Gulf of Mexico.

Activities: Guided tours, slide presentation, self-guided exhibit area, Whaleback Wharf Giftshops.

TWO RIVERS, WISCONSIN
Rogers Street Fishing Village Museum
2010 Rogers Street
Two Rivers, WI 54241
(920) 793-5905 E-mail: info@rogersstreet.com
(**See also:** Wisconsin Maritime Museum)
Location: Two Rivers is ten miles north of Manitowoc via Rte. 42, which hugs the shore of .Lake Michigan
Highlights: Tugboat, small lighthouse, shipwreck artifacts, **Website:** www.rogersstreet.com/

General Information: The Rogers Street Fishing Village Museum is a small museum on the banks of the East Twin River and tells the city's long history as a commercial fishing center. Exhibits include many artifacts highlighting famous shipwrecks off Two Rivers coast including the Christmas Tree shipwreck. A forty-foot fishing tug is on display, as well as the small 1886 Two Rivers North Pier Lighthouse, an 8,000-pound Kahlenberg operating marine diesel engine, tools, and photographs are displayed.
Admission: Entry fee. Open daily, 10 A.M.-4 P.M., mid-May-October.

PART 2

CANADIAN PROVINCES

ALBERTA, CANADA

CALGARY, ALBERTA
The Naval Museum of Alberta
1820 24 Street Southwest
Calgary, Alberta T2T 0G6   Canada
(403) 242-0002
E-mail: info@navalmuseum.ab.ca
Location: The Museum is at 17th Avenue and 24th Street, S.W. in Calgary and is alongside H.M.C.S. *Tecumseh,* the Calgary Naval Reserve facility. It is approximately ten-minutes driving time from the business center of the city of Calgary.
Highlights: Three Canadian naval aircraft, ship models, history of The Prairie Navy, gift shop, **Website:** www.navalmuseum.ab.ca
General Information: The Naval Museum of Alberta, Canada's second largest contains the only collection of three fighter aircraft used by the Royal Canadian Navy, namely a Seafire (the naval version of the Spitfire), a Sea Fury (the world's fastest piston-engine fighter aircraft, which successfully destroyed MIG (Soviet) jets in combat during the Korean War), and a Banshee jet.

The Museum possesses a superb research library of naval history. It contains, perhaps, the only surviving copy of wartime ship movements and convoy records and the photo and negative collection exceeds 20,000. The Museum has generous displays and exhibits focusing on the men and women of Alberta that played an important part in Canada's military forces.
Displays feature uniforms, badges, cap ribbons, photographs, artifacts, shipborne equipment, ship models, many written documents, and more.

The Museum commemorates the "Prairie Sailors" of the Western Canadian provinces who served in World Wars I, II, and the Korean War. It is dedicated to Lt. Robert Hampton Gray, VC, DCS, RCNVR, the RCN's only recipient of the Victoria Cross in World War II.

Admission: Entry fee. Open Summer, July to Sept. Monday – Sunday, 10 a.m. – 5 p.m.; Winter; Tuesday-Friday, 1 P.M.-5 P.M.; Weekends, 10 A.M.- 5 P.M. Closed Christmas day, New Year's Day.

BRITISH COLUMBIA, CANADA

DUNCAN, BC

Cowichan Bay Maritime Centre
Cowichan Wooden Boat Society
1761 Cowichan Bay Road, P.O. Box 22
Cowichan Bay, BC V0R 1N0 Canada
(250) 746-4955 Fax: (250) 746-9989
E-mail: on website
Location: The waterfront community of Cowichan is some 50 klms. north of Victoria on Canada Hwy 1.
Highlights: Wooden boat-building, unique maritime museum on a wharf,
Website: www.classicboats.org/
    General Information: The Cowichan Bay Maritime Centre in 1988 acquired and renovated a 350-foot pier upon which it created a very unique set of museum buildings and traditional wooden boatbuilding workshops.
    The museum illustrates the early history of the Bay and displays many of the boats built at the Centre and restored marine engines. Boatbuilding exhibits are displayed in its workshops, and the museum offers full- and part-time courses in boatbuilding.
    The Society relies on grants for the museum's operations. Much of the museum's success comes through training courses provided to the public and sponsoring the annual Cowichan Bay Boat Festival. The museum also sells and rents boats.
    Admission: No entry fee, but donations accepted. Open: daily, 9 A.M. – Dusk, year round.

GIBSON'S LANDING, BC

Sunshine Coast Museum and Archives
716 Winn Road
PO Box 766
Gibsons, BC, V0N 1V0
(604) 886-8232
Email: scm_a@dccnet.com
Location: The Museum is located in Lower Gibsons across from the Post Office in the heart of Gibsons Landing, 10 minutes from BC Ferries and just steps away from the gov't dock, marinas, & Gibsons Harbour.
Highlights: Ship models, photographs, special

maritime exhibits and events. Retired Tugboat 2005 *Rendezvous* in Gibson's Harbour.
Website: www.sunshinecoastmuseum.ca/main
    General Information: The Sunshine Coast Museum & Archives came into existence on May 29, 2002 when the two local museums, the Elphinstone Pioneer Museum and the Sunshine Coast Maritime Museum joined forces and amalgamated. The founding Museums had been separately collecting and preserving the history of the Sunshine Coast for many years but it was believed that an amalgamated Museum would be more efficient and better suited to preserving local heritage into the future. It was time to combine forces to create a joint effort for funding purposes, for management purposes and to consolidate the collections in one location. We were fortunate to have the benefit of the many years of experience from both of the founding museums as the Elphinstone Pioneer Museum had been in existence since 1969 and the Sunshine Coast Maritime Museum since 1989.
    The Sunshine Coast Museum and Archives presents the history of the Sunshine Coast and its inhabitants. Two floors of exhibits to explore! Natural History Collections (fossils, butterflies, minerals), Pioneer Period Rooms, First Nations, Small Wooden Boats & Models, The Beachcombers, Allen & Sharie Farrell Photographic Collection, and more...
    Admission: Admission by donation. Open Tuesday – Saturday 10:30 A.M. – 4:30 P.M. year round. We are wheelchair accessible & accommodate group tours by appointment.

NEW WESTMINSTER, BC

Samson *V* Maritime Museum
105-1005 Columbia St., P.O. Box 42516
New Westminster, BC V3M 3S2   Canada
(604) 527-4640 Fax: (604) 526-6358
E-mail: museum@newwestcity.ca
Location: The Samson V Maritime Museum is moored at the Westminster Quay, in New Westminster, British Columbia, Canada (30 minutes from Vancouver, by car or SkyTrain).
Highlights: The *Samson V* (sternwheeler), vessel preservation; maritime collection; photographs; steam heritage maritime history, **Website:** www.nwheritage.org/heritagesite/orgs/samson/
    General Information: Founded in 1983, *Samson V* Maritime Museum is aboard the sternwheeler of the same name, the last steam-powered sternwheeler to operate on the Fraser River. She is berthed on the Fraser River at the New Westminster waterfront. Collections include vessel preservation, maritime collection, and photographs.
    Activities: Tours arranged by appointment, and special programs.

Admission: No entry fee, but donations accepted. Open: May 1 to June 30,Saturdays, Sundays, and Holidays, Noon to 5 P.M.; daily, July 1 to Labour Day; Labour Day - 604.522.6894.

TOFINO, BC

The Whale Centre & Museum
411 Campbell Street, P. O. Box 111
Tofino, British Columbia V0R 2Z0 Canada
(250) 725-2132 Fax: (250) 725-2136
Toll Free: 1-888-474-2288
E-mail: whales@island.net
Location: From Victoria, Vancouver Island, take Rte. 1 north about 86 miles to the junction with Rte. 4. Head west about 150 miles to Tofino (on Clayoquot Sound) on the west coast of Vancouver Island. The Museum is on Campbell and 3rd Streets. *Highlights:* Whale Centre, complete gray whale skeleton, gift shop,
Website: www.tofinowhalecentre.com
General Information: The West Coast Maritime Museum, founded in 1969, is dedicated to furthering public education and interest in our magnificent marine mammals and features maritime and fishing industry history. Exhibits include a 40-foot gray whale skeleton display, equipment and artifacts from sunken ships, Nootka and Nuu Chakt Nulth Indian artifacts. The Museum also maintains a photograph archive.
Activities: Cruise—whale and nature watch excursions. Hot Springs.
Admission: No entry fee. Open March to Oct. 31, 9 A.M.-8 P.M.

VANCOUVER, BC

RV *Ben Franklin*
Vancouver Maritime Museum
1905 Ogden Avenue
Vancouver, BC V6J 1A3 Canada
(604) 257-8300 Fax: (604) 737-2621 E-mail: genvmm@vancouvermaritimemuseum.com
Location: The RV *Ben Franklin* is located at the Vancouver Maritime Museum.
Highlights: The RV *Ben Franklin* (deep ocean explorer, **Website:**
www.vancouvermaritimemuseum.com/
General Information: The RV *Ben Franklin* was built between 1966 and 1968 in Switzerland for deep ocean explorer Jacques Piccard and the Grumman Aircraft Engineering Corporation. She was christened "America's largest submersible." Her namesake, American patriot and inventor Ben Franklin, was the first to map the Gulf Stream and gave it its name.
The submersible made a famous 30-day drift dive off the East Coast of the United States and Canada in 1969, mapping the Gulf Stream's

currents and sea life. She also made space exploration history by studying the behavior of aquanauts in a sealed, self-contained, self-sufficient capsule for NASA.
She was also involved in acoustic, marine biological, chemical and other experiments as well as deep water salvage operations, pollution studies, photo mapping of the sea floor and ocean environment research for the U.S. Navy. Horton Trading Company donated her to the Vancouver Maritime Museum in December 1999.
Admission: Entry fee, senior and student rates, special group discounts. Open Monday – Saturday, 10 A.M.- 5 P.M., Sunday noon to 5 P.M. Closed Mondays from September - May.

VANCOUVER, BC

Vancouver Maritime Museum
1905 Ogden Avenue
Vancouver, BC V6J 1A2 Canada
(604) 257-8300 Fax: (604) 737-2621
E-mail:director@vancouvermaritimemuseum.com
Location: In Vancouver head west on Cornwall to Cypress Street. The site is at the foot of Cypress Street, Vanier Park.
Highlights: The *St. Roch* (pronounced ROCK), (Royal Canadian Mounted Police Arctic patrol vessel), research vessel *Ben Franklin*, International Heritage Vessels at adjoining Heritage Harbour, ship models, library/Children's Maritime Discovery Centre,
Website:www.vancouvermaritimemuseum.com/
General Information: The Vancouver Maritime Museum is dedicated to preserving the rich maritime history and traditions of the Pacific Coast and is Vancouver's link to maritime history, art, culture and technology. Step back in time onboard *St. Roch*, National Historic Site, Canada's celebrated RCMP Arctic schooner housed ashore. Wander the ship's narrow corridors, where it is still 1944 and you are one of the crew on her second and most famous voyage through the treacherous Northwest Passage.
The Maritime Museum has lots to see and do for landlubbers and old salts. Explore the many permanent and changing exhibits the museum has to offer — pirates, shipwrecks, lighthouses, the early fur trade, fireboats, warships named Vancouver, deep-ocean exploration, shipbuilding, coastal and transpacific steamship lines, cruise ships and so much more. Experience the fun of Children's Maritime Discovery Centre and see working and historic vessels in Heritage Harbour. British Columbia's rich maritime heritage is housed at the Vancouver Maritime Museum on the shores of Kitsilano's Vanier Park.
Built in 1959, the Museum is the only institution on the mainland to document the

cultural and material history of the generations of British Columbians who have drawn their livelihood from the sea. Its particular focus is on the Port of Vancouver — from the first explorers to enter our waters to today's international cruise ship facility.

Adjoining the Museum is the *St. Roch*, the RCMP Arctic patrol ship that was the first ship to sail the Northwest Passage from the Pacific to the Atlantic Ocean.

A unique feature of the Vancouver Maritime Museum is Heritage Harbour, with it's revolving display of vessels ranging from locally built yachts to restored schooners and replicas of historic ships. In July of 1987, the Museum received another important addition — a sixty-foot long mural recounting Vancouver's maritime history unveiled on the west exterior wall of the building. The mural, donated by the legal firm Rand and Edgar, under the Vancouver Legacies Programme, was created by one of Canada's foremost muralists, Frank Lewis.

In addition to featuring traveling and in-house exhibitions, the Maritime Museum offers a wide variety of public and school programming, including model boat building and sea skills, and the first-of-its-kind Children's Maritime Discovery Centre.

Activities: Guided tours of the *St. Roch*; Heritage Harbour for historic vessel interpretation.

Admission: Entry fee. Open seven days a week from 10 a.m. – 5 p.m. Closed Mondays in the Winter.

VICTORIA, BC
Maritime Museum of British Columbia
28 Bastion Square
Victoria, British Columbia V8W 1H9 Canada
(250) 385-4222 Fax: (250) 382-2869
E-mail: on website
Location: The Museum is on Bastion Square (View and Wharf Streets), several blocks north of the Parliament buildings along Victoria's harbour front.
Highlights: The *Tilikum* (dugout canoe), ship models, figureheads, naval uniforms, library, gift shop, **Website:** www.mmbc.bc.ca/
General Information: The Maritime Museum of British Columbia, founded in 1955, exhibits a collection of artifacts, documents, models and pictures on the maritime history of British Columbia, the West Coast of North America, and the Pacific Rim.

Located in the historic Provincial Court House (a national heritage building constructed in 1889), the Museum displays cover the history of British Columbia's maritime tradition, from the days of Captain Cook's early exploration and coastal

shipping to the days of the Canadian Pacific Railway ships and the U.S. Navy in the Pacific Northwest.

The famous *Tilikum*, sailed by Captain Voss from Victoria to England (1901-1904), is housed in the Museum.

An extensive library of books, photographs, and periodicals is available for Society members. Research requests mailable for anyone. Extensive collection of ships plans.

Activities: Films, lectures, and tours for members and public.

Admission: Entry fee. Memberships are available. Open: daily, 9:30 A.M.-4:30 P.M.; June 15 – Sept. 15, , 9:30 A.M.-5:30 P.M. Closed Christmas and New Year's Day.

VICTORIA, BC
Royal British Columbia Provincial Museum
675 Belleville Street
Victoria, BC V8W 9W2 Canada
(250) 356-7226 or 1-888-447-7977
Fax: (250) 387-5674 Toll free: 1-888-447-7977
E-mail: reception@royalbcmuseum.bc.ca
Location: On the southern tip of Vancouver Island, the Royal British Columbia Museum is at the corner of Belleville and Douglas Street, close to both the Parliament Buildings and the Empress Hotel in downtown Victoria.
Highlights: HMS *Discovery* cabin,
Website: www.royalbcmuseum.bc.ca/
General Information: The Royal British Columbia Provincial Museum is a general history museum. Among its many exhibits is a full-size replica of the stern section of HMS *Discovery* complete with after cabins.
Admission: Entry fee. Open Monday to Sunday 9 A.M.. to 5 P.M. year-round. Closed Christmas and New Year's Day.

MANITOBA, CANADA

SELKIRK, MANITOBA
Lower Fort Garry National Park
5981 Highway 9
St. Andrews, Manitoba R1A 1N2 Canada
1-888-773-8888 (204) 785-6050
Fax: (204) 482-5887
E-mail: On web site.
Location: The historic site is on the Red River, a half hour northeast of Winnipeg by car, on PTH-9. It can also be reached by boat and by scheduled buses from Winnipeg and Selkirk.
Highlights: Water transportation in the fur trade, York boats,
Website: www.parkscanada.gc.ca/garry

General Information: Once an important outpost of the Hudson's Bay Company, the fort is now one of Parks Canada's protected heritage sites. Its history is presented through a costumed animation program portraying the mid-19th century; museum displays, and school programs. Lower Fort Garry's position on the Red River and its proximity to an agricultural settlement, a source of produce and a source of labour for boat tripmen, were the keys to its historic importance in the context of the Canadian fur trade.

The waterways of the North had been used since ancient times by Aboriginal peoples in canoes, who were followed by the first traders when they adopted the native craft. The York boat became the workhorse of the Hudson's Bay Company from the 18th century to the early 20th century. It carried more freight for the number of men employed, than canoes. The fort houses replicas of the York boats.

Admission: Entry fee. Open mid-May-1st week in September, 9 A.M.- 5 P.M.

SELKIRK, MANITOBA
Marine Museum of Manitoba
490 Eveline Street, P.O. Box 7
Selkirk, Manitoba R1A 2B1 Canada
(204) 482-7761 Fax: (204) 785-2452
E-mail: marinemuseum@mts.net
Location: Selkirk is on the Red River, 20 minutes northeast of Winnipeg on PTH-9. The Museum is in Selkirk Park at corner of Eveline and Queen St
Highlights: The SS *Keenora* (lake steamer), The CGS *Bradbury* (steam vessel), The MS *Peguis II* (tug boat), The MS *Lady Canadian* (fish freighter), The *Chickama II* (passenger vessel), *Joe Simpson* (lake freighter), Black Bear Island lighthouse and keeper's cabin, original York boat,
Website: www.marinemuseum.com
General Information: Manitoba's history comes to life in The Marine Museum of Manitoba, founded in 1972. Lying alongside the famous Red River where nearby it enters Lake Winnipeg. The Museum reflects Selkirk's nautical past through six restored ships, all of which are safely on land next to the Red River. And other displays include outboard motors and tools used in ship building in the early 1900s. In order to protect the many Lake Winnipeg vessels in the Museum's care, all have become shore-bound where visitors have easy access to each one.

The SS *Keenora*, a steamer built in 1897, was brought to Lake Winnipeg in 1923 and houses nautical artifacts and photographs. The CGS *Bradbury*, a steam vessel built in 1915, and the CGS *Peguis II*, a tugboat, houses documents of the marine history of the Red River and Lake Winnipeg.

Other museum vessels are: MS *Lady Canadian* (1942), a former fish freighter; *Chickama II* (1944), a former York boat used for passengers and freight between the far-flung trading posts of the Hudson's Bay Company; and *Joe Simpson*, a flat-bottomed lake freighter that took the place of the *Chickama II*. Because of its shallow draft, it took passengers from Warren's Landing to Norway House, where deep-draft vessels could not go. And finally, the famous York boat displayed here on behalf of Lower Fort Garry. A lighthouse from Lake Winnipeg's Black Bear Island is also on display. A written documentary chronicles the history of water skiing.

Admission: Entry fee. Open May (long weekend-September (long weekend), Monday-Friday, 9 A.M.- 5 P.M.; Saturday/Sunday and holidays, 10 A.M.- 6 P.M.
NOTE: Nearby Lower Fort Garry houses historical information on the York Boats.

WINNIPEG, MANITOBA
Naval Museum of Manitoba
1 Navy Way
Winnipeg, Manitoba RC3 4J7
(204) 943-7745
E-mail: curator@naval-museum.mb.ca
Location: The Museum is in downtown Winnipeg. To gain access to the museum, which is located in the HMCS Chippawa building, enter through the south door. There is a doorbell/buzzer that must be used to gain entry.
Highlights: Gift shop
Website: www.naval-museum.mb.ca/contact.htm
General Information: The Naval Museum of Manitoba opened in 1980. During WWII, a large number of prairie men and women joined the navy. They flocked to recruiting divisions in cities like Winnipeg, Regina, Saskatoon, Edmonton and Calgary. During the war, recruiting in Winnipeg was the greatest of anyplace inland, and was only surpassed by recruiting on the east and west coast.
Admission: Entry fee. Open Wednesdays 9 A.M. to 3 P.M.

NEW BRUNSWICK, CANADA

GRAND MANAN, NB
Grand Manan Museum
1143 Route 776 P. O. Box 66
Grand Harbour, Grand Manan,
New Brunswick E5G 4E9 Canada
(506) 662-3524 Fax: (506) 662-3009
E-mail: gmadmin@grandmananmuseum.ca

Location: I-95 to Bangor, Maine, exiting onto SR-9. Follow SR-9 ninety-five miles into Calais, Maine, where you exit onto Rte. 1, Canada. After approximately twenty-three miles, turn onto Rte. 785 toward Blacks Harbour. The museum is located in Grand Harbour, Grand Manan Island, roughly nineteen miles off the coast of Maine in the Bay of Fundy, a thirty-mile (one and one-half-hour) ferryboat ride south from Blacks Harbour.
Highlights: Maritime history, Grand Manan Archives **Website:** www.grandmananmuseum.ca/
General Information Founded in 1967, the Grand Manan Museum exhibits a collection of local history and geology; the "Moses" collection of birds of Grand Manan Island; The Walter B. McLaughlin Marine Gallery, and a new marine gallery that investigates the history of local fishing. In addition, navigation, shipbuilding techniques, commerce, and shipwrecks are depicted through the use of marine charts, paintings, photographs, and artifacts. The lens and mechanism of the old Gannet Rock Lighthouse are also on display.
    The museum houses the Grand Manan Archives and the sales desk has several original island publications.
Activities: Summer nature school during July and August; slide shows/talks twice weekly in season.
Admission: Entry fee. Open Monday-Saturday, 10 A.M..-4:30 P.M., Sunday, 1 P.M. - 5 P.M., June 15-end-September.

HOPEWELL CAPE, NB
Albert County Museum
Albert County Historical Society
3940 Route 114 P. O. Box 3
Hopewell Cape, New Brunswick E4H 3j8 Canada
(506) 734-2003 Fax: (506) 734-3291
E-mail: albertcountymuseum@nb.aibn.com
Location: Hopewell Cape is on Rte. 114 (the Tidal Trail), midway between Moncton and Fundy National Park. The museum is in an old jail house on west bank of Petitcodiac River.
Highlights: Local historical items, ship models, **Website:** www.albertcountymuseum.ca/
General Information: Albert County Museum, founded in 1957, is a "Museum in a gaol" (former County Jail built in 1845). In addition to the "dungeon," mineral samples and early furnishings, the museum contains maritime exhibits.
    Many wooden sailing ships were built in Albert County. Among them was Rear-admiral Peary's *Roosevelt*, the ship that carried him on his successful and historic voyage in 1909 to discover the North Pole. * Models and photographs of wooden ships and the plans and tools used in building the ships are on display here.

Admission: Entry fee. Open Monday-Saturday, 10 A.M.- 6 P.M., Sunday, 10 A.M.-8 P.M. June 15-Mid September.
See also The Peary-MacMillan Arctic Museum in Maine.

ST. JOHN, NEW BRUNSWICK
New Brunswick Museum
277 Douglas Avenue
Saint John, New Brunswick E2K 1E5 Canada
(506) 643-2300 Fax: (506) 643-2360
Toll free: 1-888-268-9595
E-mail: nbmuseum@nbm-mnb.ca
Location: The museum is situated on Douglas Avenue just five minutes west of downtown Saint John. Coming from the south on Rte. 1, take the Catherwood exit to Raynes Avenue, then turn north onto Douglas. If you're coming from the north, exit at Mills Street, then turn west onto Douglas.
Highlights: New Brunswick history, New Brunswick Paleontology, New Brunswick animals/whales, Ship models and portraits, Scrimshaw, Gift shop
Website: www.nbm-mnb.ca/
General Information: The New Brunswick Museum was founded in 1842 and displays objects of the natural and human history of New Brunswick and the Atlantic region. Marine collections include half models, navigational instruments, shipbuilding tools, ship's carvings, scrimshaw, ship models and ship portraits.
Admission: Entry fee. Open daily 10 A.M.-5 P.M., May 15-Labour Day; Labor Day-May 14, Monday-Thursday, 10 A.M.-5 P.M., Friday, 10 A.M.-9 P.M., Saturday and Sunday, 12 noon – 5 P.M.

SHIPPAGAN, NB
Aquarium and Marine Center
(Centre Marin de Shippagan)
100 Aquarium Street, P. O. Box 1010
Shippagan, New Brunswick E8S 1H9 Canada
(506) 336-3013 Fax: (506) 336-3057
E-mail: info@aquariumnb.ca
Location: Reached by traveling north on Federal Highway 11 and Local Highway 345, the center is located near the northeast end of Gloucester, New Brunswick, overlooking the Bay of Chaleur.
Highlights: A new aquarium, the "touch-tank", where you can touch the aquatic life. Gift shop, **Website:** www.gnb.ca/aquarium/
General Information: Shippagan (the Micmac Indian word for "Passage of Ducks") Aquarium and Marine Center is a fascinating complex that explores the underwater life and world of fishing in the Gulf of St. Lawrence, which is home to many fish species. From the powerful wolf fish with its threatening jaw to the graceful lumpfish, you will meet typical local fish in more than thirty

tanks. Over 800 slides and a twenty-minute commentary reveal the stormy history of fishing in the Gulf, the waters of which have been the object of many revelries and much greed from the twelfth century to modern time.

An ultramodern wheelhouse equipped with electronic instruments (some of them operating while visitors watch), makes one realize the importance of electronics for today's commercial fisherman. A computerized map provides visitors with valuable information on the fisheries in the Gulf of St. Lawrence. Gears, photographs, and diagrams complete the exhibition on fishing and its techniques.

Activities: Audiovisual presentation of fishing industry of the Gulf of Saint Lawrence, and restoration of a 1904 lighthouse (with access to tower)

Admission Entry fee. Open daily, 10 A.M. to 6 P.M. May-September.

NEWFOUNDLAND, CANADA

MUSGRAVE HARBOUR, NFLND
Fishermen's Museum
4 Marine Drive P.O. Box 159
Musgrave Harbour, Newfoundland A0G 3J0
(709) 655-2119 Fax: (709) 655-2064
E-mail: bantinghti@aibn.com
Location: Ferry to Port Aux Basques from North Sydney, Cape Breton Island. Take Rte. 1 north by northeast approximately 300 miles to the intersection of Rte. 330. Bear north about thirty-six miles on Rte. 330 into Musgrave Harbour on the coast of Hamilton Sound.
Highlights: Artifacts reflecting life of fishermen in area, Ship models, Books, newspapers, pictures and more, **Web Site:**
www.musgraveharbour.com/museum.html
General Information: The Fishermen's Museum is housed in a building designed by Sir William Coaker, founder of the Fishermen's Protective Union. Collections include: items pertaining to fisheries; ship models, such as a miniature fishing boats; engines; photographs; and logbooks from the lighthouse (1902) that contain accounts of local shipwrecks.
Activities: Conducted tours.
Admission: Entry fee. Open daily 8 A.M.- 5 P.M., June-mid-September.

ST. JOHN'S, NFLND
The Rooms Provincial Museum Division
9 Bonaventure Ave. P.O. Box 1800, Stn. C.
St. John's, Newfoundland A1C 5P9
(709) 757-8000 Fax: (709) 757-8017

Highlights: Newfoundland history
Website: www.therooms.ca/ca/museum
General Information: Our museum is a study of a place and its many peoples. Come face to face with a polar bear on the trunda. Look closely at carnivorous plants in a bog. Marvel at seabirds, sea mammals, all kinds of sea life. See how a remarkable mix of plants and animals found their niche here since the glaciers retreated.

And meet the peoples who came from almost every direction to make their lives on the land and from the sea.

Activities: The Rooms Café open during regular operation until hour before closing daily.

Admission: Entry fee: Free admission on Wed. nights from 6 – 9 pm the first Sat. of each month (Nov – May); Gen. admission fees do not apply to the Archives. First time users of Archives, there is an initial ten-dollar fee to obtain permanent Researcher Registration Number.

Closed Monday. Open Tues-Sat 10 am to 5 pm. Wed. 10 am – 9 pm. Thurs – Sat 10 am-5 pm. Sun – 12 pm – 5 p.m.

The Rooms is closed on Christmas Eve/Day, Boxing Day, New Year's Day, Good Friday, Remembrance Day. On July 1 and Labour Day, open from 12 pm – 5 pm.

NOVA SCOTIA, CANADA

ANNAPOLIS ROYAL, NOVA SCOTIA
O'Dell House Museum
136 St. George Street
P.O. Box 503
Annapolis Royal, NS B0S 1A0 Canada
(902) 532-7754 Fax: (902) 532-0700
E-mail: historic@ns.aliantzinc.ca
Location: From the ferry landing at Digby, Annapolis Royal is approximately 25 klm northwest on Hwy 1.
Highlights: Local maritime History, **Website:** www.annapolisheritagesociety.com/odell.htm
General Information: The O'Dell House Museum is located at the head of the old ferry slip and is housed in the building that once faced the wharves and shipyards on which Annapolis Royal thrived. Two rooms of the display — ship's models, paintings, tools, etc. — highlight the local shipbuilding and merchatile history of the town. As well, the Museum's archival/genealogical resource centree features photo and family histories which related to this topic.
Admission: Entry fee. Open year-round; hours vary.

191

BARRINGTON, NOVA SCOTIA
Seal Island Light Museum
2401 Highway 3, RR 1
Barrington, Nova Scotia B0W 1E0 Canada
(902) 637-2185
E-mail: barmuseumcomples@eastlink.ca
Location: Barrington is 45 klms southeast of
Shelburne. The lighthouse is located across the
road from the Tourist Information Centre in
Barrington.
Highlights: Fresnel lenses, local history artifacts.
Website: www.
nslps.com/lights/lighthouse_page_01.asp?ID=363
   General Information: The Seal island light
museum is a 35-foot replica of the 67-foot
lighthouse on Seal Island. The island is located
approximately 20 miles southeast of Cape Sable
Island at the elbow of the Fundy inlet where tides
rank the highest in the world. When the light on
Seal Island was first lit in 1831, it was just a
beacon. In 1892, the seal oil was replaced with a 5-
wick-kerosene light and in 1902, to a kerosene
vapor light.
   The 2nd-order Fresnel light was fixed for 76
years, but in 1907, a revolving mechanism, counter
clockwise, was installed, giving three flashed and
one blank with flashes occurring every 10 seconds.
Finally, in 1959, the lighthouse became electrically
operated with the use of a generator electric light
was installed, all in the original Fresnel lens.
   In May 1878 the automated light took over for
the old light and the lightheeper. Earlier, in 1977,
citizens of southwest Nova Scotia learned about
the replacement of the Seal Island light and
petitioned to the Minister of Transport. It resulted
in the Cape Sable Historical Society raising the
necessary funds to construct the replica lighthouse.
The complicated operating mechanism and the
lantern were dismantled and transported by
helicopter to Cape Sable Island where they were
turned over to municipal authorities and
subsequently to the Society.
   The light Museum was opened in 1985,
providing an historical background to this
important light. Along with other important
artifacts are a 4th-order Fresnel lens from Bon
Portage Island and other items relating to local
shipping.
   Admission: Entry fee. Open June to September,
Monday-Saturday from 9:30 A.M.-
5 P.M. On Sunday, from 1 P.M. to 5:30 P.M.

BRIDGEWATER, NOVA SCOTIA
HMCS *Fraser* (DDE-233, later DDH-233)
Box 233, Unit 17
450 LaHave Street
Bridgewater, NS B4V 3T2
(902) 543-3925 Fax: (902) 624-1537
E-mail: r.welford@ns.sympatico.ca

Location: The *Fraser* is located at Bridgewater
some 10 miles upriver from the Atlantic Ocean and
187 miles west of Lunenburg.
Highlights: The HMCS *Fraser*,
   General Information: The HMCS *Fraser* is the
last surviving ship of the St. Laurent-class
destroyer escorts. When first operational, they
were known as the "Cadillacs" of the NATO fleet.
Their unusual underwater surface and rounded
hulls
allowed them to actively hunt submarines at speeds
of up to 18 knots, in any weather or sea condition.
Fraser was towed to her new home of Bridgewater
on December 18, 1997 where she is the cornerstone
of a marina and coastal cruise liner port on the
Bridgewater waterfront.
   Admission: **The Fraser may be sunk.** Contact
Museum for information.

CENTERVILLE, NOVA SCOTIA
Archelaus Smith Museum
Archelaus Smith Historical Society
P.O. Box 190
Clark's Harbour, Nova Scotia B0W 1P0   Canada
(902) 745-2411 or 3361 or 3227
E-main: blancherossoconnell@hotmail.com
Location: Cape Sable Island is about 155 miles
southwest of Halifax. The museum is located in
Centerville, roughly three miles south of the
junction of Rtes. 3 and 330 across the Cape Sable
Island Causeway.
Highlights: Boat building, Fishing industry,
Website: http://destination-
ns.com/common/property.asp?DirectoryID=1872
   General Information: The Archelaus Smith
Museum, founded in 1970, exhibits artifacts
pertaining to the marine involvement of the
community such as the fishing industry and boat
building. Other displays include artifacts from the
shipwrecks and works by local artists that
illustrate the history of Cape Sable Island and
genealogical information.
   Activities: Research projects
   Admission: No entry fee. Open daily,
9:30 A.M.-5:30 P.M., June 15-late September.

HALIFAX, NOVA SCOTIA
HMCS *Sackville* (K-181)
The Canadian Naval Memorial Trust
P.O. Box 99000 Station Forces
Halifax, NS B3K 5X5 Canada
(902) 429-2132 (Summer),
(902) 427-2837 (Winter) Fax: (902) 427-1346
E-mail: secretary@hmcssackville-cnmt.ns.ca
Location: The ship is located in downtown Halifax,
behind the Maritime Museum of the Atlantic
Highlights: HMCS *Sackville, Action Stations*
Newsletter,

192

Website: www.hmcssackville-cnmt.ns.ca/
General Information: The HMCS *Sackville* (K-181) is the last remaining Corvette of the 236 that were laid down in Canada and Britain during WW II. Her Operational career was spent escorting convoys between St. John's, Newfoundland, and engaged in oceanographic, hydrographic, and fisheries research. Retired from the Royal Canadian Navy in Londonderry, North Ireland. After the war, the *Sackville* was laid up in reserve. But in 1952, the ship was reactivated and spent the next 30 years 1982, *Sackville* was transferred to the Canadian Naval Corvette Trust and restored to her 1944 appearance. And on May 4, 1985, *Sackville* was formally dedicated as the Canadian Naval Memorial.
Admission: Entry: Open: Monday to Saturday, 10 A.M. – 5:30 P.M. and 12:00 Noon – 5:30 P.M. on Sundays.

HALIFAX, NOVA SCOTIA
Maritime Command Museum
Admiralty House
2725 Gottingen Street, P.O. Box 99000
Halifax, Nova Scotia B3K 3C9 Canada
(902) 721-8205 Fax: (902) 721-8541
E-mail: marcommuseum@forces.gc.ca
Location: The museum occupies Admiralty House, which lies between North, Gottingen, Russell and Barrington Streets, five blocks north of Citadel Hill in Halifax.
Highlights: History of the Royal Canadian Navy, Library,
General Information: Founded in 1974, the Maritime Command Museum is located in Admiralty House, which was built between 1814 and 1818. This Georgian style house first served as the official residence of the Commander in Chief of the British North American Station. Over the years it has been used as a summer residence, a hospital, and a wardroom.
The main objective of the Maritime Command Museum is to collect, preserve, and display the artifacts and history of the Canadian Maritime Military Forces. The Museum also maintains a library and archives relevant to naval history and the Dockyard since 1759. It also houses a permanent collection displaying the history of the Royal Canadian Navy which was founded on May 4, 1910.
Activities: Guided tours
Admission: No entry fee. Open Monday-Friday, 9:00 A.M.-12 noon P.M. and 1 P.M.- 5 P.M. Sat. and Sun., 12:30 P.M. to 5 P.M.

HALIFAX, NOVA SCOTIA
Maritime Museum of the Atlantic
1675 Lower Water Street
Halifax, Nova Scotia B3J 1S3   Canada
(902) 424-7490   Fax: (902) 424-0612
E-mail: lunnge@gov.ns.ca
Location: The museum overlooks the waterfront on Lower Water Street in Halifax, Nova Scotia.
Highlights: The CSS *Acadia* (retired Canadian hydrographic survey vessel built in 1913), William Robertson & Son Ship Chandlery, "Age of Steam," "Navy Shipwrecks," and "Lifesaving's and Days of Sail" galleries, Ship models and seventy-five small craft, Library (4,000 titles and 20,000 photographs),
Website: http://museum.gov.ns.ca/mma/
General Information: Maritime Museum of the Atlantic, founded in 1948, exhibits nautical history through a wide range of marine artifacts, from ship's hardware (as exhibited in the turn of the century ship chandlery) to over seventy-five small craft and an 846-ton steamship, CSS *Acadia*, Canada's first purpose-built hydrographic survey vessel.
The museum also has over 350 ship models, a large collection of navigational instruments, and shipwright's tools. Its research library contains over 4,000 titles, 20,000 photographs, and a small collection of vessel plans.
The museum is the marine history branch of the Nova Scotia Museum. Together with the Fisheries Museum of the Atlantic in Lunenburg, it collects, preserves, and interprets the material culture of the marine history of the Atlantic Provinces.
Activities: Regular interpretive programs and tours June 1-October 15, school programs, special spring oceanography program, and research.
Admission: Entry fee, but donations accepted. Open daily, October 16-June 30, 9:30 A.M. – 5 P.M. , except Monday (closed), Tuesdays, 9:30 A.M.-8 P.M. and Sundays 1 P.M.-5 P.M. Open daily, July 1-October 15, 9:30 A.M.-5:30 P.M. except Tuesday, 9:30 A.M.-8 P.M. and Sundays, 1 P.M.-5:30 P.M. *Acadia*; open from June 1 - October 15.

HANTSPORT, NOVA SCOTIA
**Churchill House and
Marine Memorial Room Museum**
Main Street, P.O. Box 396
Hantsport, Nova Scotia B0P 1P0   Canada
(902) 684-3365 or 3327 E/M: heritage@gov.ns.ca
Location: Churchill House is located in Hantsport, forty-two miles north by northwest from Halifax (just beyond Windsor) on Rte. 101. The Museum is in the Community Centre, Main Street.

Highlights: Churchill House and Museum, Ship Models, **Website:** http://museum.gov.ns.ca/musdir/churchillhouse&marineroom.htm

General Information: The Churchill House and Marine Room Museum, founded in 1967, is housed in the home (c. 1860) of Ezra Churchill, a Nova Scotia shipbuilder. The Marine Memorial Room, overlooking the Avon River, takes the visitor back to early shipbuilding days when many a fine vessel was launched to sail the seven seas. At one time, Hantsport was rated fifth in the world as a builder of fine ships, a total of 120 ships having been built there.

Exhibits include shipbuilding tool, nautical instruments, old logs, ship models, and pictures.

Admission: No entry fee, but donations accepted. Open daily, 10 A.M.-noon and 1 P.M.-5 P.M., Mar 24 - August 2.

LA HAVE ISLAND, NOVA SCOTIA
La Have Islands Marine Museum
100 Lahave Islands Road P.O. Box 69
La Have, Nova Scotia B0R 1C0 Canada
(902) 688-2973 or (902) 688-3192 (Fax too)
E-mail: limms@auracom.com
Location: Travel seventy-two miles south of Halifax on Rte. 103. At exit 15 and at the junction of Rte. 331 on the lighthouse route, turn east toward Petite Riviere and Rissers Beach Provincial Park to Crescent Beach — the road tothe La Have Islands.
Highlights: Maritime history,
Website: www.lahaveislandsmarinemuseum.ca/
General Information: The La Have Island Marine Museum, founded in 1972, was previously a church and now houses a collection of marine artifacts.
Admission: No entry fee, but donations accepted. Open daily, 10 A.M.-6 P.M., July-August; Saturdays and Sundays, 1 P.M. - 6 P.M., September.

LIVERPOOL, NOVA SCOTIA
Queens County Museum
109 Main Street, P. O. Box 1078
Liverpool, Nova Scotia B0T 1K0 Canada
(902) 354-4058 Fax: (902) 354-2050
E-mail: rafusela@gov.ns.ca
Location: Situated in the southwest tip of Nova Scotia, Liverpool is approximately eighty-five miles west of Halifax on Rte. 103.
Highlights: Shipbuilding history,
Website: www.queenscountymuseum.com/
General Information: Built in 1980, Queens County Museum is adjacent to the 200-year-old Perkin House and is designed to resemble the original buildings surrounding it.

The Main Gallery exhibit introduces Queens County with displays of its natural setting of — land, rivers, and ocean. The exhibit demonstrates historically how mankind and nature have combined to yield the lifestyle of today's residents. The museum collection of artifacts and records pertains to the history of residents and industries in the county since 1760; the development of local fishing, lumbering, and shipbuilding; the period of the privateers. History buffs and genealogists enthusiasts will find the museum a worthwhile place to visit. The Queens County Historical Society maintains extensive archives.

Admission: No entry fee, but donations accepted. Open Monday-Saturday, 9:30 A.M.-5:30 P.M., Sunday, 1 P.M.-5:30 P.M. in summer; in winter, Monday-Saturday, 9 A.M.-5 P.M.; closed Sunday.

LOUISBOURG, NOVA SCOTIA
Louisbourg Marine Museum
7548 Main Street, P. O. Box 316
Louisbourg, Nova Scotia B1C 1J4 Canada
(902) 733-2252 Fax: (902) 733-2053
Location: Once on Cape Breton Island (northeastern Nova Scotia), take either Rte. 105 or Rte. 4 to Sydney, then travel south on Rte. 22 to Louisbourg. The museum is on the ground floor of a building (c. 1895) on Main Street.
Highlights: Early local fishery artifacts, shipwreck artifacts, ship models,
Website: http://cbmuseums.tripod.com/PreviouslyFeaturedMuseums/LMM.html
General Information: The ocean embraces a rich world which that, for the most part, remains hidden from our eyes by the restless surface of its water. It's a world full of secrets into which the Atlantic Statiquarium Marine Museum will give you a glimpse.

In this unique museum, founded in 1977, you will be pleasantly introduced to many creatures and objects from the local marine environment. See the recovered sunken treasure of the *Le Chameau*, wrecked in 1725, and other historic shipwrecks of particular interest to divers and history buffs.

See also the exhibits featuring ship models, marine artifacts, and many items used by local fishermen until just a few years ago. Visitors can observe sea-creatures and their behavior from close-up at the saltwater aquarium. Their fossilized ancestors on display give evidence of life in the seas during times that even predate dinosaurs.

LUNENBURG, NOVA SCOTIA
Fisheries Museum of the Atlantic
68 Bluenose Drive, P. O. Box 1363
Lunenburg, Nova Scotia B0J 2C0 Canada
(902) 634-4794 FAX: (902) 634-8990
Free: 1-866-579-4909 E-mail: fma@gov.ns.ca

Location: The town of Lunenburg lies approximately sixty-five miles south of Halifax on Rte. 103. The museum is located at 68 Bluenose Drive on the historic Lunenburg waterfront.
Highlights: The *Theresa E. Conner* Last of Lunenburg salt bank schooners, The *Cape Sable* (steel-hulled side trawler/dragger), Aquarium, Dory Shop, Hall of Inshore Fisheries, Schooner *Bluenose* exhibit and memorabilia, Theatre of archival films and videos, Research library (1000 volumes), Photographic archives (10,000 images), *Dorymates* (bi-annual newsletter), Gift shop, Restaurant and Deli,
Website: http://museum.gov.ns.ca/fma/
General Information: The Fisheries Museum of the Atlantic, founded in 1967, has a collection that includes the *Theresa E. Conner*, built in 1938, the last of the salt- banking schooners to operate out of Lunenburg, and the *Cape Sable* , built in 1962, one of the fresh fish draggers of the Lunenburg fishing fleet.

The five buildings, which were originally part of W. C. Smith and Company's fish operations, house exhibits dealing with the Atlantic Canadian fishing industry, including inshore fishing vessels and an aquarium of fish representative of the types important to the industry; Documentation Centre and research library; photographic archives; education centre; and a Parks Canada exhibit dealing with the Grand Banks fisheries, during the Age of Sail. A theatre, gift shop, and restaurant are also on the grounds.

Activities: Films dealing with the fisheries; demonstrations of small boat construction; dory construction; dory rowing; fish filleting; net mending and knot tying; bait bag making; lobster trap making; rope and wire splicing; "hands on" participation in many activities; quilting; rug hooking; various school programmes.
Admission: Entry fee. Open daily, 9:30 A.M.- 5:30 P.M., June 1-October 15; off season by appointment.

MAHONE BAY, NOVA SCOTIA
Settler's Museum
578 Main Street
Mahone Bay, Nova Scotia B0J 2E0 Canada
(902) 624-6263 Fax: (902) 624-0646
E-mail: info@settlersmuseum.ns.ca
Location: Mahone Bay lies approximately forty-four miles southwest of Halifax via Rte. 103.
Highlights: Ship models,
Website: www.settlersmuseum.ns.ca/
General Information: The Settler's Museum, founded in 1978, contains a collection of materials used by first settlers of the district: clothing, kitchen equipment, furniture, farm equipment, pictures, quilts, dishes, boots, and shoes, together

with early shipbuilding tools and ship models from local shipyards.
Activities: Meetings, activity days; lectures
Admission: No entry fee, but donations accepted. Open Tuesday-Saturday 10 A.M.- 4 P.M., Sunday, 2 P.M.-4 P.M. year-round.

MAITLAND, NOVA SCOTIA
Lawrence House Museum
8660 Highway 215, RR#1,
Maitland, Nova Scotia B0N 1T0
(902) 261-2628 E-mail: pooledr@gov.ns.ca
Location: From Truro travel south/southwest on Rte. 102 to the junction with Rte. 236. Head toward South Maitland, then north about two miles into Maitland.
Highlights: Shipbuilding history,
Website: http://museum.gov.ns.ca/lh/
General Information: The Lawrence House, established as a museum in 1967, is located in the home of William D. Lawrence, designer and builder of the largest three-masted ship in Canada. Furnishings and memorabilia in the house relate to the Lawrence family and ship building in the Cobequid Bay area. The house is both a national and provincial historic site.

Typical of the grand homes of shipbuilders, shipowners, and captains, the Lawrence House was built about 1870 when Maitland and other towns in Nova Scotia were prosperous shipbuilding communities. In the early 1870s a number of vessels over 1,000 tons were being built; but Lawrence wanted to design and even larger one. In the fall of 1872, the keel was laid for a great ship the *William D. Lawrence*, and with the assistance of his brother Lockhart as master builder, his son John as foreman, and a work force of 75 men, Lawrence began to make his dream a reality. On October 27, 1874, over 4,000 people flocked to Maitland to witness the launching of the 2,459-ton ship.
Activities: Tours
Admission: No entry fee, but donations accepted. Open Monday -Saturday, 9:30 A.M.- 5:30 P.M., Sunday, 1 P.M.-5:30 P.M., June 15 - October 15.

PARRSBORO, NOVA SCOTIA
Ottawa House by-the-Sea
Shore Historic Society
1155 Whitehall Road, P.O. Box 98
Parrsboro, Nova Scotia, B0M 1S0 Canada
(902) 254-2376
E-mail: Ottawa.house@sympatico.ca
Location: From Moncton, New Brunswick, take Rte. 2 east/southwest through Sackville into Amherst. Parrsboro lies about thirty-eight miles south of Amherst on Rte. 2. In town, follow Main Street to Partridge Island Road.

Highlights: Shipbuilding history,
Website: www.ottawahouse.org
General Information: Ottawa House by-the-Sea, founded in 1979 as a museum, is the sole remnant of the original Partridge Island settlement. Once an inn, the house was built more than 200 years ago by James Ratchford, a prominent trader in the early history of Parrsboro.

Ottawa House is devoted to the shipbuilding and maritime heritage of the area. Exhibits include a collection of shipbuilding tools, photographs of many of the important vessels launched from local yards, and artifacts from the days of sail. Rooms on the second floor reflect the home's appearance during Sir Charles Tupper's residency.
Activities Museum tours
Admission: Entry fee. Open daily, 10 A.M. – 6 P.M., June-mid-September.

PORT GREVILLE, NOVA SCOTIA
Age of Sail Heritage Center
8334 On Highway 209, P.O. Box 14
Port Greville
Nova Scotia B0M 1T0 Canada
(902) 348-2060 (902) 254-**195**
E-mail: gbsmsageofsail@yahoo.com
Location: The Centre is on Route 209, approximately 15 km west of Parrsboro.
Highlights: Lumbering and shipbuilding, Gift Shop,
Website: www.ageofsailmuseum.ca/
General Information: Operated by the Greville Bay Shipbuilding Society the Age of Sail Heritage Centre, overlooking the tidal Greville River, pays tribute to the heritage of the communities along the Minas Channel from the Bay of Fundy to Cobequid Bay and ultimately Truro, Nova Scotia. History of lumbering and shipbuilding are brought to life through pictures, videos, story telling, artifacts, and hands-on exhibits along with activities for children.
Activities: To further your enjoyment, visit our Blacksmith Shop and tearoom Gift Shop.
Admission: Entry fee. Open June through Labor Day, 10 A.M. – 6 P.M., six days a week – closed Mondays. Open weekends in May, September, and October.

ST. PETERS, NOVA SCOTIA
St. Peters Canal
P.O. Box 8
St. Peters, Nova Scotia B0E 3B0 Canada
(902) 733-2280 Fax: (902) 733-2362
E-mail: information@pc.gc.ca
Location: St. Peters is 33 klms east of Port Hawkesbury on Rte. 4.
Highlights: Working canal, **Website:** www.pc.gc.ca/lhn-nhs/ns/stpeters/index_e.asp

General Information: St. Peters Canal is an 800 mile-long canal linking the Atlantic Ocean with Bras d'Or Lake. Work started on the canal in 1854 and was completed in 1869. The canal also boasts the only functioning lock system in Nova Scotia. View interpretive exhibits, enjoy a picnic lunch, or experience the canal by pleasure craft. The canal was declared a Canadian National Historic Site.
Activities: Reproductions in Pewter
Admission: Entry fee. Open daily, 10 A.M.-7 P.M., June-September; 10 A.M.-9 P.M., July-August.

SHELBURNE, NOVA SCOTIA
The Dory Shop
Dock Street, P. O. Box 39
Shelburne, Nova Scotia B0T 1W0 Canada
(902) 875-3219 Fax: (902) 875-4141
E-mail: beureegm@gov.ns.ca
Location: Shelburne lays approximately 109 miles south of Halifax on Rte. 103. The shop is on Dock Street, an exit off of Rte. 103.
Highlights: History of dory building,
Website: http://museum.gov.ns.ca/dory/
General Information: The Dory Shop, also known as the John Williams Dory Shop, *was* originally established in 1880 as part of the dory-building industry, which, at one time, included at least seven shops along the Shelburne waterfront. Thousands of dories were made and shipped all over the world. In 1877 Isaac Coffin Crowell designed, patented and built what was to become the famous Shelburne dory. Known for its exceptional strength, it was the dory preferred by Gloucester and other fishermen. John Williams served his apprenticeship under the guidance of Isaac Crowell.

When the John Williams Dory Shop was in operation, both the first and third floors were devoted to the storage of lumber, while the dories were built on the second floor. A visitor to the Dory Shop would have seen a number of dories in various states of completion — an early version of the assembly line. The shop's seven or so employees produced 350 dories per year.

The Dory Shop was affected by the decline in dory production and ceased operations in 1971. It was reopened in 1983 as a branch of the Nova Scotia Museum and now operated for the Museum by the Shelburne Historical Society.
Activities: Demonstration of dory building
Admission: No entry fee, but donations accepted. Open daily, 9:30 A.M.-5:30 P.M., June 1-September 15.

YARMOUTH, NOVA SCOTIA

Yarmouth County Museum
22 Collins Street
Yarmouth, Nova Scotia B5A 3C8 Canada
(902) 742-5539 Fax: (902) 749-1120
E-mail: ycmuseum@eastlink.ca
Location: Located on the southwestern tip of Nova Scotia, Yarmouth is approximately 192 miles south of Halifax on Rte. 103. Ferries leave from Portland and Bar Harbor, Maine. The museum is located at 22 Collins Street in downtown Yarmouth.
Highlights: Ship portrait collection, Library/archives, Bookshop, **Website:** http://yarmouthcountymuseum.ednet.ns.ca/
General Information: The Yarmouth County Museum contains in its exhibits and records a picture of the continuity of life in one of Canada's oldest seaport communities. Settlers from New England founded Yarmouth in 1761. Shipping and allied trades made the town prosperous in the nineteenth century, and in the 1870's was Canada's leading seaport, per capita of population, in number and tonnage of sailing ships. The museum's collection of ship paintings and models, the period rooms, costumes, and pioneer artifacts, all tell their own story for visitors.

The museum also boasts a research library and archive. Awards: 1982 Award of Merit, American Association for State and Local History and 1989 Canadian Parks Service Heritage Award.
Activities: Historical Society meeting held monthly
Admission: Entry fee. Open Monday-Saturday, 9 A.M.-5 P.M., Sunday, 2 P.M.-5 P.M., June 1-October 15; Tuesday-Saturday, 2 P.M.-5 P.M., October 16-May 31.

ONTARIO, CANADA

CHAFFEY'S LOCK, ONTARIO

Lockmaster House Museum
Chaffey's Lock and Area Heritage Society.
Director: Preston Scott, Seasonal Curator
1724 Chaffey's Lock Road, RRI P.O. Box 50
Chaffeys Lock, Ontario K0G 1E0 Canada
(613) 359-5022
E-mail: suemaclat@sympatico.ca
Location: The Museum is located on the Rideau Canal at Chaffey's Lock. From Canada Rte. 401 at the end of U.S. I-81, turn west to Exit 645. Turn north on Rte. 32, 18 kms where Rte. 32 becomes Rte. 15. Continue 18 kms to Rte. 9, near Elgin, turning west for 9 kms (6 miles) to Chaffey's Lock and hamlet.
Highlights: Chaffey's Lock lockstation, swing bridge over lock, gift shop, publications

Website: www.rideau-info.com/lockhouse/index.html
General Information: The Museum is on the site of a defensible lockmaster's house built in 1844 to defend the canal against US-based raiders, and is now restored to the 1894 period, when the building was modernized by the federal government. The hamlet of Chaffey's Lock is one of the most charming along the beautiful Rideau Canal transiting from Kingston at Lake Ontario to Ottawa, the capitol of Canada. If you arrive by boat, you will be locked through by locktenders turning cranks to raise or lower the water in the locks and turning other cranks to open the lock gates, all by hand as was done in 1832. Arrival at Chaffey's Lock by boat or auto will enthrall you.

From the swing bridge, one can easily visualize the history of this quiet lockstation. For over a century steamers passed through the lock gates towing barges loaded with cordwood, cheese, minerals, and grain. The 1872 stone gristmill was the commercial hub of the surrounding countryside. All summer long, farmers lined up in wagons, patiently waiting for their wheat and corn to be ground.

At the Lockmaster's House Museum canal life in years gone by is interpreted through exhibits illustrating the daily work of the men and women who settled the shores of the Rideau Lakes and nearby Crosby Township and the Rideau Lakes region, with a special emphasis on the turn of the century (1890-1910).

Yearly changing exhibits; audiovisual presentation; and Samuel Chaffey (1793-1827) brochures along with a fine video entitled "The Golden Times" are available.
Admission: No entry fee. Donations appreciated. Open through the summer months, 9 A.M. to 5 P.M. daily.

COLLINGWOOD, ONTARIO

Collingwood Museum
45 St. Paul Street P. O. Box 556
Collingwood, Ontario L9Y 3P1 Canada
(705) 445-4811 Fax: (705) 445-9004
E-mail: museum@collingwood.ca
Location: At the juncture of Federal Highways 401 and 400 on the top end of Toronto, proceed north on Highway 400 to the City of Barrie (about 60 miles) to Provincial Highway 27.
Follow Highway 27 northwest about 8 miles to Highway 26. Proceed west on Highway 26 into Collingwood (about 35 miles). The Town of Collingwood, population 12,500, is located on the shores of Georgian Bay. The Museum is located in Memorial Park at Highway 26 and St. Paul Street, two blocks east of the community's downtown.

197

Highlights: Nineteenth-century ship models, videos, temporary exhibits, research,
General Information: The Collingwood Museum, founded in 1904 as the Huron Institute, is housed in a reproduction 1873 railway station, known as "The Station." Exhibits are devoted to the community and area history, the town's extensive boat and shipbuilding heritage, and the Petun Indians, who lived in the area from approximately 1600 to 1650s. Numerous 19th century ship models, archives, research opportunities and Museum store are part of the operation. The Museum maintains an archive of extensive marine publications, particularly in relation to Collingwood. Appointments to access the archives are required.

Activities: Films, group tours (by appointment only). The Museum's special events throughout the year include traditional Christmas celebrations.

Admission: Entrance fee. Open May 24th weekend to Canadian Thanksgiving open Monday to Saturday 9 A.M. to 5 P.M., Sunday Noon to 5 P.M. Canadian Thanksgiving to May 24th weekend, open Monday, Tuesday, Friday 9 A.M to 5 P.M., Saturday 10am to 5 P.M., and Sunday Noon to 5 P.M.

ELGIN, ONTARIO
Jones Falls Defensible Lockmaster's House and Blacksmith Shop
Southern Area Interpretation Office
Parks Canada, Rideau Canal
Box 10
Elgin, Ontario K0G 1E0 Canada
(613) 359-5377 Fax: (613) 359-6042
E-mail: RideauCanal-info@pc.gc.ca
Location: The lockmaster's house is about 2 1/2 miles west from Rte. 15 and adjacent to the Rideau Canal in the Southern Sector/Rideau Canal National Historic Site of Canada.
Website: www.pc.gc.ca/lhn-nhs/on/rideau/natcul/natcul2d_e.asp
General Information: The lockmaster's house, opened in 1980, is in the restored defensible lockmaster's house (Sweeny House) and an operational blacksmith shop (1840s), both furnished with original reproduction artifacts
Admission: No entry fee. Open from long holiday weekend in May to Thanksgiving weekend (Canadian).

GORE BAY, ONTARIO
Mississagi Strait Lighthouse Museum
Box 10
Gore Bay, Ontario P0P 1R0 Canada
705-283-3444

E-Mail: info@themississagililighthouse.com
Location: Located at the western tip of Manitoulin Island and at the end of Mississagi Lighthouse Road, off ON 540. The Museum is nine miles west of Meldrum Bay on Lake Huron.
Website:http://lighthouse.boatnerd.com/gallery/Huron/mississagistraight.htm
General Information: The Mississagi Strait Lighthouse, built in 1874 and opened as a Museum in 1972, was furnished as the dwelling of a lighthouse keeper and now maintains local history displays.
A rare diaphone fog horn (1908) protrudes from the upper portion of the fog signal building. The light was moved to a skeletal tower in 1970 and returned to the lighthouse in May 2003; the skeletal tower has been demolished.
The fog signal building is now a restaurant. Site open; museum and restaurant open
Admission: Entry fee. Open daily June through September.

HAMILTON, ONTARIO
Hamilton-Scourge Project
c/o Hamilton Military Museum
610 York Blvd.
Hamilton, Ontario L9H 5Z9 Canada
(905) 546-2872 Fax: (905) 546-2875
E-mail: military@hamilton.ca
Location: Hamilton is about forty-six miles west of Niagara Falls on Lake Ontario's waterfront.
Highlights: The *Hamilton* and *Scourge* (1812) schooners still to be raised from Lake Ontario), gift shop,
Website: www.hamilton.ca/museums
General Information: The *Hamilton-Scourge* Project, founded in 1980, relates to two armed merchant schooners from the War of 1812 that capsized on Lake Ontario in a squall on August 8, 1813. In 1973, the vessels were discovered intact and perfectly preserved in 300 feet of water, six miles off Port Dalhousie, Ontario.
Title to the vessels was transferred in 1980 to the City of Hamilton from the U.S. Navy through the U.S. Congress and the Royal Ontario Museum. It is expected that the two ships will be raised and exhibited in a world-class museum in Hamilton, Ontario. Three levels of Canadian Government — municipal, provincial, and federal — are participating in this project.
Hamilton-Scourge Society is open to membership by the general public, sells related posters, books, "National Geographic" (March 1983) limited edition prints. (Scholars welcome to study at the Project Offices, Monday-Friday, 9 A.M.-5 P.M.)

Activities: Research on the two schooners; speakers bureau; exhibition programme; interpretation centre open July-August, Wednesday-Sunday, 12 noon-5 P.M. *Admission:* No entry fee. Visitor's Centre open Wednesday-Sunday, noon-5 P.M., July and August.

KINGSTON, ONTARIO
Marine Museum of the Great Lakes at Kingston
55 Ontario Street
Kingston, Ontario K7L 2Y2   Canada
(613) 542-2261 Fax: (613) 542-0043
E-mail: marmus@marmuseum.ca
Location: Take I-81 north from Watertown, New York, thirty miles into Canada. At the junction of Rte. 401, bear west eight miles to Kingston on northeast shore of Lake Ontario. The Museum is near the Thousand Islands tourist area five blocks west of Kingston City Hall.
Highlights: The *Alexander Henry* (3,000-ton icebreaker, a bed and breakfast), publications, library and archives with 8,400 titles, gift shop, **Website:**www.marmuseum.ca
General Information: The Marine Museum of the Great Lakes at Kingston, founded in 1976, maintains exhibits that trace the development of shipping on the Great Lakes — our freshwater seas. Main exhibits on shipbuilding (begun in 1790) are displayed in four buildings along the east side of an 1891 dry-dock. A stone building, once a powerhouse, has its original machinery still in place that used to operate the heavy dry-dock gate and the pumps for emptying it.

Artifacts collected by divers and the shipping industry of the Great Lakes are exhibited along with the 3,000-ton, 210-foot icebreaker *Alexander Henry*, acquired in 1985, which operates as a Bed and Breakfast from mid-May to Labour Day. Almost all items in the Museum are related to ships and shipbuilding. Special exhibitions are changed regularly.

An important marine library and archival collection includes over 20,000 builders' drawings of Great Lakes ships as well as nineteenth- and twentieth-century shipping and shipbuilding records. *Activities:* Annual lectures. *Admission:* Entry fee. Memberships are available. Open January-March, Monday-Friday, 10 A.M.-4 P.M., April-December, open daily 10 A.M.-5 P.M.; Library and archives: open all year by appointment. Bed and breakfast operated mid-May-Labour Day.

MALLORYTOWN, ONTARIO
St. Lawrence Islands National Park/
Brown's Bay Wreck
2 County Road 5   R.R. 3
Mallorytown, Ontario K0E 1R0   Canada
(613) 923-5261 Fax: (613) 923-1021
E-mail: ont.sli@pc.gc.ca
Location: Take I-81 north from Watertown, New York, to Canada and east on 1000 Islands Parkway to Mallorytown Landing to the St. Lawrence Islands National Park. The Park is a collection of twenty-five islands between the cities of Kingston and Brockville.
Highlights: 1812 gunboat (a flat-bottomed clinker-built, i.e., with overlapping planks/plates like the clapboards on a house), **Website**: www.parkscanada.gc.ca/sli
General Information: "When I was a youngster, we used to go skating in Brown's Bay in the winter time, and if the ice was clear of snow and the moon was full, you could see a ship frozen in the ice with its copper fasteners shining like gold," noted a Museum publication. Her ribs black against the green of the River, children used her as a diving platform, duck hunters built blinds on her bow, and fishermen lost many a lure to her oaken sides. The old wreck lay quietly in the silt and sand of Brown's Bay.

In the mid 1960s, national park staff arranged for the hulk to be raised, and, because of certain markings, she was thought to be a gunboat and probably dated around 1817. Gunboats usually mounted two cannons, were powered by sail and oar, carried supplies and escorted troops, scouted the shore, and in time of hostilities, harassed larger vessels. Although hundreds were in service on the Great Lakes, both shores of the Atlantic, the Baltic, and the Mediterranean seas, the gunboats have vanished, except for a few rare hulks such as this one.

The St. Lawrence Islands National Park was founded in 1904. The 54-foot gunboat went on display in 1968 in a special display building and cradle at St. Lawrence Islands National Park headquarters on the beautiful St. Lawrence River.
Activities: Guided tour and exhibit of the gunboat. *Admission:* Entry fee. Open daily, June 30-September 3, other times by appmt.

MANITOWANING, ONTARIO
Assiginack Historical Museum and
SS *Norisle* Heritage Park
SS *Norisle* (Great Lakes ship))
c/o Municipal Clerk, Box 147
Manitowaning, Ontario P0P 1N0   Canada
(705) 859-3905   Fax: (705) 859-2416
E-mail: assigmuse@amtelecom.net

Location: Manitowaning is on the eastern side of Manitoulin Island in northern Lake Huron, about 140 miles east of Mackinaw City, Michigan. Approachable from the north via Canadian Rte. 69 to Little Current. Follow island Rte. 6 south twenty miles to Manitowaning. The Museum is on Arthur Street.
Highlights: The SS *Norisle* (Great Lakes Steamship) **Website:** www.manitoulin-island.com/museums/assiginack_complex.htm
General Information: The Assiginack Historical Museum, founded in 1955, is housed in what was once a jail, built in 1878, and contains general displays of marine historical interest.
Located on the same grounds are a pioneer blacksmith's shop, barn, home, and school. Manitowaning Roller Mills, built 1885 as a gristmill, exhibits an agricultural display. The SS *Norisle* tour gives a full view of the workings of a large Great Lakes ship.
Activities: Tours during July and August, small-craft docking available adjacent to Heritage Park and full small-craft services, shopping, and restaurants nearby.
Admission: Entry fee. Open daily, 10 A.M.- 5 P.M., June, July, and August and September.

MATTAWA, ONTARIO
Voyageur Heritage Centre
Samuel de Champlain Provincial Park
P.O. Box 147
Mattawa, ONT   P0H 1V0
(705) 744-2276 Fax: (705)744-0587
E-mail: communications@museumsontario.com
Location: Highway 17, 13 km west of Mattawa
Highlights: Canoe replica, publications
Website: www.ontarioparks.com
General Information: The Yoyageur Heritage Centre exhibits include a replica of twelve metre Canot de Maitre, furs and trade goods, and description of voyageur history.
Activities: Conducted hikes, canoe hikes, film and slide shows, children's programmes, self-guided hikes, and amphitheatre programmes. Self-guided tour description of Museum.
Admission: Entry fee to park only. Open summer or upon appointment.

MERRICKVILLE, ONTARIO
Merrickville Blockhouse Museum
c/o Secretary, Merrickville and District Historical Society P.O. Box 294
Merrickville, Ontario K0G 1N0 Canada
(613) 269 – 3614
E-mail: info@merrickvillehistory.ca
Location: The Merrickville Blockhouse is located on the Rideau Canal in center of Merrickville at the

corner of St. Lawrence and Main Streets.
Highlights: Blockhouse, Rideau Canal and locks
Web Site: www.merrickvillehistory.org/news-harper.html
General Information: The Merrickville Blockhouse Museum, built in 1832 by Lt. Colonel By as a defence for the Rideau Canal; the Museum opened in 1980. The largest blockhouse of four built along the canal was constructed to protect the lock station from attack and to provide storage for arms and ammunition. It served as a barracks for 50 men.
The blockhouse sits beside the Rideau Canal, which was built by the British as an alternate route from the St. Lawrence River. The Americans were a constant concern due to the unsettled boundary between Canada and the U.S. in the Oregon Territory out west. Lt. Col. John By was assigned the task of building the canal, which he did between 1826 and 1832. The canal covers some 202 kms (124 miles) from Ottawa on the Ottawa River to Kingston, Ontario, on the St. Lawrence River.
The military necessity long over, the canal is now one of the favorite inland waterways taking the boater through a series of beautiful lakes and some 49 locks alongside charming villages and lockstations where most of the lock gates are
Today, the Museum is home to many interesting artifacts from the early settlement days of Merrickville and surrounding areas. Later, John Johnston became the locktender, and, while living here, he detested the cold held in by the thick-walled blockhouse. It now houses the Museum and features both military and folk collections gathered from the area.
Admission: Entry fee. Open May-September, Tuesday-Sunday, 10 A.M.- 6 P.M.

MIDLAND, ONTARIO
Huronia Museum & Wyandot Indian Village
549 Little Lake Park Road,   P.O. Box 638
Midland, Ontario L4R 4P4 Canada
(705) 526-2844   Fax: (705) 527-6622
1-800-263-7745 – Midland-Penetang Tourism Consortium E-mail: info@huroniamuseum.com
Location: The Museum and Village are located in the Town of Midland's famous Little Lake Park, just off King Street.
Highlights: History of sixty-seven shipwrecks, photograph collection (15,000), library, archival collections on Georgian Bay shipping/fishing.
Website: www.huroniamuseum.com/
General Information: The maritime focus of Huronia Museum is on the history of transportation on Georgian Bay as part of the Great Lakes system. It contains artifacts and objects relating to the shipwrecks of the

southeastern part of Georgian Bay. In addition an extensive photographic collection relating to Great Lakes marine history is partially displayed.

The Museum is in the Huron Village and Museum Complex in Little Lake Park. There is a rich heritage in this part of Ontario, much of it based in the history of marine activities and sailing vessels. The project will culminate in the Georgian Bay Marine Museum and Heritage Harbour.

Admission: Entry fee. Open: January through March, Monday-Saturday, 9 A.M.-5 P.M., closed Sundays; April through June, Monday-Sunday, 9 A.M.-5 P.M.; July/August, Monday-Sunday, 9 A.M.-6 P.M.; September through December, Monday-Sunday, 9 A.M.-5 P.M

MILFORD, ONTARIO
Mariners' Park Museum
Mariners' Park Marine Society
County Roads 10 and 13
Milford, Ontario K0K 2T0 Canada
(613) 476-2421 E-mail: pcc@reach.net
Location: South Bay is approximately 100 miles east of Toronto near Belleville. Take Rte. 49 south from Rte. 401 ten miles to Rte. 17. Follow it ten miles farther to Milford, turning onto Rte. 9 for one mile to South Bay on Lake Ontario.
Highlights: Artifacts from the *Protostatis*, *Sheboygan*, and *Acadian* (lake freighters — some of the many local shipwrecks off Prince Edward Island, False Duck Island lighthouse (1828),
Website: www.pec.on.ca/mariners-museum/
General Information: The Mariner's Park Museum, founded in 1966, encompasses several buildings, including one of the oldest lighthouses in Ontario. Displays include fishermen's nets, ships' logs, a map pinpointing the locations of wrecks offshore, and hundreds of other artifacts that depict the area's seafaring history — all that remains of a past era that came abruptly to a close about the beginning of World War II.

Nearby is the False Duck Island Lighthouse, where a Fresnel lens of French manufacture is located; it extinguished its light for the last time November 3, 1965. The sixty-two-foot-high lighthouse and lantern are memorials to the County's sailors.

The Museum also exhibits a lifeboat from the Greek freighter *Protostatis*, an anchor from the *Sheboygan*, and a wheelhouse form the *Acadian*.

Activities: Tours by appointments, Mariners' outdoor church service held annually on the second Sunday in August.

Admission: Entry fee. Memberships available. Open weekends, 9 A.M.-5 P.M., Victoria Day-Canada Day (July 1); 9 A.M.-5 P.M. daily Canada Day to Labour Day; weekends from Labour Day to Thanksgiving (Canadian).

MOORETOWN, ONTARIO
Moore Museum
94 Moore Line
Mooretown, Ontario N0N 1M0 Canada
(519) 867-2020 (Phone/Fax)
E-mail: imason@twp.stclair.on.ca
Location: Mooretown is twenty-five minutes south of Sarnia, Ontario. The Museum is located three miles west of Hwy. 40 on Moore Line or two blocks east of the St. Clair Parkway (County Road 33) on Moore Line in Mooretown.
Highlights: Local maritime history
General Information: Moore Museum is a local history museum with nine exhibits buildings, including a one-room schoolhouse, log cabin, Victorian cottage, and a historic church, railroad station, and blacksmith shop located close to the St. Clair River.

Marine history is part of the Museum's collections, and The Marine Room with highlights of the exploration of the St. Clair River and led to the settlement of Moore Township by Europeans. Early settlers often crossed the river to the United States by boat or ferry in the summer and by foot, horse, or sleigh across the ice in the winter.

Exhibited are such marine artifacts as ship's compasses, sextants, and life rings. Also included are a few ship models, a fine diorama of the wreck of the *Edmund Fitzgerald*, the ore freighter that presently lies on the bottom of Lake Superior since 1975, and the early shipping history of Father Hennepin's *Griffon*.

The wooden 1890 Corunna rear range light is also on display on the Museum grounds.

Admission: Entry fee. Open Wednesday-Sunday, 11 A.M.-5 P.M., March-June; daily, 11 A.M.-5 P.M., July-August; Monday-Friday, 9 A.M.- 4 P.M. September 1-December 15.

OTTAWA, ONTARIO
Bytown Museum
1 Canal Lane, P.O. Box 523, Station B.
Ottawa, Ontario K1P 5P6 Canada
(613) 234-4570 Fax: (613) 234-4846
E-mail: info@bytownmuseum.ca
Location: The Museum is in the Commissariat Stores Building, beside the Ottawa Locks, the northern eight-lock entrance to the Rideau Canal from the Ottawa River. Take the steps down from Wellington Street in the glen between Parliament Hill and the Château Laurier Hotel alongside the Rideau Canal.

Highlights: Archives, Rideau Canal history, library, **Website:** www.bytownmuseum.com/
General Information: Lt. Col. John By of the British Army's Royal Engineers was the founder of Bytown, which was to become Ottawa and developed between 1826 and 1832 around the major works at the Ottawa River Terminus of the Rideau Canal. The Bytown Museum's major permanent exhibit depicts John By's personal and military life and information on the construction of the Rideau Canal. Other exhibits include a lumberman's shanty, pioneer kitchen, Victorian parlour, and toy store.

The Rideau Canal, conceived in the wake of the War of 1812 to be a wartime supply route to Kingston and the Great Lakes, is a chain of beautiful lakes and canal cuts. Winding its way through varying landscapes, the Rideau Canal stretches a distance of 202 kms (124 miles) from Kingston, at the head of Lake Ontario, to Ottawa, Canada's capital city.

Visitors will view personal and household possessions from the earliest days of settlement in the Ottawa area. The Canadian Parks Service presents a self-guided exhibit called "The Builders of the Rideau Canal" on the ground floor of the Commissariat building.
Admission: Entry fee. Open April -mid-May, Monday-Friday, 10 A.M.- 2 P.M.; mid-May-mid-October, Monday-Friday, 10 A.M.- 5 P.M., Sunday/Sunday, 10 A.M.- 4 P.M.; mid-October-end of November, Monday-Friday, 10 A.M.-2 P.M.

OWEN SOUND, ONTARIO
Owen Sound Marine-Rail Museum
1155 First Avenue West
Owen Sound, Ontario N4K 4K8 Canada
(519) 371-3333   Fax: (519) 371-8628
E-mail: marinerail.museum@e-owensound.ca
Location: Owen Sound is 120 miles northwest from Toronto on Hwy. 10. The museum is one-and one-half blocks north of 10th Street.
Highlights: Boat models, CNR and CPR memorabilia, special exhibits and displays.
Website: www.e-owensound.com/marinerail/
General Information: Officially opened in 1985, The Marine and Rail Museum explains the role each industry played in shaping the area's economic history. The Museum's collection includes scale models of ships, steamers, trains, a dugout canoe, shipbuilding tools, marine and railway uniforms, various flags and many other items relating to the area's marine and rail past. The displays are rotated on a regular basis, so each Museum visit offers a different glimpse into days gone by.

For marine and rail history buffs, the Library Archives has a wide collection of books, images, maps, charts, timetables and videos available for research.
Admission: Entry fee. June to Thanksgiving: Monday - Sunday 10 A.M. - 4 P.M. Thanksgiving to May Long Weekend Tuesday - Friday 10 A.M. - 4 P.M. Weekends 11 A.M. - 3 P.M. Saturday/Sunday, Noon – 5 P.M .

PENETANGUISHENE,* ONTARIO
Discovery Harbour
93 Jury Drive
Penetanguishene, Ontario L9M 1G1   Canada
(705) 549-8064 Fax: (705) 549-4858
E-mail: hhp@hhp.on.ca
Location: From Toronto, travel ninety miles northwest on Rte. 400. Exit at Hwy 93 west and north to Penetanguishene, turn right at the water and follow the signs with the blue ship logo.
Highlights: The historic ships: *Bee* (schooner), *Perseverance* (bateau), and *Tecumseh*, Mr. Chiles' Chandlery Store, Captain Roberts' Table restaurant, *The Ship's Bell* (quarterly newsletter)
Website: www.discoveryharbour.on.ca/english/
General Information: Discovery Harbour — A Centre for Marine Heritage — was founded in 1971 and located on the shores of beautiful Penetanguishene Bay. Come board authentic ships and chat with friendly guides and period costumed staff. The site maintains a collection of 15 reconstructed and restored buildings, historic naval and military properties, original officer's quarters, a period and reproduction collection, maps and manuscripts, and replicas of the historic ships *Bee*, *Tecumseh*, and *Perseverance*.
Activities: Guided tours, historical demonstrations and dramas, education programmes, ship displays, "midday Sailaway" and "Sailor's Sunset" afternoon and evening sailing programmes, horse-drawn wagon rides.
Admission: Entry fee. Open: Mon/Fri, 10 A.M.- 5 P.M.; May 23 – June 30, Mon/Fri 10 A.M. – 5 P.M.: July 1-Sept. 3, daily 10 A.M. – 5 P.M.
pn: Pen-et-ANG-wish-een. An Abenaki Indian word meaning "Place of the rolling white sands."

PETERBOROUGH, ONTARIO
The Canadian Canoe Museum
910 Monaghan Road
Peterborough, Ontario K9J 5K4   Canada
Toll free: 1-866-34-CANOE (22663)
(705) 748-9153 Fax: (705) 748-0616
E-mail: inquiries@canoemuseum.net
Location: Peterborough is sixty-two miles northeast of Toronto, a 90-minute drive.
Highlights: Kanawa International (canoe) Collection **Website:** www.canoemuseum.net/

General Information: The Canadian Canoe Museum is where you will discover the enduring significance of the canoe to the people of Canada in North America's only canoe museum. With more than 600 canoes and kayaks and 1,000 related artifacts, the Museum's collection is the largest of its kind.

Experience a dramatic waterfall upon entering, hear creation stories inside a traditional Mi'Kmaq wigwam, or try your hand building a birch bark canoe in the new Preserving Skills Gallery. Feel what it was like living as a voyageur during the Fur Trade era, plan a prospecting expedition from the Klondike gold rush days, and enjoy the cottage lifestyles of the early 19th century. The canoe is the ultimate link to Canada's rich cultural heritage, connecting the people, the past, and the unique Canadian landscape.

Admission: Entry fee. Memberships available. Open year-round: Summer hours, May-October, 10 A.M.-5 P.M. 7-days a week; Winter hours, November-April, Monday-Friday, 10 A.M.– 5 P.M.

PETERBOROUGH, ONTARIO

Peterborough Centennial Museum and Archives
300 Hunter Street E. (Armour Hill)
P.O. Box 143
Peterborough, Ontario K9J 6Y5 Canada
(705) 743-5180 Fax: (705) 743-2614
E-mail:administration@peterboroughmuseum.ca
Location: Peterborough is sixty-two miles northeast of Toronto. The lock is accessible either by footpath along the waterway or via Hunter Street East.
Highlights: Hydraulic lift lock, Trent Severn Waterway, archives, Peterborough canoes
Website: www.pcma.ca/
General Information: The Peterborough Centennial Museum is in the region known as the home of the "Canadian" canoe, as it was in this area in the 1850s where this new type of canoe was developed out of the traditional birch bark and dugout canoe technologies. There were a number of local manufacturers from about 1860 up to 1960.

The Museum portrays the settlement and domestic life of Peterborough through various collections and exhibits. The archives contain local records, historical photographs, maps, and waterway charts. The Museum overlooks the Trent Canal lock and has several examples of Peterborough-built canoes in its collection.

Admission: Entry fee. Open Monday-Friday, 9 A.M.-5 P.M., weekends and holidays, Noon – 5 P.M. The Archives are open Monday-Friday. **NOTE: due to space restrictions, public appointments are now MANDATORY.**

PETERBOROUGH, ONTARIO

Peterborough Hydraulic Lift Lock and Visitor Centre
Hunter Street E. P.O. Box 567
Peterborough, Ontario K9J 6Z6 Canada
(705) 750-4950
E-mail: ont.trentsevern@pc.gc.ca
Location: The lock is on the Trent-Severn Waterway in Peterborough.
Highlights: Hydraulic lift lock, Trent-Severn Waterway and archives
Website: www.cruising.ca/trent/docs/L-21.html
General Information: The Peterborough Hydraulic Lift Lock 21 was built between 1896 and 1904 on the Trent-Severn Waterway, which meanders 240 miles (386 kms) across Central Ontario, linking the Bay of Quinte (Trenton) with Georgian Bay to the west. The concrete and steel monolith slowly emerged. The purpose was to overcome the considerable rise between Little Lake and the Otonabee River at Nassau Mills, with the Waterway providing a through-route from the Great Lakes to the West.

To visualize a lift lock, think of two giant out-door water-filled chambers (like cake pans) 140 feet long and 33 feet wide with a water depth of 8 feet. When one chamber is at the upper level (65 feet above the lower chamber), the gates are opened, boats float into it. It is a counterbalance to the lower chamber, and they move opposite to each other — full of water and boats — up/down some 65 feet.

Once in their proper positions, the end-gates are opened to allow the boats/boats to float out and travel on to their destinations.

This lift lock is the highest in the world of its type. The lock is operated mid-May through October, and a working model of the lock can be seen in the Visitor Centre. Nearby, the Peterborough Centennial Museum and Archives overlook the lift lock. The Trent-Severn Waterway is a historical canal operated and maintained by Parks Canada.

Admission: Entry fee. Open daily, 10 A.M.-5 P.M., May-October.

PORT CARLING, ONTARIO

Muskoka Lakes Museum
1 Joseph Street   P. O. Box 432
Port Carling, Ontario P0B 1J0 Canada
(705) 765-5367 Fax: (705) 765-7682
E-mail: info@mimuseum.com
Location: Port Carling is approximately 140
miles north of Toronto. Take Rte. 400 north
eighty-five miles to Barrie, then north to Braler
Bridge, then west nine miles to Port Carling. The
Museum is located in Island Park adjacent to the
locks.
Highlights: Boat building, history of building
small boats, including Dispro (disappearing
propeller) boat and canoes, ship models **Websites**:
www.muskoka.com/tourism/mlm/
General Information: The Muskoka Lakes
Museum, founded in 1967, is the home of
Ditchburn launches, runabouts, and the
Disappearing Propeller (DISPROS) Boat Co.
    The Museum maintains a collection of artifacts
used by early settlers in the Muskoka area from
1865. Also displayed are artifacts relating to the
wooden launches built in Muskoka. The Museum
has a room devoted to small boat construction,
steamers on the lakes, and is a repository for
information on the locks.
Admission: Entry fee. Open Jul/Aug,
Wed/Sat, 10 A.M.-5 P.M.; Sunday Noon-5 P.M.,
Sept/Oct Wed/Sat, 10 A.M. – 4 P.M. , Sun,
12 Noon – 4 P.M.

PORT COLBORNE, ONTARIO

**Port Colborne Historical and Marine
Museum**
280 King Street (Box 572)
Port Colborne, Ontario L3K 5X8 Canada
(905) 834-7604 Fax: (905) 834-6198
E-mail: museum@portcolborne.ca
Location: Port Colborne lies 30 miles directly
west of Buffalo, NY, on Canadian Rte. 3.
Highlights: Welland Canal, wheelhouse from
steam tug *Yvonne Dupré Jr.*, Arabella's Tearoom,
lifeboat from S.S. *Hochelaga*
Website:www.portcolborne.on.ca/page/museum
General Information: The Port Colborne
Historical and Marine Museum, founded in
1974, is housed in a Georgian Revival-style
home built in 1869. It exhibits artifacts pertaining
to the early history of this area, including the
Welland Canal; a heritage village site with an
1818 log school house; blacksmith shop c. 1880's;
1946 wheelhouse; 1915 tea room; and an 1850's
log house.
    Canal Days is held on Canada's Civic Holiday
Weekend (the first Monday in August) and
features marine displays, an outdoor art and craft
show, demonstrations, entertainment, and food.

Activities: Group tours, Canal Days, and a
Christmas Festival held the first Sunday in
December. Arabella's Pie Social, last Sunday in
May.
Admission: No entry fee. Open May/Dec 12
Noon – 5 P.M. for the Museum and village.
Various fees for special events. Open daily,
Noon-5 P.M., May-December.

PORT DOVER, ONTARIO

Port Dover Harbour Museum
44 Harbour Street Box 1298
Port Dover, Ontario N0A 1N0   Canada
(519) 583-2660
E-mail: portdover.museum@norfolkcounty.ca
Location: Port Dover lies approximately
seventy-two miles west of Niagara Falls on Lake
Erie. Take Rte. 3 to Jarvis, then Rte. 6, and south
thirteen miles to Port Dover.
Highlights: Schooner trade history, freshwater
commercial fishing history,
Website:www.norfolkcounty.ca/harbourmuseum
General Information: Founded in 1976, the
Port Dover Harbour Museum exhibits artifacts
and photos relating to schooner trade and fishing
on north shore of Lake Erie.
Activities: Research facilities and slide shows
Admission: No entry fee, but donations
accepted. Open daily, 11 A.M.-6 P.M., July 1 –
Labor Day.

PRESCOTT, ONTARIO

The Forwarders' Museum
201 Water and Centre Streets   P.O. Box 2179
Prescott, Ontario K0E 1T0   Canada
(613) 925-1861 E-mail: On web site
Location: Prescott is eighty miles northeast from
Kingston toward Montreal on the St.
Lawrence River at 201 Water St. W., Centre &
Water Streets The Museum is on the waterfront
in Prescott in Forwarders' Building.
Highlights: History of freight forwarders along
the St. Lawrence River, **Web Site**:
www.prescott.ca/tourism/area-attractions-
directory/forwarders-museum-and-visitor-
center.aspx
General Information: The Forwarders'
Museum, opened in 1978, was established to
preserve the history of the freight forwarders who
moved all the goods from the "civilized"
world to the settlers on the frontier via boat.
Goods and travelers were put ashore on the docks
at Prescott, where the forwarders' building, now
the museum, stands. Goods needing protection
were stored in the lower level of the building, and
offices occupied the upper floor.
    The operators of the several forwarding
companies were the entrepreneurs of their day and
contracted to send the travelers and their
goods to their destinations at Brockville,
Kingston,

York (Toronto), and other ports on the lakes. Huge rafts of squared timbers (some rescued from the lake bottom to be shown at the Museum) came down river (St. Lawrence), tied up a Prescott to "tighten their chains" before venturing through the rapids. Other larger vessels that could not navigate the lower St. Lawrence rapids off-loaded their cargo at Prescott to be reloaded on shallow-draft vessels for the continued transport to the Atlantic Ocean.

The restored building maintains a variety of exhibits reflecting the forwarders' work and lifestyle. The Museum will bring history to life before your eyes.

Admission: Entry fee, but donations accepted. Open Sunday-Friday 11 A.M.-5 P.M., Saturdays 10 A.M.-6 P.M.

ST. CATHARINES, ONTARIO

St. Catharines Museum
1932 Welland Canals Parkway P.O.Box 3012
St. Catharines, Ontario L2R 7K6
(905) 984-8880 1-800-305-5134 (toll-free)
E-mail: museum@stcatharines.ca
Location: Welland Canals Centre at Lock 3 on the Welland Canal. Exit at QEW at Glendale Ave. West and follow the Welland Canals Centre signs for approximately 1 km. (2/3 mile.)
Highlights: History of 4 Welland Canals and city that grew up around them, video presentation, Ontario Lacrosse Hall of Fame and Museum, Black History Tour *Follow the North Star*, Lock 3 viewing platform, Tourist Information Centre, Gift Shop, Snack Bar and full service restaurant,
Website: www.stcatharineslock3museum.ca/
General Information: St. Catharines was built around the Canal. At the St. Catharines Museum, one can learn about the history of the four Welland Canals; how they were built and how they operate. William Hamilton Merritt (1793-1862), was the driving force behind the engineering the marvel of the Welland Canal. The Canal was built first in 1829, with 39 locks and wooden gates. The second and third canals were opened in 1845 and 1887. In 1932, the forth canal was completed. It has a total of eight locks and is 43 kilometres (27 miles) long. Portions of the old canal can still be seen today in downtown St. Catharines and Port Dalhousie, complete with lock tender shanties.

Activities: The Welland Canals Past and Present 12-minute video presentation, play in the "hands-on" Discover Room, tour the *Follow the North Star* exhibit which recounts the history of the Underground Railroad and the rich heritage of Niagara's African Canadians, visit the Library/Archives and extensive photograph collection, lectures, special events, guided tours to all pre-booked groups, educational programming, Discovery Park is being developed to expand the Museum walls out of doors.

Admission: Entry fee. Open Mon/Fri - 9 A.M to 5 P.M., Sat/Sun - 11 A.M. to 4 P.M.. (winter hours) Administration office hours – Mon/Fri – 9 A.M. to 5 P.M.Library and Archives open Mon, Wed, Fri - 12:30 P.M. to 4:30 P.M. daily.

SAULT STE. MARIE, ONTARIO

Museum Ship *Norgoma*
Station Mall P. O. 23099
Sault Ste. Marie, Ontario P6A 6W6 Canada
1-800-461-6020 (705) 256-7447
E-mail: Norgoma@shaw.ca
Location: Sault Ste. Marie lies on the Canadian-Michigan border where Lakes Huron and Superior meet. The twin cities are about 175 miles west of Sudbury on Canadian Rte. 178. The Museum ship is at the Roberta Bondar Park Marina in Sault Ste. Marie, Ontario.
Highlights: The *Norgoma* (Great Lakes cruise ship),
Website: www.geocities.com/TheTropics/5508/
General Information: The Museum Ship *Norgoma*, founded in 1976, exhibits motorship *Norgoma*, 188-ft diesel-powered passenger vessel (built in 1950), featuring historical artifacts on the main deck.

The *Norgoma*, presently under volunteer restoration, was the last overnight cruise ship built on the Great Lakes. She ran from Owen Sound to Sault Ste. Marie between 1950 and 1963, after which she served as an auto ferry to Manitoulin Island until 1974.

Activities: Entire ship open for touring and restaurant on board; lunch/dinner.
Admission: Entrance fee. Open daily: June to Labour Day: 10 A.M. to 8 P.M.; Labour Day to mid-October: seasonal.

SAULT STE. MARIE, ONTARIO

Sault Ste. Marie Canal Visitor Center
National Historic Site of Canada
1 Canal Drive
Sault Ste. Marie, Ontario P6A 6W4 Canada
(705) 941-6262 Fax: (705) 941-6206
E-mail: info-saultcanal@pc.gc.ca
Location: The Sault Ste. Marie Canal and St. Marys River is the link between Lake Superior and Lake Huron.
Highlights: Archive with drawings and land plans **Website**: www.pc.gc.ca/lhn-nhs/on/ssmarie/index_e.asp
General Information: Two cities face each other across the St. Marys River: both named Sault (Soo) Ste. Marie, one in Ontario and the other in Michigan. The St. Marys River's rapids

were first discovered by Etienne Brule in 1622, and the first permanent mission was founded by Père Marquette in 1669. Since then, the area has become an important transportation center for Great Lakes traffic. The canal, closed for some time due to deterioration and lack of need because of the larger American "Soo Locks," was rebuilt to handle mostly pleasure craft. The recreational lock opened in 1998.

The Sault Ste. Marie Canal Visitor Center, where the canal is the centerpiece of lake traffic, maintains 1,100 engineering drawings and land plans related to development and operation of the canal. Also available for research are eight feet of archival files and documents and a site-specific artifact collection.

Publications: "The Sault Ste. Marie Canal: A Chapter in the History of Great Lakes Transport."

Admission: No entry fee. Open all year. June/Sept 9 A.M. – 9 P.M.

SMITHS FALLS, ONTARIO

Lockmaster Anglin's Interpretive Centre
Parks Canada, Rideau Canal
34A Beckwith Street South
Smiths Falls, Ontario, K7A 1E0   Canada
Mail: Southern Area P.O. Box 10
Elgin, Ontario K0G 1E0   Canada
(613) 395-5377 (Direct)
Location: Lockmaster Anglin's Interpretive Centre is two kms north of Hwy 401 at Kingston Mills Lockstation.
Highlights: Rideau Canal history
Website: www.billanglin.com/story3.2.html
General Information: The Lockmaster Anglin's Interpretive Centre maintains a collection of photographs and textual materials describing the military history of the Rideau Canal and the social and economic development of the Kingston Mills area. The Rideau Canal and its locale provide the setting for recreational activities, including boating, picnicking, jogging, and biking.
Admission: Entry fee to Park, no entry fee. Open mid-May-mid-October daily, other times by request. Call or write for times.

SMITH FALLS, ONTARIO

Rideau Canal Museum
34 Beckwith Street South
Smiths Falls, Ontario, K7A 2A8   Canada
(613) 284-0505, Fax: (613) 284-0505
E-mail: rcmchin@superaje.com
Location: From Ottawa travel southwest on Rte. 7 approximately 30 miles to Rte. 15. Then bear south sixteen miles to Smiths Falls.From Watertown, New York, north on I-87 29 miles to Canadian Route 401. Then east 37 km to Rte. 29;

turn north some 32 miles to Smiths Falls. Museum is in heart of the Rideau.
Highlights: The Rideau Canal
Website: www.rideau-info.com/museum/
General Information: The Rideau Canal Museum, opened in 1991, offers five floors of a unique blend of historic displays, artifacts, and modern technology to interpret one of the first engineering triumphs of Canadian History: the building and development of the Rideau Canal. This recreational waterway, which links Kingston and Ottawa, was built by Lt. Col. John By between 1826 and 1832 as a military alternative route where blockhouses provided protection from a feared American invasion.

Housed in a restored mill, the Museum provides a 20-foot (6m) animated detailed model of the waterway, a Look-Out Tower, a Tunnel of History, user-friendly computer quizzes, information mini-theatre programmes, and a narrated slide presentation. During high season, interpretive walks along the canal provide an interesting view of the old winches and massive gates, which still operate as they did 160 years ago.

Admission: Entry fee. Open daily, mid-May-mid-October, 10 A.M.-4:30 P.M. October 12 to Dec. 19, open weekends 10 A.M. – 4:30 P.M.

THUNDER BAY, ONTARIO

Old Fort William Historical Park
1350 King Road
Thunder Bay, Ontario P7K 1L5 Canada
(807) 577-8461 Fax: (807) 473-2387
E-mail: info@fwhp.ca
Location: The fort is two- and one-half miles south of the junction of Hwys. 11B, 17B, and 61, then two- and one-half miles southwest on Broadway Avenue.
Highlights: Perseverance schooner (replica), Great Lakes history,
Website: www.fwhp.ca/index.php
General Information: Thunder Bay was formed with the joining of two cities: Fort William and Port Arthur located on Lake Superior — a major grain-shipping port. Tied closely to the fur trade, Old Fort William, consisting of forty-two carefully constructed historical buildings, was an important inland outpost headquarters of the North West Company, serving from the early nineteenth century. The energy of those early days is recaptured through interpretive guide programs along with guided tours and special events during the winter.

The Fort includes craft shops that were typical of the early period where today much of the activity and spirit of those early days can be relived. Included are a naval yard, a farm, dairy, Indian encampment, and a site where large cargo birchbark canots (canoes) are built.

Admission: Entry fee. Open daily, 10 A.M.-
6 P.M., Jun 17-Aug 19; Mon-Fri, 10 A.M.-
4 P.M.,Sat-Sun 10 A.M.-5 P.M., May 20-June 16
and Aug 20- Sept 30.

TOBERMORY, ONTARIO
Fathom Five National Marine Park
P.O. Box 189
Tobermory, Ontario N0H 2R0 Canada
(519) 596-2233 Fax: 519-596-2298
E-mail: bruce-fathomfive@pc.gc.ca
Location: Fathom Five Park is located in the
Bruce Peninsula National Park at the northern end
of Rte. 6 about 260 kms northwest of Toronto on
Georgian Bay.
Highlights: Shipwreck sites,
Website: www.pc.gc.ca/amnc-
nmca/on/fathomfive/index_e.asp
   General Information: Built in 1852, the
schooner *John Walters* is a true old timer. This
108-foot wooden schooner met its fate off Russell
Island circa 1883. The remains of this vessel lie in
shallow water (maximum 15 feet), making it a site
suitable for both novice divers and snorkelers.
   Fathom Five National Marine Park protects the
historical shipwrecks, aquatic ecosystem, and
island archipelago at the mouth of Georgian Bay.
   Wreck sites include the schooner *China*
wrecked in 1871, the schooner *John Walters*, the
steamer *W. L. Wetmore* sunk in 1901, the
schooner/barge *James C. King* sunk in 1901, the
steamer *Newaygo* wrecked in 1903, the schooner
Philo Schoville, the schooner *Charles P. Minch*
driven onto the rocks in 1898, and the barque
Arabia that foundered in 1884. There are 12 other
wreck sites to dive. Divers must check in at the
Diver Registrations Centre open 7-day-a-week
from June to Laboure Day Reduced hours at other
times of year. There is a hyperbaric chamber at
the local medical clinic.
   Admission: Administration Office: Monday -
Friday, 8 A.M. - 4:30 P.M. Closed holidays.

TORONTO, ONTARIO
HMCS *Haida* Naval Museum
Ontario Place Corporation
955 Lakeshore Blvd. W.
Hamilton, ONT   M6K 3B9
(416) 314-9755 Fax: (416) 314--9878
E-mail: Carla.Morse@pc.gc.ca
Location: **Site location Canada Marine
Discovery Centre at 658 Catharine Street
North**
Highlights: Friends of HMCS *Haida* (newsletter),
library and archival collection, gift shop,
Website: http://hmcshaida.ca/
   General Information: HMCS *Haida* National
Historic Site of Canada is the last remaining

Tribal Class Destroyer in the world and is
Canada's most decorated warship. HMCS
Haida served in the Royal Canadian Navy from
1943 – 1963 serving in World War II and the
Korean War.
   The Museum, founded in 1965, exhibits a
collection housed in a Royal Canadian Navy
Destroyer and serves as a Naval Memorial and
Maritime Museum. The Museum also maintains a
library and archival collection with access by
appointment only.
   Activities: Self-conducted tours with guides
stationed at points throughout the ship to answer
questions. Special tours for school groups by
appointment.
   Admission: Entry fee. Open May 17-
September 2, daily, 10:00 A.M.-6:30 P.M.

TORONTO, ONTARIO
Toronto Port Authority Archives
60 Harbour Street
Toronto, Ontario M5J 1B 7   Canada
(416) 863-2011 Fax: (416) 863-0391
E-mail:jhubbell@torontoport.com
Location: The archives are located in Toronto,
Ontario. **Website:**
www.infosource.gc.ca/inst/tor/fed07_e.asp
   General Information: The Toronto Port
Authority Archives maintains a wide variety of
information which includes: annual reports, 1853
to the present; minutes of the Board of
Commissioners, 1887-1970s; harbour dues,
manifest and tonnage registers, 1848-1970s;
financial records, 1850-1980s; harbour police
logbooks; correspondence, legal documents,
photographs, and engineering and architectural
drawings concerning waterfront development, the
construction and administration of Sunnyside
Beach and Amusement Area and the Toronto
Island and Malton Airports, the development
ofthe St. Lawrence Seaway, and the activities of
North American port and harbour associations.
   Publications include: Satinson, Jeffrey, "The
Heritage of the Port Industrial District," Toronto:
Toronto Harbour Commissioners, 1990.
   Admission: No entry fee. Open all year.

WASAGA BEACH, ONTARIO
Nancy Island Historic Site
Wasaga Beach Provincial Park
11-22nd Street, P.O. Box 183,
Wasaga Beach, Ontario L9Z 2V9
Telephone: (705) 429-2516 (Nancy Island) or
(Office) (705) 429-2516 Fax: (705) 429-7983
Email: nancyisland@wasagabeachpark.com
Location: The historic site is located in the
Wasaga Beach Provincial Park on the
Nottawasaga River and Gerogian Bay in the
Province of Ontario, Canada.

Highlights: Hull of the *Nancy*, ship models, theatre, museum, and lighthouse replica, bateau (flat-bottom freight boat),
Website: www.wasagabeachpark.com/
General Information: Nancy Island Historic Site, founded in 1928, provides a vital moment in history. It is here that the story of the Schooner *Nancy* is told.

The *Nancy*, built as a private cargo vessel in 1789 at Detroit, which was then British. She was a fur-trading vessel but was pressed into service as a British supply ship during the War of 1812. The *Nancy* was burned and sunk by the British to avoid capture in a battle August 14, 1814. Soon after, on September 10th, Admiral Perry defeated the British on Lake Erie. Her hull rested in the river until the charred remains were recovered in 1928. Today, the hull is located inside the museum along with a wide variety of artifacts and ship models.
Admission: Entry fee. Open weekends, 10 A.M.-6 P.M., Victory Day (near May 24th) through third Friday in June; daily, 10 A.M.-6 P.M. third Friday in June to Labour Day.

PRINCE EDWARD ISLAND, CANADA

PORT HILL, PEI
Green Park Shipbuilding Museum
Port Hill, Rte. 12, west of Summerside
Phone: 902-831-7947 Fax: 902-831-7944
E-mail Contact: green_park@gov.pe.ca **OR** mhpei@gov.pe.ca Off Season: 902-368-6600
Location: Take the new Confederation Bridge to Prince Edward Island: toll one way only — off island. Then 8 klms to Rte. 1-A west some 26 klms to Rte. 2. Then west on Rte. 2 a short distance to the intersection to Rte. 12. Turn north on 12 traveling 16 klms into Port Hill and Green Park Provincial Park where the shipyard is located.
Highlights: History of wooden shipbuilding, Annual Blue Berry Social, gift shop,
Website: www.
gov.pe.ca/peimhf/index.php3?number=1015695
General Information: During the nineteenth century, shipbuilding was major industry on Prince Edward Island. Green Park includes the Green Park Shipbuilding Museum, founded in 1973, tracing the history and craft of shipbuilding in the 1800s in a re-created nineteenth-century wooden shipbuilding yard, and an interpretive centre. The museum includes the restored 1865 Victorian residence of ship owner James Yeo, Jr. Exhibits also include carpenter and blacksmith shops, and a partially completed full-size vessel.
Activities: July Blueberry Social, Concerts on the Green, and Ghost Story.

Admission: Entry Fee. Open daily mid-June-September, 10 A.M.-6 P.M.

SOURIS, PEI
Basin Head Fisheries Museum
Hwy 16, P.O. Box 248
Souris, P. E. I. C0A 2B0 Canada
(902) 357-7233 Fax: (902) 357-7232
(Off season: (902) 368-6600, Fax: (902) 368-6608)
E-mail: basin_head@gov.pe.ca
Location: The museum is located high on a bluff overlooking Singing Sand" beach and the Northumberland Strait off Rte. 16, east of Souris on Prince Edward Island.
Highlights: View, dioramas, lobster fishery, coastal ecology exhibit, and gift shop, **Website:** gov.pe.ca/peimhf/index.php3?number=1015692
General Information: Located in a former fishing port, the Basin Head Fisheries Museum, founded in 1973, tells the story of the inshore fishery through artifacts, dioramas, and photographs that depict the life style of an inshore fisherman through displays of regional small craft and fishing gear. As the lobster industry boomed, canneries sprang up all along the Prince Edward Island coast. In 1903, the island had 190 canneries. On site are dioramas illustrating fishing industry techniques and the variety of boats used and various types of trawl nets, fish sheds, and small-craft. The large building down by the wharf below the Museum once housed the Smith fish cannery, which put up tins of salt fish and chicken haddy and now houses a coastal ecology exhibit that complements the other exhibits.
Activities: Variety of workshops including art, tole painting, child craft workshops, craft and kite demonstrations, as well Share History Talks. Call for information.
Admission: Entry fee. Open daily Spring to Fall, 9 A.M. – 5 P.M.; mid-season, 9 A.M. 6 P.M. Special rates for bus tours.

QUÉBEC, CANADA

COTEAU-DU-LAC, QUÉBEC
Coteau-du-Lac National Historic Site
308 A Chemin du Fleuve
P.O. Box 250
Coteau-du-lac, Québec J0P 1B0 Canada
Toll Free: 1-888-773-8888
(450) 763-5631 Fax: (450) 763-1654
E-mail: parcscanada-que@pc.gc.ca
Location: Coteau-du-Lac lies along the north side of the St. Lawrence River. From Rte 40, take Exit 17 south on Rte. 201 past Rte. 20 and 338 to end of road. Turn west 1 klm to site.

Highlights: First lock canal in North America,
Website:
www.pc.gc.ca/lhn-nhs/qc/coteaudulac/index_e.asp
  General Information: Coteau-du-Lac was a
strategic gateway from the days of the nomadic
Indian tribes to the 19th century. It is situated on
the north side of the St. Lawrence River. In the
early 1800s, to avoid the turbulent rapids which
blocked the ascent of people and supplies to the
West and the Great Lakes, the first lock canal in
North America was built at the point of Coteau-du-
Lac in 1780, where the Delisle and St. Lawrence
Rivers meet. It is remarkable in its short length and
simple design.
  British troops passed through on boats and
Durham barges. During the armed conflicts of
1776 and 1812, imposing fortifications were built,
consisting of a variety of earthworks, defensive
buildings, and an octagonal blockhouse.
  Now you can stroll along the short but now-dry
canal as far as the fortified bastion to admire the
low rapids in the St. Lawrence that the canal by-
passed. Unique boats and figures, outlined in
steel, positioned in and around this canal, give the
visitor a real sense of perspective of its original use.
  Activities: Guided tours and group activities are
available daily at the site.
  Admission: Entry fee. Open: from May 13 to
June 20: Wed to Sun 10 A.M. to 5 P.M.;
From June 21 to Aug 27: Everyday 10 A.M. to
5 p.m.; From Aug 28 to Oct 8th: Sat and Sun
10 A.M. to 5 P.M.

L'ISLET-SUR-MER, QUÉBEC
Bernier Maritime Museum
(Musée Maritime Bernier)
55 chemin des Pionniers Est,
Québec G0R 2B0 Canada
(418) 247-5001 Fax: (418) 247-5002
E-mail: info@mmq.qc.ca
Location: Approximately sixty miles northeast of
Quebec City, L'Islet-sur-Mer lies on the south side
of the St. Lawrence River on Rte. 132.
Highlights: The *Bras d'Or 400* (hydrofoil), The
Ernest Lapointe (icebreaker), ship models and
boatworks, library, gift shop,
Website: www.mmq.qc.ca/a_propos_en.html
  General Information: Founded in 1968, the
mission of the Musée Maritime du Québec Inc. is
to safeguard, study, and promote the maritime
heritage of the St. Lawrence River, from its entry
point to the Great Lakes to the high seas including
the Arctic territories.
  Visitors to the Musée du Québec discover not
only an exceptional natural site in an enchanting
setting on the shores of the St. Lawrence River, but
also a cultural site focused on history and the
world. The Museum offers them a change to

explore our maritime heritage, to the real and
contemporary and based on traditions and dreams.
  The Museum's collections naturally reflect its
dual mandate. On the program: four interactive
thematic exhibits, the *Ernest Lapointe* icebreaker,
the *Bras d'Or 400* hydrofoil, an experimental ship
developed for anti-submarine defense, and the
Hydro-Québec park and boatworks, complete with
a boat-maker plying his traditional trade in the
presence of visitors.
  The collections also contain more usual
maritime artifacts as navigational instruments
equipment and furnishings, dishes and cutlery,
weapons, flags, and scale models. Finally, the
museum's holding also includes archival
manuscripts, photographs, maps and plans,
drawings, and posters.
  Activities Guided tours; animation sessions,
documentary films, documentation center,
illustration of navigation on the Saint Lawrence
River and demonstration of ancient Maritime
techniques.
  Admission: Entry fee according to selected
activities. Various packages are sold on site. For
groups with reservation, the museum is open at all
times. Museum open daily, 10 A.M.-5 P.M., May
20-September 3. The rest of the year, 10 A.M.-
Noon and 1 P.M.-4 P.M. Tuesday-Friday
The hydrofoil is open from June 23-September 3.
Picnic areas, out-door cafe and playgrounds on site.

MONTRÉAL, QUÉBEC
TEMPORARY CLOSED – OPEN WINTER
2011
David M. Stewart Museum
Old Fort - St. Helen's Island
P. O. Box 12000, Station "A"
Montreal, Québec H3C 4G6   Canada
(514) 861-6701
E-mail: info@stewart-museum.org
Location: Via the Port de la Concorde bridge or
the Jacques Cartier Bridge to the Park des Lies
Exit. This exit is the only one on the bridge and has
a very short entry — be prepared. Follow signs for
parking and Fort/Museum's parking. Via Metro:
Take Line 4 from Berri LIQAM Station or
Logueuil to Ile Sainte Hélène, about a ten minute
walk, following the signs for the Vieux Fort. Via
bus: Line 70, from Papineau Metro Station.
Highlights: Marine Gallery, ship models,
book/gift shop,
Website: www.stewart-museum.org/
  General Information: Founded in 1955, is
housed in the 1822 Arsenal. Among the buildings
and exhibits to see are the armory, workshops and
cannon store-sheds (even a full-time gun-smith is
on site), and ammunition magazines. Other
buildings include the powder magazine and
barracks.

The fortified arsenal was built by the British to defend the city of Montreal from potential attack by the Americans. The unique artifacts take you back to the life and times of another era, when bold new discoveries were opening vast new frontiers and changing the face of the world. The collections include artifacts from kitchen utensils to firearms, ancient maps, scientific instruments navigational aids, Navigational aids and historic documents. During the summer, you'll see the precision drills of two historic regiments who perform 18th century maneuvers reflecting the daily routine of the troops, which were garrisoned in France's New World outposts from 1683 to 1760. And the Olde 78th Fraser Highlanders add another historic dimension to events at the Fort.

Admission Entry fee. In the summer, the Fort/Museum is open from 10 A.M. to 6 P.M. During winter, open until 5 P.M., closed Tuesdays.

POINTE-AU-PÈRE, QUÉBEC
Pointe-Au-Père Sea Museum
1034, rue du Phare
Pointe-au-Père, Québec G5M 1L8 Canada
(418) 724-6214 Fax: (418) 721-0815
E-mail: On web site.
Location: Pointe-Au-Père is about five miles east of Rimouski on Rte. 132 (on the south side of the St. Lawrence River, approximately 180 miles northeast of Quebec.)
Highlights: The Wreck of the *Empress of Ireland* (Canada's worst maritime tragedy), Pointe-Au-Père, Aid Center, Lighthouse (second highest in Canada), The saltwater marsh of Pointe-au-Père, Website:www. .rimouski.
worldweb.com/SightsAttractions/Museums/ - 51k
General Information: Because of its unique location at the frontier between inland waters and the maritime environment, Pointe-au-Père (Father Point) played an important historic role for more than a century. Because of its many navigational aid facilities and a St. Lawrence pilot station, it was well known to navigators by the beginning of the twentieth century. In 1976 the lighthouse and associated buildings were declared a national historic site.

Visitors may tour the lighthouse, the foghorn shed, and the first keeper's house, and the *Empress of Ireland,* which sank off Rimouski on May 29, 1914, with a loss of 1,012 lives. Displays include original artifacts, montages, models, dioramas, videos, 3-D projection, and photographs depicting the maritime patrimony of the region.
Activities: Illustrations; exhibitions, educational programs, historical research, and historical preservation.
Admission: Entry fee; special fee for groups. Open daily, 9 A.M.-6 P.M., June-October 7 days a week.

QUÉBEC, QUÉBEC
Cartier-Brébeuf National Historic Park
(Parc Historique National Cartier-Brebeuf)
175 l'Espiany, CP 10, Station B
Québec, Québec G1K 7A3 Canada
Toll Free: 1-888-773-8888
(418) 648-4038 Fax: (418) 948-9181
E-mail: parcscanada-que@pc.gc.ca
Location: You can reach the park by heading north via Cote d'Abraham and rue Dorchester (follow 175 nord) approximately two miles from the city center.
Highlights: A 1/20 scale model of a sixteenth-century flagship and a life-sized reproduction of an amerindian loghouse, life-size reproduction of *La Grande Hermine* (flagship),
Website: www.pc.gc.ca
General Information: The information center commemorates Jacques Cartier, first European known to have spent a winter in Canada (1535-36) and Jean de Brébeuf, a martyred Jesuit priest. The museum contains documents that illustrate Cartier's second voyage, the mixing of sixteenth-century European and American Indian cultures, and the initial implantation of the Jesuits in "New France."

The life-size reproduction of *La Grande Hermine,* the flagship of Jacques Cartier, contains an exposition in the mooring basin. Visitors may tour only the hull. *Activities:* Guided tours of the interpretation centre, hands-on display of navigation instruments, maps and photographs illustrating the site's different historical themes. Special activities from the beginning of July to mid-August.
Admission: Entry fee. Call or write the museum for information about their opening hours and special activities.

QUÉBEC, QUÉBEC
Grosse Ile National Historic Site
2 rue d'Auteuil
P.O. Box 10, Station B
Québec, Québec, G1K 7A1 Canada
(418) 234-8841 1-800-773-8888
E-mail: parkscanada-que@pc.gc.ca
Location: Grosse Ile is in the middle of the St. Lawrence River dominating L'Isle-aux-Grues Archipelago. River transportation may be obtained at Berthier sur Mer, Montmagny, Quebec City (48 km), Levis, and St. Laurent.
Highlights: Immigration quarantine station, ice canoe (1920s), Marconi station (1919)
Website: www.parkscanada.gc.ca/grosseile
General Information: Situated in the upper St. Lawrence estuary, this island served as a quarantine station from 1832 to 1937 for the port of Québec, the main gateway to Canada for immigrants until the First World War. In 1847, it was the site of a tragedy when more than 5,000 immigrants, for the most part Irish, fell victims of typhus. Canadian heritage is the focus

of this historical site's nineteenth and twentieth century immigration in the development of Canada.
Artifacts reflecting the maritime history of the island include an ice canoe. The canoe dates from the 1954-55 era. And a Marconi station dating to 1919 is also on the island. Around 40 historical buildings, some of which are open to the public, are located on the island.

Guided tours are offered and excursions are available, but require reservations.
Admission: The entry fee is included in the transport-carrier's river transport rate. Open early May to October, Wednesday-Sunday. Call for rates and telephone number for carriers.

QUÉBEC, QUÉBEC

Naval Museum of Québec
170, rue Dalhousie
Québec, G1K 8M7 Canada
Tel. : (418) 694-5387
Fax : (418) 694-5550
E-mail: info@mnq-nmq.org
Location: The Museum is located at Bassin Louise
Highlights: Canadian naval history
Web site: www.mnq-nmq.org/enter.html
General Information: The Naval Museum of Québec tells naval stories, the story of the Saint Lawrence, and the story of the Naval Reserve of Canada. Even though the museum is small, one can learn the strategic importance of the Saint Lawrence and the roles it played in many historical events. Here, you will learn unknown stories: naval battles on the Saint Lawrence that shaped Canadian history, and tales of men and women who gave life to the Canadian Navy.
Activities: Bring your little sailors to the Naval Museum and let them discover the traditions of the Canadian Navy and our great river's naval history.
Admission: Open July – January. Call or write the Museum for information about opening hours.

QUÉBEC, QUÉBEC

Port of Québec in the Nineteenth Century National Historic Site (Lieu Historique National le Port de Québec au XIXe Siecle)
Historical National Site
100, Saint-Andre Street, P. O. Box 2474
Québec, Québec G1K 7R3 Canada
(418) 648-3300
Location: The site is located at 100, Saint-Andre Street in the ancient cement works, and integrated into the harbor installations of the Louise Basin in the heart of the Old Port.
Highlights: The history of the Port of Québec
General Information: The Old Port of Québec

interpretation Centre has been offering high quality interpretation services since 1984.

The hands-on exhibitions relate to the port's principal activities in the nineteenth century: shipbuilding and timber trade. Scale-models, reproductions, soundtracks and mannequins in period costume recreate the hustle and bustle of Québec's harbour fruont at the time of tall ship building.
Activities: Guided tours of the exhibitions. Guided tour of the port in the 19th century.
Admission: Entry fee. Open May 2nd-September 3rd: everyday, from 10 A.M.-5 P.M.; September 4th – October 7th: every day from 1 P.M. to 5 P.M.

YUKON TERRITORY, CANADA

DAWSON CITY, YUKON
SS *Keno* (Sternwheeler)
The Klondike National Historic Sites
Front Street, P. O. Box 390
Dawson City, Yukon Y0B 1GO Canada
(867) 993-7221 Fax: (867) 993-7203
Email: dawson.info@pc.gc.ca
Location: From Anchorage, Alaska, via Rte. 1 243 miles to Tok, then Rte. 5/9 106 miles to Dawson City. The *Keno* is in the dry-dock on Front Street between King and Queen Streets.
Highlights: SS *Keno* (sternwheeler), **Website:** www.pc.gc.ca/voyage-travel/pv-vp/itm13-/page8_e.asp **Website:** www.yukoneh.com
General Information: The SS *Keno* (sternwheeler), relocated to Dawson City in 1961, now sits on the bank of the Yukon River. Built in 1922 at Whitehorse, it was the last riverboat to run between that city and Dawson.

Because the sternwheeler used wood-fired boilers, wood camps were established along the waterway. The SS *Keno* was part of the fleet which played a major part in the history of the Yukon Territory bringing out the ore each spring and doing so until the railroad was built, thus eliminating the need for river transportation. The Museum has photo exhibits depicting its career as part of a fleet of steamers.

Today, the *Keno* is getting ready for restoration work will hopefully be open for tours in 2002. An outdoor exhibit shows the role that the SS *Keno* played in the Yukon.
Activities: Ground tours
Admission: No entry fee. Call or write the sponsors for information about opening hours.

CANAL PARKS

LISTED BELOW ARE THE NAMES OF
SELECTED CANAL PARKS. FOR MORE

Albemarle and Chesapeake Canal
(Great Bridge, VA)
Alexandria Canal Tide Lock Park
(Alexandria, VA)
Armory Canal (Harper's Ferry, WV)
Battery Creek Lock Restoration
(Near Lynchburg, VA)
Ben Salem Lock Wayside
(Between Lexington and
Buena Vista, VA)
Big Sandy Lock and Dam 3
(LA, KY, & Fort Gay, WV)
*Black River Canal (NY)
*Blackstone Canal (MA)
Canal Basin Square (Scottsville, VA
*Cayuga-Seneca Canal (NY)
*Champlain Canal (NY)
*Chemung Canal (NY)
*Chenango Canal (NY)
Chessie Nature Trail (Lexington, VA)
Crofton Lock (Near Charlottesville, VA)
Deep Creek Lock Park (Deep Creek, VA)
*Delaware and Raritan Canal (NJ/PA)
Dismal Swamp Canal
(Deep Creek, VA, and South Mills, NC)
Eagle Rock Lock Park (Eagle Rock, VA)
Explore Park Batteau Living History Program
(Roanoke, VA)
Fredericksburg Canal (Fredericksburg, VA)
*Genesee Valley Canal (NY)
Goose Creek State Scenic River
(Loudoun County, VA)
Great Dismal Swamp National Wildlife Refuge
Suffolk, VA)
Great Falls Park (Great Falls, VA)
Great Ship Lock Park (Richmond, VA)
*Hocking Canal (OH)
Humpback Bridge Wayside Park
(W of Covington, VA)
Kanawha River Navigation
(Winfield, Marmet-London, WVA)
*Lehigh Navigation (PA)
Little Kanawha River Navigation
(Leachtown, WVA)
*Louisville and Portland Canal (KY)
Marmet Park (Near Charleston, WV)

NOTE:
CANAL PARKS NOT IN VA/WV/NC

INFORMATION ABOUT
A SPECIFIC PARK, PLEASE WRITE TO
THE FOLLOWING:

The American Canal Society
117 Main Street
Freemansburg, PA 18017
http://www.americancanals.org/
Or
Virginia Canals and Navigation Society
6826 Rosemont Drive
McLean, VA 22101
http://organizations.rockbridge.net/canal/
- -

*Miami and Erie Canal (OH)
Monongahela River Navigation
(Morgantown, Hildebrand &
Opekiska, WV)
*New Haven and Northampton (CT)
New River Gorge National River
(Hinton and Fayetteville, WV)
*Ohio and Pennsylvania Canal (OH)
Ohio River Navigation (WVA Border)
Old Dominion Railway Transportation Museum
(Richmond, VA)
Palmyra Lock (Palmyra, VA)
Patowmack Canal (Great Falls, VA)
Pump House/Three-Mile Locks Park,
(Richmond, VA)
Rappahannock State Scenic River
(Faquier County, VA)
Richmond Riverfront & Canal Walk,
(Richmond, VA)
Rivanna Canal Trail, (Palmyra, VA)
Rivanna State Scenic River
(Fluvanna County, VA)
Whitewater Canal (IN)
Roanoke Canal Museum (Roanoke Rapids, NC)
*Sandy and Beaver Canal (OH)
*Santee and Cooper Canal (SC)
*Schuylkill Navigation (Philadelphia, PA)
Shenandoah Canal (Harper's Ferry, WV)
Shenandoah State Scenic River
(Clarke County, VA)
Staunton State Scenic River
(Between Long Island and
Brookneal, VA)
*Susquehanna and Tidewater (PA)
Union Mills Canal Towpath Trail
(Lake Monticello, VA)
Upper Appomattox Canal (Petersburg, VA)
Upper James State Scenic River
(Botetourt County, VA)
*Wabash and Erie Canal (IN)

212

LIST OF MUSEUMS-ALPHA

Absecon Lighthouse
(Atlantic City, NJ) 102
Adirondack Museum
(Blue Mountain Lake, NY) 110
Age Of Sail Heritage Center
(Port Greville, NS) 196
Aircraft Carrier *Hornet* Museum
(Alameda, CA) 3
Albert County Museum
(Hopewell Cape, NB) 190
Alexandria Seaport Foundation &
Seaport Center, (Alexandria, VA) 161
Alfred S. Brownell Collection of Atlantic
Coast Fishing Craft Models
(Providence, RI) 152
Allie Ryan Maritime Collections
(Castaine, ME) 44
American Merchant Marine Museum
U.S. Merchant Marine Academy,
(Kings Point, NY) 117
American Philosophical Society
Library (Philadelphia, PA) 145
Annapolis Maritime Museum
(Annapolis, MD) 50
Antique Boat Museum (Clayton, NY) 113
Apalachicola Maritime Museum
(Apalachicola, FL) 22
Apostle Islands National Lakeshore
(Bayfield, WI) 181
Aquarium and Marine Centre
(Centre Marin de Shippaga
(Shippagan, NB) 190
Arabia Steamboat Museum
(Kansas City, MO) 98
Archelaus Smith Museum
(Centreville, NS) 192
Arkansas River Historical Society
Museum (Catoosa, OK) 140
Arkansas Inland Marine Museum
(North Little Rock, AR) 3
Ashtabula Maritime Museum
(Ashtabula, OH) 133
Assiginack Historical Museum
and SS *Norisle* Heritage Park
(Manitowaning, ONT) 199
Atlantic Heritage Center Museum
(Somers Point, NJ) 107
Bainbridge Island Historic Museum
(Bainbridge Island, WA) 170
Baltimore Maritime Museum
(Baltimore, MD) 52
Baltimore Museum of Industry
(Baltimore, MD) 52
Banning Residence Museum
(Wilmington, CA) 15
Barn Museum (Bellport, NY) 109

Barnacle State Historical Site
(Miami, FL) 22
Barnegat Lighthouse
(Barnegat Light, NJ) 102
Basin Head Fisheries Museum
(Souris, PEI) 208
Battery Point Lighthouse
(Crescent City, CA) 5
Battleship Cove (Fall River, MA) 65
Battleship *New Jersey* (Camden, NJ) 103
Battleship *South Dakota* Museum
(Sioux Falls, SD) 156
Battleship *Texas* State Historical Park
(La Porte, TX) 159
Bay Model Visitor Center
(Sausalito, CA) 14
Bayfield Heritage Association Inc.,
(Bayfield, WI) 181
Beavertail Lighthouse & Museum
(Jamestown, RI) 148
Belle of Louisville Steamer
(Louisville, KY) 6 39
Bernier Maritime Museum,
(Musée Maritime Bernier),
(L'Islet-sur-Mer, Québec, QBC) 209
Beverly Historical Society/ Museum
(Beverly, MA) 60
Big Sandy Lake Lock and Dam
(McGregor, MN) 94
Binghamton (Ferry) (Edgewater, NJ) 104
Bishop Museum (Honolulu, HI) 31
Block Island Southeast Lighthouse
and Museum(Block Island, RI) 147
Boothbay Region Historical
Society (Boothbay Harbor, ME) 43
Border Historical Society
(Eastport, ME) 44
Boston Marine Society (Boston, MA) 60
Boston Tea Party Ship and Museum
(Boston, MA) 60
Bremerton Naval Museum
(Bremerton, WA) 171
Brick Store Museum (Kennebunk, ME) 45
Buffalo and Erie Counties Naval and
Servicemen's Park, (Buffalo, NY) 111
Buffalo Bill Museum of Le Claire
(Le Claire, IA) 38
Burke Museum (Seattle, WA) 175
Bytown Historical Museum
(Ottawa, ONT) 201

C and D Canal Museum
(Chesapeake/Delaware Canal
Museum) (Chesapeake City, MD) 54
C & O Canal of Cumberland MD
(Cumberland, MD) 55
C. Howard Heister Canal Center
(Wyomissing, PA) 147

CSS *Neuse* State Historic Site
(Kinston, NC) 130
Cabrillo National Monument
(San Diego, CA) 11
Cairo Custom House Museum
(Cairo, IL) 33
Calvert Marine Museum
(Solomons, MD) 59
Canadian Canoe Museum
(Peterborough, ONT) 202
Canal Fulton Heritage Society
(Canal Fulton, OH) 134
Canal Museum (Greenville, PA) 144
Canal Society of New Jersey
Museum at Waterloo Village
(Morristown, NJ) 106
Canal Society of New York State
(Syracuse, NY) 126
Canastota Canal Town Museum
(Canastota, NY) 112
Cannon Ball House & Marine Museum
(Lewes, DE) 21
Cape Ann Historical Museum
(Gloucester, MA) 67
Cape Cod Maritime Museum
(Hyannis, MA 68
Cape Fear Museum (Fayetteville, NC) 129
Cape Fear Museum
(Wilmington, NC) 132
Cape Florida Lighthouse
(Miami, FL) 25
Cape Henry Lighthouse
(Virginia Beach, VA 167
Cape May County Historical and
Genealogical Society Museum
In the John Holmes House/Barn
(Cape May, NJ) 104
Capt. Charles H. Hurley Library
(Buzzards Bay, MA) 61
Captain Robert Bennet Forbes House
(Milton, MA) 70
Carroll County Wabash and Erie
Canal, Inc. (Delphi, IN) 35
Cartier-Brébeuf National Historical Park
(Québec, QBC) 210
Cascade Locks and Marine Park
(Cascade Locks, OR) 141
Castle Museum of Saginaw County
History (Saginaw, MI) 90
Catalina Island Museum
(Catalina Island, CA) 5
Center for the Wooden Boat
(Seattle, WA) 175
Chafee Blackstone National Corridor
(Woonsocket, RI) 154
Chaffey's Lockhouse Museum
(Chaffey's Lock, ONT) 196
Channel Islands National Park
(Ventura, CA) 15

"Chapel Hill" Museum
(Shag Harbour, NS) 196
Charleston Museum
(Charleston, SC) 154
Charlestown Navy Yard
(Charlestown, MA) 62
Chautauqua Lakes Historic Vessels Co.
(Mayville, NY) 119
Chesapeake & Ohio National
Historic Park (Hagerstown, MD) 57
Chesapeake Bay Maritime Museum
(St. Michaels, MD) 58
Chicago Maritime Society (Chicago, IL) 34
Chicamacomico Life-Saving Station
(Rodanthe, NC) 132
China Cabin (Belvedere, CA) 3
Chittenango Landing Canal Boat
Museum (Chittenango, NY) 113
Churchill House and Marine
Memorial Room Museum
(Hantsport, NS) 193
Cigna Museum and Art Collection
(Philadelphia, PA) 145
City Island Nautical Museum
(City Island, NY) 113
Civil Engineer Corps/Seabee Museum
(Port Hueneme, CA) 10
Clarke Museum (Eureka, CA) 6
Clatsop County Historical Museum
(Astoria, OR) 140
Clinton County Historical Museum
(Plattsburg, NY) 122
Coast Guard Cutter *Bramble*
(Port Huron, MI) 88
Coast Guard Museum/Northwest
(Seattle, WA) 176
Cohasset Maritime Museum
(Cohasset, MA) 64
Collingwood Museum
(Collingwood, ONT) 197
Columbia Pacific Heritage Museum
(Ilwaco, WA) 172
Columbia River Maritime Museum
(Astoria, OR) 140
Connecticut River Museum (Essex, CT) 16
Coos Historical & Maritime Museum
(North Bend, OR) 142
Copper Harbor Lighthouse Museum
(Copper Harbor, MI) 80
Coquille River Lighthouse
(Bandon, OR) 141
Corpus Christi Museum of Science & Industry
(Corpus Christi, TX) 157
Coteau-du-Lac National Historical
Site (Coteau-du-Lac, QBC) 208
Counting-House-Old Berwick Historical
Society (South Berwick, ME) 49
Cowichan Bay Maritime Center
(Duncan, BC) 186

Crown Point State Historic Site
   (Crown Point, NY)   114
Custom House Maritime Museum of
   Newburyport, (Newburyport, MA) 72
Custom House Museum
   (New London, CT)   18

David M. Stewart Museum
   (Montréal, Québec, QBC)   209
David Warther Carving Museum
   (Sugarcreek, OH)   137
Decatur House (Washington, D.C.)   179
Delaware and Hudson Canal Museum
   (High Falls, NY)   116
DeTour Passage Historical Museum
   (De Tour Village, MI)   81
DiscoverSea Shipwreck Museum
   (Fenwick Island, DE)   19
Discovery Harbour
   (Penetanguishene, ONT)   202
Door County Maritime Museum
   (Gills Rock, WI)   182
Door County Museum at Cana Island
   Lighthouse (Gills Rock, WI)   182
Door County Maritime Museum
   (Sturgeon Bay, WI)   184
Dorchester Heritage Museum
   (Cambridge, MD)   53
Dorothy (The Iron Tugboat),
   (Newport News, VA)   162
Dory Shop (Shelburne, NS)   196
Dossin Great Lakes Museum
   (Detroit, MI)   81
Downeast Maritime Museum
   (Eastport, ME)   44
Dunkirk Historical Lighthouse and
   Veteran's Park (Dunkirk, NY)   115
Dutra Museum of Dredging
   (Rio Vista, CA)   10
Dwight D. Eisenhower Lock
   (Massena, NY)   119

Eagle Harbor Lighthouse and Museums
   (Eagle Harbor, MI)   82
Eagle Bluff Lighthouse
   (Fish Creek, WI)   182
East Brother Light Station
   (Point Richmond, CA)   9
East End Seaport Maritime Museum
   (Greenport, NY)   116
East Hampton Town Marine Museum
   (East Hampton, NY)   115
East Martello Gallery & Museum
   (Key West, FL)   24
Edmonds Historical Museum
   (Edmonds, WA)   171
Egan Institute of Maritime Studies
   (Nantucket Island, MA)   70

Erie Canal Museum (Syracuse, NY)   126
Erie Canal Village (Rome, NY)   123
Erie Maritime Museum Homeport
   U.S. Brig *Niagara* (Erie, PA)   144
Essex Shipbuilding Museum
   (Essex, MA)   65
Expedition *Whydah* (Pirate Ship)
   (Provincetown, MA)   74

Fairbanks Historical Preservation
   Foundation (Fairbanks, AK)   2
Fairport Marine Museum
   (Fairport, OH)   137
Falls of the Ohio State Park
   (Jeffersonville, IN)   36
Falmouth Historical Society's Museums
   (Falmouth, MA)   66
Fathom Five National Marine Park
   (Tobermory, ONT)   207
Fells Point Maritime Museum now at
   Maryland Historical (Baltimore, MD) 52
Fire Island Lighthouse Preservation
   Society (Captree, NY)   112
Fisheries Museum of the Atlantic
   (Lunenburg, NS)   194
Fishermen's Museum
   (Musgrave Harbour, NFLD)   191
Fishermen's Museum and Pemaquid Point
   Lighthouse (Pemaquid Point, ME) 47
Fort Fisher Historic Site
   (Kure Beach, NC)   130
Fort Hancock Museum
   (Highlands, NJ)   105
Fort Hunter-Schoharie State Historic Site
   (Fort Hunter, NY)   115
Fort Morgan Museum (Gulf Shores, AL) 1
Forwarder's Museum (Prescott, ONT) 204
Franklin D. Roosevelt Library/Museum
   (Hyde Park, NY)   117
Freedom Park, Inc. (Omaha, NE)   100
Friendship Museum (Friendship, ME) 44

Gates House (Machiasport, ME)   46
Gig Harbor Peninsula Historical Society
   & Museum, (Gig Harbor, WA)   172
Gilbert's Bar House of Refuge
   (Stuart, FL)   27
Glacier Society Museum
   (Stratford, CT)   19
Gloucester *Adventure* (schooner)
   (Gloucester, MA)   67
Gloucester Maritime Heritage Center
   (Gloucester, MA)   67
Golden Eagle River Museum
   (St. Louis, MO)   98
Governor J. Millard Tawes Historical
   Museum (Crisfield, MD)   55

Smith's Guide to Maritime Museums of North America

Grand Manan Museum and Walter B.
McLaughlin Marine Gallery
(Grand Manan, NB) 189
Grand Marais Maritime Museum
(Grand Marais, MI) 83
Grand Traverse Lighthouse Museum
(North Point, MI) 87
Graveyard of the Atlantic Museum
(Hatteras, NC) 129
Gray & Blue Naval Museum
(Vicksburg, MS) 97
Grays Harbor Historical Seaport
(Aberdeen, WA) 169
Great Harbor Maritime Museum
(Northeast Harbor, ME) 45
Great Lakes Marine/U.S. Coast Guard
Memorial Museum
(Ashtabula, OH) 132
Great Lakes Naval Memorial &
Museum, (Muskegon, MI) 86
Great Lakes Naval Museum
(Great Lakes, IL) 34
Great Lakes Shipwreck Museum
(Paradise, MI) 87
Green Park Shipbuilding Museum
(Port Hill, PEI) 208
Greenville Canal Museum
(Greenville, PA) 145
Grosse Ile and the Irish Memorial
National Historic Site
(Québec, QBC) 210
Guest House Museum (Fort Bragg, CA) 6

H. L. Hunley Museum
(North Charleston, SC) 155
H. Lee White Marine Museum
(Oswego, NY) 121
HMCS Fraser (DDE-223)
(Bridgewater, NS) 192
HMCS Haida Naval Museum
(Toronto, ONT) 207
HMCS Sackville (K-181)
(Halifax, NS) 192
Half Moon Visitor Center/ New
Netherland Museum (Albany, NY) 108
Hamilton-Scourge Project
(Hamilton, ONT) 198
Hampton Roads Naval Museum-
Nauticus (Norfolk, VA) 164
Harry Lundberg School of Seamanship
(Piney Point, MD) 57
Hart Nautical Collections
(Cambridge, MA) 61
Havre de Grace Maritime Museum
(Havre de Grace, MD) 56
Hawaii Maritime Center
(Honolulu, HI) 31
Hereford Inlet Lighthouse
(North Wildwood, NJ) 106

Heritage Hjemkomst Interpretive
Center (Moorhead, MN) 94
Herman T. Pott National Inland
Waterways Library (St. Louis, MO) 99
Hermann River Memorial
(Hermann, MO) 96
Herreshoff Marine Museum/
Monument (Bristol, RI) 148
Hiram Chittenden Locks (Seattle, WA) 176
Historic Annapolis (Annapolis, MD) 50
Historic Gardener's Basin
(Atlantic City, NJ) 102
Historic Hermann Museums
(Hermann, MO) 98
Historic Roscoe Village
(Coshocton, OH) 136
Historic St. Mary's City
(St. Mary's City, MD) 58
Historical Collections of the Great Lakes
(Bowling Green, OH) 134
Historical Museum of Bay County
(Bay City, MI) 79
Historical Museum of Southern
Florida (Miami, FL) 26
Historical Society of Old Yarmouth
(Yarmouth Port, MA) 78
Hokenson Brothers Fishery
(Bayfield, WI) 181
Hopkins and Bros. Store
(Onancock, VA) 165
Houston Maritime Museum
(Houston, TX) 158
Howard Steamboat Museum
(Jeffersonville, IN) 36
Hudson River Maritime Museum
(Kingston, NY) 118
Hudson River Sloop Clearwater
(Beacon, NY) 109
Hull Lifesaving Museum (Hull, MA) 68
Humboldt Bay Maritime Museum
(Eureka, CA) 6
Hunting Island State Park
(St. Helena Island, SC) 156
Huron City Museums
(Port Austin, MI) 88
Huron Lightship Museum (See Port
Huron Lightship Museum) 89
Huronia Museum & Huron Indian
Village (Midland, ONT) 200

Ice Harbor - Lower Monumental Project
Historical Society (Pasco, WA) 174
Illinois and Michigan Canal Museum
(Lockport, IL) 34
Independence Seaport Museum
(Philadelphia, PA) 146
Indian River Life-Saving Station
(Bethany Beach, DE) 23

Inland Rivers Library
  (Cincinnati, OH)   134
Inland Seas Maritime Museum
  (Vermilion, OH)   139
International Yacht Restoration School
  (Newport, RI)   149
Intrepid Sea-Air-Space Museum
  (New York City, NY)   119
Iowa Great Lakes Maritime Museum
  (Arnolds Park, IA)   37
Isle Royal National Park
  (Houghton, MI)   84
Islesford Historical Museum
  (Bar Harbor, ME)   42

Jacksonville Maritime Museum Society
  (Jacksonville, FL)   23
James B. Richardson Maritime Museum
  (Cambridge, MD)   54
James Kirk Maritime Museum
  (Linwood, NJ)   106
Jamestown Museum (Jamestown, RI) 147
Jamestown Settlement
  (Williamsburg, VA)   168
Jeremiah Lee Mansion
  (Marblehead, MA)   69
Jesse Besser Museum (Alpena, MI)   79
John Dubois Maritime Museum
  (Greenwich, NJ)   104
John Hancock Warehouse and Wharf/
  Old York Historical Society
  (York, ME)   50
John Paul Jones House
  (Portsmouth, NH)   100
Jones Falls Defensible Lockmaster's
  House (Elgin, ONT)   198
Jupiter Inlet Lighthouse and Museum
  (Jupiter, FL)   23

Kalmar Nyckel Shipyard & Museum
  (Wilmington, DE)   21
Keewatin Maritime Museum
  (Douglas, MI)   81
Kennebunkport Maritime Museum
  (Kennebunkport, ME)   45
Keokuk River Museum (Keokuk, IA)   38
Key West Shipwreck Historeum
  (Key West, FL)   24
Kittery Historical and Naval
  Museum (Kittery, ME)   46
Kodiak Maritime Museum (Kodiak, AK) 2

La Have Island Marine Museum
  (La Have Island, NS)   194
Lake Champlain Maritime Museum
  (Basin Harbor, VT)   160
Lake Erie Islands Historical Society
  Museum (Put-in-Bay, OH)   138

Lake Pontchartrain Basin Maritime
  Museum (Madisonville, LA)   41
Lake Superior Maritime Visitor Center
  (Duluth, MN)   93
Landsford Canal (Catawba, SC)   154
Lawrence House (Maitland, NS)   195
Leif Erickson Restoration Project
  (Duluth, MN)   94
Les Cheneaux Maritime Museum
  (Cedarville, MI)   80
Light Station Mulkiteo 1906
  (Mulkiteo, WA)   173
Lighthouse Museum (Key West, FL)   24
Lighthouse Park Museum
  (Port Hope, MI)   88
Lighthouse Point and Harbor Museum
  (Two Harbors, MN)   95
Lightship *New Bedford*
  (New Bedford, MA)   71
Lightship *Relief* (Oakland, CA)   8
Lloyd Taber-Marina del Rey Library
  (Marina del Rey, CA)   7
Lockmaster Anglin's Interpretive
  Center (Smiths Falls, ONT)   206
The Lockmaster's House Museum
  (Chaffey's Lock, NS)   196
Lockport Canal Museum
  (Lockport, NY)   118
Log Cabin Museum (Newport, OR)   141
Long Island Maritime Museum
  (West Sayville, NY)   127
Longship Company, Ltd.
  (Avenue, MD)   51
Los Angeles Maritime Museum
  (San Pedro, CA)   13
Louisbourg Marine Museum
  (Louisbourg, NS)   194
Louisiana State Museum
  (New Orleans, LA)   41
Louisiana State Museum-Baton Rouge
  (Baton Rouge, LA)   40
Lowell's Boat Shop (Amesbury, MA)   59
Lower Fort Garry National Park
  (Selkirk, MTB)   188
Lower Lakes Marine Historical Society
  (Buffalo, NY)   111

Madeline (Replica Schooner)
  (Traverse City, MI)   92
Maine Lighthouse Museum
  (Rockland, ME)   48
Maine Maritime Museum (Bath, ME)   42
Makah Museum (Neah Bay, WA)   173
Manistee County Historical Museum
  (Manistee, MI)   85
Marblehead Historical Society
  (Marblehead, MA)   69
Marine Museum (St. James, MI)   91

Marine Museum at Fall River
(Fall River, MA) 66
Marine Museum of Manitoba
(Selkirk, MAN) 189
Marine Museum of the Great Lakes at
Kingston, (Kingston ONT) 199
Mariners' Museum
(Newport News, VA) 163
Mariner's Park Museum
(Milford, ONT) 201
Marinship 1942-1945 (Shipyard)
(Sausalito, CA) 13
Maritime & Irish Mossing Museum
(Scituate, MA) 76
Maritime & Yachting Museum
(Stuart, FL) 27
Maritime Aquarium (Norwalk, CT) 18
Maritime Command Museum
(Halifax, NS) 193
Maritime Industry Museum/Fort Schuyler
(Bronx, NY) 110
Maritime Museum of British Columbia
(Victoria, BC) 188
Maritime Museum of Sandusky
(Sandusky, OH) 138
Maritime Museum of the Atlantic
(Halifax, NS) 193
Maritime Seafood Industry Museum
(Biloxi, MS) 96
Mark Twain Home Foundation
(Hannibal, MO) 97
Marquette Maritime Museum
(Marquette, MI) 86
Marshall Point Lighthouse Museum
(Port Clyde, ME) 47
Martha's Vineyard Historical Society
and Museum (Edgartown, MA) 64
Mary Celeste Museum (Marion, MA) 69
Mary Woods II Riverboat Museum
(Jacksonport, AR) 3
Masters, Mates, & Pilots Museum
(Linthicum, MD) 56
Mather House Museum
(Port Jefferson, NY) 123
Mayor Andrew Broaddus (Coast
Guard Station) (Louisville, KY) 40
Medford Historical Society Museum
(Medford, MA) 69
Mel Fisher Maritime Heritage Society
(Key West, FL) 24
Mel Fisher's Treasure Museum
(Sebastian, FL) 27
Merrickville Blockhouse Museum
(Merrickville, ONT) 200
Michigan Historical Museum
(Lansing, MI) 84
Michigan Maritime Museum
(South Haven, MI) 92

Middlesex Canal Museum
(North Billerca, MA) 73
Milwaukee Public Library
(Milwaukee, WI) 183
Minnesota Lakes Maritime Museum
(Alexandria) 93
Minnesota Marine Art Museum
(Winona) 96
Mississagi Strait Lighthouse Museum
(Gore Bay, ONT) 198
Mississippi River Museum at
Mud Island (Memphis, TN) 156
Mississippi River Visitor Center
(Rock Island, IL) 35
Missouri Historical Society
(St. Louis, MO) 99
Montauk Point Lighthouse
Museum (Montauk, NY) 119
Monterey Maritime Museum
(Monterey, CA) 7
Moore Museum (Mooretown, ONT) 201
Moosehead Marine Museum
(Greenville, ME) 44
Museum of Florida History
(Tallahassee, FL) 28
Museum of History and Industry
(Seattle, WA) 176
Museum of Missouri River History
(Brownville, NE) 100
Museum of Mobile (Mobile, AL) 1
Museum of Newport History
(Newport, RI) 150
Museum of Science (Boston, MA) 60
Museum of the Albemarle
(Elizabeth City, NC) 128
Museum of the Berkeley Springs
(Berkeley Springs, VA) 180
Museum of the City of New York
(New York City, NY) 120
Museum of the Confederacy
(Richmond, VA) 166
Museum of the Jefferson County
Historical Society
(Port Townsend, WA) 174
Museum of the Man in the Sea
(Panama City, FL) 26
Museum of the Sea/Hatteras Island
Visitor's Center-Cape Hatteras
Lighthouse, (Buxton, NC) 128
Museum of Yachting (Newport, RI) 150
Museum of Yarmouth History
(Yarmouth, ME) 50
Museum Ship *Norgoma*
(Sault Ste. Marie, ONT) 205
Museum Ship *Valley Camp*
(Sault Ste. Marie, MI) 91
Muskoka Lakes Museum
(Port Carling, ONT) 204
Mystic Seaport Museum (Mystic, CT) 17

Nancy Island Historic Site
(Wasaga Beach, ONT)   207
Nantucket Lifesaving Museum
(Nantucket Island, MA)   70
National Canal Museum and
Hugh Moore Park (Easton, PA)   144
National Maritime Historical Society
(Peekskill, NY)   122
National Maritime Heritage Initiative
(Washington, D.C).   179
National Mississippi River Museum   38
National Museum of Ship Models &
Sea History, (Sadorus, IL)   35
National Museum of the Pacific
War (Fredericksburg, TX)   156
Nautical Museum at Horton Point
Lighthouse (Southold, NY)   126
Nauticus. The National Maritime Center
(Norfolk, VA)   164
Nautilus and Submarine Force Museum
(Groton, CT)   16
Naval Museum of Alberta
(Calgary, ALB)   184
Naval Museum of Manitoba
(Winnipeg, MTB)   189
Naval Museum of Québec
(Québec, Québec)   211
Naval Undersea Museum
(Keyport, WA)   173
Naval War College Museum
(Newport, RI)   150
Navy Museum (Washington, D.C.)   179
Neversink Valley Area Museum/
D and H Canal Park
(Cuddebackville, NY)   115
New Bedford Free Public Library
(New Bedford, MA)   71
New Bedford Whaling Museum
(New Bedford, MA)   71
New Brunswick Museum
(Saint John, NB)   190
New England Pirate Museum
(Salem, MA)   75
New Hampshire Boat Museum
(Wolfeboro, NH)   102
New Hope Canal Boat Company
(New Hope, PA)   145
New Jersey Maritime Museum
(Beach Haven, NJ)   103
New Jersey Naval Museum/
Submarine USS *Ling,*
(Hackensack, NJ)   105
New-York Historical Society
(New York City, NY)   120
New York State Canal System
(Albany, NY)   109
Newport Harbor Nautical Museum
(Newport Beach, CA)   8

Noble Maritime Collection
(Staten Island, NY)   126
Nordic Heritage Museum
(Seattle, WA)   177
North Carolina Maritime Museum
(Beaufort, NC)   128
North Carolina Maritime Museum at
Roanoke Island, (Manteo, NC)   130
North Carolina Maritime Museum at
Southport, (Southport, NC)   132
Northport Historical Museum
(Northport, NY)   121
Northwest Seaport (Seattle, WA)   177

Ocean City Historical Museum
(Ocean City, NJ)   107
Ocean City Life-Saving Station
Museum (Ocean City, MD)   57
Ocean Liner Museum
(New York City, NY)   120
O'Dell House Museum
(Annapolis Royal, NS)   191
Odyssey, The Maritime Discover
Center (Seattle, WA)   177
Ohio River Museum (Marietta , OH) 137
Old and New Lighthouses
(Virginia Beach, VA)   167
Old Coast Guard Station Museum
(Virginia Beach, VA)   168
Old Fort Jackson (Savannah, GA)   30
Old Fort William Historical Park
(Thunder Bay, ONT)   206
Old Harbor Life-Saving Station
(Wellfleet, MA)   77
Old Lighthouse (Biloxi, MS)   96
Old Lighthouse Museum
(Michigan City, IN)   37
Old Lighthouse Museum
(Stonington, CT)   19
Old Mackinac Point Lighthouse
Museum (Mackinac City, MI)   85
Old Sacramento Waterfront and
Riverboat *Delta King*
(Sacramento, CA)   11
Old Santee Canal State Park
(Moncks Corner, SC)   154
Old Sardine Village Museum
(Lubec, ME)   45
Old State House-The Bostonian
Society (Boston, MA)   61
Oregon History Center (Portland, OR) 142
Oregon Maritime Center and Museum
(Portland, OR)   143
Oregon Museum of Science and
Industry (Portland, OR)   143
Osher Map Library (Portland, ME)   48
Osterville Historical Society
(Osterville, Cape Cod, MA)   73

219

Oswego Maritime Foundation
(Oswego, NY)   122
Ottawa House By-the-Sea
(Parrsboro, NS)   195
Owen Sound Marine-Rail Heritage
Museum, (Owen Sound, ONT)   202
Oxford Museum (Oxford, MD)   57
Oyster & Maritime Museum
(Chincoteague, VA)   162

P.A. Denny (Towboat)
(Charleston, VA)   180
PT Boat Museum and Library
(Fall River, MA)   66
PT Boats, Inc. Headquarters
(Germantown, TN)   156
Palm Beach Maritime Museum
(Palm Beach, FL)   26
Pate Museum of Transportation
(Fort Worth, TX)   156
Paterson Museum (Paterson, NJ)   107
Patowmack Canal (Great Falls, VA) 162
Patowmack Presidential Yacht
(Oakland, CA)   8
Patriot's Point Naval and Maritime
Museum, (Mt. Pleasant, SC)   155
Peabody Essex Museum
(Salem, MA)   76
Peary-MacMillan Arctic Museum
(Brunswick, ME)   43
Penobscot Marine Museum
(Searsport, ME)   48
Pensacola Historical Museum
(Pensacola, FL)   27
Peterborough Centennial Museum
(Peterborough, ONT)   203
Peterborough Hydraulic Lift Lock and
Visitor Center,
(Peterborough, ONT)   203
Philadelphia Ship Preservation Guild
(Philadelphia, PA)   6
Phyllis A and Maritime Heritage Society
(Kennebunkport, ME)   46
Pilgrim (Snow Brig)
(Dana Point, CA)   5
Pilgrim Hall Museum
(Plymouth, MA)   74
Piney Point Lighthouse Museum
(Piney Point, MD)   58
Piqua Historical Area
(Piqua, OH)   138
Pirate Soul Museum
(Key West, FL)   25
Piscataqua Gundalow Project
(Portsmouth, NH)   101
Plainville Historic Center
(Plainville, CT)   19
Plaquemine Lock
(Plaquemine, LA)   42

Plimoth Plantation (Plymouth, MA)   74
Point Arena Lighthouse and Museum
(Point Arena, CA)   9
Point Iroquois Lighthouse & Maritime
Museum (Brimley, MI)   80
Point Pinos Lighthouse
(Pacific Grove, CA)   9
Point Sur Light Station Carmel, CA)   4
Pointe-au-Père Sea Museum
(Pointe-au-Père, Québec, QBC)   210
Ponce de Leon Inlet Lighthouse
Museum (Ponce Inlet, FL)   27
Port Colborne Historical and Marine
Museum (Port Colborne, ONT)   204
Port Columbus Civil War Naval
Center (Columbus, GA)   29
Port Dover Harbour Museum
(Port Dover, ONT)   204
Port Huron Lightship Museum
(Port Huron, MI)   89
Port Huron Museum (Port Huron, MI)   89
Port Isabel Historical Museum
(Port Isabel, TX)   159
Port Isabel Lighthouse Complex
(Port Isabel, TX)   159
Port of Portsmouth Maritime Museum
(Portsmouth, NH)   99
Port Orford Lifeboat Station
(Port Orford, OR)   142
Port Penn Interpretive Center
(Port Penn, DE)   21
Port of Québec in the Nineteenth Century
National Historic Site
(Québec, QBC)   211
Portage Canal Society, Inc.
(Portage, WI)   184
Portland Harbor Museum
(South Portland, ME)   49
Portland Head Light
(Cape Elizabeth, ME)   43
Portland Museum (Louisville, KY)   40
Portsmouth Athenaeum
(Portsmouth, NH)   101
Portsmouth Lightship Museum
(Portsmouth, VA)   165
Portsmouth Naval Shipyard
Museum (Portsmouth,, VA)   165
Port Washington Light Station
(Port Washington, WI)   184
Presque Isle County Historical
Museum (Rogers City, MI)   90
Presque Isle Lighthouses
(Presque Isle, MI)   90
Pride & Heritage Museum and
Peche Island Lighthouse
(Marine City, MI)   86
Pride of Baltimore II, Inc.
(Baltimore, MD)   52

Providence (Reproduction-18th
    Century Sloop) (Providence, RI)   152
Puget Sound Maritime Historical
    Society (Seattle, WA)   177
Putnam Museum (Davenport, IA)   38

Queen Mary (Ocean Liner)
    (Long Beach, CA)   7
Queens County Museum
    (Liverpool, NS)   194
Quoddy Maritime Museum
    (Eastport, ME 04361)   44

RV *Ben Franklin* (Vancouver, BC)   187
Reedville Fisherman's Museum
    (Reedville, VA)   166
Rhode Island Historical Society Library
    (Providence, RI)   153
Rideau Canal Museum
    (Smiths Falls, ONT)   205
Rier's Old Sardine Village Museum
    (Lubec, ME)   46
Ripley's Believe It Or Not!
    Museum (Key West, FL)   25
River Heritage Center Museum
    Paducah, KY   40
Roanoke Canal Museum & Trail
    (Roanoke Rapids, NC)   132
Roanoke Island Festival Park
    (Manteo, NC)   131
Roanoke River Lighthouse Replica &
    Museum (Plymouth, NC)   131
Rogers Street Fishing Museum
    (Two Rivers , WI)   185
Rose Island Lighthouse & Museum
    (Newport, RI)   151
Royal British Columbia Museum
    (Victoria, BC)   188
Ruark Boatworks (Cambridge, MD)   52
Rutherford B. Hayes Presidential Center
    (Fremont, OH)   137

Sackets Harbor Battlefield State Historic
    Site, (Sackets Harbor, NY)   123
Sag Harbor Whaling Museum
    (Sag Harbor, NY)   124
Sailor's Memorial Museum and
    Lighthouse (Islesboro, ME)   45
St. Augustine Lighthouse and Museum
    (St. Augustine, FL)   27
St. Catharines Historical Museum
    (St. Catharines, ONT)   205
St. Clements Island-Potomac River
    Museum (Coltons Point, MD)   54
St. Lawrence Islands National Park/
    Brown's Bay Wreck
    (Mallorytown, ONT)   199
St. Peters Canal (St. Peters, NS)   196

St. Simons Island Lighthouse Museum
    (St. Simons Island, GA)   30
Salem Maritime National Historical
    Site (Salem, MA)   76
Salt Pond Visitor Center
    (Eastham, MA)   64
Samson V Maritime Museum
    (New Westminister, BC)   186
San Diego Aircraft Carrier Museum
    (San Diego, CA)   11
San Diego Maritime Museum
    (San Diego, CA)   12
San Francisco Maritime National
    Historical Park (San Francisco, CA) 12
Sand Point Lighthouse
    (Escanaba, MI)   82
Sandy Bay Historical Society &
    Museums (Rockport, MA)   75
Sandy and Beaver Canal
    (East Liverpool, OH)   136
Sanilac Historical Museum and
    Village (Port Sanilac, MI)   90
Santa Barbara Maritime Museum
    (Santa Barbara, CA)   14
Saugerties Lighthouse Museum
    (Saugerties, NY)   124
Sault Ste. Marie Canal Visitor Centre
    (Sault Ste. Marie, ONT)   205
Schooner/*Ernestina* Commission
    (New Bedford, MA)   72
Science Museum of Virginia
    (Richmond, VA)   166
Scituate Lighthouse (Scituate, MA)   77
Scranton Floating Museum
    (Pascagoula, MS)   97
Seal Island Light Museum
    (Barrington, NS)   192
Seawolf Park (Galveston, TX)   158
Semiahmoo Park Museum
    (Blaine, WA)   170
Settler's Museum (Mahone Bay, NS)   195
Seul Choix Point Lighthouse
    (Gulliver, MI)   83
Shelburne Museum, Inc.
    (Shelburne, VT)   161
Ships of the Sea Maritime
    Museum (Savannah, GA)   30
Ship's Wheel Gallery & Nautical
    Museum (Kewaunee, WI)   182
Sims' Store Museum (Camillus, NY)   112
Singlehanded Sailors Hall of Fame
    (Newport, RI)   152
Skenesborough Museum
    (Whitehall, NY)   127
Sleeping Bear Point Coast Guard Station
    Maritime Museum (Empire, MI)   82
Smithsonian Institution
    (Washington, D.C.)   180

Society of the Cincinnati
(Washington, D.C.)   180
Sodus Bay Lighthouse Museum
(Sodus Point, NY)   125
Soo Locks Information Center
(Sault Ste. Marie, MI)   91
South County Museum
(Narragansett, RI)   149
South Florida Museum
(Bradenton, FL)   22
South Street Seaport Museum
(New York City, NY)   120
Southampton Historical Museum
(Southampton, NY)   125
Split Rock Lighthouse Historic
Site (Two Harbors, MN)   95
SS *American Victory* Mariners Memorial
and Museum, (Tampa, FL)   29
SS *City of Milwaukee* (Manistee,, MI) 85
SS *Jeremiah O'Brien* (Liberty
Ship) (San Francisco, CA)   13
SS *John W. Brown* (Liberty Ship)
(Baltimore, MD)   53
SS *Keno* (Sternwheeler)
(Dawson City, YT   211
SS *Lane Victory* (Victory Ship)
(San Pedro, CA)   14
SS *Meteor* Maritime Museum
(Superior, WI)   184
SS *Milwaukee Clipper* (Passenger Ship)
(Muskegon, MI)   87
SS *Red Oak Victory* (Victory Ship)
(Richmond, CA)   10
SS *William A. Irvin* Ore Boat
(Duluth, MN)   93
SS *Willis B. Boyer* Museum Ship
(Toledo, OH)   139
State Historical Society of North
Dakota (Bismarck, ND)   133
Steamboat *Bertrand* Cargo Collection
(Missouri Valley, IA)   39
Steamboat Dock Museum
(Keyport, NJ)   106
Steamer *Virginia V* Foundation
(Seattle, WA)   178
Steamer *William G. Mather* Museum
(Cleveland, OH)   135
Steamship Historical Society of America
(Providence, RI)   153
Stone House (Deep River, CT)   16
Strawbery Banke Museum
Collection, (Providence, RI)   101
Sturgeon Point Lighthouse &
Museum (Harrisville, MI)   84
Suffolk Historical Museum
(Riverhead, NY)   123
Sunshine Coast Maritime & Archives
(Gibson's Landing, BC)   186

Susquehanna Museum
(Havre de Grace, MD)   56
Tahoe Maritime Museum
(Carnelian Bay, CA)   4
Tennessee-Tombigbee Waterway
Tom Bevill Visitor Center
(Carrollton, AL)   1
Texas Maritime Museum
(Rockport, TX)   160
Texas Seaport Museum/*Elissa*
(Galveston, TX)   158
The Rooms Provincial Museum Div.
(St. John's, NFLD)   191
Thunder Bay Underwater Preserve
(Alpena, MI)   79
Toms River Seaport Society
(Toms River, NJ)   108
Toronto Port Authority
(Toronto, ONT)   207
Torpedo Factory Art Center
(Alexandria, VA)   162
Treasurers of the Gulf Museum
(Port Isabel, TX)   160
Treasurers of the Sea Exhibit
(Georgetown, DE)   20
Tri-Cities Historical Museum
(Grand Haven, MI)   83
Truro Historical Society Museum
(North Truro, MA)   73
Tuckerton Seaport (Tuckerton, NJ)   108
Tugboat *Urger* (Waterford, NY)   127
Twin Lights State Historic Site
(Highlands, NJ)   105
Tybee Island Historical Society
(Tybee Island, GA)   31
U-505 (German Submarine)
(Chicago, IL)   33
UDT - SEAL Museum
(Ft. Pierce, FL)   23
U.S. Coast Guard Museum
(New London, CT)   18
U.S. Merchant Marine Museum
(Anderson, IN)   34
U.S. Marine Corps Museum
(Triangle, VA.)   167
U.S. Naval Academy Museum
(Annapolis, MD)   51
U.S. Navy Supply Corps Museum
(Athens, GA)   29
USS *Alabama* Battleship Memorial
Park (Mobile, AL)   2
USS *Albacore* (submarine)
(Portsmouth, NH)   101
USS *American Victory*
(Anderson, IN)   28
USS *Arizona* Memorial (Honolulu, HI) 32

USS *Batfish* /Muskogee War Memorial
   Park and Military Museum and
   (Submarine) (Muskogee, OK)   140
USS *Bowfin* Submarine Museum& Park
   (Honolulu, HI)   32
USS *Cairo* Museum (Vicksburg, MS)   97
USS *Cassin Young* (DD-793)
   (Charlestown, MA)   62
USS *Cod* Submarine Museum
   (Cleveland, OH)   135
USS *Constellation* (sloop of war)
   (Baltimore, MD)   53
USS *Constitution*
   (Charlestown, MA)   63
USS *Constitution* Museum
   (Charlestown, MA)   63
USS *Hornet*, Aircraft Carrier Museum
   (Alameda, CA)   3
USS *Kidd* Nautical Center
   (Baton Rouge, LA)   41
USS *Lexington* Museum on the Bay
   (Corpus Christi, TX)   157
USS LST 325 (Evansville, IN)   36
USS *Missouri* Memorial Association
   (Honolulu, HI)   32
USS *Monitor* Ironclad
   (Newport News, VA)   163
USS *New Jersey,* Battleship
   (Camden, NJ)   102
USS *North Carolina* Battleship
   Memorial (Wilmington, NC)   133
USS *Pampanito* (SS-33) Submarine
   (San Francisco, CA)   13
USS *Radford* National Naval Memorial
   (Newscomertown, OH)   137
USS *Requin* (SS-481) Submarine
   (Pittsburgh, PA)   147
USS *Saratoga* Museum
   (Providence, RI)   151
USS *Slater* (Destroyer Escort)
   Albany, NY   109
USS *Texas* State Historical Park
   (La Porte, TX)   157
USS *Turner Joy*/Bremerton Historic
   Ships Assoc., (Bremerton, WA)   171
USS *Utah* (BB-31, AG-16)
   (Honolulu, HI)   33
Umpqua Discovery Center Museum
   (Reedsport, OR)   143
United States Naval Shipbuilding
   Museum (Quincy, MA)   75
University of Rhode Island Special
   Collections (Kingston, RI)   149
Upper Bay Museum
   (North East, MD)   57

Vallejo Naval and Historical Museum
   (Vallejo, CA)   15

Vancouver Maritime Museum
   (Vancouver, BC)   187
Vanderbilt Mansion, Marine Museum
   (Centerport, NY)   112
Varnum Memorial Armory
   (East Greenwich, RI)   148
Ventura County Maritime Museum
   (Oxnard, CA)   9
Virginia Canals & Navigations Society
   (Richmond, VA)   167
Voyageur Heritage Centre, Samuel
   de Champlain Provincial Park
   (Mattawa, ONT)   200

W. T. PRESTON (Sternwheeler)
   (Anacortes, WA)   170
Warroad Heritage Museum
   (Warroad, MN)   95
Warther Carving Museum
   (Sugarcreek, OH)   139
Waterfront Museum and Showboat
   Barge (Brooklyn, NY)   110
Watermen's Museum
   (Yorktown, VA)   168
Watson Curtze Mansion and Planetarium
   (Erie, PA)   145
Wellfleet Historical Society Museum
   (Wellfleet, MA)   77
Western Reserve Historical Society
   (Cleveland, OH)   135
Westport Marine Museum
   (Westport, WA)   178
Whale Centre and Museum
   (Tofino, BC)   187
Whale Museum - Friday Harbor-
   (San Juan Island, WA)   175
Whaling Museum
   (Cold Spring Harbor, NY)   114
Whaling Museum
   (Nantucket Island, MA)   71
Whalers Cabin & The Whaling Station
   Museum, (Carmel, CA)   4
Whatcom Museum of History and Art
   (Bellingham, WA)   170
White Pine Village (Ludington, MI)   84
White River Light Station Museum
   (Whitehall, MI)   93
Whitewater Canal State Historic Site
   (Metamora, IN)   37
Willowbrook at Newfield
   (Raymond, WA)   174
Willowbrook at Newfield
   (Newfield, ME)   47
Wisconsin Maritime Museum
   (Manitowoc, WI)   183
Woods Hole Historical Collection
   (Woods Hole, MA)   78
Working Waterfront Maritime Museum
   (Tacoma, WA)   178

Wrecker's Museum (Key West, FL)   25

Yaquina Bay Lighthouse
   (Newport, OR)   142
Yarmouth County Museum
   (Yarmouth, NS)   197
Yorktown Battlefield Visitor Center
   (Yorktown, VA)   169
Yorktown Victory Center
   (Yorktown, VA)   169

SUBJECT
INDEX
CONTENTS

BED AND BREAKFAST and
OVERNIGHT ENCAMPMENTS   225
BOAT/SHIP BUILDING   226
GIFT/BOOK SHOPS   227
HALLS OF FAME   231
LIBRARIES   231
LIGHTHOUSES   234
LOCKS AND CANALS   236
NAVY YARDS   237
NEWSLETTERS & PERIODICALS   237
PIRATE MUSEUMS   239
SCRIMSHAW   239
SHIP CHANDLERS   239
SHIP MODELS   239
SHIPS AND BOATS BY TYPE   242

CANAL BOATS/BARGES

CANOES   242
ICE BREAKERS   242
IRONCLADS   242
LIGHTSHIPS   242
SMALLCRAFT   243
SUBMARINES   243
TUGBOATS   244
SHIPS AND BOATS – GENERAL   244
WHALING   248

BED AND BREAKFAST
and OVERNIGHT
ENCAMPMENTS

*Alexander Henry (*210-foot icebreaker)
Mid-May to Labour Day (Kingston, ONT)   199
East Brother Light Station
(Point Richmond, CA)   9
Light Station Mukilteo (Mukilteo, WA)   171
Lighthouse Point and Harbor Museum
(Two Harbors, MN)   95
Marine Museum of Great Lakes/Kingston
(Kingston, ONT)   198
New Jersey Naval Museum
Submarine USS *Ling* (Hackensack, NJ)   105
Point Arena Lighthouse and Museum
(Point Arena, CA)   9
Rose Island Lighthouse (Newport, RI)   151
Saugerties Lighthouse Museum (Year round)
(Saugerties, NY)   124
SS *City of Milwaukee* Railroad Car Ferry
Program runs May September
(Manistee, MI)   85
SS *Milwaukee Clipper* Passenger Ship
(Muskegon, MI)   87

BED AND BREAKFAST and
OVERNIGHT
ENCAMPMENTS - Continued

USCGC *Taney* Coast Guard Cutter
Capacity: 70, Grades: 3 12
(Baltimore, MD)   50
USS *Alabama* Battleship, Capacity: 375
Ages 68, (Mobile, AL)   2
USS *Blueback* Submarine,
Recommended grades 2 - 8, Capacity: 50
(Portland, OR)   142
USS *Cobia* Submarine (Manitowoc, WI)   182
USS *Hornet* Aircraft Carrier Capacity: 275,
Minimum age: 7 (Alameda, CA)   3
USS *Kidd* Destroyer, Capacity: 165,
Minimum age: 6 (Baton Rouge, LA)   41
USS *Lexington* Aircraft Carrier
Capacity: 450   (Corpus Christi, TX)   157
USS *Little Rock* Cruiser Capacity: 250
(Buffalo, NY)   109
USS *Massachusetts* Battleship
Capacity: 400 youths, 100 adults.
Min. age: 6 (Fall River, MA)   64
USS *Missouri* Battleship Capacity: 130,
Minimum age: 6 (Honolulu, HI)   32
USS *Pampanito* Submarine Capacity: 48,
Minimum age: 6, (San Francisco, CA)   13
USS *Requin* Submarine Capacity: 30 youths,
10 adults Minimum age: 10
(Pittsburgh, PA)   145
USS *Salem* Cruiser Capacity: 250,
Minimum age: 5 (Quincy, MA)   75
USS *Silversides* Submarine &
USCGC Cutter *McLane*
(Muskegon, MI)   86
USS *Slater* Museum Ship (DE766)
(For youths) (Albany, NY)   109
USS *Texas*, Battleship Capacity: 46,
Minimum age: 8   (La Porte, TX)   157
USS *Yorktown* Aircraft Carrier
(Mount Pleasant, SC)   155
William M. Black (1934 riverboat) Boat &
Breakfast, (Dubuque, IA)   37

NOTE: The following lighthouses also have bed and breakfast accommodations but are not listed in general text of guide:
BIG BAY POINT LIGHTHOUSE
#3 Lighthouse Road
Big Bay, Michigan 49808
Phone: (906) 345-9957
Email: keepers@BigBayLighthouse.com
BROWNS POINT LIGHT
(Commencement Bay)
5125 Tok A Lou Ave
Write:
201 N. Tulalip St. NE
Tacoma, WA 98421
(253) 305-1000

CAPE DISAPPOINTMENT
Cape Disappointment State Park
(formerly Fort Canby State Park)
P.O. Box 488 • Ilwaco, WA 98624
(360) 642-3078 Fax (360) 642-4216
E-mail: info@fortcanby.org

HECETA HEAD LIGHT
92072 Hwy. 101 South
Yachats, OR 97498 USA
Reservations: Voice / Voice mail,
Toll free 1-(866)-547-3696

ISLE AU HAUT LIGHT
The Keeper's House
P.O. Box 26
Isle au Haut, ME 04645
(207) 367-2261

LIGHTHOUSE INN
Post Office Box 128
1 Lighthouse Inn Road
West Dennis, MA 02670
(508) 398-2244 Fax: (508) 398-5658

NEW DUGENESS LIGHT
P.O. Box 1283
Sequim, WA 98382
(360) 683-9166   E-mail:
lightkeepers@newdungenesslighthouse.com

POINT MONTARA LIGHT
American Youth Hostels, Incorporated
1-650-728-7177 for further information.

SAND HILLS LIGHT
Five Mile Point Road
P.O. Box 298
Ahmeek, MI 49901
(906) 337-1744

SELKIRK LIGHTHOUSE
6 Lake Road Extension
PO Box 228
Pulaski, NY 13142-0228
(315) 298-6688 Fax: (315) 298-6685
E-mail: selkirklight@hotmail.com

THACHER ISLAND LIGHT
Thacher Island Association
P.O. Box 73
Rockport, MA 01966
(617) 599-2590

TIBBETS POINT LIGHT
Tibbetts Point Lighthouse Hostel
Cape Vincent, NY
(315) 654-3450

BOAT/SHIP BUILDING

Adirondack Museum	
(Blue Mountain Lake, NY)	110
Age of Sail Heritage Center	
(Port Greville, NS)	196
Alexandria Seaport Foundation and Seaport	
Center (Alexandria, VA)	161
Archelaus Smith Museum	
(Centerville, NS)	192
Atlantic Heritage Center	
(Somers Point, NJ)	107
Bainbridge Is. Historical Museum	
(Bainbridge Island, WA)	170
Bayfield Heritage Association	
(Bayfield, WI)	181
Brannock Maritime Museum	
(Cambridge, MD)	53
Center for Wooden Boats, The	
(Seattle, WA)	175
Chesapeake Bay Maritime Museum	
(St. Michaels, MD)	58
City Island Nautical Museum	
(City Island, NY)	111
Coos Historical & Maritime Museum	
(North Bend, OR)	142
Cowichan Bay Maritime Centre	
(Duncan, BC)	186
Dory Shop (Lunenburg, NS)	193
Dory Shop (Shelburne, NS)	196
East End Seaport Maritime Museum	
(Greenport, LI, NY)	116
East Hampton Town Marine Museum	
(East Hampton, NY)	115
Green Park Shipbuilding Museum	
(Port Hill, PEI)	208
Historical Museum of Bay County	
(Bay City, MI)	79
Howard Steamboat Museum, Inc.	
(Jeffersonville, IN)	35
Independence Seaport Museum	
(Philadelphia, PA)	146
International Yacht Restoration School	
(Newport, RI)	149
James B. Richardson Maritime Museum	
(Cambridge, MD)	54
Kalmar Nyckel Shipyard and Museum	
(Wilmington, DE)	21
Lake Champlain Maritime Museum	
(Basin Harbor, VT)	160
Lawrence House (Maitland, NS)	195
Les Cheneaux Maritime Museum	
(Cedarville, MI)	80
Lowell's Boat Shop (dories)	
(Amesbury, MA)	59
Maine Maritime Museum (Bath, ME)	42
Marinship 1942-1945 (Sausalito, CA)	15
Maritime & Irish Mossing Museum	
(Scituate, MA)	76

BOAT/SHIP BUILDING –
Contunied

Maritime and Yachting Museum
(Stuart, FL) 27
Maritime Aquarium at Norwalk
(Norwalk, CT) 18
Maritime Museum of Sandusky
(Sandusky, OH) 138
Muskoka Lakes Museum
(Port Carling, ONT) 204
Mystic Seaport (Mystic, CT) 17
Newport Harbor Nautical Museum
(Newport Beach, CA) 8
North Carolina Maritime Museum
(Beaufort, NC) 128
Ottawa House By-the-Sea
(Parrsboro, NS) 195
Queens County Museum
(Liverpool, NS) 194
Richardson Maritime Museum
(Cambridge, MD) 54
Ruark Boatworks
(Cambridge, MD) 52
South Florida Museum (Bradenton, FL) 22
United States Naval Shipbuilding Museum
(Quincy, MA) 75
Vancouver Maritime Museum
(Vancouver, BC) 187
Working Waterfront Maritime Museum
(Tacoma, WA) 178

GIFT/BOOK SHOPS

Adirondack Museum
(Blue Mountain Lake, NY) 110
Age of Sail Heritage Center
(Port Greville, NS 196
Aircraft Carrier *Hornet* Museum
(Alameda, CA) 3
Antique Boat Museum (Clayton, NY) 113
Aquarium and Marine Center
(Shippagan, NB) 190
Arabia Steamboat Museum
(Kansas City, MO) 98
Arkansas River Historical Society Museum
(Catoosa, OK) 140
Baltimore Maritime Museum
(Baltimore, MD) 52
Banning Residence Museum
(Wilmington, CA) 15
Barn Museum (Bellport, NY) 109
Basin Head Fisheries Museum
(Souris, PEI) 208
Battleship Cove (Fall River, MA) 65
Battleship *Texas* (La Porte, TX) 159
Bay Model Visitor Center (Sausalito, CA) 14
Belle of Louisville Steamer (Louisville, KY) 39

GIFT/BOOK SHOPS Continued

Bernier Maritime Museum
(L'Islet-sur-Mer, QBC) 209
Bishop Museum (Honolulu, HI) 31
Boston Tea Party Ship and Museum
(Boston, MA) 60
Bremerton Historic Ships Association
(Bremerton, WA) 170
Bremerton Naval Museum
(Bremerton, WA) 171
Brick Store Museum (Kennebunk, ME) 45
Brig *Niagara* (reconstructed ship) (Erie, PA) 144
Buffalo Bill Museum of Le Claire, Iowa, Inc.
(Le Claire, IA) 38
Burke Museum (Seattle, WA) 175
Bytown Museum (Ottawa, ONT) 200
CEC/Seabee Museum (Port Hueneme, CA) 10
CSS *Neuse*, (ironclad) State Historic Site (Kinston, NC) 128
Cabrillo National Monument Memorial
(San Diego, CA) 11
Calvert Marine Museum (Solomons, MD) 57
Canadian Canoe Museum
(Peterborough, ONT) 202
Canal Fulton Heritage Society
(Canal Fulton, OH) 134
Canal Society of New Jersey Museum
(Morristown, NJ) 106
Cape Ann Museum (Gloucester, MA) 65
Cape Cod Maritime Museum
(Hyannis, MA) 68
Cape Fear Museum (Fayetteville, NC) 129
Cape Fear Museum (Wilmington, NC) 132
Cape May Historical Society
(Cape May, NJ) 101
Captain Robert Bennet Forbes
(Milton, MA) 70
Carroll County Wabash and Erie Canal, Inc.
(Delphi, IN) 35
Castle Museum of Saginaw County
(Saginaw, MI) 90
Catalina Island Museum (Avalon, CA) 5
Center for Wooden Boats (Seattle, WA) 175
Chaffey's Lockmaster House Museum
(Chaffey's Lock, ONT) 197
Channel Islands National Park
(Ventura, CA) 15
Charleston Museum (Charleston, SC) 154
Charleston Navy Yard (Boston, MD) 61
Chesapeake & Ohio National Historic
Park (Sharpsburg, MD) 57
Chesapeake Bay Maritime Museum
(St. Michaels, MD) 58
Chicago Maritime Society (Chicago, IL) 34
Chicamacomico Life-Saving Station
(Rodanthe, NC) 132
Chittenango Landing Canal Boat Museum
(Chittenango, NY) 113

GIFT/BOOK SHOPS Continued

Civil Engineer Corps/Seabee Museum
(Port Hueneme, CA)   10

Clinton County Historical Museum
(Plattsburg, NY)   122

Collingwood Museum
(Collingwood, ONT)   196

Columbia Pacific Heritage Museum
(Ilwaco, WA)   171

Columbia River Maritime Museum
(Astoria, OR)   139

Connecticut River Museum (Essex, CT)   16

Coos Historical & Maritime Museum
(North Bend, OR)   142

Coquille River Lighthouse (Bandon, OR)   141

Corpus Christi Museum of Science
and Industry (Corpus Christi, TX)   157

Coteau-du-Lac National Historic Site
(Québec, QBC)   208

Custom House Maritime Museum
(Newburyport, MA)   72

David M. Stewart Museum
(Montréal, QBC)   209

Discovery Harbour
(Penetanguishene, ONT)   202

Dossin Great Lakes Museum (Detroit, MI)   81

East End Seaport Maritime Museum
(Greenport, NY)   116

East Martello Gallery & Museum
(Key West, FL)   24

Edmonds Historical Museum
(Edmonds, WA)   171

Erie Canal Museum (Syracuse, NY)   126

Erie Canal Village (Rome, NY)   123

Erie Maritime Museum/Homeport
U.S. Brig *Niagara* (Erie, PA)   144

Essex Shipbuilding Museum (Essex, MA)   65

Expedition *Whydah* (Pirate Ship)
(Provincetown, MA)   75

Falls of the Ohio State Park
(Jeffersonville, OH)   36

Fisheries Museum of the Atlantic
(Lunenburg, NS)   194

Fort Fisher Historic Site (Kure Beach, NC)   130

Fort Hancock Museum (Highlands, NJ)   105

Fort Hunter (Fort Hunter, NY_)   114

Fort Morgan Museum (Gulf Shores, AL)   1

Forwarder's Museum (Prescott, ONT)   204

Franklin D. Roosevelt Library
and Museum (Hyde Park, NY)   117

Gilbert's Bar House of Refuge (Stuart, FL)   27

Gloucester *Adventure* (Gloucester, MA)   67

Gloucester Maritime Heritage Center
(Gloucester, MA)   68

Grand Manan Museum
(Grand Manan, NB)   189

Grand Marais Maritime Museum
(Grand Marais, MI)   83

GIFT/BOOK SHOPS Continued

Grand Traverse Lighthouse Museum
(Northport, MI)   87

Graveyard of the Atlantic Museum
(Hatteras, NC)   129

Grays Harbor Historical Seaport
(Aberdeen, WA)   169

Ashtabula Maritime Museum
(Ashtabula, OH)   133

Great Lakes Naval Memorial Museum
(Muskegon, MI)   86

Great Lakes Shipwreck Museum
(Paradise, MI)   87

Green Park Shipbuilding Museum
(Port Hill, PEI)   208

HMCS *Haida* (WW II Cutter)
(Toronto, ONT)   207

HMCS *Sackville* (K181) (Halifax, NS)   192

Hamilton-Scourge Project
(Hamilton, ONT)   198

Hawaii Maritime Center (Honolulu, HI)   31

Heritage *Hjemkomst* Interpretive Center
(Moorhead, MN)   94

Herreshoff Marine Museum (Bristol, RI)   148

Hiram M. Chittenden Locks Visitor Center
(Seattle, WA)   175

Historic Gardener's Basin
(Atlantic City, NJ)   102

Historic Roscoe Village
(Coshocton, OH)   136

Historical Museum of Bay County
(Bay City, MI)   79

Historical Museum of Southern Florida
(Miami, FL)   26

Historical Society of Old Yarmouth
(Yarmouth Port, MA)   78

Hopkins & Bros. Store (Onancock, VA)   164

H. L. Hunley Museum (N. Charleston, SC)   155

Hudson River Maritime Museum
(Kingston, NY)   118

Hull Lifesaving Museum (Hull, MA)   68

Humboldt Bay Maritime Museum
(Eureka, CA)   6

Hunting Island State Park (St. Helena Is. SC) 156

Huron Lightship (Port Huron, MI)   87

Houston Maritime Museum (Houston, TX)   158

Hyde Street Pier (San Francisco, CA)   11

Independence Seaport Museum
(Philadelphia, PA)   146

Inland Seas Maritime Museum
(Vermilion, OH)   139

Intrepid Sea-Air-Space Museum
(New York, NY)   119

Isle Royal National Park (Houghton, MI)   84

Jacksonport State Park (Newport, AR)   2

Jacksonville Maritime Museum Society, Inc.
(Jacksonville, FL)   23

Jeremiah O'Brien, SS (San Francisco, CA)   12

GIFT/BOOK SHOPS - Continued

John Hancock Warehouse and Wharf	
(York, ME)	50
Jones Falls Defensible Lockmaster's House	
(Elgin, ONT)	198
Jupiter Inlet Lighthouse (Jupiter, FL)	23
Kalmar Nyckel Shipyard & Museum	
(Wilmington, DE)	21
Keewatin Maritime Museum	
(Douglas, MI)	81
Kennebunkport Maritime Museum	
(Kennebunkport, ME)	45
Keokuk River Museum (Keokuk, IA)	38
Kittery Historical/Naval Museum	
(Kittery, ME)	45
Lake Champlain Maritime Museum	
(Basin Harbor, VT)	160
Lake Erie Islands Historical Society Museum	
(Put-in-Bay, OH)	138
Lake Superior Maritime Visitor Center	
(Duluth, MN)	92
Les Cheneaux Maritime Museum	
(Cedarville, MI)	80
Light Station Mulkilteo (Mulkiteo, WA)	173
Lighthouse Museum (Key West, FL)	24
Lockmaster's House Museum	
(Chaffey's Lock, ONT)	197
Log Cabin Museum (Newport, OR)	141
Los Angeles Maritime Museum	
(San Pedro, CA)	14
Maine Lighthouse Museum (Rockland, ME)	48
Maine Maritime Museum (Bath, ME)	43
Makah Museum (Neah Bay, WA)	173
Marblehead Historical Society	
(Marblehead, MA)	69
Marine Museum at Fall River	
(Fall River, MA)	66
Marine Museum of the Great Lakes	
(Kingston, ONT)	199
Mariners' Museum (Newport News, VA)	163
Marinship 1942-1945 (Sausalito, CA)	14
Maritime & Irish Mossing Museum	
(Scituate, MA)	76
Maritime Aquarium (Norwalk, CT)	18
Maritime Industry Museum/Fort Schuyler	
(Bronx, NY)	110
Maritime Museum of British Columbia	
(Victoria, BC)	188
Maritime Museum of the Atlantic	
(Halifax, NS)	193
Maritime Museum of Sandusky	
(Sandusky, OH)	138
Maritime Seafood Industry Museum	
(Biloxi, MS)	96
Marquette Maritime Museum	
(Marquette, MI)	86
Marshall Point Lighthouse	
(Port Clyde, ME)	48

GIFT/BOOK SHOPS - Continued

Mary Woods II Riverboat Museum	
(Jacksonport, AR)	3
Mel Fisher Maritime Heritage Society	
(Key West, FL)	24
Mel Fisher's Treasure Museum	
(Sebastian, FL)	27
Michigan Maritime Museum	
(South Haven, MI)	92
Minnesota Lakes Maritime Museum	
(Alexandria, MN)	93
Minnesota Marine Art (Winona, MN)	96
Missouri Historical Society (St. Louis, MO)	100
Monterey Maritime Museum	
(Monterey, CA)	7
Maritime & Irish Mossing Museum	
(Scituate, MA)	76
Museum of Florida History	
(Tallahassee, FL)	28
Museum of History and Industry	
(Seattle, WA)	176
Museum of Science (Boston, MA)	60
Museum of Man in the Sea	
(Panama City Beach, FL)	26
Museum of the Albemarle	
(Elizabeth City, NC)	128
Museum of The Berkeley Springs	
(Berkeley Springs, WV)	180
Museum of the Confederacy	
(Richmond, VA)	166
Museum of the Sea/Hatteras Island	
Visitor's Center (Buxton, NC)	126
Museum of Yachting (Newport, RI)	150
Museum of Yarmouth History	
(Yarmouth, ME)	50
Museum Ship *Norgoma*	
(Sault Ste. Marie, ONT)	205
Museum Ship *Valley Camp*	
(Sault Ste. Marie, MI)	91
Muskogee War Memorial Park and	
Military Museum (Muskogee, OK)	139
Mystic Seaport Museum (Mystic, CT)	17
Nantucket Lifesaving Museum	
(Nantucket Island, MA)	70
National Canal Museum and Hugh	
Moore Park (Easton, PA)	144
National Maritime Historical Society	
(Peekskill, NY)	122
National Museum of the Pacific War	
(Fredericksburg, TX)	157
National Mississippi River Museum &	
Aquarium (Dubuque, IA)	38
Nauticus National Maritime Center	
(Norfolk, VA)	164
Nautilus and Submarine Force Museum	
(Groton, CT)	16
Naval Museum of Alberta, The	
(Calgary, ALB)	185

GIFT/BOOK SHOPS - Continued

Naval Museum of Manitoba,
Winnipeg, MTB   189
Naval Undersea Museum (Keyport, WA)   173
Naval War College (Newport, RI)   148
Navy Museum (Washington, D.C.)   179
Neversink Valley Area Museum
(Cuddebackville, NY)   115
New Bedford Whaling Museum
(New Bedford, MA)   72
New Brunswick Museum
(Saint John, NB)   190
New Jersey Naval/USS *Ling* (Submarine)
(Hackensack, NJ)   104
New York Historical Society
(New York, NY)   118
Newport Harbor Nautical Museum
(Newport Beach, CA)   8
Nordic Heritage Museum (Seattle, WA)   177
North Carolina Maritime Museum
(Beaufort, NC)   128
North Carolina Maritime Museum
(Manteo, NC)   129
North Carolina Maritime Museum at
Southport (Southport, NC)   132
Northport Historical Museum
(Northport, L.I., NY)   121
Ocean City Historical Museum
(Ocean City, NJ)   107
Ocean City Life Saving Station Museum
(Ocean City, MD)   56
Odyssey, The Maritime Discovery Center
(Seattle, WA)   177
Ohio River Museum (Marietta, OH)   137
Old Coast Guard Station Museum
(Virginia Beach, VA)   168
Old Fort Jackson (Savannah, GA)   30
Old Fort William (Thunder Bay, ONT)   206
Old Sacramento Waterfront and
Riverboat *Delta King* (Sacramento, CA)   11
Old Santee Canal State Park
(Moncks Corner, SC)   154
Old State House (Boston, MA)   61
Oregon History Center (Portland, OR)   142
Oregon Museum of Science and Industry
(Portland, OR)   143
PT Boat Museum and Library
(Fall River, MA)   66
PT Boats, Inc. Headquarters
(Germantown, TN)   156
Patriots Point Naval and Maritime Museum
(Mt. Pleasant, SC)   153
Peabody Essex Museum (Salem, MA)   76
Penobscot Marine Museum
(Searsport, ME)   48
Pilgrim (Replica ship) (Dana Point, CA)   5
Pilgrim Hall Museum (Plymouth, MA)   74
Piney Point Lighthouse Museum
(Piney Point, MD)   58

GIFT/BOOK SHOPS - Continued

Piqua Historical Area (Piqua, OH)   138
Plainville Historical Center (Plainville, CT)   18
Plimoth Plantation (Plymouth, MA)   74
Ponce de Leon Inlet Lighthouse
(Ponce Inlet, FL)   26
Port Colborne Historical & Marine Museum
(Port Colborne, ONT)   204
Port Columbus Civil War Naval Center
(Columbus, GA)   29
Port Huron Museum (Port Huron, MI)   89
Portsmouth Lightship Museum
(Portsmouth, VA)   165
Portsmouth Naval Shipyard Museum
(Portsmouth, VA)   165
Queen Mary (passenger liner)
(Long Beach, CA)   7
Quoddy Maritime Museum (Eastport, ME)   44
Roanoke Island Festival Park *Elizabeth II*
(Manteo, NC)   130
Sag Harbor Whaling Museum
(Sag Harbor, NY)   124
Sailor's Memorial Museum,
Grindle Point Light (Islesboro, ME)   45
St. Augustine Lighthouse and Museum
(St. Augustine, FL)   26
St. Catharines Historical Museum
(St. Catharines, ONT)   205
St. Clements Island Potomac River Museum
(Colton Points, MD)   54
St. Simons Island Lighthouse Museum
(St. Simons Island, GA)   30
Salem Maritime National Historical Site
(Salem, MA)   76
San Diego Aircraft Carrier Museum
(USS *Midway*) (San Diego, CA)   11
San Diego Maritime Museum
(San Diego, CA)   11
San Francisco Maritime National
Historical Park (San Francisco, CA)   12
Sandy and Beaver Canal
(East Liverpool, OH)   136
Sanilac County Historical Society Museum
(Port Sanilac, MI)   88
Santa Barbara Maritime Museum
(Santa Barbara, CA)   14
Saugerties Lighthouse Museum
(Saugerties, NY)   124
Science Museum of Virginia
(Richmond, VA)   166
Semiahmoo Park Museum (Blaine, WA)   170
Seul Choix Point Lighthouse (Gulliver, MI)   83
Shelburne Museum (Shelburne, VT)   161
Sims' Store Museum (Camillus, NY)   112
Skenesborough Museum (Whitehall, NY)   127
Smithsonian Institution (Washington, D.C.)   180
Sodus Bay Lighthouse (Sodus Pont, NY)   125
South Street Seaport Museum & Ocean
Liner Museum (New York, NY)   120

GIFT/BOOK SHOPS - Continued

Split Rock Lighthouse Historic Site	
(Two Harbors, MN)	95
SS *Jeremiah O'Brien* (Liberty Ship)	
(San Francisco, CA)	13
SS *John W. Brown* (Liberty Ship)	
(Baltimore, MD)	53
SS *Lane Victory* (victory ship)	
(San Pedro, CA)	14
SS *Meteor* Maritime Museum	
(Superior, WI)	184
SS *William A. Irvin*, (ore boat)	
(Duluth, MN)	93
SS *Willis B. Boyer* Mus. Ship (Toledo, OH)	139
Steamboat *Bertrand* (Missouri Valley, IA)	39
Steamer *William G. Mather* Museum	
(Cleveland, OH)	135
Sturgeon Point Lighthouse	
(Harrisville, MI)	82
Suffolk Historical Museum	
(Riverhead, NY)	122
Texas Maritime Museum (Rockport, TX)	160
Texas Seaport Museum (Galveston, TX)	158
Treasures of the Gulf (Port Isabel, TX)	159
Treasures of the Sea Exhibit	
(Georgetown, DE)	20
Tri-Cities Historical Museum	
(Grand Haven, MI)	83
Truro Historical Society Museum	
(N. Truro, MA)	72
Tuckerton Seaport (Tuckerton, NJ)	108
Twin Lights State Historic Site	
(Highlands, NJ)	105
U-505 (Submarine) (Museum of Science and	
Industry) (Chicago, IL)	34
UDT-SEAL Museum (Ft. Pierce, FL)	23
U.S. Coast Guard Museum	
(New London, CT)	18
U.S. Marine Corps Museum (Triangle, VA)	167
U.S. Naval Academy Museum	
(Annapolis, MD)	51
U.S. Navy Supply Corps Museum	
(Athens, GA)	29
USS *Alabama* Battleship Memorial Park	
(Mobile, AL)	2
USS *Arizona* Memorial (Honolulu, HI)	32
USS *Bowfin* (Honolulu, HI)	32
USS *Cairo* Museum (Vicksburg, MS)	97
USS *Constellation* (sloop of war)	
(Baltimore, MD)	53
USS *Constitution* Museum (Boston, MA)	63
USS *Kidd* Nautical Center	
(Baton Rouge, LA)	41
USS *Lexington* Museum	
(Corpus Christi, TX)	157
USS *Midway* Aircraft Museum	
(San Diego, CA)	11
USS *Missouri* Memorial Association	
(Honolulu, HI)	32

GIFT/BOOK SHOPS - Continued

USS *North Carolina* Battleship Memorial	
(Wilmington, NC)	133
USS *Slater* Museum Ship (DE766)	
(Albany, NY)	109
USS *Turner Joy* (DD) (Bremerton, WA)	171
Umpqua Discovery Center (Reedsport, OR)	143
Vallejo Naval and Historical Museum	
(Vallejo, CA)	15
Vancouver Maritime Museum	
(Vancouver, BC)	187
Vanderbilt Mansion (Centerport, NY)	112
Ventura County Maritime Museum	
(Oxnard, CA)	9
Waterfront Museum and Showboat Barge	
(Brooklyn, NY)	110
Watermen's Museum (Yorktown, VA)	168
Watson Curtze Mansion and Planetarium	
(Erie, PA)	145
Whale Centre and Museum (Tofino, BC)	187
Whaliing Museum (Cold Spring Harbor,NY)	114
White Pine Village (Ludington, MI)	84
Willowbrook at Newfield (Newfield, ME)	47
Wisconsin Maritime Museum	
(Manitowoc, WI)	183
Woods Hole Historical Collection	
(Woods Hole, MA)	78
Working Waterfront Maritime Museum	
(Tacoma, WA)	178
Yaquina Bay Lighthouse (Newport, OR)	142
Yarmouth County Museum (Yarmouth, NS)	197
Yorktown Victory Center (Yorktown, VA)	169

HALLS OF FAME

American Merchant Marine Museum	
(Kings Point, NY)	117
America's Cup Museum (Bristol, RI)	146
Arkansas River Hall of Fame (Catoosa, OK)	139
Great Lakes Hall of Fame	
(Sault Ste. Marie, MI)	90
Hall of Inshore Fisheries (Lunenburg, NS)	195
National Rivers Hall of Fame	
(Dubuque, IA)	37
Singlehanded Sailors Hall of Fame	
(Museum of Yachting) (Newport, RI)	152

LIBRARIES

Alexandria Seaport Foundation &	
Seaport Center (Alexandria, VA)	161
Alfred S. Brownell Collection	
(Providence, RI)	152
Allie Ryan Maritime Collection	
(Castaine, ME)	44
American Philosophical Museum	
(Philadelphia, PA)	144
Antique Boat Museum (Clayton, NY)	113
Apalachicola Maritime Museum	
(Apalachicola, FL)	22

LIBRARIES - Continued

Apostle Islands National Lakeshore
  (Bayfield, WI)   181
Arkansas River Historical Society Museum
  (Catoosa, OK)   140
Atlantic Heritage Center (Somers Point, NJ)   107
Bainbridge Island Historical Museum
  (Bainbridge Island, WA)   170
Baltimore Museum of Industry
  (Baltimore, MD)   50
Banning Residence Museum
  (Wilmington, CA)   15
Battery Point Lighthouse (Crescent City, CA)   5
Battleship Cove (Fall River, MA)   65
Bayfield Heritage Association
  (Bayfield, WI)   181
Bernier Maritime Museum
  (L'Islet-sur-Mer, QBC)   209
Beverly Historical Society and Museum
  (Beverly, MA)   60
Bishop Museum (Honolulu, HI)   31
Brick Store Museum (Kennebunk, ME)   45
Burke Museum (Seattle, WA)   175
Bytown Museum (Ottawa, ONT)   201
Calvert Marine Museum (Solomons, MD)   57
Canal Society of New York State, Inc.
  (Syracuse, NY)   126
Cape Ann Historical Museum
  (Gloucester, MA)   67
Cape May County Historical Museum
  (Cape May, NJ)   104
Capt. Charles H. Hurley Library
  (Buzzards Bay, MA)   61
Catalina Island Museum (Avalon, CA)   5
Charleston Museum (Charleston, SC)   154
Chesapeake Bay Maritime Museum
  (St. Michaels, MD)   58
Chicamacomico Life-Saving Station
  (Rodanthe, NC)   132
Chittenango Landing Canal Boat Museum
  (Chittenango, NY)   113
City Island Nautical Museum
  (City Island, NY)   113
Coast Guard Museum/Northwest
  (Seattle, WA)   176
Collingwood Museum
  (Collingwood, ONT)   196
Columbia River Maritime Museum
  (Astoria, OR)   139
Connecticut River Museum (Essex, CT)   16
Corpus Christi Museum of Science and
  Industry (Corpus Christi, TX)   157
Counting House (South Berwick, ME)   49
Custom House Maritime Museum
  (Newburyport, MA)   72
Delaware and Hudson Canal Museum
  (High Falls, NY)   115
Dossin Great Lakes Museum (Detroit, MI)   81

LIBRARIES - Continued

Dutra Museum of Dredging, (Rio Vista, CA)   10
Edmonds Historical Museum
  (Edmonds, WA)   171
Egan Institute of Maritime Studies
  (Nantucket Island, MA)   70
Erie Maritime Museum (Erie, PA)   144
Fisheries Museum of the Atlantic
  (Lunenburg, NS)   194
Franklin D. Roosevelt Library and Museum
  (Hyde Park, NY)   117
Gates House/Machiasport Historical Society
  (Machiasport, ME)   46
Gig Harbor Peninsula Historical Society &
  Museum (Gig Harbor, WA)   172
Golden Eagle River Museum
  (St. Louis, MO)   99
Grand Manan Museum
  (Grand Manan, NB)   189
H. Lee White Marine Museum
  (Oswego, NY)   121
HMCS *Haida* (WW II cutter)
  (Hamilton, ONT)   199
Herman T. Pott National Inland Waterways
  Library (St. Louis, MO)   99
Historic Hermann Museums
  (Hermann, MO)   98
Historical Collections of the Great Lakes
  (Bowling Green, OH)   134
Historical Museum of Bay County
  (Bay City, MI)   79
Historical Museum of Southern Florida
  (Miami, FL)   26
Houston Maritime Museum (Houston, TX)   158
Hudson River Maritime Museum
  (Kingston, NY)   118
Huron City Museum (Port Austin, MI)   88
Huronia Museum & Huron Indian Village
  (Midland, ONT)   200
Independence Seaport Museum
  (Philadelphia, PA)   146
Inland Rivers Library (Cincinnati, OH)   134
Inland Seas Maritime Museum
  (Vermilion, OH)   139
Intrepid Sea-Air-Space Museum
  (New York, NY)   118
Isle Royale National Park
  (Houghton, MI)   82
James Kirk Maritime Museum
  (Linwood, NJ)   106
John Dubois Maritime Museum
  (Greenwich, NJ)   104
John Hancock Warehouse and Wharf
  (York, ME)   50
Kalmar Nyckel Shipyard and Museum
  (Wilmington, DE)   21
Kendall Institute
  (New Bedford, MA)   71

LIBRARIES - Continued

Kennebunkport Maritime Museum (Kennebunkport, ME)	45
Kynett Library and Research Center (Life Saving) (Nantucket, MA)	70
Kittery Historical and Naval Museum (Kittery, ME)	46
Lake Champlain Maritime Museum (Basin Harbor, VT)	160
Lake Erie Islands Historical Society Museum (Put-in-Bay, OH)	138
Lake Pontchartrain Basin Maritime Museum (Madisonville, LA)	41
Lake Superior Maritime Visitor Center (Duluth, MN)	92
Lloyd Taber Marina del Rey Library (Marina del Rey, CA)	7
Log Cabin Museum (Newport, OR)	141
Long Island Maritime Museum (West Sayville, L.I., NY)	127
Lower Lakes Marine Historical Society (Buffalo, NY)	111
Maine Maritime Museum (Bath, ME)	43
Manistee County Historical Museum (Manistee, MI)	85
Marine Museum (St. James, MI)	91
Marine Museum at Fall River (Fall River, MA)	66
Marine Museum of the Great Lakes at Kingston (Kingston, ONT)	199
Mariners' Museum (Newport News, VA)	163
Maritime & Yachting Museum (Stuart, FL)	27
Maritime Command Museum (Halifax, NS)	193
Maritime Industry Museum at Fort Schuyler (Bronx, NY)	110
Maritime Museum of British Columbia (Victoria, BC)	188
Maritime Museum of the Atlantic (Halifax, NS)	193
Martha's Vineyard Historical Society and Museum (Edgartown, MA)	64
Masters, Mates, and Pilots Museum (Linthicum Heights, MD)	55
Mel Fisher Maritime Heritage Society (Key West, FL)	24
Mel Fisher's Treasure Maritime (Sebastian, FL)	27
Michigan Historical Museum (Lansing, MI)	84
Michigan Maritime Museum (South Haven, MI)	92
Milwaukee Public Library (Milwaukee, WI)	183
Missouri Historical Society (St. Louis, MO)	99
Monterey Maritime Museum (Monterey, CA)	7
Museum of Florida History (Tallahassee, FL)	28

LIBRARIES - Continued

Museum of History and Industry (Seattle, WA)	176
Museum of Mobile (Mobile, AL)	1
Museum of Newport History (Newport, RI)	150
Museum of the Albemarle (Elizabeth, NC	128
Museum of the City of New York (New York, NY)	118
Museum of the Confederacy (Richmond, VA)	166
Museum of the Jefferson County Historical Society (Port Townsend, WA)	174
Museum of the Man in the Sea (Panama City, FL)	26
Museum of Yachting (Newport, RI)	150
Museum of Yarmouth History (Yarmouth, ME)	50
Mystic Seaport Museum (Mystic, CT)	17
Nantucket Lifesaving Museum (Nantucket, MA)	70
National Canal Museum and Hugh Moore Park (Easton, PA)	144
National Maritime Heritage Initiative (Washington, D.C.)	179
National Museum of the Pacific War (Fredericksburg, TX)	157
Naval Undersea Museum (Keyport, WA)	173
Naval War College Museum (Newport, RI)	150
Navy Museum (Washington, D.C.)	179
New Bedford Free Public Library (New Bedford, MA)	72
New Bedford Whaling Museum (New Bedford, MA)	72
New Jersey Maritime Museum (Beach Haven, NJ)	103
New-York Historical Society (New York, NY)	120
Noble Maritime Collection (Staten Island, NY)	126
Nordic Heritage Museum (Seattle, WA)	177
North Carolina Maritime Museum (Beaufort, NC)	128
North Carolina Maritime Museum on Roanoke Island, NC (Manteo, NC)	130
North Carolina Maritime Museum at Southport (Southport, NC)	132
Ocean City Historical Museum (Ocean City, NJ)	107
Old Lighthouse Museum (Michigan City, IN)	37
Old State House Bostonian Society (Boston, MA)	61
Oregon History Center (Portland, OR)	142
Osher Map Library (Portland, ME)	48

LIBRARIES - Continued

Osterville Historical Society
  (Osterville, Cape Cod, MA)   73
Oswego Maritime Foundation
  (Oswego, NY)   122
Owen Sound Marine Rail Museum
  (Owen Sound, ONT)   202
PT Boat Museum and Library
  (Fall River, MA)   65
Peabody Essex Museum(Phillips Library)
  (Salem, MA)   76
Peary MacMillan Arctic Museum
  (Brunswick, ME)   42
Penobscot Marine Museum (Searsport, ME)   48
Pensacola Historical Museum
  (Pensacola, FL)   27
Peterborough Centennial Museum
  (Peterborough, ONT)   203
Plainville Historic Center (Plainville, CT)   19
Plimoth Plantation (Plymouth, MA)   74
Port Isabel Historical Museum
  (Port Isabel, TX)   159
Portsmouth Athenaeum (Portsmouth, NH)   101
Portsmouth Naval Shipyard Museum
  (Portsmouth, VA)   165
Puget Sound Maritime Historical Society
  (Seattle, WA)   177
Lake Erie Islands Historical Society
  Museum (Put-in-Bay, OH)   138
Putnam Museum (Davenport, IA)   38
Rhode Island Historical Society Library
  (Providence, RI)   153
Rutherford B. Hayes Presidential Library
  (Fremont, OH)   137
Sackets Harbor (Sackets Harbor, NY)   123
Sag Harbor Whaling Museum
  (Sag Harbor, NY)   124
St. Catharines Historical Museum
  (St. Catharines, ONT)   205
St. Clements Island Potomac River Museum
  (Colton Points, MD)   55
San Diego Maritime Museum
  (San Diego, CA)   11
San Francisco Maritime National Historical
  Park (San Francisco, CA)   12
Sault Ste. Marie Canal Visitor Centre
  (Sault Ste. Marie, ONT)   206
Scituate Lighthouse (Scituate, MA)   77
Shelburne Museum (Shelburne, VT)   161
Sleeping Bear Point Coast Guard Maritime
  Museum (Empire, MI)   82
South Street Seaport Museum
  (New York, NY)   120
Southampton Historical Museum
  (Southampton, NY)   125
Steamship Historical Society of America
  Collection (Providence, RI)   153

LIBRARIES - Continued

Suffolk Historical Museum
  (Riverhead, NY)   122
Texas Maritime Museum (Rockport, TX)   160
Toms River Seaport Society
  (Toms River, NJ)   108
Toronto Port Authority (Toronto, ONT)   207
Treasures of the Gulf (Port Isabel, TX)   158
Treasures of the Sea Exhibit
  (Georgetown, DE)   20
Tri-Cities Historical Museum
  (Grand Haven, MI)   83
U.S. Coast Guard Museum
  (New London, CT)   18
U.S. Naval Academy Museum
  (Annapolis, MD)   51
U.S. Navy Supply Corps Museum
  (Athens, GA)   29
USS *Arizona* Memorial (Honolulu, HI)   32
USS *Bowfin* Submarine Museum and Park
  (Honolulu, HI)   32
USS *Cairo* Museum (Vicksburg, MS)   96
USS *Constitution* Museum
  (Charlestown, MA)   63
United States Naval Shipbuilding Museum
  (Quincy, MA)   75
University of Rhode Island
  (Kingston, RI)   149
Vancouver Maritime Museum
  (Vancouver, BC)   187
Vicksburg National Military Park
  (Vicksburg, MS)   96
Virginia Canals and Navigations Society, Inc.
  (Richmond, VA)   167
Waterfront Museum and Showboat Barge
  (Brooklyn, NY)   110
Watson Curtze Mansion and Planetarium
  (Erie, PA)   145
Western Reserve Historical Society
  (Cleveland, OH)   135
Whale Museum –San Juan Island
  (Friday Harbor, WA)   175
Whaling Museum (Nantucket Island, MA)   69
Whatcom Museum of History and Art
  (Bellingham, WA)   170
White Pine Village (Ludington, MI)   84
Willapa Seaport Museum
  (Raymond, WA)   174
Woods Hole Historical Museum
  (Woods Hole, MA)   78
Working Waterfront Maritime Museum
  (Tacoma, WA)   178
Yarmouth County Museum
  (Yarmouth, NS)   197

LIGHTHOUSES

Absecon Lighthouse (Atlantic City, NJ)   102

LIGHTHOUSES - Continued

Apostle Islands National Lakeshore (6)
(Bayfield, WI) 181
Baltimore Maritime Museum
(Baltimore, MD) 52
Barnegat Lighthouse (Barnegat Light, NJ) 102
Battery Point Lighthouse
(Crescent City, CA) 5
Beavertail Lighthouse Museum
(Jamestown, RI) 148
Black Bear Island Lighthouse
(Selkirk, MTB) 189
Block Island Southeast Lighthouse
and Museum (Block Island, RI) 147
Bug Island Lighthouse
(Greenport, NY) 114
Calvert Marine Museum (Solomons, MD) 57
Cana Island Lighthouse
(Bailey's Harbor, Gills Rock, WI) 182
Cannon Ball Museum (Lewes, DE) 20
Cape Cod Lighthouse (N. Truro, MA) 72
Cape Florida Lighthouse (Miami, FL) 25
Cape Hatteras Lighthouse
(Buxton, NC) 128
Cape Henry Lighthouse
(Virginia Beach, VA) 167
Cape May County Historical & Genealogical
Society Museum (Cape May, NJ) 104
Champlain Lighthouse (Crown Point, NY) 114
Colchester Reef Lighthouse
(Shelburne, VT) 159
Copper Harbor Lighthouse Museum
(Copper Harbor, MI) 80
Coquille River Lighthouse (Bandon, OR) 139
Cove Point Lighthouse (Solomons, MD) 58
Derby Wharf Lighthouse (Salem, MA) 76
Drum Point Lighthouse (Solomons, MD) 58
Dunkirk Historical Lighthouse (Dunkirk, NY)115
Eagle Harbor Lighthouse and Museums
(Eagle Harbor, MI) 82
Eagle Bluff Lighthouse (Fish Creek, WI) 182
East Brother Lightstation
(Point Richmond, CA) 9
Fairport Marine Museum
(Fairport Harbor, OH) 137
False Duck Island Lighthouse
(Milford, ONT) 201
Fire Island Lighthouse Preservation Society
(Captree Island, NY) 111
Fishermen's Museum
(Musgrave Harbor, NFLND) 191
Fishermen's Museum and Pemaquid
Point Lighthouse (Pemaquid, ME) 46
Fort Hancock Museum (Highlands, NJ) 105
Fort Morgan Museum (Gulf Shores, AL) 1
Grand Traverse Lighthouse
(Northport, MI) 87
Ashtabula Maritime Museum
(Ashtabula, OH) 133

LIGHTHOUSES - Continued

Great Lakes Shipwreck Museum
(Paradise, MI) 87
Grindel Point Lighthouse (Islesboro, ME) 44
Hereford Inlet Lighthouse
(North Wildwood, NJ) 6
Hooper Strait Lighthouse
(St. Michaels, MD) 57
Horton Point Lighthouse (Horton Point, NY) 125
Hudson River Maritime Museum
(Kingston, NY) 118
Hunting Island Lighthouse
(St. Helena Island, SC) 155
Huron City Museum (Port Austin, MI) 88
Inland Seas Maritime Museum
(Vermilion, OH) 139
Jupiter Lighthouse (Jupiter, FL) 23
Lake Superior Maritime Visitor Center
(Duluth, MN) 92
Lightship New Bedford (New Bedford, MA) 71
Light Station Mulkiteo (Mulkiteo, WA) 173
Lighthouse Museum (Key West, FL) 24
Lighthouse Park Museum (Port Austin, MI) 88
Lighthouse Point Museum
(Two Harbors, MN) 95
Marine Museum (St. James, RI) 91
Marine Museum of Manitoba
(Selkirk, MTB) 189
Marshall Point Lighthouse
(Port Clyde, ME) 47
Mississagi Strait Lighthouse Museum
(Gore Bay, ONT) 198
Montauk Point Lighthouse Museum
(Montauk, NY) 119
Museum of the Sea/Hatteras Island
Visitor's Center (Buxton, NC) 126
Nancy Island Historic Site
(Wasaga Beach, ONT) 207
Nautical Museum at Horton Point
Lighthouse (Southold, L.I., NY) 126
Northwest Seaport (Seattle, WA) 177
Old and New Lighthouses
(Virginia Beach, VA) 167
Old Lighthouse (Biloxi, MS) 96
Old Lighthouse Museum
(Michigan City, IN) 37
Old Lighthouse Museum (Stonington, CT) 19
Old Mackinac Point Lighthouse
(Mackinac City, MI) 85
Peche Island Lighthouse
(Marine City, MI) 86
Pemaquid Point Lighthouse
(Pemaquid Point, ME) 47
Piney Point Lighthouse Museum
(Piney Point, MD) 58
Point Arena Lighthouse and Museum
(Point Arena, CA) 9
Point Gratiot Lighthouse (Dunkirk, NY) 113
Point Iroquois Lighthouse (Brimley, MI) 80

LIGHTHOUSES - Continued

Point Loma Lighthouse (San Diego, CA) 10
Point Pinos Lighthouse (Pacific Grove, CA) 9
Point Sur State Historic Park (Carmel, CA) 4
Pointe-au-Père Sea Lighthouse
    (Point-au-Père, QBC) 209
Ponce De Leon Lighthouse
    (Ponce Inlet, FL) 27
Port Isabel Lighthouse Complex
    (Port Isabel, TX) 159
Pointe-au- Père Lighthouse (QBC) 209
Port Orford Lighthouse (Port Orford Lifeboat
    Station) (Port Orford, OR) 142
Portland Head Light
    (Cape Elizabeth, ME) 43
Port Washington Light Station
    (Port Washington, WI) 184
Presque Isle Lighthouses (Presque Isle, MI) 90
Roanoke River Lighthouse Replica &
    Museum (Plymouth, NC) 131
Rock Harbor Lighthouse (Isle Royale
    National Park) (Houghton, MI) 82
Rogers Street Fishing Museum
    (Two Rivers, WI) 185
Rondout Lighthouse (Kingston, NY) 116
Rose Island Lighthouse and Museum
    (Newport, RI) 151
Sailor's Memorial Museum,
    Grindle Point Light (Islesboro, ME) 45
St. Augustine Lighthouse and Museum
    (St. Augustine, FL) 27
St. George Reef Lighthouse
    (Crescent City, CA) 5
St. Simons Island Lighthouse Museum
    (St. Simons Island, GA) 30
Salem Maritime National Historic Site
    (Salem, MA) 76
Sand Point Lighthouse (Escanaba, MI) 82
Sandy Hook Lighthouse (Highlands, NJ) 104
Saugerties Lighthouse Museum
    (Saugerties, NY) 124
Scituate Lighthouse (Scituate, MA) 77
Seal Island Light Museum
    (Barrington, NS) 192
Seul Choix Point Lighthouse (Gulliver, MI) 83
Shelburne Museum (Shelburne, VT) 161
Sodus Bay Lighthouse (Sodus Point, NY) 125
Split Rock Lighthouse Historic Site
    (Two Harbors, MN) 95
Spring Point Lighthouse
    (South Portland, ME) 49
Sturgeon Point Lighthouse
    (Harrisville, MI) 82
Texas Maritime Museum (Rockport, TX) 160
Thomas Point Lighthouse (Annapolis, MD) 50
Tuckerton Seaport (Tuckerton, NJ) 108
Twin Lights State Historic Site
    (Highlands, NJ) 105

LIGHTHOUSES - Continued

Tybee Island Historical Society
    (Tybee Island, GA) 31
Valcour Island Lighthouse
    (Plattsburg, NY) 122
White River Light Station Museum
    (Whitehall, MI) 93
Whitefish Shoal Lighthouse
    (Paradise, MI) 88
Yaquina Bay Lighthouse (Newport, OR) 142

LOCKS AND CANALS

Arkansas River Historical Society Museum
    (Catoosa, OK) 140
Big Sandy Lake Lock and Dam
    (McGregor, MN) 94
Bytown Museum (Ottawa, ONT) 200
C & D Canal Museum (Chesapeake, MD) 53
C & O Canal (Cumberland, MD) 55
C. Howard Hiester Canal Center
    (Wyomissing, PA) 147
Canal Fulton Heritage Society
    (Canal Fulton, OH) 134
Canal Museum (Greenville, PA) 144
Canal Society of New Jersey Museum
    at Waterloo Village (Morristown, NJ) 106
Canal Society of New York State
    (Syracuse, NY) 125
Canastota Canal Town Museum
    (Canastota, NY) 112
Carroll County Wabash and Erie Canal, Inc.
    (Delphi, IN) 35
Cascade Locks and Marine Park
    (Cascade Locks, OR) 141
Chafee Blackstone National Corridor
    (Woonsocket, RI) 154
Chaffey's Lock (Chaffey's Lock, ONT) 196
Champlain Canal (Skenesborough Museum)
    (Whitehall, NY) 127
Chesapeake & Ohio National Historical Park
    (Hagers Town, MD) 55
Chittenango Landing Canal Boat Museum
    (Chittenango, NY) 113
Coteau-du-Lac Canal (First in No. America) 208
    (Québec, QBC) 207
Delaware and Hudson Canal Museum
    (High Falls, NY) 116
Dwight D. Eisenhower Lock
    (Massena, NY) 119
Erie Canal (Canastota, NY) 110
Erie Canal (Chittenango, NY) 111
Erie Canal (Fort Hunter, NY) 116
Erie Canal (Lockport, NY) 117
Erie Canal Museum (Syracuse, NY) 126
Erie Canal Village (Rome, NY) 123
Falls of the Ohio (Jeffersonville, IN) 35
Farmington Canal (Plainville, CT) 18
Fort Hunter Schoharie Crossing;
    State Historic Site (Fort Hunter, NY) 114

LOCKS AND CANALS Continued

Greenville Canal Museum
  (Greenville, PA)   145
H. Lee White Marine Museum
  (Oswego, NY)   121
Hiram M. Chittenden Locks
  (Seattle, WA)   176
Historic Roscoe Village (Coshocton, OH)   136
Ice Harbor Lock and Dam (Pasco, WA)   174
Illinois and Michigan Canal Museum
  (Lockport, IL)   34
Jones Falls Defensible Lockmaster's
  House (Elgin, ONT)   198
Lake Champlain Canal (Whitehall, NY)   125
Landsford Canal (Catawba, SC)   154
Lockmaster Anglin's Interpretive Centre
  (Smith's Falls, ONT)   206
Lockmaster's House Museum
  (Chaffey's Lock, ONT)   197
Lockport Canal Museum
  (Lockport, NY)   118
McAlpine Locks and Dam
  (Jeffersonville, IN)   35
Merrickville Blockhouse Museum
  (Merrickville, ONT)   200
Middlesex Canal Museum and Visitor Center
  (N. Billenca, MA)   73
Mississippi River Visitor Center
  (Rock Island, IL)   35
Muskoka Lakes Museum
  (Port Carling, ONT)   204
National Canal Museum and Hugh
  Moore Park (Easton, PA)   144
Neversink Valley Area Museum/ D and H
  Canal Park (Cuddebackville, NY)   115
New Hope Canal Boat Company
  (New Hope, PA)   145
New York State Canal System
  (Albany, NY)   109
Old Santee Canal State Park
  (Moncks Corner, SC)   154
Oswego Canal (Oswego, NY)   119
Patowmack Canal (Great Falls, VA)   162
Peterborough Centennial Museum
  (Peterborough, ONT)   203
Peterborough Hydraulic Lift Lock and
  Visitor Center (Peterborough, ONT)   203
Piqua Historical Area (Piqua, OH)   138
Plainville Historic Center (Plainville, CT)   18
Plaquemine Lock (Plaquemine, LA)   42
Port Colborne Historical and Marine Museum
  (Port Colborne, ONT)   204
Portage Canal Society, Inc. (Portage, WI)   184
Rideau Canal (Merrickville, ONT)   199
Rideau Canal (Ottawa, ONT)   201
Rideau Canal Museum (Smiths Falls, ONT)   206
Roanoke Canal Museum & Trail
  (Roanoke Rapids, NC)   132

LOCKS AND CANALS Continued

St. Catharines Historical Museum
  (St. Catharines, ONT)   205
Sault Ste. Marie Canal Visitor Centre
  (Sault Ste. Marie, ONT)   204
  (Sault Ste. Marie, MI)   92
St. Peters Canal (St. Peters, NS)   196
Schoharie Crossing State Historic Site
  (Fort Hunter, NY)   114
Sandy and Beaver Canal (East Liverpool, OH)136
Sims' Store Museum (Camillus, NY)   112
Skenesborough Museum (Whitehall, NY)   127
Soo Locks (Sault Ste. Marie, MI)   91
Susquehanna Museum
  (Havre de Grace, MD)   56
Tennessee-Tombigbee Waterway
  (Carrollton, AL)   1
Virginia Canals and Navigations
  Society (Richmond, VA)   166
Welland Canal (Port Colborne, ONT)   203
Whitewater Canal State Historic Site
  (Metamora, IN)   37

NAVY YARDS

Charlestown Navy Yard (Boston, MA)   62
Navy Museum (Washington, D.C.)   179
Sackets Harbor Battlefield State
  Historic Site (Sackets Harbor, NY)   123
Vallejo Naval and Historical Museum
  (Vallejo, CA)   15
Ventura County Maritime Museum
  (Oxnard, CA)   9

NEWSLETTERS & PERIODICALS

A Whaling Account (Whaling Museum Society)
  (Cold Spring Harbor, L.I., NY)   114
Action Stations (HMCS *Sackville*)
  (Halifax, NS)   192
Anchor Light (*SS Lane* Victory)
  (San Pedro, CA)   13
Anchor News (Wisconsin Maritime Museum)
  (Manitowoc, WI)   183
Anchor Watch newsletter (Historic Naval
  Ships Association) U.S. Naval Academy
  Museum (Annapolis, MD)   49
Bay Chronicle Journal (Newsletter)
  (Searsport, ME)   49
Broadside US Naval Academy Museum
  (Annapolis, MD)   50
Broadside (USS *Missouri*) (Honolulu, HI)   32
Bugeye Times (Calvert Marine Museum)
  (Solomons, MD)   57
Calendar (Monthly) (Corpus Christi, TX)   156
Canal Currents (newsletter)
  (Erie Canal Museum) (Syracuse, NY)   126
Canal Routes (Middlesex Canal Museum)
  (North Billerica,, MA)   67
Cape Fear Museum (Wilmington, NC)   132

NEWSLETTERS Continued

Clarke Museum (Eureka, CA)   6
Cod Chronical (USS Cod) (Submarine)
    (Cleveland, OH)   134
Constitution Chronicle (newsletter)
    (USS Constitution Museum)
    (Boston, MA)   63
Courier (Bayfield Heritage Association)
    (Bayfield, WI)   181
Dorymates (biannual newsletter)
    (Fisheries Museum of Atlantic)
    (Lunenburg, NS)   195
Fall River Line Journal (quarterly)
    (Marine Museum at Fall River)
    (Fall River, MA)   66
Fire in the Hole (UDT-SEAL Museum)
    (Ft. Pierce, FL)   22
Focs'le News (Hudson River Maritime
    Museum) (Kingston, NY)   116
Forbes House Jottings (Capt. Robert
    Bennet Forbes House) (Milton, MA)   70
Friends of HMCS Haida
    (Toronto, ONT)   199
Full & By (newsletter) (San Diego, CA)   11
Glacier Icebreaker (News, Stratford, CT)   19
Historical Happenings (Bayfield, WI)   180
Illinois and Michigan Canal Museum
    (Lockport, IL)   34
Katahdin Knots (Newsletter)
    (Greenville, ME)   45
Kidd's Compass (newsletter)
    (Baton Rouge, LA)   40
LCHS (Log Cabin Historical Society)
    (Newport, OR)   139
LCMMnews (Lake Champlain Maritime
    Museum) (Basin Harbor, VT)   159
Lex Letter (USS Lexington)
    (Corpus Christi, TX)   157
Liberty Log (SS John W. Brown)
    (Baltimore, MD)   53
Long Reach Log (Bath, ME)   42
Maine Lighthouse Museum (newsletter)
    (Rockland, ME)   48
Mains'l (Biloxi, MS)   96
Mains'l Haul (historical journal)
    (San Diego, CA)   11
Maritimes (newsletter) (Oswego, NY)   121
Mel Fisher Maritime Heritage Society
    (Key West, FL)   24
National Mississippi River Museum
    And Aquarium (Dubuque, IA)   38
Navy Museum News (The Navy Museum)
    (Washington, D.C.)   178
Niagara League News
    (Erie Maritime Museum) (Erie, PA)   142
Now and Then (Old Fort Jackson,
    (Savannah, GA)   30
Nordic News (Nordic Heritage Museum,
    (Seattle, WA)   177

NEWSLETTERS Continued

OHC Spectator Magazine (Portland, OR)
OMF Ontario, Maritimes (Oswego, NY)   121
Old Lighthouse Museum News
    (Michigan City, IN)   37
Olympia Update (Independence
    Seaport Museum) (Philadelphia, PA)   143
On the Beam (newsletter)
    (St. Michaels, MD)   58
Ponce de Leon Inlet Lighthouse
    (Ponce Inlet, FL)   26
Port of Entry (Oxford, MD)   57
Portland Harbor Museum
    (South Portland , ME)   49
Rose Island Lighthouse News
    (Newport, RI)   151
Science and History Quarterly
    (Corpus Christi, TX)   156
Sea Chest Journal (Seattle, WA)   177
Sea History Magazine (Peekskill, NY)   122
Shavings (Center for Wooden Boat)
    (Seattle, WA)   175
Shelburne Museum, Inc. (Shelburne, VT)   161
Slater Signals (USS Slater) (Albany, NY)   107
Soundings (historical quarterly)
    (Milwaukee, WI)   183
Spinnaker (Museum of Yachting)
    (Newport, RI)   150
Steamboat Log (newsletter) (Essex, CT)   16
Steaming as Before (SS American Victory)
    (Tampa, FL)   28
Tea Times (newsletter) (Boston, MA)   60
Telescope (Detroit, MI)   80
The Annunciator (USS North Carolina)
    (Wilmington, NC)   131
The Bay Chronicle (Penobscot Marine
    Museum) (Searsport, ME)   48
The Bulletin from Johnny Cake Hill
    (New Bedford, MA)   71
The Chadburn (Inland Seas Maritime
    Museum) (Vermilion, OH)   138
The Daybook (Hampton Roads Naval
    Museum) (Norfolk, VA)   163
The Dolphin (West Sayville, NY)   126
The Icebreaking News (The Glacier Society)
    (Stratford, CT)   19
The Inland Seas (Vermilion, OH)   138
The Jeremiah (SS Jeremiah O'Brien)
    (San Francisco, CA)   12
The Keeper (Old Coast Guard Station
    Museum) (Virginia Beach, VA)   166
The Lock Tender (newsletter)
    (Natl. Canal Museum) (Easton, PA)   144
The Log (Mystic Seaport) (Mystic, CT)   17
The Log Line (Rockport, TX)   159
The Manifest (newsletter) (Kings Point, NY)   117
The Mariners' Pipe (Newport News, VA)   162
The Masthead (Philadelphia, PA)   143
The Nor'easter (Duluth, MN)   92

NEWSLETTERS Continued

The PT Boater (PT Boats, Inc.)
(Fall River, MA) 64
The Ship's Bell (Discovery Harbor)
(Penetanguishene, ONT) 201
The Ship's Lamp (South Haven, MI) 90
The Tiller (Virginia Canals & Navigation
Society (Richmond, VA) 167
The Ugly Duckling (newsletter)
(SS *John W. Brown*)(Baltimore, MD) 53
The Windrose (Mystic Seaport)
(Mystic, CT) 17
To The Point (Patriot's Point Naval &
Maritime Museum) (Patriot's Point, SC) 155
Towpath Topics
(Lowell, MA) 67
US Coast Guard Newsletter (Lewes, DE) 20
Undersea Quarterly (Naval Undersea
Museum) (Keyport, WA) 173
Waterlines
(Kodiak Maritime Museum, Kodiak, AK) 2
Weather Gauge (semiannual publication)
(St. Michaels, MD) 58
Woods Hole Historical Museum
(Woods Hole, MA) 78

PIRATE MUSEUMS

Expedition *Whydah*
(Provincetown, MA) 75
New England Pirate Museum
(Salem, MA) 75
Pirate Soul Museum (Key West, FL) 25
Ripely's Believe-it-or-Not Museum
(Key West, FL) 25

SCRIMSHAW

Alfred S. Brownell Collection
(Providence, RI) 152
Barn Museum (Bellport, NY) 109
Custom House Maritime Museum
(Newburyport, MA) 73
Kennebunkport Maritime Museum
(Kennebunkport, ME) 46
Maine Lighthouse Museum
(Rockland, ME) 48
Mariners' Museum
(Newport News, VA) 163
Monterey Maritime Museum
(Monterey, CA) 7
Mystic Seaport Museum (Mystic, CT) 17
New Bedford Whaling Museum
(New Bedford, MA) 72
New Brunswick Museum
(Saint John, NB) 190
Old Coast Guard Station Museum
(Virginia Beach, VA) 168
Old State House (Boston, MA) 61

SCRIMSHAW – Continued

Peabody Essex Museum (Salem, MA) 76
Sag Harbor Whaling Museum
(Sag Harbor, NY) 124
San Francisco Maritime National
Historic Park (San Francisco, CA) 12
Shelburne Museum (Shelburne, VT) 161
Ships of the Sea Maritime Museum
(Savannah, GA) 30
Whaling Museum (Nantucket Island, MA) 69
Whaliing Museum (Cold Spring Harbor,NY) 114

SHIP CHANDLERS

Cohasset Historical Museum (Cohasset, MA) 64
Discovery Harbour
(Penetanguishene, ONT) 202
Robertson & Son Ship Chandlery
(Halifax, NS) 193
Ships of the Sea Maritime Museum
(Savannah, GA) 30

SHIP MODELS

Albert County Museum
(Hopewell Cape, NB) 190
Alfred S. Brownell Collection of Atlantic
Coast Fishing Craft Models
(Providence, RI) 152
American Merchant Marine Museum
(Kings Point, NY) 117
American Philosophical Society Library
(Philadelphia, PA) 145
Ashtabula Maritime Museum
(Ashtabula, OH) 133
Atlantic Heritage Center
(Somers Point, NJ) 107
Barn Museum (Bellport, NY) 109
Barnacle State Historical Site
(Coconut Grove, FL) 23
Battleship Cove (Fall River, MA) 65
Battleship *South Dakota* Museum
(Sioux Falls, SD) 156
Bishop Museum (Honolulu, HI) 31
Bernier Maritime Museum
(L'Islet-sur-Mer, QBC) 208
Boston Marine Society (Boston, MA) 60
Bremerton Naval Museum
(Bremerton, WA) 170
Brickstore Museum (Kennebunk, ME) 44
Buffalo and Erie County Naval and
Military Park (Buffalo, NY) 111
Burke Museum (Seattle, WA) 175
CEC/Seabee Museum (Port Hueneme, CA) 10
Cape Fear Museum (Wilmington, NC) 132
Capt. Charles H. Hurley Library
(Buzzards Bay, MA) 61
Captain Robert Bennet Forbes House
(Milton, MA) 70

SHIP MODELS Continued

Cartier-Brébeuf National Historic Park
(Québec, QBC) 209
Catalina Island Museum (Avalon, CA) 5
Churchill House and Marine Memorial
Room Museum (Hantsport, NS) 193
Cigna Museum and Art Collection
(Philadelphia, PA) 145
Clarke Museum (Eureka, CA) 6
Coast Guard Museum/Northwest
(Seattle, WA) 176
Cohasset Maritime Museum
(Cohasset, MA) 64
Collingwood Museum
(Collingwood, ONT) 196
Columbia River Maritime Museum
(Astoria, OR) 139
Connecticut River Museum (Essex, CT) 16
Counting House (South Berwick, ME) 47
David M. Stewart Museum
(Montreal, QBC) 209
David Warther Carving Display
(Sugarcreek, OH) 138
Dossin Great Lakes Museum (Detroit, MI) 81
East Hampton Town Marine Museum
(East Hampton, NY) 115
East Martello Gallery and Museum
(Key West, FL) 24
Edmonds Historical Museum
(Edmonds, WA) 171
Essex Shipbuilding Museum
(Essex, MA) 65
Falls of the Ohio State Park
(Jeffersonville, OH) 36
Fishermen's Museum
(Musgrave Harbour, NFLD) 191
Fishermen's Museum
(Pemaquid Point, ME) 46
Franklin D. Roosevelt Library and
Museum (Hyde Park, NY) 117
Gates House/Machiasport Historical Society
(Machiasport, ME) 47
Golden Eagle River Museum (St. Louis, MO) 98
Grand Manan Museum (Grand Harbor, NB) 189
Granville Island Model Ships Museum
(Vancouver, B.C.) 187
Gray & Blue Naval Museum
(Vicksburg, MS) 97
Gates House/Machiasport Historical Society
Machiasport, ME) 46
Golden Eagle River Museum River Towboat
Models (St. Louis, MO) 99
Great Northeast Harbor Maritime Museum
(Northeast Harbor, ME) 45
Gundalow ship models
(South Berwick, ME) 48
H. L. Hunley Museum (N. Charleston, SC) 155
H. Lee White Marine Museum
(Oswego, NY) 121

SHIP MODELS Continued

Hampton Roads Naval Museum
(Norfolk, VA) 164
Hart Nautical Collections
(Cambridge, MA) 61
Herman T. Pott National Inland Waterways
Library (St. Louis, MO) 99
Herreshoff Marine Museum (Bristol, RI) 148
Historic Hermann Museums
(Hermann, MO) 98
Historical Museum of Bay County
(Bay City, MI) 79
Historical Museum of Southern Florida
(Miami, FL) 26
Houston Maritime Museum (Houston, TX) 158
Howard Steamboat Museum and Mansion
(Jeffersonville, IN) 35
Independence Seaport Museum
(Philadelphia, PA) 146
Inland Rivers Library (Cincinnati, OH) 134
Inland Seas Maritime Museum
(Vermilion, OH) 139
Intrepid Sea-Air-Space Museum
(New York, NY) 119
Jacksonville Maritime Museum Society, Inc.
(Jacksonville, FL) 23
James Kirk Maritime Museum
(Linwood, NJ) 106
Jamestown Museum (Jamestown, RI) 148
Jesse Besser Museum (Alpena, MI) 79
Kennebunkport Maritime Museum
(Kennebunkport, ME) 46
Keyport Steamboat (Keyport, NJ) 104
Kittery Historical and Naval Museum
(Kittery, ME) 46
Lake Erie Islands Historical Society
Museum (Put-in-Bay, OH) 138
Lake Superior Maritime Visitor Center
(Duluth, MN) 92
Long Island Maritime Museum
(West Sayville, NY) 127
Los Angeles Maritime Museum
(San Pedro, CA) 14
Louisbourg Marine Museum
(Louisbourg, NS) 194
Maine Lighthouse Museum
(Rockland, ME) 48
Manistee County Historic Museum
(Manistee, MI) 84
Marine Museum at Fall River
(Fall River, MA) 66
Mariners' Museum (Newport News, VA) 163
Maritime & Yachting Museum
(Stuart, FL) 27
Maritime Industry Museum at Fort Schuyler
(Bronx, NY) 110
Maritime Museum of Sandusky
(Sandusky, OH) 138

SHIP MODELS Continued

Maritime Museum of British Columbia
(Victoria, BC) 188
Maritime Museum of the Atlantic
(Halifax, NS) 193
Mark Twain Home Foundation
(Hannibal, MO) 97
Marquette Maritime Museum
(Marquette, MI) 86
Masters, Mates, and Pilots Museum
(Linthicum Heights, MD) 57
Medford Historical Society Museum
(Medford, MA) 69
Meteor, SS, Maritime Museum
(Superior, WI) 184
Milwaukee Public Library
(Milwaukee, WI) 183
Mississippi River Museum at Mud Island
(Memphis, TN) 156
Model Ships Museum, Granville Island
(Vancouver, B.C.) 187
Monterey Maritime Museum
(Monterey, CA) 7
Moore Museum (Moore Town, ONT) 201
Museum of History and Industry
(Seattle, WA) 176
Museum of Newport History
(Newport, RI) 150
Museum of Science (Boston, MA) 60
Museum of the City of New York
(New York, NY) 120
Museum of Yachting (Newport, RI) 150
Museum Ship *Valley Camp*
(Sault Ste. Marie, MI) 91
Muskoka Lakes Museum
(Port Carling, ONT) 204
Mystic Seaport Museum (Mystic, CT) 17
Nancy Island Historic Site
(Wasaga Beach, ONT) 207
National Museum of Ship Models &
Sea History, (Sadorus, IL) 35
Nautilus and Submarine Museum
(Groton, CT) 16
Naval Museum of Alberta, The
(Calgary, ALB) 185
Naval War College Museum
(Newport, RI) 150
Navy Museum (Washington, D.C.) 179
New Bedford Whaling Museum
(New Bedford, MA) 72
New Brunswick Museum
(Saint John, NB) 190
Newport Harbor Nautical Museum
(Newport Beach, CA) 8
North Carolina Maritime Museum
(Beaufort, NC) 128
North Carolina Maritime Museum
(Southport, NC) 132

SHIP MODELS Continued

Ohio River Museum (Marietta, OH) 137
Old Coast Guard Station Museum
(Virginia Beach, VA) 168
Old Lighthouse Museum
(Stonington, CT) 18
Old State House (Boston, MA) 61
Oregon History Center (Portland, OR) 142
Oregon Maritime Center and Museum
(Portland, OR) 143
Owen Sound Marine-Rail Museum
(Owen Sound, ONT) 202
Peabody Essex Museum (Salem, MA) 76
Penobscot Marine Museum
(Searsport, ME) 48
Port Columbus Civil War Naval Center
(Columbus, GA) 29
Port Huron Museum (Port Huron, MI) 89
Portsmouth Athenaeum (Portsmouth, NH) 101
Portsmouth Naval Shipyard Museum
(Portsmouth, VA) 165
Presque Isle County Historical Museum
(Rogers City, MI) 90
Presque Isle Lighthouses (Presque Isle, MI) 90
Pride and Heritage Museum
(Marine City, MI) 85
Puget Sound Maritime Historical Society
(Seattle, WA) 177
Putnam Museum (Davenport, IA) 38
Reedville Fisherman's Museum
(Reedville, VA) 166
Rier's Old Sardine Village Museum
(Lubec, ME) 46
River Heritage Center Museum
Paducah, KY 40
Sag Harbor Whaling Museum
(Sag Harbor, NY) 124
San Diego Maritime Museum
(San Diego, CA) 11
San Francisco National Historic Park
(San Francisco, CA) 12
Sandy Bay Historical Society and
Museums (Rockport, MA) 75
Sanilac County Historical Museum
(Port Sanilac, MI) 88
Santa Barbara Maritime Museum
(Santa Barbara, CA) 14
Settler's Museum (Mahone Bay, NS) 195
Ships of the Sea Maritime Museum
(Savannah, GA) 30
Skenesborough Museum
(Whitehall, NY) 127
Smithsonian Institution
(Washington, D.C.) 180
SS *Meteor* Whaleback Ship
(Superior, WI) 184
State Historical Society of North Dakota
(Bismarck, ND) 133

SHIP MODELS Continued

Steamboat Dock Museum	
(Keyport, NJ)	106
Steamboat models (Hannibal, MO)	96
Steamboat models (Hermann, MO)	96
Strawbery Banke (Portsmouth, NH)	99
Suffolk Historical Museum	
(Riverhead, NY)	123
Sunshine Coast Museum and Archive	
(Gibson's Landing, B.C.)	186
Texas Maritime Museum (Rockport, TX)	160
Toms River Seaport Society	
(Toms River, NJ)	108
Tri-Cities Historical Museum	
(Grand Haven, MI)	83
Truro Historical Society Museum	
(N. Truro, MA)	73
U.S. Naval Academy Museum	
(Annapolis, MD)	51
U.S. Navy Supply Corps Museum	
(Athens, GA)	29
USS *Constitution* Museum	
(Boston, MA)	63
USS *Kidd* & Nautical Center	
(Baton Rouge, LA)	41
Umpqua Discovery Center (Reedsport, OR)	143
United States Shipbuilding Museum	
(Quincy, MA)	75
Vallejo Naval and Historical Museum	
(Vallejo, CA)	15
Vancouver Maritime Museum	
(Vancouver, BC)	187
Vanderbilt Mansion (Centerport, NY)	112
Ventura County Maritime Museum	
(Oxnard, CA)	9
Warther Carving Display, David	
(Sugarcreek, OH)	139
Watson Curtze Mansion and Planetarium	
(Erie, PA)	145
Wellfleet Historical Society Museum	
(Wellfleet, MA)	77
Whaling Museum	
(Cold Spring Harbor, L.I., NY)	111
Willapa Seaport Museum (Raymond, WA)	174
Willowbrook at Newfield (Newfield, ME)	47
Wisconsin Maritime Museum	
(Manitowoc, WI)	183
Wrecker's Museum (Key West, FL)	25

SHIPS AND BOATS – BY TYPE

Canal Boats/Barges
Canoes
Icebreakers
Iron Clads
Lightships
Small Craft Collections
Submarines
Tugboats

CANAL BOATS/BARGES

Canal barge (replica) Coshocton, OH)	134
Canal boat (Easton, PA)	144
Canal boat (Erie Canal Museum)	
(Syracuse, NY)	126
Canal barge (New Hope, PA)	143
Centennial (Beverly, MA)	59
Chief Engineer of Rome (horse drawn	
canal packet boat) (Rome, NY)	122
Capt. Edward H. Adams (opendecked barge)	
(Portsmouth, NH & York Maine)	49/99
General Harrison (replica canal boat)	
(Piqua, OH)	137
Monticello III, (replica canal boat)	
(Coshocton, OH)	134
Poplar (barge) (Philadelphia Ship	
Preservation Guild (Philadelphia, PA)	145
Rufus A. Reed (replica canal barge)	
(Greenville, PA)	145

CANOES

Burke Museum (Seattle, WA)	175
Canadian Canoe Museum	
(Peterborough, ONT)	202
Grosse Isle National Historical Site	
(Québec, QBC)	211
H. Lee White Marine Museum	
(Oswego, NY)	121
Hokule'a (Polynesian double hull	
voyaging canoe) (Honolulu, HI)	30
Ice Canoe (1920s) (Québec, Québec)	210
Makah Museum (whaling and sealing)	
(Neah Bay, WA)	173
Muskoka Lakes Museu (Port Carling, ONT)	202
Peterborough Canoe (Peterborough, ONT)	203
Shelburne Museum (Shelburne, VT)	161
Tilikum (dugout canoe) (Victoria, BC)	187
Voyageur Canoe (Mattawa, ONT)	200
Voyageur freight canoe (Saginaw, MI)	89
Whaling canoes (Neah Bay, WA)	173

ICE BREAKERS

Alexander Henry (ice breaker)	
(Kingston, ONT)	198
Ernest Lapointe (icebreaker	
(L'Islet sur Mer, QBC)	209
Glacier Society Museum, The	
(Stratford, CT)	19

IRONCLADS

USS *Cairo* (Union ironclad)	
(Vicksburg, MS)	97
CSS *Chattahoochee* (gun boat)	
(Columbus, GA)	28
CSS *Georgia* (Savannah, GA)	30
CSS *Jackson* Ironclad (Columbus, GA)	28
CSS *Little David* (Moncks Corner, SC)	153

IRONCLADS – Contd.

USS *Monitor* Ironclad (Newport News, VA) 163
CSS *Neuse* (ironclad) State Historical
  Site (Kinston, NC) 130

LIGHTSHIPS

Ambrose (lightship) (New York, NY) 118
Chesapeake (Lightship) (Baltimore, MD) 50
Columbia (lightship) (Astoria, OR) 138
Huron Lightship Museum (Port Huron, MI) 87
Chesapeake (Baltimore Maritime Museum)
  (Baltimore, MD) 52
Columbia (Columbia River Maritime
  Museum) (Astoria, WA) 139
New Bedford, Lightship (New Bedford, MA) 70
Overfalls (Cannon Ball Marine Museum)
  (Lewes, DE) 21
Port Huron Lightship (Port Huron, MI) 89
Portsmouth Lightship Museum
  (Portsmouth, VA) 165
Relief #83 (Lightship) (Oakland, CA) 8
Swiftsure (Lightship) (Seattle, WA) 176

WHALE BOATS

Dominy & Edwards Whaleboats
  (East Hampton, NY) 115

SMALLCRAFT COLLECTIONS

Adirondack Museum
  (Blue Mountain Lake, NY) 108
Antique Boat Collection (Clayton, NY) 113
Basin Head Fisheries Museum
  (Souris, P.E.I.) 208
Calvert Marine Museum (Solomons, MD) 57
Center for Wooden Boats (Seattle, WA) 175
Chesapeake Bay Maritime Museum
  (St. Michaels, MD) 58
DeTour Passage Historical Museum
  (DeTour Village, MI) 81
Iowa Great Lakes Maritime Museum
  (Arnolds Park, IA) 37
Lake Pontchartrain Basin Maritime Museum
  (Madisonville, LA) 41
Lifeboat from SS *Hochelaga*
  (Port Colborne, ONT) 204
Local small craft (De Tour Village, MI) 79
Madeline (ship) (Traverse City, MI) 92
Maritime Heritage Alliance
  (Traverse City, MI) 91
Maine Maritime Museum (Bath, ME) 43
Mariners' Museum (Newport News, VA) 163
Maritime Museum of the Atlantic
  (Halifax, NS) 193
Museum of Yachting (Newport, RI) 150
New Hampshire Boat Museum
  (Wolfeboro Falls, NH) 102
North Carolina Maritime Museum
  (Beaufort, NC) 128

SMALLCRAFT COLLECTIONS – Cntd.

North Carolina Maritime Museum at
  (Roanoke (Manteo, NC) 130
St. Clements Island-Patomac River Mus.
  (Coltons Point, MY) 53
Tahoe Maritime Museum
  (Carnelian Bay, CA) 4
Toms River Seaport Societ (Toms River, NJ) 108
Tuckerton Seaport (Tuckerton, NJ) 108
Upper Bay Museum (North East, MD) 57
Watermen's Museum (Yorktown, VA) 167
Willowbrook at Newfield (Newfield, ME) 47
Chesapeake Boats (Yorktown, VA) 167
Watermen's Museum (Yorktown, VA) 168
Woods Hole Historical Collection
  (Woods Hole, MA) 78
Working Waterfront Maritime Museum
  (Tacoma, WA) 178

SUBMARINES

Aluminaut (research submarine)
  (Richmond, VA) 166
American Turtle (first submarine)
  (Essex, CT) 15
German Submarine Black Panther
  ((Piney Point, MD) 58
Deep Quest (Keyport, WA) 173
German Seahund Submarine
  (Hackensack, NJ) 102
Holland I, Holland II, Fenian Ram
  (Paterson, NJ) 107
Hunley, H.L. (Confederate submarine)
  (North Charleston, SC) 155
Japanese Mini-Sub (Fredericksburg, TX) 157
Kaiten (Japanese submarine)
  (Hackensack, NJ) 103
Pioneer II Submersible (Santa Barbara
  Maritime Museum) (Santa Barbara, CA) 14
ROV Submarine (Santa Barbara
  Maritime Museum) (Santa Barbara, CA) 14
RV *Ben Franklin* (Vancouver, BC) 187
Trieste II (deep submergence vehicle)
  (Keyport, WA) 173
Trieste (Research Vessel)
  (Washington, D.C.) 179
U-505 (German submarine) (Chicago, IL) 34
U-1105 (sunken German submarine)
  (Piney Point, MD) 56
USS *Albacore* (Portsmouth, NH) 101
USS *Batfish* (Muskogee, OK) 86
USS *Becuna* (Philadelphia, PA) 143
USS *Blueback* (Portland, OR) 143
USS *Bowfin* (Honolulu, HI) 32
USS *Clamagore* (Mt. Pleasant, SC) 155
USS *Cavalla* (Galveston, TX) 158
USS *Cobia* (Manitowoc, WI) 183
USS *Cod* (Cleveland, OH) 135

SUBMARINES - Continued

USS *Croaker* (Buffalo, NY)   111
USS *Drum* (Mobile, AL)   2
USS *Growler* (New York, NY)   117
USS *Holland* (replica) (Greenport, NY)   115
USS *Ling* (Hackensack, NJ)   105
USS *Lion Fish* (Fall River, MA)   66
USS LST-393 (Muskegon, MI)   85
USS *Marlin* (Omaha, NE)   98
USS *Nautilus* (nuclear sub) (Groton, CT)   16
USS *Pampanito* (San Francisco, CA)   13
USS Razorback (North Little Rock, AR)   3
USS *Requin* Pittsburgh, PA   145
USS *Silversides* (Muskegon, MI)   85
USS *Torsk* (Baltimore, MD)   50

TUGBOATS

Arthur Foss (Northwest Seaport)
   (Seattle, WA)   177
Baltimore (steam tug) (Baltimore, MD)   50
Charlotte (1880s tugboat)
   (West Sayville, NY)   126
Dorothy (iron tugboat) (Newport News, VA) 162
Edna G Tug (Two Harbors, MN)   93
Fish tug (Great Lakes) (Gills Rock, WI)   182
Fish tug (Great Lakes) (Two Harbors, MN)   94
Jupiter (tug) (Philadelphia Ship
   Preservation Guild) (Philadelphia, PA) 146
Mathilda (an 1898 steam tug)
   (Kingston, NY)   116
P. A. Denny (towboat) (Charleston, WV)   180
Peguis II, MS (Tug boat) (Selkirk, MTB) 189
Reiss (steam tug) (Steamship *Keewatin*)
   (Douglas, MI)   81
Rendezvous (Retired Tug)
   (Gibson's Landing, BC)   186
Tugboat (Two Rivers, WI)   185
Tugboat *Urger* (Waterford, NY)   127
Tugboat (LT5) (World War II)
   (Oswego, NY)   119
W.O. Decker (Tug) (New York City, NY)   118

SHIPS AND BOATS - GENERAL

Acadia, CSS (Canadian Hydrographic
   Survey Vessel) (Halifax, NS)   193
Alma (scow schooner) (San Francisco, CA) 12
Admiral's Barge (Fredericksburg, TX)   156
Adventure (sailing fishing schooner)
   (Gloucester, MA)   66
Alabama, USS (battleship) (Mobile, AL)   2
Balclutha (Square rigger)
   (San Francisco, CA)   11
Barge (Lehigh valley Rail Road)
   (Brooklyn, NY)   109
Bateau (flat bottom freight boat)
   (Wasaga Beach, ONT)   206
Beaver II, Tea Party Ship (Boston, MA)   60

SHIPS AND BOATS Continued

Bee (schooner) (Penetanguishene, ONT)   201
Belle of Louisville Steamer (Louisville, KY) 39
Bemus Point Stowe ferry (cable drawn)
   (Mayville, NY)   119
Ben Franklin, RV (Vancouver, BC)   186
Berkeley (1898 San Francisco ferry)
   (San Diego, CA)   11
Bertrand (river steamboat)
   (Missouri Valley, IA)   39
Binghamton (ferry) (Edgewater, NJ)   104
Bluenose, Schooner (Lunenburg, NS)   193
Bradbury, CGS (steam vessel)
   (Selkirk, MTB)   189
Bras d'Or (hydrofoil) (Bernier Maritime
   Museum) (L'Islet-sur-Mer, QBC)   208
Bristol Bay (sailboat) (Blaine, WA)   170
Buoy Tender (USCG) (CG 52303)
   (Basin Harbor, VT)   159
C.A. Thayer (schooner)
   (San Francisco, CA)   12
CGS *Bradbury* (Steam Vessel)
   (Selkirk, MTB)   188
CSS *Acadia* (hydrographic survey vessel)
   (Halifax, NS)   193
CSS *Florida* (Hampton Roads Nav. Mus.,
   (Norfolk, VA)   163
Californian (Replica Revenue Cutter)
   (San Diego, CA)   11
Capt. Matt Peasley (18th Cent. longboat
   reproductions) (Aberdeen, WA)   169
Captain Meriwether Lewis (Steamboat
   dredge) (Brownville, NE)   100
Cape Sable (Trawler/dragger)
   (Lunenburg, NS)   193
Charles W. Morgan (whale ship)
   (Mystic, CT)   17
Chautauqua Belle (sternwheeler)
   (Mayville, NY)   119
Chickama II (passenger vessel)
   (Selkirk, MTB)   189
Chris Craft Classic Wooden Runabouts
   (Arnolds Park, IA)   36
Chris Craft Classic Wooden Runabouts
   (Newport News, VA)   160
City of Milwaukee, SS (ferry)
   (Manistee, MI)   84
Civil War gunboat (Memphis, TN)   156
Civil War gunboat (Vicksbuurg, MS)   97
Claude Somers (Skipjack)
   (Reedville, VA)   166
Clearwater Hudson River Sloop
   (Beacon, NY)   109
Coast Guard Buoy Tender (Lake
   (Basin Harbor, VT)   159
Coast Guard Cutter *Bramble*
   (Port Huron, MI)   88

244

SHIPS AND BOATS Continued

Daisy (whaleboat)	
(Cold Spring Harbor, L.I., NY)	114
Delta King Riverboat (Sacramento, CA)	10
Derrick Boat No. 8 (Oswego, NY)	119
Discovery (replica ship) (Jamestown	
Settlement) (Williamsburg, VA)	167
Dixie II (Gold Cup racer)	
(Clayton, NY)	113
Dory Boat, (Potomac River)	
(Alexandria, VA)	161
Double Nickel Deuce (Coast Guard vessel)	
(Marquette, MI)	85
Eagle (training barque) (U.S. Coast Guard	
Museum) (New London, CT)	17
Elissa (1877 iron barque)	
(Galveston, TX)	158
Elizabeth II (replica ship) Roanoke Is.	
Festival Park (Manteo, NC)	130
Empire State (Merchant Marine Training Ship)	
(Bronx, NY)	109
Eppleton Hall (paddle-wheel tug)	
(San Francisco, CA)	12
Ernest Lapointe (Ice Braker	
(L'Islet-Sur-Mer, QBC)	208
Eureka (Walking beam ferry)	
(San Francisco, CA)	12
Eluac (Buyboat) (Reedville Fisherman's	
Museum) (Reedville, VA)	166
Ernestina Commission, Schooner	
(New Bedford, MA)	71
Evelina M. Goulart (schooner)	
(Essex, MA)	64
Falls of Clyde (tall ship) (Honolulu, HI)	30
Fishing vessels Great Lakes	
(St. James, MI)	89
Fred W. Woodward Riverboat	
(Dubuque, IA)	37
Fyrdraca (Viking warship)	
(Avenue, MD)	51
Gazela (tall ship) (Independence Seaport	
Museum) (Philadelphia, PA)	145
George M. Verity (Paddlewheel)	
(Keokuk, IA)	37
Glenn L. Swetman (schooner)	
(Biloxi, MS)	96
Godspeed (replica ship)	
(Jamestown Settlement)	
(Williamsburg, VA)	168
Governor Stone (schooner)	
(Apalachicola, FL)	21
Great Republic (Beverly, MA)	59
Gunboat (War of 1812) Brown's Bay Wreck	
(Mallorytown, ONT)	199
Gunboat (Civil War) (Memphis, TN)	156
Gundalow Captain Edward H. Adams (barge)	
(Piscataque NH)	101

SHIPS AND BOATS Continued

Gunning boat (waterfowl) (aka-Punt Gunning)	
(Cambridge, MD)	53
Gyrfalcon (landing boat)	
(Avenue, MD)	51
HMCS Fraser (DDE233)	
(Bridgewater, NS)	192
HMCS Haida Naval Museum	
(Toronto, ONT)	206
HMCS Sackville (K181) (Corvette)	
(Halifax, NS)	192
HMS Rose (reproduction ship)	
now HMS Surprise) (San Diego, CA)	11
HMS Surprise (reproduction ship)	
(previous HMS Rose) (San Diego, CA)	11
Halve Maen (Half Moon) (replica ship)	
(Albany, NY)	108
Hercules (steam tug), San Francisco, CA	12
Hewitt R. Jackson (18thCent. longboat	
reproductions) (Aberdeen, WA)	169
Hiddensee (Russian Naval vessel)	
(Fall River, MA)	64
Hjemkomst (Viking ship reproduction)	
(Moorhead, MN)	93
Historic Vessels (NY State Canal System)	
(Albany, NY)	106
Hochelaga Life Boat (Port Colborne, ONT)	203
Jacksonville (tall ship) (Jacksonville, FL)	23
Joe Simpson (Lake Freghter (Selkirk, MTB)	189
John W. Brown (liberty ship)	
(Baltimore, MD)	51
Joseph Conrad (fishing schooner)	
(Mystic, CT)	17
Kalmar Nyckel (replica ship) (Delaware	
State Ship)(Wilmington, DE)	21
Katahdin (steamboat) (Moosehead Marine	
Museum) (Greenville, ME)	45
Keno, SS (sternwheeler)	
(Dawson City, Yukon)	210
Keenora, SS (lake steamer)	
(Selkirk, MTB)	189
Keewatin, Steamship (Douglas, MI)	82
Krestine (Ketch) (Raymond, WA)	174
L.A. Dunton (Fishing schooner)	
(Mystic, CT)	17
LST 325 (Evansville, IN)	36
LST 393 (Muskegon, MI)	86
LSM 45 (Amphibious Landing Craft)	
(Omaha, NE)	98
Lady Canadian (fish freighter)	
(Selkirk, MTB)	189
Lady Washington (brig) (Aberdeen, WA)	169
La Grande Hermine (Cartier flagship)	
(Québec, QBC)	210
Leif Erickson (replica Viking vessel)	
(Duluth, MN)	94
Life Saving boats (Hull, MA)	66
Life Saving boats (South Haven, MI)	90

SHIPS AND BOATS Continued

Lifeboat (from S.S. *Hochelaga*)
(Port Colborne, ONT) 203
Lobster Boat (Pemaquid Point, ME) 46
Lone Star Steamer (sternwheeler)
(Le Claire, IA) 37
MS *Lady Canada* (fish freighter)
(Selkirk, MTB) 189
MSB 5 (mine sweeper) (Fort Worth, TX) 156
Madaket (1910 diesel launch)
(Eureka, CA) 6
Madeline (replica schooner)
(Traverse City, MI) 92
Manitou (yacht) (Harry Lundberg School
of Seamanship) (Piney Point, MD) 57
Mary Celeste (ship)
(Marion, MA) 69
Mary Woods No. 2, Riverboat Museum
(Newport, AR) 3
Martha Lewis (skipjack)
(Havre de Grace, MD) 56
Maryland Dove (replica)
(Historic St. Mary's City, MD) 58
Mayflower II (replica ship)
(Plimoth Plantation) (Plymouth, MA) 73
Mayor Andrew Broaddus River Coast
Guard Station (Louisville, KY) 40
Meriwether Lewis, Captain (steamboat
dredge) (Brownville, NE) 98
Medea (1904 steam yacht) (San Diego, CA) 11
Mike Sekul (Scooner) (Biloxi, MS) 96
Miss Canada III (Gold Cup racer)
(Clayton, NY) 113
Miss Kathy (motor launch)
(Wilmington, DE) 21
Modesty (oyster sloop)
(West Sayville, NY) 126
Montgomery (U.S. snagboat)
(Carrollton, AL) 1
Nenana (riverboat) (Fairbanks, AK) 2
Niagara (1812 reconstructed brig)
(Erie, PA) 144
Norgoma (museum ship)
(Sault Ste. Marie, ONT) 204
Norisle, SS (Manitowaning, ONT) 198
OMF Schooner) (Oswego, NY) 120
PT boats (Battleship Cove)
(Fall River, MA) 65
PT 309 (Natl. Mus. of Pacific War)
(Fredericksburg, TX) 157
Patomack Presidential Yacht
(Oakland, CA) 8
Peking (bark) (New York, NY) 118
Perseverance (bateau)
(Penetanguishene, ONT) 201
Perseverance (schooner replica)
(Thunder Bay, ONT) 206

SHIPS AND BOATS Continued

Philadelphia II (Revolutionary War gunboat)
(Basin Harbor, VT) 159
Phyllis A (motor vessel)
(Kennebunkport, ME) 46
Pilgrim (Snow Brig) (Dana Point, CA) 5
Pilot (Port Pilot Boat) (San Diego, CA) 11
Pioneer (Schooner) (New York, NY) 118
Portland (restored sternwheeler)
(Portland, OR) 143
Pride of Baltimore II, Inc.
(Baltimore, MD) 52
Priscilla (oyster vessel) (West Sayville, NY) 126
Providence (replica sloop) (Newport, RI) 152
Queen Mary (passenger liner)
(Long Beach, CA) 7
Rattlesnake (privateer replica)
(Jacksonville, FL) 23
Russian Naval vessel *Hiddensee*
(Fall River, MA) 64
Sackville, HMCS (Halifax, NS) 193
Saginaw Gig (from 1870) (Saginaw, MI) 90
St. Helena III (canal freighter)
(Canal Fulton, OH) 133
St. Roch (RCMP patrol boat)
(Vancouver, BC) 186
Salem, USS (heavy cruiser) (Quincy, MA) 75
Samson V (sternwheeler)
(New Westminster, BC) 186
Schooner *Bluenose* (Lunenburg, NS) 193
Scranton (shrimp boat) (Pascagoula, MS) 97
Schooner *Ernestina* Commission
(New Bedford, MA) 72
San Diego Aircraft Carrier Museum
(USS *Midway*) (San Diego, CA) 11
Sea Lion (16thcentury merchant ship)
(Mayville, NY) 117
Sherman Zwicker (Grand Banks Schooner)
(Bath, ME) 42
Snow Squall (clipper)
(South Portland, ME) 49
SS *American Victory* (Mariners Memorial
and Museum) (Tampa, FL) 29
SS *City of Milwaukee* (ferry) (Manistee, MI) 85
SS *Jeremiah O'Brien* (Liberty Ship)
(San Francisco, CA) 12
SS *John W. Brown* (Victory Ship)
(Baltimore, MD) 53
SS *Keenora* (Lake steamer) (Selkirk, MTB) 188
SS *Keno* (Sternwheeler) (Dawson City, YK) 211
SS *Lane Victory* (Victory Ship)
(San Pedro, CA) 14
SS *Meteor* (Whaleback) Maritime Museum
(Superior, WI) 184
SS *Milwaukee Clipper* Passenger Ship
(Muskegon, MI) 87
SS *Norisle* Heritage Park
(Manitowaning, ONT) 199

SHIPS AND BOATS Continued

SS *Red Oak Victory* (Victory Ship)
(Richmond, CA) 10
SS *Ticonderoga* (lake paddlewheeler)
(Shelburne, VT) 160
SS *William A. Irvin* (ore boat)
(Duluth, MN) 94
SS *William G. Mather* (Great Lakes ore
carrier) (Cleveland, OH) 134
SS *Willis B. Boyer* Museum Ship
(Toledo, OH) 139
Star of India (1863 Iron-hull barque)
San Diego, CA) 11
Steamer *Virginia V* (passenger steamer)
(Seattle, WA) 178
Steamship *Keewatin* (Douglas, MI) 82
Surfboat – 1930s (Hyannis, MA) 67
Surfboat reproduction (Gilbert's Bar House
of Refuge) (Stuart, FL) 27
Swift boat (Navy Museum, Wash., D.C.) 179
Susan Constant (replica ship)
(Jamestown Settlement, VA) 168
Tecumseh (bateau) (Discovery Harbour)
(Penetanguishene, ONT) 202
Theresa E. Connor (salt bank schooner)
(Lunenburg, NS) 193
U.S. Brig *Niagara* (Erie, PA) 144
USCGC *Ingham* (destroyer)
(Mt. Pleasant, SC) 155
USCGC *McLane* (Muskegon, MI) 86
USCGC Cutter *Taney*
(Baltimore, MD) 50
USS *Alabama* Battleship Memorial Park
(Mobile, AL) 2
USS *Arizona* Memorial (Honolulu, HI) 32
USS *Barry* (DD 933) (The Navy Museum)
(Washington, D.C.) 179
USS *Becuna* (Independence Seaport
Museum (Philadelphia, PA) 146
USS *Cassin Young* (WW II destroyer)
(Boston, MA) 62
USS *Cod* Submarine Museum
(Cleveland, OH) 135
USS *Constellation* (sloop of war)
(Baltimore, MD) 53
USS *Constitution* ("Old Ironsides")
(Boston, MA) 63
USS *Cumberland* (Civil War) (Mariners'
Museum, Newport News, MD) 162
USS *Edson* (destroyer)
(New York, NY) 117
USS/USCGC *Glacier* (icebreaker)
(Stratford, CT) 19
USS *Hazard* (minesweeper) (Omaha, NE) 98
USS *Hornet* Aircraft Carrier Museum
(Alameda, CA) 3
USS *Intrepid* (aircraft carrier
(New York, NY) 119

SHIPS AND BOATS Continued

USS *Joseph P. Kennedy, Jr.*(Fall River, MA) 64
USS *Kidd* (destroyer) (Baton Rouge, LA) 41
USS *Laffey* (destroyer) (Mt. Pleasant, SC) 155
USS *Lexington* (aircraft carrier)
(Corpus Christi, TX) 157
USS *Little Rock* (cruiser) (Buffalo, NY) 111
USS *Massachusetts* (BB 59)
(Battleship Cove) (Fall River, MA) 65
USS *Midway* Aircraft Carrier Museum
(San Diego, CA) 11
USS *Missouri* Memorial Association
(Honolulu, HI) 32
USS *New Jersey* (BB62) (Camden, NJ) 103
USS *North Carolina* (Battleship)
(Wilmington, NC) 133
USS *Olympia* (flagship) (Penn's Landing)
(Philadelphia, PA) 146
USS *Radford* (DD) (Newscomerstown, OH) 137
USS *Saratoga* (Aircraft carrier)
(Providence, RI) 151
USS *Salem* (CA 139) (Quincy, MA) 75
USS *Slater* (destroyer escort)(DE766)
(Albany, NY) 109
USS *Stewart* (destroyer escort)
(Galveston, TX) 158
USS *The Sullivans* (destroyer) (Buffalo, NY) 111
USS *Texas* (battleship) (La Porte, TX) 158
USS *Turner Joy* (destroyer)
(Bremerton, WA) 170
USS *Utah* (battleship) (Pearl Harbor, HI) 33
USS *Wisconsin* (battleship)
(Norfolk, VA) 163
USS *Yorktown* (aircraft carrier)
(Mt. Pleasant, SC) 155
Valley Camp (museum ship)
(Sault Ste. Marie, MI) 90
Vessels boardable (San Francisco, CA) 11
Vessels historic (Northwest Seaport)
(Seattle, WA) 177
Virginia V (passenger steamer)
(Seattle, WA) 177
Voyageur freight canoe
(Saginaw, MI) 90
W. P. Snyder, Jr. (sternwheeler)
(Marietta, OH) 136
W. T. Preston (sternwheeler)
(Anacortes, WA) 170
Wawona (Coastal schooner) (Seattle, WA) 177
Wapama (lumber cargo ship)
(Sausalito, CA) 14
Wavertree (fullrigged ship)
(New York, NY) 118
William M. Black (1934 riverboat)
(Dubuque, IA) 37
Wm. B. Tennison (historic bugeye)
(Solomons, MD) 58
William A. Thompson (dredge)
(Winona, MI) 96

SHIPS AND BOATS Continued

Whydah , Expedition (Provincetown, MA)   75
York boats (Hudson Bay freight boats)
  (Selkirk, MTB)   189

WHALING

Young American (tall ship)
  (Atlantic City, NJ)   100
Alfred S. Brownell Collection
  (Providence, RI)   152
Barn Museum (Bellport, NY)   109
Brannock Maritime Museum
  (Cambridge, MD)   53
Cabrillo National Monument Memorial
  (San Diego, CA)   11
Canadian Canoe Museum
  (Peterborough, ONT)   202
Cold Spring Harbor Museum Society
  (Cold Spring Harbor, L.I., NY)   113
Columbia River Maritime Museum
  (Astoria, OR)   139
East Hampton Town Marine Museum
  (East Hampton, NY)   113
Egan Institute of Maritime Studies
  (Nantucket, MA)   70
Falmouth Historical Society's Museum
  (Falmouth, MA)   67
Makah Museum (Neah Bay, WA)   173
Martha's Vineyard Historical Society
  and Museum (Edgartown, MA)   64
Monterey Maritime Museum
  (Monterey, CA)   7
Mystic Seaport Museum (Mystic, CT)   17
New Bedford Free Public Library
  (New Bedford, MA)   71
New Bedford Whaling Museum
  (New Bedford, MA)   71
Old Lighthouse Museum (Stonington, CT)   18
Peabody Essex Museum (Salem, MA)   76
Rhode Island Historical Society Library
  (Providence, RI)   153
Sag Harbor Whaling Museum
  (Sag Harbor, NY)   124
Southampton Historical Museum
  (Southampton, NY)   125
Suffolk Historical Museum
  (Riverhead, NY)   123
Wellfleet Historical Society Museum
  (Wellfleet, MA)   77
Whaleboat (Cold Spring Harbor, NY)   111
Whaleboat (Edgartown, MA)   65
Whaleboat (East Hampton, NY)   113
Whaleboat (Pemaquid Point, ME)   46
Whaleboat (Sag Harbor Whaling Museum)   124
Whale Centre and Museum (Tofina, BC)   187
Whale Museum (Friday Harbor)
  San Juan, WA)   174

WHALING – Contd.

Whaling canoes (Neah Bay, WA)   173
Whaling Museum
  (Cold Spring Harbor, L.I., NY)   111
Whaling Museum (Nantucket Island, MA)   69
Whalers Cabin and Whaling Station Museum
  (Carmel, CA)   4

Robert H. Smith

Here, is the one essential guide, sought by all lovers of maritime history, of ships, canals, and the sea. ROBERT H. SMITH thoroughly describes, in this sixth update, more than 630 maritime, lighthouse, canal, and canal lock museums in the North American Continent, including in each entry such essential information as location; directions for motorists; telephone, fax, and e-mail addresses; web sites for museums that have web sites, visiting hours; collection highlights; history of the organizations; special activities such as lectures and film shows; admission policies; and gift shops. Several elaborately cross-referenced indices will guide the reader to any area of specialized interest, such as geographical locations, location by

state, specialized interests indexed by submarine, ships, scrimshaw, research libraries and photographic collections. Smith has written four other maritime and boating guides, all well received by the public and specialists alike. He travels extensively visiting the museums he describes, from his home base in Del Mar, California. Robert H. Smith is a longtime supporter of marine and maritime organizations and is a member of the board of trustees of the San Diego Maritime Museum. Formerly, he was Assistant to the Chancellor of the University of California, San Diego (the home of Scripps Institution of Oceanography) and vice-president of development at Scripps Clinic and Research Foundation in La Jolla, California for many years.

A NOTE TO MUSEUMS DIRECTORS

An effort was made to include all the maritime, lighthouse, canal, and canal lock museums in North America. But, in all likelihood some may have been missed. If you'd like to suggest a listing for your museum in the next edition, please complete the this form

The following maritime, lighthouse, canal, or canal lock museum was not included in this guide (2005).

_____

(Name of museum, lighthouse, canal, or canal lock museum)

_____

(Street and/or Post Office Box number)

_____

(City/State or Province/Zip or Canadian Mail Code)

_____

(Phone Number(s), Fax numbers, E-mail address)

_____

Please send to:

R. H. Smith
P.O. Box 176
Del Mar, CA 92014-0176
(858) 755-7753
or by
E-mail: cbooks@san.rr.com

Made in the USA
Lexington, KY
01 October 2011